Manufacturing Processes
and Materials for Engineers

Contributing Authors

JOE L. MORRIS

Research Engineer, Lawrence Radiation Laboratory
University of California, at Berkeley

JAMES L. LEACH

Professor of Mechanical Engineering
University of Illinois

GEORGE F. SCHRADER

Assistant Professor of Mechanical Engineering
University of Illinois

Manufacturing Processes

and Materials for Engineers

LAWRENCE E. DOYLE

Professor of Mechanical Engineering
University of Illinois

PRENTICE-HALL, INC.

Englewood Cliffs, N.J.

Second printing ....June, 1962

© 1961 by Prentice-Hall, Inc.
Englewood Cliffs, New Jersey

Library of Congress Catalog Card Number 61–13503

PRINTED IN THE UNITED STATES OF AMERICA
55585—C

Preface

The trend today in engineering education is to emphasize fundamentals and give secondary attention to practices. That is being done in the manufacturing processes courses at the University of Illinois and is the theme of this book. Throughout this text the approach is to explain the principles upon which manufacturing processes are based and to describe practices to illustrate the principles.

Manufacturing processes are looked upon in this book as engineering problems. One aim is to show how scientific and economic principles are applied to evaluate and solve these problems. Then similar problems are presented at the ends of the chapters to afford the students exercises in applying engineering principles.

To the many manufacturers of machines and tools who have furnished illustrations and information, credit is extended throughout the book. Their generous cooperation is a mark of their sincere interest in promoting engineering education.

Lawrence E. Doyle
Joe L. Morris
James L. Leach
George F. Schrader

Contents

WELDING AND ALLIED PROCESSES—Continued

facing and hard facing, 358. Braze welding, brazing, and soldering, 359.

Introduction

THE PURPOSE OF THIS TEXT

Manufacturing processes. Manufacture means to make goods and wares by industrial processes. Manufacturing is the largest segment of industry in the United States today and embraces many branches of industry. If we consider only a few, the drug, food, machinery, electrical, and shoe and leather industries, we see that each has its own technology. In the aggregate, all encompass a much larger store of knowledge than could be contained in one textbook. To keep within bounds, this book must be confined to the processes that are basic to all industry.

The derivation of the word manufacture reflects its original meaning; to make by hand. Today, however, manufacturing is done largely by machinery. The activity upon which all branches of manufacturing depend is the fabrication and use of machinery. In some areas, such as the machine tool and automobile industries, machinery is the end product as well as the means of manufacture. In those like the textile and furniture industries, machinery is the means of production. On the whole, those processes that produce machinery and hardware are basic to all forms of industry and are the ones treated in this book.

Mechanization of industry started with the industrial revolution during the 18th century. Early impetus was given the textile industry in England by the great inventions of machines for spinning and weaving. At the end of that century and the beginning of the next, the basic machines were brought forth in England and Europe for forming, shaping, and cutting metal. At about the same time in the United States, Eli Whitney gave practical effect to the principle of interchangeable manufacture, so that mechanical parts could be assembled without hand fitting. This provided the basis for full utilization of machines to make mechanical parts.

Early in the 19th century the rudimentary processes and concepts for producing mechanical parts were known and practiced. The course of events furnished the products upon which the practices were nurtured. Inventions after inventions were made of mechanical devices that men wanted and would buy; sewing machines, repeating guns, locomotives, engines, low cost watches, and automobiles were among the leaders. Others have followed in the present century. The demand to produce the growing host of industrial and consumers goods gave the impetus to developing and refining the processes, machinery, and systems of manufacturing.

Manufacturing has always been and is today a growing and a changing art. Processes of the present can be expected to change in years ahead. Metal cutting is an example. For a hundred years cutting tools were made of plain hardened high-carbon steel with little alloying. In 1900 Taylor and White introduced high-speed steel containing alloys that enabled tools to operate at red heat and up to several times faster than ever before. Designs of machine tools were appreciably strengthened to get the benefits of the improved tools. Then about 1930 industry was given tools of hard carbides instead of steel. As they became accepted, they were found able to cut metal faster and give better finishes than steel tools. Again metal cutting changed; new machines were needed to drive the tools to their full capacities. Within the last few years tools of ceramic materials have been discovered able to cut at heretofore fantastic rates. Merely to describe current practices and processes in any area is not enough. In this text the emphasis is placed upon the principles and underlying physical phenomena. The processes are described to illustrate the principles.

Materials. Manufacturing is dependent upon materials. The main ingredients of mechanical devices are metals because they provide an optimum balance of strength, ductility, hardness, resilience, endurance, dimensional stability, resistance to wear, appearance, and economy for most applications. During this century plastics have become important supplements to metals because they offer corrosion-resistance, pliability, formability, colorability, and lightness in various forms. These are the materials that will be given prime attention.

Costs. Manufacturing has given us an abundance of goods to satisfy our needs and wants at prices most people can afford to pay. To meet competition, the manufacturer must ever seek the lowest cost for acceptable quality. A meaningful basis for understanding a manufacturing process is in its elements of cost. What determines costs and how the costs of processes can be controlled, estimated, and compared are stressed throughout this text.

Manufacturing is commonly thought to connote large quantity production. Many products, particularly consumers' goods, are manufactured in large quantities, but many others are made in only small or moderate quantities. Special-purpose machines, experimental or prototype models of aircraft, and huge turbo-generators may be manufactured one or a very few at a time. Railroad locomotives, commercial aircraft, and most machine tools are manufactured in lots of a few dozen to a few hundred. Quantity is the factor that has the most bearing upon the cost of a manufacturing process. A process for a few pieces must have features and a basis of cost quite different from those of a process to produce the same results on millions of parts if the least cost is to be realized in each case. The relationships between quantity and cost are pointed out for processes throughout this text.

Because machinery is essential to manufacturing, almost any manufacturing process requires a sizeable investment. To give an appreciation of the relative amounts needed for comparable processes, approximate costs of major units of equipment are stated in the text. It can be expected that such costs will change from year to year with economic conditions, but the relative costs will stay about the same in most cases. The prices specified are those for the year 1960. Guides are available for adjusting these costs to any other years, should the reader wish to do so. These guides are the published index numbers of prices of industrial machinery and equipment. Two outstanding ones are the *Wholesale Price Index of the U. S. Bureau of Labor Statistics* and the *American Machinist Index of Metalworking Prices*. These offer index numbers for metal-working machinery, general-purpose machinery and equipment, electrical machinery, fabricated metal products, and the like.

As an example of how index numbers may be used, the case may be cited of a machine tool that cost $9000 in 1951. An index of metal-working machinery stood at 134.3 in that year and 178.3 in 1957. The cost of the same type of machine in 1957 was estimated to be $9000(178.3/134.3) \cong \$12,000$. An index number represents an average of individual prices. However, studies have indicated that most machinery and equipment costs can be estimated in the manner suggested within 10%, and practically all within 20% of actual costs.

PREPARATION FOR MANUFACTURING

Efficient manufacturing methods do not just happen. They are carefully planned. Typical steps taken to plan and coordinate the processes

and their elements are depicted in Fig. 1–1. Most of these functions are
performed by engineers, and surveys have shown that most engineers are
engaged at some stage or other in such work. A knowledge of the principles of manufacturing processes is essential for the majority of engineers.

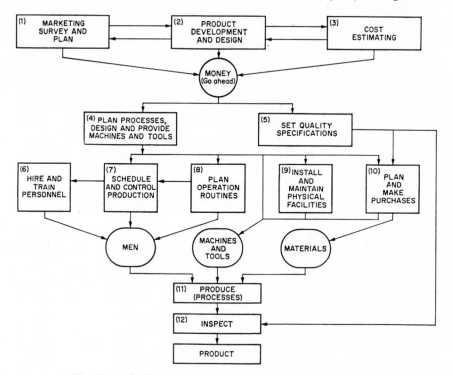

Fig. 1–1. The functions that lead to efficient manufacturing.

Planning the product. The first stage in preparation for manufacturing
is the development and design of a salable product, an analysis of its
potential sales, and an estimate of the costs of making it. These are steps
(1), (2), and (3) in Fig. 1–1.

The product design engineer must select the proper materials, ascertain the proportions and physical properties needed, and arrange the parts
for efficient performance. He usually encounters two major problems.
First, the product must function properly for a reasonable period of time.
Second, it must be possible to manufacture the product at a competitive
cost to earn a profit. The designer must select material that satisfies the
two requirements. He must proportion the parts so they perform satisfactorily and can be made by the processes of lowest cost. As for materials, the designer may have to choose from among plain-carbon steel,
alloy steel, aluminum, brass, plastics, or others. For processes, he may
have to decide from among casting, forging, welding, machining, or a combination. From the standpoint of raw materials, he may have available

castings, forgings, plates, standard structural shapes like I-beams, bar-stock, or others. His judgment and final selection will be influenced partly by the labor skills, types of machines, and raw materials available. For example, if the base and frame of a machine is to be manufactured, a choice may be presented between casting and welded shape construction. If the plant's principal installation is a foundry, the design may take advantage of the facilities. On the other hand, if welding skills and equipment are on hand and favorably priced rolled steel shapes and plates are readily available, the units may be made advantageously from steel and weld fabricated. In most cases, the alternatives need to be studied carefully for the quantity of output required to find the processes that promise lowest costs. To do that efficiently, the design engineer must be acquainted with the fundamentals of manufacturing processes and materials.

Planning for production. When the management of an enterprise decides on the basis of market surveys and cost estimates that a product as designed can be manufactured profitably, the money is appropriated and budgeted for the project. The first step is to delineate the processes on paper. Common practice is to list the steps or operations for each process on a *routing* or *process sheet,* which usually specifies also the machines, equipment, and tools needed and performance expected. Routings have many forms; one is shown in Fig. 1–2. Commercial machines and equip-

SPECIAL MFG. CO. PRODUCTION AND MACHINE TOOL ROUTING MIDWEST, IND.

PART NAME Cover - Gear Housing PART NO 72845

MATERIAL Cast Iron ROUGH SIZE As Cast ROUGH WEIGHT 3 pounds DATE EFFECTIVE 8/15/48

MODEL E-33 QUANTITY PER ASSEMBLY 1 SHEET NO 1 OF 1

OP NO.	DEPT. NO	OPERATION NAME	MACHINE NAME	MACH NO	TOOLS & GAGES	TOOL NO	GROUP NO	REQ NO	STD TIME MINS	STD TIME HRS	CAP EACH MACH PER HOUR
	307	Receive	Receiving Dept.		(1) Foundry Insp. Fixture (1) Cutter Driver (2) Cutter	72845-T-1 72845-T-2 72845-T-3					
	327	Laboratory test	Laboratory		(1) Receiving						
	317	Inspection	Bench		Insp. Fixture	72845-T-4					
	338	Stock	Stock Room		(1) Tool						
5	355	Locate-from (3) Foundry pads on edge of flange and on (3) foundry pads on back side of flange. Face end of casting to 1.3915 ± .005 from foundry pads on back side of flange. Finish face joint face of bolt flange to .829 ± .003 dim. from end of casting. Leave 1/32 rad. in corner. Finish turn pilot to 3.998 ±.001 dia. Leave 1/32 radius in corner. Break edges.	12" x 5' Leblond Engine Lathe.	777	Layout (1) Face Plate Fixture (1) Tool Bit #DSF-2-NF (1) Flush Pin Gage to Check 1.3915 ± .005 dim. (1) Flush Pin Gage to check .829 ± .003 dim. (1) 3.998 ±.001 Snap Gage.	72845-T-5 72845-T-6 Std. 72845-T-7 72845-T-8 Std.			3.60	.06	13.89
10	366	Final Inspection.	Bench		(1) Flush pin gage to check 1.3915 ± .005 dim. (1) Flush pin gage to check .829 ± .003 dim. (1) 3.998 ±.001 snap gage.	72845-T-7 72845-T-8 Std.					

REMARKS:	ENGR GROUP INDEX	ASSEMBLY NO	WRITTEN BY	TOTALS		
		93724	C.E.M.	PER PC	.06	
				PER JOB		

Fig. 1–2. An example of a process planning sheet.

ment are ordered and special tools are designed to conform to the process plan. A number of other forms, such as purchase and design orders, may also enter into the planning procedure. Quality specifications are set as a basis for procuring the gaging equipment and planning for inspection.

On the basis of the process plans, activities are initiated to prepare the physical means for production, as indicated by steps (6) through (10) in Fig. 1–1. Individual operation routines are planned and specified in detail; production schedules are set up; and steps are taken to hire and train the necessary personnel. Orders are issued to purchase machines, tools, and materials. The layout of the plant is planned and physical equipment installed accordingly as soon as available. When all is ready, the elements are brought together to carry out the processes. Certainly those who bear the responsibility for the planning and preparation described must be well acquainted with the principles of manufacturing processes.

The engineer's viewpoint. Evidence has been given to show that a knowledge of manufacturing processing is necessary for most engineers to do their work efficiently. There is yet another compelling reason for all engineers to study manufacturing processes. Manufacturing is beset with many challenging engineering problems. A study of processes shows how these problems are solved in realistic ways. Specific instances are pointed out, and many more are evident in this text. It is not proposed that a student will apply these solutions to the same problems when he meets them in later years. Rather it is expected that he will improve upon them. On the other hand, an ingenious solution in one area can often be turned to good advantage in another. A control system on a machine tool may serve admirably on excavation equipment also, for example. But most of all, a glimpse of the ingenuity, finesse, and good judgment that have been exercised by other engineers can do much to arouse those traits and bolster the self-confidence of the young engineer when he comes to pit his knowledge of science and economics against the problems of the world.

References

Doyle, L. E., *Tool Engineering: Analysis and Procedure,* Prentice-Hall, Inc., Englewood Cliffs, N. J., 1950.

Handbook of Industrial Engineering and Management, Prentice-Hall, Inc., Englewood Cliffs, N. J., 1955.

2

Fundamentals of Metals and Alloys

In general, a metal may be described as body or material which is a solid at room temperature, has relatively high density, is reflective when polished, behaves elastically up to its elastic limit and plastically at higher loads, and is a good conductor of heat and electricity. Metals may exist in the gaseous, liquid, and solid states. Upon freezing from a liquid it becomes a solid crystalline mass. Metal crystals are microscopically small and, therefore, are seldom observed by the unaided eye.

Most commercial metals are of the alloy types; that is, they consist of two or more elements. Gold, silver, zinc, tin, and copper are examples of metal which are often employed in their pure state. Well-known alloys are steel, brass, bronze, Monel, and the aluminums.

With the exception of gold, silver, and a few others, commercial metals are derived from earth deposits of their oxides, carbonates, hydrides, and other chemical compound forms. The extraction of metals from the parent ores involve processing such as reduction, roasting, flotation, leaching, electrolysis, etc.

The control of solidification, transformation, and gain size in metal is the means by which important mechanical and physical properties are obtained in structural and machine members. The performance of space

rockets, reliability and comfort of automobiles, and the miracle of television are the outgrowth of controlling the characteristics of metals.

STRUCTURES AND PROPERTIES OF METALS

Unit cells in the metal crystal. Metals are composed of many individual crystals secured together at their boundaries. Crystals are composed of atoms. Elemental metals have widely varying individualities; a
chief characteristic is their atomic arrangement.

In general, the basic concept of an atom is that it consists of a nucleus
and a fixed number of orbital electrons. The atom of any element differs
from the atom of another element in the mass of the nucleus and the
number of associated electrons. In the gaseous and liquid states, several
atoms may be associated to form a molecule. The molecules in liquids
are free to move among themselves, but to a lesser degree than in the
gaseous state. Molecules in the two fluid states behave differently because, as a gas, the molecules will fill their container; but, as a liquid,
they generally have no tendency to change in volume if the temperature
remains constant.

When the state changes to that of a solid crystalline body, the dis-
order that was so evident in gases and liquids becomes an ordered one
of very precise nature. In the new order the atoms are in exact geometric
patterns. Cubic, hexagonal, and other geometric shapes are some of the
common systems, as given in Fig. 2–1. A solid formed by change of
state is defined by the surrounding container and by planes within the
solid. The basic geometric body created upon changing from the liquid
to the solid state is referred to as the *unit cell*. In the body-centered-cubic
(BCC) type the distribution of atoms consists of one at each corner of
the cube and one at its geometric center. The face-centered-cubic (FCC)
unit cell has an atom at each corner and one in the center of each
face.

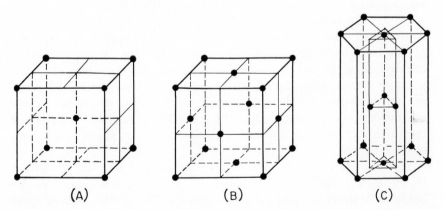

Fig. 2–1. Arrangement of atoms in unit cell.

The nature of the unit cell, and hence the crystal, depends largely upon the kinds of elemental atoms present and the temperature. It is primarily these factors that indicate whether the atoms will exist in an alloy as separate crystals side by side and joined by grain boundaries, or as crystals of solid solutions. In two different elemental metals the atom size and physical features of the unit cells may be so dissimilar that solubility is impossible; and, therefore, the two metals are termed insoluble, as lead in iron. On the other hand, if two elements have similar unit cells and the atoms are of compatible size they may combine to form entirely different crystals and both elements lose their crystalline identity. At elevated temperatures complete solubility between elements may be obtained; at some lower temperature only partial solubility; and at an even lower temperature, complete insolubility. An alloy of carbon and iron is an example of the type in which the carbon unit cell is hexagonal and is somewhat soluble in iron which is face-centered-cubic at elevated temperatures. At room temperatures iron is body-centered-cubic, the carbon is unchanged, and the solubility of carbon in iron is very low.

Crystals of the body-centered-cubic type, such as chromium and molybdenum, have high tensile strength and hardness and are limited in the amount of cold-work which they will sustain. Face-centered-cubic crystals are softer, more ductile, have lower yield strength; and will cold-form, usually without difficulty. They are good conductors of electricity and heat. The hexagonal type hardens rapidly when cold-worked.

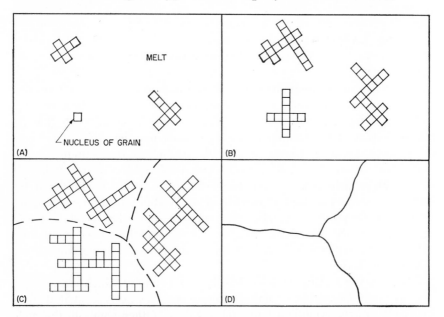

Fig. 2–2. Process of forming metal grain from melt. Views (A), (B), and (C) show growth of dendrites. The metallographical grain boundary is shown in (D).

Formation of grains. At some point in the falling temperature of a melt, several atoms from the melt associate themselves to form a very small crystal, called a *nucleus.* Just why these particular atoms join in this manner is one of the mysteries of metallurgy; nevertheless, an instant before the nucleus forms, all atoms move and shift freely in the liquid, and an instant afterward the small plastic particle exists. The embryonic crystal increases in size by addition of atoms to its several plane faces (Fig. 2–2). Rate of growth is a function of the heat withdrawal rate. In a cubic crystal the direction of growth is normal to the cubic faces (in six directions), giving rise to the dendritic appearance shown in Fig 2–3. Under most conditions of cooling the size of the crystal is limited by interference from a neighboring crystal. If a melt could be cooled under ideal conditions, theoretically a single crystal would be obtained. In commercial practice this is neither desirable nor possible.

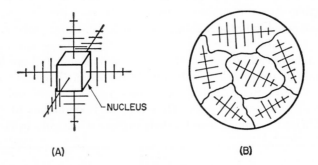

Fig. 2–3. (A) Dendritic growth of crystal.
(B) Relationship of dendrites in polycrystalline metal.

Nuclei form at numerous points in the melt upon incipient freezing. When nuclei start forming with the drop in temperature, the first freezing action will be at points where the heat dissipation is greatest; that is, at the surface of the container. An ingot mold may be such a container (Fig. 2–4). Crystals enlarge by initially starting at the container walls and growing into the liquid, thus causing a column-like shape. It is evident that growth in any other direction would finally be hindered by neighboring crystals and thus individual crystals are limited in size. Columnar (dendrite) crystals, after encountering other crystals, make additional growth by atomic additions at right angles to the main axis. The crystal completes its form by filling in the interstices, thus resembling a tree (Fig. 2–3).

When a nucleus forms, it evolves heat, a behavior which discourages atomic additions to that crystal until more heat has been dissipated from the melt and the attendant temperatures drop. Other points in the melt will have slightly lower temperatures momentarily and will form other nuclei. Because of the numerous nuclei, it is easily seen that a single crystal could not form in the freezing of commercial metals.

A solid rapidly formed from a fast-cooling melt will have a greater abundance of nuclei and, therefore, have crystals (grains) of smaller size. Grain size is significant in metallurgical practice, since the number of individual grains contained in a unit volume of metal has an important bearing on its properties. For example, large grain size will promote greater hardenability in steels; and small grain size tends to improve shock-resistance and ductility.

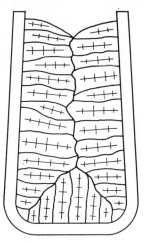

Because nuclei usually start at a number of places in the melt on cooling, the final solid will contain many crystals and is said to be *polycrystalline*. Important atomic planes within a crystal have orientations, if considered in reference to a neighboring crystal, which results in an interlocking effect and general strengthening of the crystalline aggregate.

Fig. 2–4. Columnar crystals in an ingot.

Dendritic growth does not progress with uniform speed; thus, grains will be of varying size and irregular in shape. Figure 2–5 depicts this aspect of grain structure.

Grain boundaries. The nature of grain boundaries which attach grains together is little understood. The definition of the grain boundaries is, in most cases, good; in fact, the boundaries are used more frequently than any other distinguishing feature for the identification of certain microstructures. Some metallographers support the theory that grain boundaries are made up of impurities expelled from the freezing melt. Others insist that boundaries are *amorphous* (noncrystalline) material; that is, the atoms last to freeze which were not in the correct numbers to form perfect unit cells. Whatever the case is, the boundaries of the grains play an important role in the properties of the polycrystalline metal.

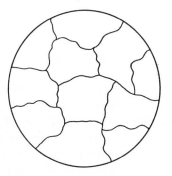

Fig. 2–5. Polycrystalline structure.

Grain (crystal) size. Single crystals produced by slow cooling and other idealized treatments seldom have value outside of the academic field. Commercial metals are aggregates of many crystals or grains. With incipient freezing, nuclei start forming in the region of the mold, or at the points of lowest temperature, and with subsequent drop in temperature the crystals grow as previously explained. Because the heat from the metal is dissipated through the mold walls, the crystals will grow inward and thus form column-like microstructure. Under more uniform conditions of cooling, nucleation or origin of the individual grains may be uniformly distributed throughout the cooling melt and, for this reason, the crystals tend to be equiaxed. The size of the grain is a function of the speed of cooling, the impurities present, and other factors.

After the melt is entirely exhausted and freezing is complete, a sample may be taken from the metal for examination. If a section is taken through the sample and prepared by an approved metallographic technique, the relationship of each grain to its neighbor may be seen through a microscope. The microscope shows, among other things, the diverse angles of orientation of the individual equiaxed grains. The average size of the grain seen in the examination necessarily indicates that some grains are smaller than others (Fig. 2–6). In designating the size of grain, the average size is always given. The grain size has a direct bearing on such properties as endurance strength, impact resistance, and machinability of the metal.

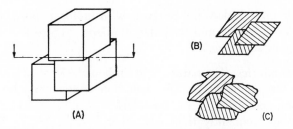

Fig. 2–6. Orientation of grain in metallurgical specimen. (A) Theoretical grain. (B) Section through theoretical grain. (C) Typical polyhedral grain in section.

The ductility of a metal is thought to derive from the nature of the grain boundaries and the grain orientation. Plastic strain occurs when atomic planes slip past each other. In commercial metal, grains are variously oriented so that the path of plastic slip has to change direction from one grain to the next one. By this means planes are more abundantly available for slip in response to stresses applied from any direction. If this were not true only those grains properly oriented with respect to the stresses, and rather accurately so, would contribute to the plasticity of a metal. This explains why fine-grain metals exhibit greater ductile properties.

The mutual attraction of atoms. A metal displays strength in normal service by resisting its loads. In calculating the resistance of a material in most design areas, no consideration is given to permanent or plastic deformation, although structural designers sometimes rely on limited plastic deformation to distribute loads. Generally, designers of machine elements compute their stresses to some value below which plastic deformation occurs.

Elasticity is inherent in any constructional material. It is from this property that dependability and long life are built into modern machinery and structures. The elastic character of many metals permits loading with a given amount of displacement or deformation but they resume their original dimensions when the loads are removed, providing, of course, that the elastic limit is not exceeded. There is a rough likeness between a metal tensile member and a coiled door spring, although the elastic effect is obviously exaggerated in the spring. The spring may be extended by loading but will return to its original length on release of the load. However, if a great enough load is imposed the coils of the spring are permanently separated and after release of the deforming load, the length will be somewhat greater than before.

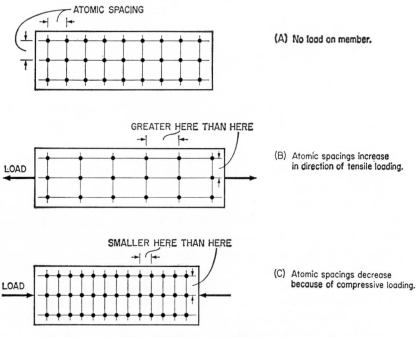

Fig. 2–7. Elastic behavior of member loaded in tension and in compression.

An analogy also exists between the door spring and the atoms in a metal. In the crystal the atoms are bonded together, presumably, by some manner of magnetic attraction and spaced apart at exact distances. Elasticity is one of the important features of magnetism; therefore this theory of magnetic attraction appears to be reasonable and acceptable, for if the compression load is applied to a crystal, it changes in shape in such a way that the atoms appear to be closer together in line with the load and further apart transverse to the load. In tension, the reverse effect is observed. Figure 2–7 illustrates this principle. If the elastic limit of the material is exceeded, the atoms will shift with respect to one another along the path of displacement and permanently remain in the new position if the load becomes no greater. With increased loading the member may fail by complete separation of the atoms.

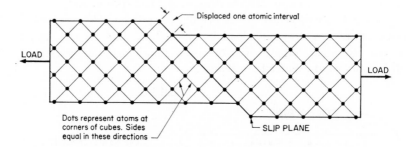

Fig. 2–8. Permanent deformation as a result of slip along plane of high atomic polulation.

In the unit cell certain planes within the geometric solid have higher atomic population and the most favorable orientation for slip with respect to the crystal faces (Fig. 2–8). In permanent deformation the change in dimension is affected by slip along the planes of greatest atomic populations since they are further apart than other planes and oriented at angles of best gliding action.

Recent investigations show that plastic gliding action within a crystal is by dislocation. Figure 2–9 illustrates the principle. The initial effects of plastic deformation by force F is to shift the top layers of atoms to the right a distance of one atomic interval. As noted by the circle, several atoms are displaced from their normal spacing to create the dislocation. This condition can be detected by metallographical etching, since an etchant attacks a dislocation more rapidly than elsewhere along the gliding plane. As the stress increases, the dislocation moves to the right, and strain increases until the dislocation meets a barrier, such as a grain boundary. When that is completed, the atoms to the left are normally spaced.

A few impurity atoms, either larger or smaller than the normal atoms, cause some distortion of the normal atoms, and, therefore, impede dislocation behavior. Precipitated particles also impede dislocation. Alloying to introduce such impediments and thus strengthen and harden metals is common metallurgical practice.

Just why a particular plane is selected over another of the same orientation for the initial deformation is not known, but it is generally thought that the impurities in the atomic arrangement are responsible. Strangely enough, after the first plane has displaced through one or more atomic intervals, that plane is strengthened and hardened. For subsequent deformation, other planes successively slip, the overall action being conducive to less favorable orientation for slip by reason of the slight rotation of the crystal which is induced. The hardness, which reflects resistance to slip, becomes increasingly greater, more stress must be applied for further deformation, and finally complete failure may occur from brittleness. This hardness is, in the metal-working industry, termed *work-hardening* or *cold-work* and is the result of working below the recrystallization temperature.

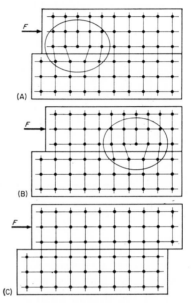

Fig. 2–9. Dislocation behavior. (A) The circle shows dislocation at the start of plastic deformation. (B) The circle shows that the dislocation has moved as loading becomes greater.

A secondary mode of crystal deformation is called *twinning*, which is a limited and ordered movement of a large number of atoms in a definite section of a crystal. Twinning can account for only small strains and does not occur in some materials but has some importance in that it can reorient atomic planes more favorably for slip.

Rupture. A failure by rupture is complex. Under a load, the first effect on the member is elastic deformation. With additional load the elastic limit may be exceeded and the plasticity of the metal must be utilized for further deformation. Failure occurs with loading if slip cannot accommodate the strain. High ductility or slip is facilitated by reorientation of grains. Where such action is obstructed or expended, the atoms in unit cells move further apart, beyond a critical distance, and the loaded member ruptures.

Types of failures. Failures or ruptures are generally of two types—ductile and brittle. The ductile failure is silky in appearance, thus suggesting two surfaces that wiped each other during the rend, and failed by slip along a plane at an angle to the axis of loading. Brittle failures are usually dull, irregular, and tend to break square rather than at a shearing angle. Frequently the two types exist in the same rupture as a result of progressive hardening. The outside portion may shear in a ductile manner while the center may fail as a brittle section. Figure 2–10 shows the combined types in a standard tensile test bar.

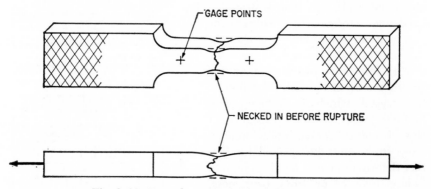

Fig. 2–10. Typical rupture in a tensile test piece.

Effects of temperature. Metals are hot-worked to shape at elevated temperatures and then cooled to room temperature. Whether a metal survives the stresses imposed by heating, shaping, and cooling without failure depends not only upon its mechanical properties at the elevated temperature but also upon the nature of the stresses.

Upon an increase in temperature the atomic mobility of a metal is accelerated. If the structure of a metal has been distorted, its atoms begin to reform into new undeformed grains when a certain temperature, called the *recrystallization temperature,* is reached. As temperature is increased, tensile strength drops and ductility rises, except immediately above the recrystallization temperature where the ductility of metal drops off rather sharply. Depending upon which metal or alloy is considered, there are other temperature ranges of low ductility. For example, free-cutting steel containing a high percentage of sulfur has a certain degree of brittleness at forging temperature which is referred to as *hot short.*

At high service temperatures a member carrying a load may change its dimensions by an effect called *creep.* A deformation of this type may lead to rupture even with stress at a reasonably low magnitude. The use of molybdenum as an alloying element in steel is effective in reducing deformation caused by creep. Alloys of molybdenum, columbium, tungsten, and titanium are viewed with favor for use in high-temperature environments.

Notches. If stress lines in a member are imagined to be similar to rubber bands, the effect of a discontinuity in the shape of a member becomes evident. Figure 2–11 shows a notch in a tensile link and its attending

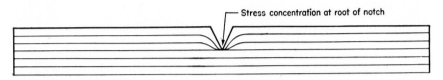

Fig. 2–11. Concentration of stresses at root of a notch.

stress concentration. The magnitude of a stress such as this cannot be calculated with any satisfactory degree of accuracy. The complications arising from the notch effect are those of confinement or restraint; that is, the full amount of plasticity reported for the material may not be available at the highly stressed point because of restraining effects of adjacent metal. With this condition of stresses surrounding a notch, brittleness may cause a crack or tear to start and be propagated to cause total failure of the member. Intermittent loads often cause fatigue failures at notches even though the design stress for the member is well within the elastic range of the material. Fine-grain metals are less likely to fail from notches combined with dynamic loading. Common notches are grinder scratches, hammer marks, arc scars, and corrosion pits.

Hot-work. If a commercial metal is deformed by hammering, rolling, pressing, or shaping by other means, the member is elongated in at least one direction. Such changes in shapes are referred to as hot-working or cold-working, depending upon whether the process is done above or below the recrystallization temperature. At temperatures sufficiently high to effectively roll or forge steels and other metals, grain growth may occur; therefore, the practice is to continue the work down to a temperature which is below the grain growth zone. Where the only purpose is to give shape—as in turning flanges—the need for improvement in the properties of the metal are generally nonexistent.

Cold-work. Deformation given a metal below the recrystallization temperature of that metal will elongate the grain, increase the tensile strength, etc., as well as introduce stresses. Wire drawing and coining are typical of this effect. Table 2–1 shows the result of the cold-working of some common materials. Hot- and cold-working of metals are discussed further in Chap. 12.

TABLE 2–1. COMPARISON BETWEEN PROPERTIES OF (1) HOT- AND
(2) COLD-WORKED METALS

Alloy	Ultimate tensile strength (psi)	Yield strength (psi)	Hardness
Aluminum 1100:			
"O" condition	16,000	6,000	28 Bhn
H18 condition	29,000	25,000	55 Bhn
Electrolytic tough pitch copper:			
Hot-rolled	34,000	10,000	45 R_F
Extra spring	57,000	53,000	95 R_F
Steel, SAE 1010:			
Hot-rolled	62,000	32,000	60 R_B
Cold-rolled	81,000	50,000	90 R_B
Brass, yellow:			
Annealed	49,000	17,000	68 R_F
Spring hard	91,000	62,000	90 R_B

EQUILIBRIUM DIAGRAMS

Solidification of pure and impure metals. When a *pure metal* freezes, it changes state at a fixed temperature known as its freezing point. On a falling temperature, if data are taken of time and temperature and plotted on Cartesian coordinates, a typical freezing curve may be obtained as shown in Fig. 2–12. It is noted that the mid-section of the curve is horizontal and represents the evolution of latent heat at the freezing point. If the purity of the metal is extremely high, it may evidence some difficulty in forming nuclei to initiate freezing and, consequently, tends to cool to a temperature somewhat lower than the normal freezing temperature before solidification starts. It is then said to be *super-cooled*. At this subtemperature nuclei appear to form suddenly and vigorously, evolving heat. When freezing is complete, the temperature rises to the normal freezing point.

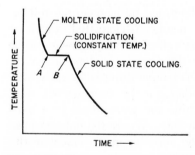

Fig. 2–12. Time-temperature cooling curve of a pure metal.

In contrast to pure metals, an *impure metal* (one containing more than one element, such as an alloy) has a tendency to solidify through a temperature range. Steel is an example of an alloy or an impure metal which cools through a mushy range as shown in Fig. 2–13. As an example, steel having 0.5% carbon, on a falling temperature, will start to freeze at 2720°F; it continues to freeze progressively and remain more or less in a mushy state until the temperature drops to 2630°F, where it is completely solid. The lead-antimony and copper-silver alloys are also typical of those which freeze through a mushy range rather than at a constant temperature.

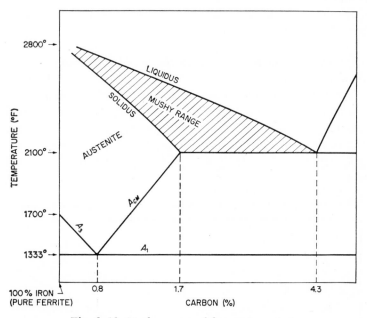

Fig. 2–13. Mushy range of low-carbon steel.

Types of alloys. Metallic elements combine into alloys in three ways. In some cases they do not mix and, if they do not separate into layers while molten, exist in an intimate *mechanical mixture.* The elements keep their individual identities and properties in adjacent and interspersed grains.

A second way elements may combine is by dissolving one in the other to form a *solid solution.* This may be a *substitutional form,* with the atoms of one element replacing those of the other at random in the base lattice, or the *interstitial form,* with the atoms of one occupying spaces at random between the atoms of the other.

A third type of alloy is an *intermetallic compound* in which the atoms of one element replace those of the other in definite positions and proportions in the base lattice. All the elements need not be metals. Commonly the atoms of the constituents are of different sizes, and the lattice of an intermetallic compound lacks symmetry and has fewer planes along which atomic slip is easy.

Further benefits are obtained in some alloys by combinations of the basic types of alloys just described. For instance, certain tool steels are quite hard because of particles of metallic carbides distributed but not dissolved in an iron matrix.

A picture of how two or more metals in various proportions combine at various temperatures is called an *equilibrium diagram*. Such diagrams are available in reference books for all common alloys. The three basic forms are described in the following sections to show what they reveal and how they are read.

Two metals completely soluble in the liquid state and completely insoluble in the solid state. In Fig. 2–14, two metals, A and B, are graphically shown to be soluble in the molten state and completely insoluble in the solid state. Examination of the figure shows *LEL′* and *LSES′L′* to be liquidus and solidus lines, respectively. The incipient freezing temperature is a function of the alloy composition. On a falling temperature the first or *primary crystals* form at *LEL′*. Upon further lowering of the temperature, additional crystals form and, finally, at *SES′* all of the remaining melt solidifies at constant temperature.

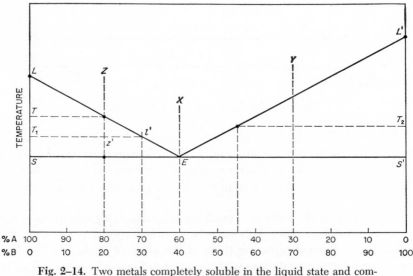

Fig. 2–14. Two metals completely soluble in the liquid state and completely insoluble in the solid state.

Consider three alloys of composition X, Y, and Z. X has a composition of 60% metal A and 40% metal B. As noted on the diagram, an alloy of this composition has no mushy range and, therefore, freezes at a constant temperature. The alloy is a *eutectic* because it has the lowest freezing (or melting) point of any proportion of metals A and B. A frozen eutectic is a finely divided aggregate or mechanical mixture of pure crystals A and B.

Composition Z (80% A, 20% B) starts to freeze at temperature T, forming pure crystals of A (the predominating metal). Further drop in temperature causes additional freezing until, at temperature S, the remaining melt is of eutectic composition and solidifies at constant temperature. Therefore, the final microstructure is pure crystals A in a matrix of eutectic, the latter being finely divided crystals of both A and B.

At any temperature during solidification of composition Z, the composition of the solid and the liquid in equilibrium may be found by drawing a horizontal line from the temperature value in question, say T_1, to l' on liquidus line LE. A vertical line to the composition scale shows the melt to be 70% A and 30% B. The solid crystals are pure metal A. Using the lever method, the ratio of solid to liquid is inversely proportional to the line segments through z'. This is expressed as $z'T_1/l'T_1 = 66\frac{2}{3}\%$ liquid and $z'l'/l'T_1 = 33\frac{1}{3}\%$ solid. The lever system is also employed in finding the relative amounts of eutectic in solid alloy Z of crystals A.

$$\text{eutectic} = \frac{100 - 80}{100 - 60} = \frac{20}{40} \text{ or } 50\%,$$

and

$$\text{crystal A} = \frac{80 - 60}{100 - 60} = \frac{20}{40} \text{ or } 50\%.$$

In composition Y, the primary crystals start forming at EL' on a falling temperature and are pure B. Similar to the behavior of alloy Z, a eutectic freezes at ES', forming a matrix around crystals B. The composition of the melt at any temperature within the mushy region—for example, T_2—may be found by drawing a horizontal line from T_2 to EL'; then, by dropping a vertical line from the intersection to the composition line, the melt is seen to be 45% A and 55% B. Again using the lever system,

$$\text{eutectic} = \frac{30 - 0}{100 - 40} = 0.5 \text{ or } 50\%,$$

and

$$\text{crystal B} = \frac{60 - 30}{100 - 40} = 0.5 \text{ or } 50\%.$$

Two metals completely soluble in both liquid and solid states. If curves show the slow cooling of two metals which are mutually soluble in both liquid and solid states for several compositions, and have their corresponding break points connected with a smooth line, an equilibrium relationship for the alloy will appear as in Fig. 2–15.

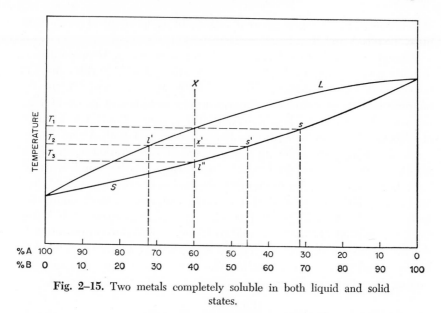

Fig. 2–15. Two metals completely soluble in both liquid and solid states.

An example of the 60A–40B alloy is shown. The first crystals form at T_1 (falling temperature). Their composition are found by drawing a horizontal line T_1s. Since s is shown on the solidus line, a vertical line from this point to the composition line shows the crystals in equilibrium to be 32% A and 68% B. Upon cooling to T_2, the intersections of horizontal line $l' - s'$ and curves L and S indicate proportions of the molten and the solid phases at temperature T_2. Vertical lines drawn from l' and s' show the compositions of the remaining liquid and the solid formed to T_2. At T_3 solidification is complete, and the solid is of composition l''.

The alloy becomes progressively richer in metal B as it freezes at progressively lower temperatures as shown, and the individual crystal grows by adding successive layers of the richer alloy. This effect is called *coring*. The heterogeneity caused by coring is easily discernible in a properly prepared metallographical specimen viewed through a microscope. Coring may be destroyed by: (1) hot-working, (2) cold-working followed by recrystallization, and (3) heating for an extended period at a temperature just below the solidus for the particular composition. Coring is undesirable in alloys which are to have optimum properties.

The lever system is employed to calculate the amounts of the two phases (solid and liquid) at any temperature within the mushy range. A vertical line is drawn through the composition under consideration—in this case, 60A–40B. Horizontal segment $x's'$ is the amount of liquid and $x'l'$ is the amount of solid. Using metal A as the basis of reference, alloy $X = 60\%$ A, $l' = 72\%$ A,   and $s' = 46\%$ A.

Also $x's' = 60 - 46 = 14$,

           $x'l' = 72 - 60 = 12$,

and $l's' = 72 - 46 = 26$.

Amount of liquid at T_2 equals

$$\frac{x's'}{l's'} = \frac{14}{26} = 0.54 = 54\%.$$

Amount of solid at T_2 equals

$$\frac{x'l'}{l's'} = \frac{12}{26} = 0.46 = 46\%.$$

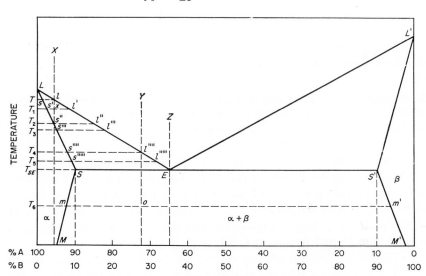

Fig. 2–16. Two metals completely soluble in the liquid state and partially soluble in the solid state.

Two metals completely soluble in the liquid state and partially soluble in the solid state. Many metals retain at least small amounts of other metals in solution at temperatures approaching ambient, but less at lower temperatures. Figure 2–16 depicts this relationship; LEL' is the liquidus, $LSES'L'$ the solidus, and LSM and $L'S'M'$ the limits of solubility on each end of the diagram. At the eutectic line, S is the solubility limit of B in A; and S' is the solubility limit of A in B. Vertical lines drawn to the composition line show the proportions of B in A at S and A in B at S', both at the eutectic temperature. Too, it is noted that solubilities decrease as the temperature drops; that is from S to M and S' to M'.

Considering alloy X, solidification starts at l, and is completed at s'', and the alloy then drops to room temperature at constant solubility. The composition of crystals formed at any temperature within the mushy range can be found by drawing a horizontal line to intersect LS and LE and thence vertically to the composition line. The lever system may be employed here to calculate the relative amounts of liquid and solid, as previously explained. For example:

Liquid at T_1 equals

$$\frac{S'x}{s'l'} \times 100 = \text{per cent}$$

Solid at T_1 equals

$$\frac{xl'}{s'l'} \times 100 = \text{per cent}$$

For any composition of 10% to 35% B, crystals start to form along LE with compositions designated by LS. Crystals which form subsequently will be richer in B as noted by the slope of LS. At SES' (temperature T_{SE}) all of the remaining liquid is of composition E and, as a eutectic, freezes at a constant temperature. The eutectic is a mixture of a saturated solution of B in A and A in B. Thus, at the eutectic temperature, all crystals are solid solutions of varying proportions.

In alloy Y crystals start forming at l'''' on a falling temperature. Their composition may be found by drawing a horizontal line to s'''' and then vertically to the composition line. At T_5 both liquid and solid exist and their compositions and relative amounts can be found as shown for alloy X at T_1. At the eutectic temperature, line SE, all remaining liquid is of composition E, and freezes at constant temperature.

Characteristic of this alloy system, below SE the solubilities of B in A and A in B decrease with the temperature as shown by the slopes of the lines SM and $S'M'$. At T_6 the amount of B in A is somewhat less than at the eutectic temperature and likewise for A in B. Thus at T_6 (or any temperature below T_{SE}) the solid is an agglomeration of two solid solutions which are usually denoted as alpha (α) and beta (β), left- and right-hand sides of the diagram, respectively. The composition of alpha crystals at T_6 is found by drawing a vertical line from m to the composition line; the composition of beta is similarly determined by drawing a vertical line through m'.

To calculate the relative amounts of alpha and beta in alloy Y at temperature T_6, the line mm' is the basis of reference. Using the lever principle:

$$\text{amount of } \alpha = \frac{om'}{mm'} \times 100 = \%, \qquad \text{amount of } \beta = \frac{mo}{mm'} \times 100 = \%$$

Alloy Z, the eutectic composition for the system, will solidify at constant temperature T_{SE} without the formation of primary crystals (mushy). The compositions and proportions of the α and β solid solutions existing below T_{SE} may be calculated as in the example of alloy Y.

Properties of metals and alloys. The mechanical properties of metals and their alloys are largely dependent upon the microconstituents they contain.

Solid solutions are comparatively ductile, soft, and malleable, and tend to confer these properties on alloys in which they are present. Softness and malleability are important in the cold-rolling and deep-drawing of ferrous and nonferrous alloys. Many of the brasses and bronzes are examples of soft nonferrous alloys containing solid solutions. Ductility also bears a relationship to shock-resistance and, therefore, for most uses metals must have this property.

Intermetallic compounds are of greater hardness than the elements from which they are derived; with brittleness, low shock-resistance, and reduced tensile strength as their outstanding characteristics. Generally speaking, the presence of compounds in proper distribution improves the properties of alloy cutting tools. Examples of alloys containing intermetallic compounds are Babbit and aluminum alloys containing nickel or tin.

Eutectics of nonferrous alloys are brittle but not to the extent of intermetallic compounds. Since primary crystals are imbedded in a matrix of eutectic, the mechanical properties of these types of alloys are largely governed by the eutectic. These alloys are principally used for low-melting solders and bearing metals.

MICROCONSTITUENTS AND GRAIN IN STEEL

Generally speaking, the microstructure of steel consists of ferrite and cementite arranged with each other in numerous patterns. Under varying conditions of heat treating, as discussed in Chap. 5, iron and carbon may be related in an extremely complex manner to produce steel workpieces which have selectively varying mechanical and physical properties. A simplified equilibrium diagram for iron and carbon is shown in Fig. 2–13.

Ferrite. Ferrite is pure iron (BCC), a metallic element which is capable of holding in solution such elements as nickel, silicon, phosphorus, sulfur, and carbon. The solubility of these elements will vary according to the temperature; in particular the element carbon has very little tendency to dissolve in ferrite at room temperature. Ferrite has the property known as *allotropy;* on a rising temperature and at 1670°F it transforms from the BCC to the FCC type—a reversible reaction. Face-centered-cubic ferrite is nonmagnetic. Ferrite has a specific gravity of 7.86, a tensile strength of 38,000 to 40,000 psi, an elongation of 40%, and a hardness of about 50 Rc. In the average plain-carbon steel ferrite will constitute 99% or more of the metal.

A properly prepared metallographic specimen of a fully annealed steel containing less than 0.83% carbon will show light polyhedral areas (ferrite) intermixed with gray polyhedral areas (pearlite), all grains being attached together to form a continuous, tenacious aggregate (Fig. 2–17).

Cementite. Cementite is a chemical compound of carbon and iron which exists in some quantity in all steels. It consists of 6.67% carbon and 93.33% iron by weight.

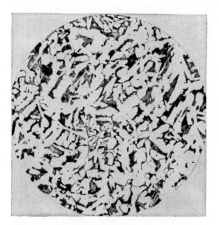

Fig. 2–17. Polyhedral hypo-eutectoid steel (X100).

Cementite is the hardest phase in steel, having a Rockwell C hardness number of 62, a tensile strength of 5000 psi, elongation nil, and a specific gravity of 7.66. As a microconstituent it may appear as globular particles, membranes at grain boundaries, interlayered with ferrite, as precipitated individual particles, and in many other forms. It is from the controllable distribution of cementite in heat treatments that a multiplicity of mechanical and physical properties are obtained in steel. With ordinary techniques of metallographic preparation, cementite appears white when observed under the microscope.

Cementite is practically insoluble in iron up to 1333°F. Above this temperature it is gradually dissolved by the iron on heating, the dissolution being complete at line A_3 or A_{CM} as shown in Fig. 2–13. Above these temperatures it is in complete solid solution with iron.

Austenite. Austenite is a solid solution of carbon and iron (other elements may also exist). Austenite is nonmagnetic, since the BCC (alpha) unit cell has changed to the FCC (gamma), and by this characteristic it may be detected. At the austenitizing temperatures, above the A_3 and A_{CM} lines in Fig. 2–13, forging, rolling, pressing, and many heat treatments are done. It is also in this temperature range that grain growth and burning may occur; hence temperatures should be selected with care and should be based on the nature of the processing that is to follow.

Austenite is unstable at room temperature in ordinary steels. It may, however, exist at room temperature by: (1) quenching sufficiently rapidly to set up a high state of rigidity before transformation occurs, and (2) introducing alloys which are predominately of the face-centered-cubic types. It is by the latter method that such alloy steels as 18-8 stainless and 14% manganese steel are made austenitic at normal temperatures.

Primary constituents. Primary constituents in hardened steels are those microstructures that result directly from quenching. The geometric forms and patterns assumed by primary constituents depend mainly upon the speed of cooling and the tendency of a steel to transform. It is well to mention again that transformation from austenite to cementite and ferrite requires a period of time. If less time is allowed than that required to assume the equilibrium condition, steels tend to harden. By the formation of primary constituents varying degrees of hardness may be obtained upon quenching.

Martensite. This hard constituent is an interlacing, needle-like structure which evolves from the rapid quenching of steel. Two factors govern the formation of martensite—the amount of carbon present (along with intensifying alloying elements, if present) and the speed of cooling. Steels must contain at least 0.2% carbon and the rate of heat dissipation must be above a certain specified amount (*critical cooling speed*) for martensite to form.

When heated, iron becomes face-centered-cubic (gamma iron) and dissolves carbides. When the iron is quenched, transformation occurs at a low temperature, and the carbides tend to precipitate out of solution and coalesce. If a sufficient amount of carbon is present and the rate of heat dissipation equals or exceeds the critical cooling rate, the resulting microstructure will be hard (martensite). The carbides ejected from solution are dispersed as submicroscopic particles and occupy interstatial spaces in the unit cells. Considerable distortion of the cells results from this behavior and causes the hardened steel to be unstable but hard. The precipitated carbides presumably have a keying effect which tends to deprive the steel of its property of plastic flow and thus produces high strength and brittleness.

As depicted in Fig. 2–18, martensite will appear under the microscope, at about ×1000, to be a needle-like or acicular structure; the needles appear in shades from dark to black, depending upon the amount of etching, and are contrasted against a light-colored matrix background. Whether martensite has grain boundaries is a polemical point. Hypoeutectoid and hypereutectoid steels may have martensitic areas outlined by ferrite and cementite, respectively, if quenched from immediately above the lower critical temperature.

Fig. 2–18. Martensite. (X1000).

Primary troostite. This primary constituent is a product of quenching a steel from its austenitizing temperature at a cooling rate somewhat lower than the critical cooling speed but higher than that necessary to form coarse pearlite. Primary troostite is most predominately found in plain-carbon steels. These steels are martensitic in their surface areas, and their interiors, which have cooled at a somewhat lower rate, are of primary troostite. As might be supposed, primary troostite is somewhat softer than martensite but considerably harder than the pearlites in annealed steels. Compared to martensite, primary troostite is tougher and more shock-resistant but lower in tensile strength.

Primary troostite is observed to be dark to black rosette patterns, and is often referred to as a radial pearlite.

Bainite. Bainite is a primary constituent obtained by direct quenching and its formation, as related to the S-curve (Fig. 5–5), occurs between the temperature limits of 950 to 1150°F. In general, metallurgists have failed to make very convicing statements with regards to the nature of this transformation product. It was found to be derived from isothermal transformation and, while varying somewhat in its appearance throughout the temperature range in which it is obtained, it is a feathery, needle-like, constituent and thought by most observers to be lamellar. Depending upon the region of the S-curve in which its transformation takes place, bainite is a dark-etching microstructure, and its hardness is about 40 Rc.

Evidently, isothermal transformation of steels is of advantage where the ultimate mechanical properties sought are those of bainite because it avoids the risk of losing work pieces by severe quenching directly to martensite. With this advantage in mind, increasing use is being made of the principle, which is illustrated in Fig. 5–5.

Pearlite. Normal pearlite consists of alternate layers of iron carbide and alpha iron, appearing as a stratified and wavy microstructure. The basic form of pearlite is an equilibrium product most commonly derived at slow rates of cooling as in annealing. As such, pearlite grains have 0.83% carbon and are most predominant as the carbon content approaches the eutectoid amount (100% pearlite). Slowly cooled, all austenite at 1333°F transforms to pearlite at constant temperature. Thus, if the steel has less than the eutectoid amount of carbon (hypoeutectoid), all grains of ferrite form between the upper and lower critical points as the temperature falls, and pearlite forms at 1333°F. Finally, at all lower temperatures the microstructure is an aggregate of ferrite and pearlite grains of polyhedral shape. In steels having greater than the eutectoid amount of carbon (hypereutectoid), the excess microconstituent is iron carbide, and the final aggregate is iron carbide and pearlite, the former usually being at the grain boundaries.

When viewed under the microscope, pearlite appears in varying shapes of darkness and, under normal conditions of etching, ranges from almost white to almost black (Fig. 2–19).

Ferrite has a tensile strength of approximately 40,000 psi and elongation of 40% while the tensile strength of iron carbide is about 5000 psi and elongation nil. The interlayering of these two phases in pearlite with an overall carbon content of 0.83% results in a steel that has a tensile strength of about 125,000 to 150,000 psi with an elongation of 10 to 15%.

Pearlites are ordinarily defined on the basis of an eutectoid amount of carbon and slow cooling; however, wide variations of pearlites may be derived by employing different rates of cooling, changing the alloy content, changing the austenite grain size, or by other means.

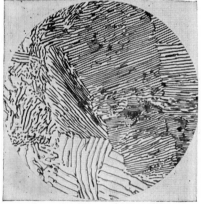

Fig. 2–19. Pearlite (X1000).

Secondary micronstituents. The secondary microconstituents are obtained by reheating martensite to a selected temperature below 1333°F. This is called *tempering* or *toughening* and is described in Chap. 5. The microconstituent produced by tempering is called *secondary troostite*, a tough, shock-resistant, relatively hard microstructure. Toughening forms *sorbite*. Both are granular rather than needle-like.

Amounts of microconstituents present in slowly cooled carbon steels. By use of the equilibrium diagram of Fig. 5–1, along with the knowledge that pearlite and cementite contain 0.83% and 6.76% carbon, respectively, the amounts of microconstituents in a slowly cooled steel may be calculated. In compositions having 0.83% carbon, the grains are all pearlite; steels of less carbon have correspondingly less pearlite and more ferrite. If a hypothetical steel has 6.67% carbon, it is 100% cementite, and, therefore, the full range of cementite is from 0.83% carbon (zero cementite) to 6.67% carbon (100% cementite).

To determine mathematically the amounts of microconstituents present in annealed steels, the following examples may be followed.

A plain-carbon steel has 0.45% carbon and is slowly cooled from 1500°F. Find the percentages of ferrite and pearlite.

$$\frac{0.83 - 0.45}{0.83} \times 100 = 45.8\% \text{ ferrite.}$$

$$\frac{0.45}{0.83} \times 100 = 54.2\% \text{ pearlite.}$$

A plain-carbon steel has 1.10% carbon and is slowly cooled from 1600°F. Find the percentages of pearlite and cementite.

$$\frac{6.67 - 1.10}{6.67 - 0.83} \times 100 = 95.4\% \text{ pearlite.}$$

$$\frac{1.10 - 0.83}{6.67 - 0.83} \times 100 = 4.6\% \text{ cementite.}$$

Grain size. The fitness of a steel for a specific application depends largely upon its chemical composition, the method used to make the steel, the hot- and cold-work it is given, and the heat treatments to which it is subjected. All of these factors affect the steel, more or less, with respect to its grain size and, therefore, its physical and mechanical properties. It is by varying the size of grain in a steel that a wide choice in properties is possible. Consistent observation has shown that fine-grain steels are more suited to certain applications than coarse-grain types, and vice versa.

The grains of steels heated to above their upper critical temperatures tend to grow; the amount depending largely upon the intensity of the heat and the length of time held at the temperature. Strangely enough, one steel may appear to enlarge appreciably in grain size at a given temperature; while another steel, which closely resembles the first one, appears to sustain the temperature without grain growth. Steels that show a tendency to coarsen when heated within the limits of ordinary heat-treating temperatures are called *coarse-grained* steels; steels which show little tendency to coarsen at ordinary treating temperatures are called *fine-grained* steels.

Factors affecting grain size. The size of grain obtained in a steel at room temperature is an outgrowth of the scavenging and deoxidizing practice, the alloying elements present, and the amount of hot- and cold-rolling given. A deoxidizer (added to a molten bath of steel to eliminate dissolved gases and to reduce FeO) tends to be retained in the bath as minute oxide particles. Most metallurgists believe that these particles act as nuclei; and, if the particles are numerous, they cause the formation of a fine-grain steel. Aluminum scavenging is particularly effective in the making of fine-grained steels. Where it is especially desired to produce steels which have little tendency to increase in grain size at relatively high temperatures of shaping and heat treating, such alloying elements as vanadium, molybdenum, and tungsten are frequently used.

Questions

1. Define a metal and describe its structure.

2. Name and describe three common types of unit cells in crystals. How does each react to stresses?

3. How is crystalline structure important in alloying of metals?

4. What occurs when a molten metal solidifies?

5. Why are fine-grained metals more shock-resistant and ductile than coarse?

6. Describe the mechanism of metallic strain in the elastic and the plastic regions.

7. What is meant by work-hardening or cold-work?

8. Explain how rupture takes place and describe the two types of failure of metals.

9. How do notches affect the strength of metallic pieces and why?

10. What is an eutectic?

11. What is coring and how may its effects be destroyed?

12. What are the properties of metals in the forms of solid solutions, inter-metallic compounds, and eutectics?

13. Describe the appearance under a microscope of a properly prepared met-allographic specimen of fully annealed steel containing less than 0.83% carbon.

14. What is cementite and what properties does it confer on iron and steel?

15. What is austenite and under what conditions does it occur?

16. What is martensite and when does it occur?

17. What are troostite and bainite?

18. Describe pearlite and its place among steel structures.

19. What are coarse-grained and fine-grained steels?

20. What factors affect the grain size of a steel?

Problems

1. Refer to Fig. 2–14. Find the compositions midway between the liquidus and solidus temperatures and at the solidus temperature of the following alloys.

Alloy designation:	R	S	T	U
Per cent A:	20	40	70	90
Per cent B:	80	60	30	10

2. Refer to Fig. 2–15. For the following alloys specify the composition (1) of the first crystals that separate out of the metal, (2) of the mixture half way between liquidus and solidus lines, and (3) of the last crystals to form on solidification.

Alloy designation:	K	L	M
Per cent A:	20	50	70
Per cent B:	80	50	30

3. Refer to Fig. 2–16. Specify the constituents and specify their proportions for:
   (a) Alloy X at temperatures T, T_1, T_2, T_3, T_4, T_5, and T_6.
   (b) Alloy Y at temperatures T_4, T_5, T_{SE}, and T_6.
   (c) Alloy Z at temperatures T_{SE} and T_6 and room temperature.
   (d) An alloy of 30% A and 70% B at T_4, T_{SE}, T_6, and room temperature.

4. The equilibrium diagram for steel (iron-carbon) is shown in Fig. 5–1. From that ascertain the constituents and their proportions for steels containing the following percentages of carbon: (a) 0.10, (b) 0.40, (c) 0.83, (d) 1.00, (e) 1.30.

References

Metals Handbook, American Society for Metals, Cleveland, 1948, 1954 and 1955 supplements.

Barrett, C. S., *Structure of Metals*, McGraw-Hill Book Co., Inc., New York, 1952.

Seitz, F., *The Physics of Metals*, McGraw-Hill Book Co., Inc., New York, 1952.

Testing of Engineering Materials

Purpose of testing. In general, testing is for the purpose of providing an engineer with the necessary data for his design calculations and determining whether a material, either in the raw or fabricated form, meets specifications. It is only by means of adequate testing and evaluating of materials that a favorable combination of high mechanical properties and low cost may be obtained.

The validity of a materials test will depend upon how nearly the test simulates field loading and environment, or how accurately the test results are interpreted for design application where the test is dissimilar to actual conditions.

Nondestructive tests, in which workpieces are left intact after testing, are seldom like the environmental conditions, but they indicate the quality of the workpieces in question. Destructive tests which destroy, or tend to destroy, the workpieces or specimens usually resemble environmental conditions.

The commonly used destructive and nondestructive tests will be discussed in this chapter.

DESTRUCTIVE TESTS

Tensile and compressive testing. Tensile testing is one of the more common types of mechanical tests given engineering materials. It is usually imposed to determine the unit tensile strength and ductility of a

· material. *Tensile strength* is the property of a material which enables it to resist being pulled apart. *Ductility* is the property of a material which enables it to deform permanently without failure. In useful articles, tensile strength, while important, usually is not considered alone; other properties which may be desired in combination are shock-resistance, fatigue strength, creep strength, etc.

A machine for loading a specimen for tensile testing is called a *tensile testing machine*. The machine applies the load mechanically or hydraulically at a constant rate and accurately indicates, either by balancing beam or some other means, the amount of load. The amount of elongation in the specimen caused by the load is measured accurately by a mechanical, electrical, or optical device called an *extensometer*. In Fig.

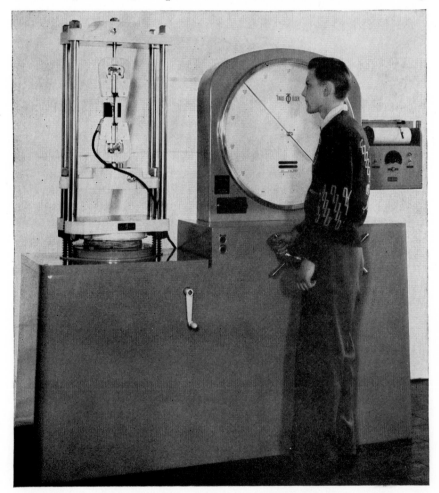

Fig. 3–1. A tensile testing machine. (Courtesy Tinius Olsen Testing Machine Co.)

3–1 is depicted a modern tensile testing machine. Rectangular, round, square or threaded standard test specimens are gripped between suitable jaws that transmit the test load.

The stress-strain curve. As the loading of the specimen progresses, load and deformation readings are taken simultaneously. To obtain engineering stress (lb/in.²), the original cross section of the test specimen is divided into the total load. Only that elongation is considered that appears between the testing points of the extensometer, or the gage length of uniform initial cross section. Deformation does occur in the specimen outside of the gage length but has little effect on the test and is disregarded. The *strain* is the total elongation recorded by the extensometer divided by the gage length (in./in.).

The most important use made of the data obtained from tensile testing is the plotting of a curve from points whose ordinate values are stress and abscissa values are strain. Such a curve is shown in Fig. 3–2 and is typical of tensile testing low-carbon steel.

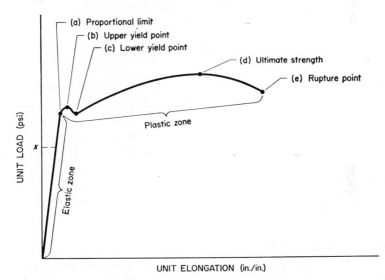

Fig. 3–2. A typical stress-strain curve.

It is observed that for the lower values of stress and strain the curve is linear. Obviously, within certain limits the stress is proportional to the strain and represents the pure elastic behavior of the test piece. It is seen that the relationship is no longer linear after the stress exceeds that represented by point *a*. Some load deviation is observed at this point, and at point *b* a sharp deviation from the straight line is observed. In low-carbon steel, as the load increases to a point which causes permanent deformation, it is not uncommon for the load to drop to a value somewhat less than obtained previously; and, when the points are plotted, a hook will appear in the curve as shown at *c*. This phenomenon indicates that a rapid yielding occurs in the test piece at that load magnitude. From the yielding point onward, the load increases to a maximum value *d* normally referred to as the *ultimate tensile strength;* after which, the load drops off to rupture value *e*. Point *a* is called the *proportional limit; b* the *elastic limit* or *upper yield point; c* the *lower yield point; d* the *ultimate tensile strength;* and *e* the *failure* or *breaking point.*

Soft metals that deform considerably before breaking show a distinct reduction in cross-sectional area as the test progresses beyond the yield point. *Reduction in area* continues up to the breaking point. Most soft alloys reduce considerably in area prior to their final failure. This is referred to as *necking-in.*

In the elastic section of the stress-strain curve—that is, that section of the curve below *a*, the test specimen responds entirely in an elastic manner. If the load is taken to some value *x* and then removed, the markings on the specimen representing the gage length will return to their original dimension. This is Hooke's law for elastic members. If the stress is divided by the strain, the quotient obtained is Young's modulus, also known as the *modulus* of *elasticity.* Moduli are fairly well fixed for all the commonly known construction materials and may be found in standard materials hand-books.

Many metals, particularly the nonferrous metals and some types of heat treated steels, do not show a sharp break in a stress-strain curve at the yield point. Therefore, yield strength is found by drawing a line parallel to the elastic section of the curve a distance to the right usually equalling 0.2% of the gage length. The intersection of this line with the stress-strain curve gives the elastic limit of stress. This graphic solution is ordinarily referred to as the *offset* method of yield strength determination. The amount of offset should always be included with the test data.

Results of tensile testing. In commercial tensile testing the two broken parts of the specimen are fitted together and the distance between the gage marks measured with dividers and rule. The *elongation* is reported as the per cent of gage length and is equal to the total extension observed divided by the original gage length, all multiplied by 100. *Yield strength* is equal to the total load at yielding divided by original cross-sectional area of the test piece. *Reduction in area,* per cent, is equal to the original cross-sectional area minus the final cross-sectional area divided by the original cross-sectional area, all multiplied by 100.

Table 1–1 shows the ultimate tensile strength, yield strength and per cent elongation of some of the more common types of commercial metals and alloys.

TABLE 3–1. Ultimate Tensile Strength, Yield Strength, and Per Cent Elongation of Common Metals and Alloys

Metal or alloy	Ultimate tensile strength (psi)	Yield strength (psi)	Elongation (%)
Steel, 0.2% C:			
Hot-rolled	60,000	35,000	30
Steel, 0.8% C:			
Oil-quenched	180,000	120,000	2
Wrought iron:	50,000	30,000	30
Cast iron, gray:			
(Class 20)	20,000	. . .	0
Red brass, leaded:			
Sand cast	32,000	15,000	24
Aluminum, 7075:			
"O" condition	33,000	15,000	15
T6 (heat treated)	82,000	72,000	10

Compressive test. Compressive tests provide design information on engineering materials that are to be compressively loaded in use. The compressive loading of a specimen is obtained in the tensile testing machine by pushing against the material. The usual information derived from a test of this type is the unit stresses at failure and the modulus of elasticity of the material.

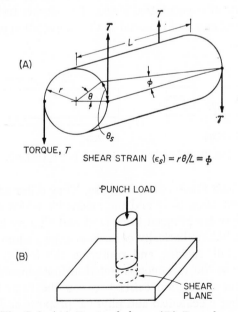

Fig. 3–3. (A) Torsional shear; (B) Pure shear.

Shear test. Shear tests are ordinarily of two types: torsional loading and pure shearing; both are shown in Fig. 3–3. Such engineering members as shafting and tubular torsional members may be torsionally-strained to evaluate their strength properties. From torsion tests the modulus of rigidity, ultimate shear strength, and the modulus of rupture are ascertained. The *modulus of rigidity* is the ratio of shear stress to shear strain in the elastic range. The *modulus of rupture* is the breaking stress.

Members may be tested by loading in pure shear, as depicted in Fig. 3–3 by means of shear punches and dies. The unit shear load is calculated in pounds per sq in. (load divided by the area sheared).

Bend test. This test, wherein a metal specimen is bent in a shaped die or is free-bent at room temperature, is usually for the purpose of determining the ductility of the test piece, although certain stress constants may be calculated too.

The bend test is found to be particularly valuable in checking the quality of welded joints. Ordinarily if voids or slag inclusions exist in the deposited metal, the test piece will not satisfactorily bend. The test has the advantage of being convenient and rapid and requires no expensive apparatus as in tensile and other tests.

Impact test. This test is to determine the suitability of a material for engineering applications at low temperatures. The test also provides a means for studying the resistance of a material to failures at discontinuities or points of concentrated stress. The impact test may also serve to measure the resistance of material to the propagation of a crack after it has once formed.

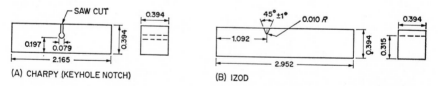

Fig. 3–4. Notched bar impact test specimens.

Two impact tests are in recognized use. They differ only in the shapes of specimens used (Fig. 3–4) and the means by which they are held in the machine. They are referred to as Izod and Charpy impact tests.

The testing machine basically consists of a pendulum which is raised and allowed to fall, striking and rupturing the test piece (Fig. 3–5). Energy given up to the specimen is stated in foot-pounds.

Apparently no correlation exists between the impact strength of a metal and its other mechanical and physical properties. Table 3–2 shows the impact values of some of the common commercial metals.

Fig. 3–5. An impact testing machine.
(Courtesy Lincoln Electric Co.)

TABLE 3–2. Impact Strength (ft-lb) of Common Commercial Metals

Steel:
    Low carbon, hot-rolled .... 3–20 Charpy
    Low carbon, cold-rolled .... 3–35 Charpy (with grain)
    Copper, light-drawn (15%) .... 79 Izod
    Red brass, annealed, cast .... 33 Izod
Inconel:
    Annealed .... 230 Charpy
    Cold-drawn .... 151 Charpy
Zinc die casting:
    4% Al, 1% Cu, 0.04 Mg .... 48 Charpy
Aluminum, 2024–T4 (75°F) .... 12 Izod

Hardness test. Hardness is a relative term which is often loosely used. This property will generally be evidenced by the ability of a material to resist wear by scrubbing action of another material against its surface, by the ability of the material to maintain a cutting edge (as a lathe tool), or its resistance to surface denting from impact. Hardness varies with the tensile strength of a given metal and its condition.

Brinnell hardness test. The Brinnell hardness test is made by imposing a standard load, usually 500 or 3000 kilograms, on a hardened steel ball ten millimeters in diameter which is in contact with the test material. After ten to thirty seconds the load is released and the impression formed on the test piece is measured with a calibrated microscope. The value thus obtained, when applied to the Brinnell formula or a set of prepared tables, gives the hardness intensity.

The equation for Brinnell hardness is

$$\text{Bhn} = \frac{2P}{\pi D(D - \sqrt{D^2 - d^2})}$$

where

     Bhn = Brinnell harness number
     P = load applied, kg
     D = diameter of ball, mm
     d = diameter of ball impression, mm.

Fig. 3–6. Brinell Hardness testing machine. (Courtesy Steel City Testing Machines, Inc.)

Figure 3–6 shows the Brinnell hardness testing machine.

The Brinnell hardness test has its widest application in the soft and medium hard materials. If applied to extremely hard materials, such as machine cutting tools, the penetrator ball may be damaged.

Rockwell hardness test. The Rockwell hardness test differs fundamentally from the Brinnell hardness test in that the penetrator is first applied to the surface of the test material under a minor load of 10 kg, the purpose being to penetrate the imperfections of the work surface. After the minor load is applied, a lever is actuated to apply the major load. A calibrated dial on the machine indicates in Rockwell scale units the difference in depth of penetration caused by the major and minor loads on the penetrator. For testing hard and comparatively thick materials, a 120° diamond penetrator is used with a major load of 150 kg and is designated as Rc (Rockwell "C"). For testing soft materials, a $\frac{1}{16}$ in. diameter steel ball is used with 100 kg major load. When using the $\frac{1}{16}$ in. steel ball the scale is designated as R_B.

In using the Rockwell "C" scale (150 kg major load and diamond penetrator) the depth of penetration may be as much as 0.005 in., a magnitude too great for testing thinner materials. The Rockwell Superficial is designed to test thin materials.

Rockwell testers which have ⅛ and ¼ in.-diameter steel spherical penetrators are available for the hardness testing of soft materials such as rubber and plastic.

Figure 3–7 shows the Rockwell testing machine.

Scleroscope hardness test. The Scleroscope method of hardness testing is based upon the principle of a bouncing hammer. The Scleroscope tester consists of a diamond-pointed hammer encased by a graduated tube. In use, the hammer is lifted to a predetermined height from which it is dropped upon the test material. Obviously the harder the material, the higher the hammer will bounce; and, if a provision is made to determine the amount of hammer rebound, a relative hardness value may be noted.

Fig. 3–7. Rockwell Hardness Tester. Picture taken in the laboratory of Georgia Institute of Technology.

Vickers hardness test. The Vickers hardness test also employs the penetration principle. The penetrator is a small diamond pyramid whose apex angle is 136°. The load imposed on the penetrator may be varied from 1 to 120 kg in selected increments. The hardness is determined by swinging a microscope over the impression made by the penetrator and measuring the diagonals of the impression. By referring to a prepared table, the hardness value may be obtained; or the following equation may be used:

$$\text{Vickers hardness} = 1.8544 \times \frac{\text{load (kg)}}{\text{diagonal}^2 \text{ (mm}^2)}$$

Inasmuch as the impression made by a Vickers hardness penetrator is comparatively small, it is particularly useful in measuring hard materials and polished surfaces. For the same reason, it is somewhat less accurate for measuring hardness in soft materials such as cast iron and forgings.

For practical purposes, Vickers and Brinnell hardness numbers are the same up to 300. Above this value Vickers readings tend to be somewhat higher and should not be used as true Brinnell readings.

Microcharacter hardness test. This method of hardness testing is designed to measure the hardness of isolated microconstituents, and metals of extremely thin sections. The penetrator is an accurately ground diamond point having three facets at right angles to one another (representing the corner of a perfect cube). The load is 3 g for testing average materials and 9 g for harder materials. The hardness reading is determined by measuring the width of the impression or scratch with a calibrated microscope. By using this shape of penetrator the hardness is inversely proportional to the square of the impression width, thus the hardness mathematically becomes:

$$K = \lambda^{-2}10^4$$

where

$$K = \text{microhardness}$$
$$\lambda = \text{width of impression in microns.}$$

Creep testing. *Creep* is permanent deformation resulting from the loading of members over a long period of time. High temperature creep may lead to the failure of loaded units such as high-pressure steam piping and petroleum cracking stills.

To simulate industrial conditions, the creep test would involve a long period of time. The present practice is to impose short-term tests and extrapolate the results to obtain the probable *creep strength* of a metal. Creep testing apparatus is generally a loading device, equipped with an electric furnace to supply heat to the specimen, and a suitable extensometer to measure the elongation of the specimen. Usually the duration of the test is for periods of 1000, 10,000 and 100,000 hr, each test using the necessary load to produce 1% elongation. This load is said to be the creep strength of the material.

From the standpoint of design, elongation caused by creep will occur below the yield strength of a metal. Such factors as heat treatment, grain size, chemical composition, etc., appreciably affect the creep strength of a metal.

Fatigue testing. A flexural member carrying a cyclic load is subject to cracks that spread until the cross section of a member is so reduced that it will no longer support the smallest load. These types of failures are sometimes observed in automobile axles and similar members. The term fatigue is a misnomer, inasmuch as, once the failure is initiated in a member, the metal has no ability to recuperate with rest.

The fatigue strength or endurance strength of metal is determined by loading standard test specimens repetitiously or cyclically, and determining the number of cycles sustained by the specimen before failing at some given intensity of loading. To run such a test from which engineering design information may be obtained, a considerable number of test pieces and much time is required. The usual practice is to test the first specimen at relatively high stress so that it will fail from a small number of stress applications. By successively reducing unit tensile stress on the specimen, a load value will be found which the specimen will apparently sustain indefinitely. If the load cycles reach ten million in number, the member is considered to have indefinite life. The load sustained at this level is called the *endurance strength.*

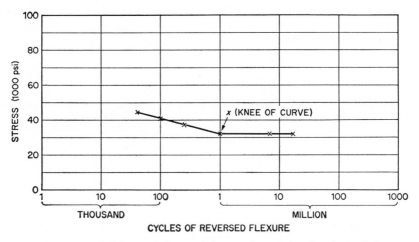

Fig. 3–8. Typical S–N (stress-cycle) curve for 0.2% carbon hot rolled steel.

In Fig. 3–8 the abscissa values are the number (log) of cycles of load imposed and the ordinate values are the stresses. The typical test of a low-carbon steel shows a curve that appears to become horizontal at about 32,000 psi. The knee formed by the curve at point *x* is taken as the endurance strength of the material. For some types of steels and for nonferrous metals the curve does not become asymptotic at any stress value, and endurance strength is specified for a definite number of cycles. Therefore, in the use of these materials if strength-weight ratio is a point in design, it may become necessary to operate the member for a predetermined period of time and then retire it as being unfit for further use. This practice is common in the aircraft industry.

Table 3–3 shows the endurance strengths of some common commercial metals.

TABLE 3–3. ENDURANCE STRENGTH OF COMMON METAL ALLOYS

Material	Steel 0.02% C Hot-rolled	Aluminum 2024—T4	Red brass ⅛ hard	Inconel annealed	Zinc 4% Al, 0.04 Mg Die cast
Endurance strength (psi)	32,000	18,000	20,000	31,000—45,000	6,800
Number of cycles	indefinitely large	5×10^8	3×10^8	10^8	10^8

The more common fatigue tests are the rotating-beam and the flexure-beam types. The rotating beam has two end supports and a load applied at the center. The testing device is designed so that when the specimen fails the machine will shut down. Figure 3–9 shows the rotating beam type. The flexural-beam test may be either a cantilever or end-supported

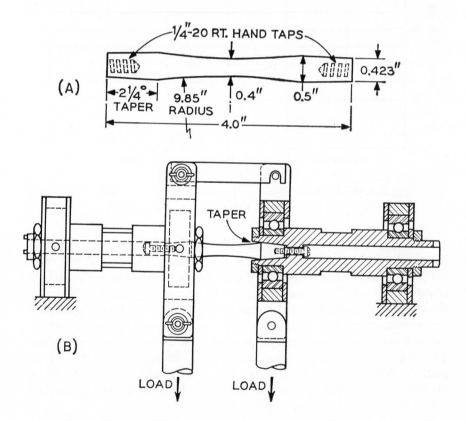

Fig. 3–9. Rotating beam endurance testing machine.

type, both being loaded by weights, cams, or hydraulic action. In comparing the endurance limits of materials, the method of testing should be known.

A failure caused by repetitious loading generally initiates at an imperfection or notch in the surface of the member. Common examples of notches are hammer marks, grinder scratches, chisel marks, and arc marks. Fatigue test results unquestionably indicate that surface finishes have a marked bearing on the enduring strength of the member, the smooth surfaces tending to promote higher fatigue limits. In an effort to improve fatigue strength, surface finishes obtained by peening and cold-working have been investigated. These finishes set up a state of compression on the surface and tension in the core of the load-supporting member. If in compression, a notch will have little tendency to initiate a failure and, therefore, the cold-working of such parts as crankshafts and pump shafts has been employed to extend their useful lives.

Corrosion tests. Because of the lack of standardization in corrosion testing, it is difficult to present a very exact discussion on the testing procedures employed. Losses from corrosion generally occur over a long period of time; thus, to simulate a corrosive condition for purposes of testing would often be impractical. Experience has shown that short-period test or accelerated tests and extrapolated results are feasible for evaluating a metal for design use.

Laboratory corrosion tests usually consist of exposing the test metal to brine spray, atmosphere, or corrosive immersion. Earth is the corrosive medium if the member is to be used underground; or corrosive atmospheric gases may be employed if the expected industrial exposure is to be of this type.

The usual observations made are those of determining whether change has occurred in the physical and mechanical properties of the metal during the test, the maximum depth of penetration if excessive pitting is present, and the loss of weight as a result of the corrosion. Frequently this type of data is not very precise and in many cases can not serve for the final evaluation of a material.

Cupping tests. This method of testing, wherein the test piece is deep-drawn in dies, is used to determine the suitability of a work material for deep-drawing operations described in Chap. 13. In deep-drawing, two features of the metal behavior are of special significance: the surface finish and the depth to which the material may be drawn. These facts will generally indicate the suitability of a material for its intended use. Most production plants have cupping tests which impose the necessary drawing severity to test adequately the purchased sheet or plate metal,

NONDESTRUCTIVE TESTING

X-ray and gamma-ray tests. Metal-penetrating energy rays may be employed to photograph materials to determine the presence of fissures, cracks and other kinds of defects. In ordinary photography use is made of visible light rays that vary in intensity to form an image on light-sensitive film. Although X-rays are invisible to the human eye, they do affect photographic film in a way similar to light rays. X-rays vary in intensity inversely as the density of the metal through which they pass and, therefore, a void in the metal being examined allows more rays to pass and greater exposure on the film in that particular area. By this means, areas of high intensity and low intensity will be registered on the film to form the image. After an exposed film is developed, it may serve as a means of checking the parts examined and as a permanent record of the inspection.

X-rays penetrate through greater thicknesses as the densities of work pieces decrease and as the wave length of the rays becomes shorter. The wave length is inversely proportional to the X-ray tube voltage. The higher voltages of the more recent X-ray apparatus make possible the examination of thicker sections of metals. The greater percentage of parts to be radiographed (X-rayed or gamma-rayed) will be two inches in thickness or less. For such sections, a 200 kv tube has been found to be satisfactory. In thicknesses of 2 to 7 in., the million-volt tube is recommended. Figure 3–10 shows schematically the X-ray apparatus.

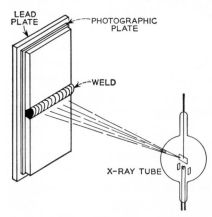

Fig. 3–10. X-ray schematic.

X-ray equipment consists primarily of a transformer and its rectification unit, the X-ray tube, and auxiliary equipment such as intensifying screens, filters, grids, and film holders. A 200 kv X-ray complete, including the more common kinds of accessories, can be purchased for about $15,000.

Sensitive film emulsion for X-ray application has been developed to give optimum detail. Sensitivity to shorter rays, such as those emitted in radiographic exposure, is a special property of these films. They are processed in the same general way as ordinary photographic film.

Gamma rays, those rays emanating from radium or its salts, correspond to X-rays generated at approximately 2½ million volts. They are much more penetrating than X-rays and do not scatter to any great extent. Radium salts (contained in a capsule) give constant radiation and are a convenient source of penetrating rays for many radiographic purposes. Cobalt 60 is now in common use as a radiation source. Detail is about equally clear in exographs and gammagraphs, but the contrast is somewhat lower in the latter. Lower contrasts do, however, make possible satisfactory radiographs of metals varying considerably in thickness. Gammagraphing is possible in heavier sections where exographing would not be applicable (Fig. 3–11).

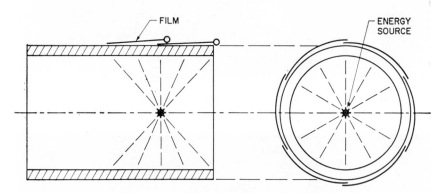

Fig. 3–11. Gammagraphing a large casting.

Areas to be radiographed are usually designated by specifications or marked by an inspector. If the location on the member is to be identified, this is done by appropriate marks; the film is identified by attaching lead numerals to the test area with wax so they will be included in the exposure.

After development, the negative should be examined with an illuminator designed for this purpose. Voids which decrease the density of the exposed metal allow more rays to pass; thus subjecting the film to greater exposure and producing darker emulsion areas. Imperfections, such as cracks, gas and slag pockets, and overlap from rolling, show up on the X-ray negative as dark areas and the denser metal corresponds to the lighter areas. Figure 3–12 depicts an industrial X-ray machine and Fig. 3–13 shows a typical X-ray film.

Magnetic particle test. This method of testing is applied only to ferromagnetic metals.

If a member to be tested is made a part of a strong magnetic path, irregularities, such as holes, cracks, and slag pockets, will cause distortion of the magnetic path. Because the permeability of the material is changed

Fig. 3–12. Mobile X-ray machine used in industrial plants. (Courtesy General Electric X-Ray Corporation.)

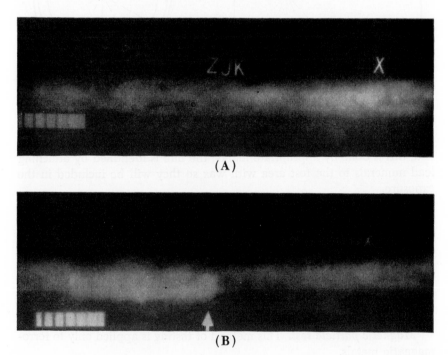

(A)

(B)

Fig. 3–13. (A) X-ray showing defect in welded seam. (B) The defect has been chipped out and rewelded. The X-ray now shows that the deposited weld has no voids or other defects. (Courtesy General Electric X-Ray Corp.)

in this way, irregularities or discontinuities in the workpiece may be detected. A change in permeability causes a flux leakage or a distortion of the field of flux, a fact which may be demonstrated by sprinkling the workpiece with magnetic particles—such as iron filings. These become arrayed along the lines of flux. A sharp discontinuity in ferrous metal causes the powder lines to distort, thus disclosing its presence, location, and extent.

Magnetic testing is particularly valuable in exploring for surface defects, although if the magnetizing forces are sufficiently strong, a subsurface defect may be indicated. The success in finding a subsurface defect also depends on its distance from the surface, width, and the ratio of its height to the thickness of the section being examined. The pattern of the magnetic flux is indicative of its distance from the defect; therefore, with experience the technician can judge the depth of a defect with reasonable accuracy.

Magnetic fields are established in the member to be tested by: (1) passing a current of the required intensity through the member, (2) use of an external winding or placing the workpiece in a strong field created by an electro-magnet or permanent magnet, and (3) passing the energizing current along a conductor located through a hollow workpiece.

Alternating current is advantageous as a magnetizing force where the detection of surface defects is of most importance. For subsurface exploration, direct current is more effective.

Magnetic powders of high permeability and suitable particle shape are applied to the surface to be inspected either in the dry or wet form. The dry powders are dusted, blown, or sifted on, while the wet powders—those suspended in oil—are sprayed or brushed on, or the workpieces may be dipped.

Demagnetization of low-carbon steel is rarely required after testing. Hardened and alloy members having a higher degree of retentivity may be demagnetized by passing the parts through a powerful a-c field or by passing an alternating current of high intensity and low voltage through the parts and then gradually decreasing the intensity.

The patterns formed by the particles applied are shown in Fig. 3–14.

The magnetic particle test equipment to be used for the testing of pieces up to five feet long and in a variety of shapes is valued at about $3000. A paste, which contains the magnetic particles and is mixed with a light oil vehicle for application, sells for about $2 per lb.

Ultrasonic inspection. Section thickness of $\frac{1}{16}$ to 35 in. or more may be explored for defects, such as cracks, slag inclusions, and other defects, by use of ultrasonic wave propagation. For inspection and testing purposes, this method is capable of detecting defects too small to be discernible in the average radiograph.

Fig. 3–14. Powder magnetization being used on a fillet weld sample. The sharp indication of the dry Magnaflux powder shows a surface crack. (Courtesy Magnaflux Corp.)

Ultrasonic testing is not intended to supplant radiographic and other nondestructive tests but to complement them. Many applications in the field have shown substantial savings in time and costs through the use of this method of testing.

The ultrasonic apparatus operates on the principle of the echo. A quarts crystal is energized by an ultrasonic generator and sends ultrasonic vibrations of short durations into the object being tested. Between transmissions the vibrations are reflected back upon the crystal which changes this vibrational energy into electrical energy of the same frequency as the original vibrations. The indicating instrument is a cathode ray tube. The time base or horizontal trace is deflected vertically at the same time that the original wave enters the test medium. If imperfections are present in the material, some of the waves are reflected back by them. These cause jumps on the screen along the trace, which indicates the distance to the imperfections.

The searching unit is a transducer which propagates ultrasonic waves into the material under test at an angle to the surface. These waves follow a zigzag path from one surface to another in the material under test until they encounter an obstruction at such an angle to the beam to cause a reflection to the source (Fig. 3–15).

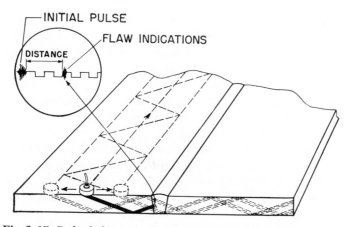

Fig. 3-15. Path of ultrasonic vibrations transmitted by a Reflectoscope with angle searching unit. (Courtesy Sperry Products, Inc.)

The sensitivity of ultrasonic testing is a function of the frequency used, the crystal size, and the grain level as set on a standard test block. By selecting the proper (low) searching frequency, small defects will not be readily indicated, thus, in many instances, accelerating the inspection procedure.

Ultrasonic test equipment complete for the more common types of inspections sells for $9-10,000.

Fluorescent-dye penetrant test. This is a nondestructive testing method wherein a fluorescent or dye penetrant is employed for locating cracks, pores or other surface discontinuities in metal and nonmetals. It is particularly valuable for nonmagnetic materials.

The surfaces of a part are brushed or sprayed with liquid penetrant, and time is allowed for the agent to enter any openings. This time may vary from a minute to several hours, depending upon the type of material and nature of the defect. After the surplus penetrant is completely removed, and the part is dried, a developer is applied to the surface. It may be a dry powder or a liquid and shows up penetrant that seeps out of the flaws. A fluorescent penetrant is viewed under black light, and a dye under visible light.

Fluorescent-dye penetrant test equipment, including work racks, drier, and fluid handling apparatus, suitable for inspecting small work pieces up to five feet in length is valued at about $2000.

Comparison of nondestructive test methods. Generally, no single method of nondestructive testing is capable of solving all inspection problems; more often they are regarded as companion expedients.

X-ray apparatus, as well as its subsequent use, is relatively expensive.

It has the drawbacks of sometimes being awkward to use, and poses a health hazard problem from radiation. The advantages of X-ray are that it gives good resolution from which a permanent photographic record is obtained of the shape, size, and location of a defect.

The ultrasonic inspection method is rapid and sensitive, but provides no pictorial record of the defect. A workpiece is often radiographed after defects are found by ultrasonics and, therefore, the two methods are often employed as companion tools.

The magnetic particle and dye penetrant methods are advantageous because of their reasonably low first cost and their speed and simplicity of use. They are particularly suitable for detecting defects on or near surfaces. These methods fit into production lines efficiently.

Questions

1. What are the relative merits of destructive and nondestructive testing?

2. What is a stress-strain curve and how is it obtained?

3. Explain the meanings of proportional limit, elastic limit, yield point, ultimate tensile strength, and breaking point.

4. How are elongation, yield strength, ultimate tensile strength, and reduction in area determined for a metal specimen?

5. How and for what purposes are compressive, shear, bend, and impact tests conducted?

6. Describe and compare the Brinnell, Rockwell, Scleroscope, Vickers, and Microcharacter hardness tests.

7. What is creep testing and what does it show?

8. How and for what purpose is fatigue testing done?

9. How and for what purpose are corrosion tests conducted?

10. How do X-ray and gamma-ray tests reveal defects in metals?

11. How is magnetic particle testing done? What are its advantages and limitations?

12. How does ultrasonic testing apparatus operate and what does it reveal?

13. Describe the fluorescent-dye penetrant testing method.

14. Compare the various nondestructive testing methods described.

Problems

1. A specimen of steel has a proportional limit of 60,000 psi. Its dimensions are 1 in. by 1 in. by 3 inches. The modulus of elasticity of steel is 30,000,-000. How much energy is stored in the piece when it is subjected to a uniform longitudinal stress of 50,000 psi? How much when it is compressed transversely to the same stress?

2. A machine tool has a heavy reciprocating table. If the drive to the table should break, the momentum of the table would carry it off the end of the machine, and considerable damage might result. For such an emergency, a safety catch is provided to break and absorb the energy of the table. Which of the following materials would you select for this catch? State the reason for your choice.

Material	Ultimate tensile strength (psi)	Yield strength (psi)	Elongation to failure (% in 2 in. gage length)
Cast iron	60,000	60,000	0.3
Mild steel	75,000	40,000	20
Low-alloy steel	180,000	160,000	15
High-alloy steel	290,000	235,000	8

3. What tests would you recommend for each of the following products to assure that its physical properties were adequate for service?
   (a) A gear for an aircraft engine.
   (b) A gear for an automobile transmission.
   (c) A crankshaft for a metal forming press.
   (d) A boom of a crane.

4. In a sheet metal forming shop, the crankshafts of the presses become fatigued in time and break. This can be a serious matter because a heavy flywheel is carried on the end of each shaft and may be dropped by a broken shaft. As a result the crankshafts are inspected periodically for incipient cracks so that the shafts may be replaced before failure. Cracks do not always start at the surface. Methods that give good inspection yet avoid the need of completely dismantling a press are desirable. Describe and discuss the relative merits of the methods that you would recommend for inspecting the crankshafts.

References

Davis, H. E., G. E. Troxell, and C. W. Wiskocil, *The Testing and Inspection of Engineering Materials*, 2nd Edition, McGraw-Hill Book Co., Inc., New York, 1955.

Keyser, Carl A., *Materials of Engineering*, Prentice-Hall, Inc., Englewood Cliffs, N. J., 1956.

Metals Handbook, American Society for Metals, Cleveland, 1948 and supplements.

Moore, H. F., and M. Moore, *Textbook of Materials of Engineering*, McGraw-Hill Book Co., Inc., New York, 1953.

4

Extraction and Development of Ferrous and Nonferrous Metals

Commercially pure metals—such as iron, aluminum, copper, tin, zinc, and others—are derived from their ores contained in the earth's crust. Usually elemental metals do not exist in a pure state but in chemical combination with other elements; the compounds being called minerals.

A mineral is regarded as an ore only if it can be processed profitably to produce a commercial metal. Although minerals are distributed fairly uniformly throughout the earth's crust, occasionally concentrated formations occur which are mined as ore bodies. The iron ores in Minnesota and the copper ores in Montana are examples of mineral concentrations which are classed as ores.

Ores as mined almost invariably contain earthy materials called *gangue* which lowers their concentrations. If gangue accompanies the ore through the extraction process, the cost of extraction might become unprofitable. To avoid this additional expense, the mine-run ore is processed to remove a high percentage of the worthless content, the operation being called *beneficiation*. Such processes as roasting, gravity and magnetic separation, leaching, etc., are employed to concentrate or beneficiate ores.

DEVELOPMENT OF FERROUS METALS

Pig iron, a ferrous metallic product of the blast furnace, is the result of iron ore reduction. It is from pig iron that all commercial ferrous products such as steel, wrought iron, and cast iron are obtained.

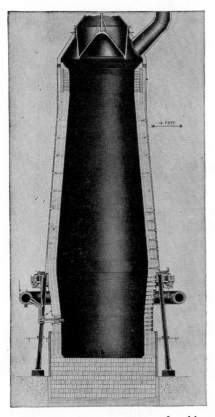

Fig. 4–1. A cross section of a blast furnace. (Courtesy Harbison-Walker Refractories Co.)

The blast furnace. The present-day blast furnace is a circular structure 90 to 100 ft high built of fire brick and encased with a protective steel shell. Three fundamental zones make up the blast furnace space: the bottom part, called the *hearth;* the second section, the *bosh;* and the third or top section, the *stack.* In height, the hearth is about 10 ft, the bosh section about 9 to 12 ft, and the stack normally about 70 ft. The general proportions and shapes are shown in Fig. 4–1. All interior parts of the furnace subject to high temperatures are lined with refractory brick.

The tapping hole is located at a suitable place in the hearth and is unplugged periodically to remove the molten iron. Also located in the hearth is the cinder notch, a hole through which collected liquid slag is removed. The slag formed in the process floats on top of the heavier iron. The cinder notch is six to eight feet above the tapping hole to leave room for a reasonable amount of iron to collect between each tapping.

Tuyeres are holes through which blast air enters the furnace; 10 to 16 tuyeres are distributed uniformly around the circumference of the hearth just below the bosh. A large cast iron torus pipe, called a *bellypipe,* completely encircles the furnace somewhat above the tuyeres, to which it is connected by suitable passages. It serves to supply the necessary blast air.

The apparatus shown at the top of the furnace in Fig. 4–1 is an arrangement which serves to admit and properly distribute raw materials at the top of the furnace without allowing any appreciable escape of the furnace gases and to draw off the furnace gases, which are sent to a washer and ultimately used for fuel.

The stoves are essential accessories to the blast furnace. They are brick wall cylinders enclosing a combustion chamber and a system of regenerative flues. A portion of the combustible gases drawn from the furnace top is burned in one of the stoves and heats the brick work. After that the combustible gases are directed to another stove, and the blast air going to the blast furnace is passed through the heated stove. It is by this regenerative principle that blast air is heated, and the efficiency of the blast furnace is appreciably increased.

Pig iron. The smelting of iron consists essentially of reducing the iron oxide ore, the final products of the furnace being iron of varying purity, a slaggy material, flue dust, and gas. In present-day practice and with average ores, to make one ton of finished pig iron consumes about two tons of iron ore, one ton of fuel, four tons of air, and 0.35 tons of flux. Along with the ton of pig iron, there are produced six tons of gas, 0.6 tons of slag, and 75 to 375 pounds of fine dust.

Chemically speaking, the reduction of pig iron consists of the combustion of the fuel (coke), from which is derived CO gas, which is brought in contact with and reduces the heated iron ore. In a lower zone of the furnace the iron becomes liquid. The limestone flux acts as a general cleansing agent and vehicle to carry off the gangue.

Upon being tapped, the liquid iron is directed through runners to pig beds in which the iron is cast into small pieces or pigs weighing approximately 50 pounds. In another practice to save the cost of reheating the pig iron, it is tapped into thermos tank cars and delivered to the open-hearth, Bessemer, or electric furnace in the molten condition. Pig iron is the basic product from which most ferrous products are made and contains 3 to 4% of carbon and small amounts of impurities such as sulfur, phosphorus, silicon, manganese and other elements. Average pig iron sells for about $66 per ton, depending upon location and market fluctuations.

Sponge iron. Iron ore may be reduced by bringing it in contact with CO gases whose temperatures are somewhat lower than those of the blast furnace. The iron obtained is a spongy mass that is never brought to its fusion temperature in reduction. There is a growing interest in pulverized iron for powder metallurgy as described in Chap. 10.

Wrought iron. "Wrought iron is a ferrous material, aggregated from a solidifying mass of pasty particles of highly refined metallic iron, with which, without subsequent fusion, is incorporated a minute and uniformly distributed quantity of slag"—ASTM. Wrought iron is a pure metallic iron interlayered with approximately 3% of silicate slag. It is easily identified by microscopic examination, inasmuch as the slag seams are in striking evidence in the direction of forging and rolling (Fig. 4–2). In contradistinction to steel making, in the making of wrought iron the silicate slag is included intentionally and is an important feature of the product.

Puddling of wrought iron. The puddling furnace has a capacity of about 600 pounds of wrought iron per heat; it is a small reverberatory type and coal fired. As depicted in Fig. 4–3, the furnace consists essentially of three parts, the grate or fire compartment located at one end of the furnace, the flue at the opposite end, and the hearth or puddling basin located between the flue and the grate. The furnace is constructed entirely of refractory brick with a metal plate encasement and reinforced roof.

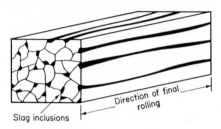

Fig. 4–2. Sketch of microdistribution of slag in wrought iron.

The bottom or hearth of the furnace, composed largely of magnetic oxide of iron, Fe_3O_4, is built up by adding successive layers of the oxide and sintering until a monolithic basin is formed.

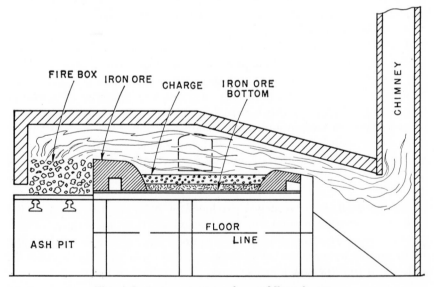

Fig. 4–3. A cross section of a puddling furnace.

With the furnace up to temperature, it is charged with about 600 pounds of cold pig iron, and thereafter the puddling proceeds through stages known as melting, clearing, boiling, and drawing.

Pig iron ordinarily used for puddling contains about 3½ to 4% carbon; ½ to 1% manganese; ¾ to 1.25% silicon; 0.04 to 0.08% sulfur; and 0.3 to 0.4% phosphorus. Strangely enough, aside from the slag content of wrought iron, its mechanical properties are largely regulated by varying the phosphorus content. In spite of its high carbon content, pig iron has a low melting rate at the start of the process due to the low surface-mass ratio of the pigs. During the initial heating period, some silicon is oxidized and forms a slag with the iron oxide lining material. This tends to blanket the pig iron that remains unfused. The melting period requires about twenty minutes. The following period of eight or ten minutes serves to remove the silicon, a condition indicated by a white fracture of the test sample taken.

After the silicon is removed, roll scale which is largely iron oxide, is charged to start the burning of the carbon. The turmoil caused by the escaping CO_2 is called "boil". After about 20 minutes the carbon is practically all removed, effervescence subsides, and the slag ceases to flow from the door. With reduction in carbon content the fusion temperature of the purified burden appreciably increases, which results in the partial solidification of the metal. Thus, the mixture of semi-solid iron and slag becomes pasty, and the charge is said to have "come to nature." The temperature of the furnace is raised to a welding heat and the pasty material is manipulated with a bar or paddle to form a large mass or ball. The metal may be separated into several smaller balls of convenient size, and these placed in different regions of the furnace. These may be removed one at a time and, by means of a crane, transferred to a squeezer where they are compressed into blooms. All but about 3% of the slag is squeezed out, and the bloom is then ready for rolling.

Rolling of wrought iron consists of one or more rolling steps to produce a convenient standard bar stock (done from the initial heat). However, to derive a higher quality but more expensive iron, the bar from the first rolling step is cut into convenient lengths and stacked. Then the stack is reheated in a suitable furnace to a welding temperature and rerolled to the desired sections. To produce further refinement and uniformity of wrought iron bar, a second or third cutting, stacking and rerolling procedure may be employed.

The Aston process for producing wrought iron. Because of the great amounts of hand labor required to produce wrought iron by the puddling process, its cost is higher than that of carbon steel. Doctor Aston recognized the limitations of the puddling process and reasoned, that, inasmuch as wrought iron was basically pure iron and slag, a mechanical mixture of these should be possible by preparing the slag and the iron in separate furnaces and finally bringing them together in proper proportions to produce the wrought iron.

In the Aston process pig iron is melted in a cupola and refined in a Bessemer converter. The iron-siliceous slag required for the wrought iron is made up in a basic-lined open-hearth furnace, the charge consisting of mill scale, iron ore, and silica sand. The "shotting" step is accomplished by pouring a stream of the Bessemer-purified metal at a temperature of about 2750°F into a bath of the prepared slag. The temperature of the slag is about 2400°F. Ordinarily, 3 volumes of slag to 1 volume of metal are used. The violence of pouring and oscillation of the shotting ladle causes the metal to be distributed uniformly throughout the slag. Upon coming in contact with the comparatively cool slag, the metal is immediately solidified and the dissolved gases have sufficient force in liberation to disintegrate the metal within the liquid or semi-liquid slag. After the shotting process is complete, all uncombined slag is poured off and finally the shotted ball of iron weighing about 2500 pounds is discharged onto a table and sent to the squeezer for removal of the excess slag. Thereafter, the steps are basically the same as those employed in the puddling process.

The Aston process for making wrought iron has the two important advantages over the puddling processes of close control of specifications and much higher production output per man.

Uses of wrought iron. Wrought iron is more expensive than plain carbon steel, but in spite of this it does have at least three properties in which its proponents claim superiority: the slag makes wrought iron excel in corrosion-resistance; wrought iron has high resistance to shock and fatigue; and it has better machining properties than some low-carbon steels. Its common uses are in the manufacture of pipe, staybolts, drawbars, blacksmith iron and crucible steel. The price of wrought iron bar is about $0.15 per lb.

Steel-making processes. Steel, an alloy of carbon and iron, was not unknown to the artificers of the Middle Ages. The steel products of that period were referred to as "blister or cementation" steel, an alloy obtained by heating wrought iron in contact with a carbonaceous material for a long period of time. By infusion of carbon into the surface of the material, the carbon content of the latter increases, which results in the improvement of its mechanical properties. The Wootz steel of India, the famous Damascus steel, and the Toledo steels of Spain, are examples of blister or cementation steels.

Because of the slag inclusions and heterogeneity in steel that resulted in early failures of clock springs, Benjamin Huntsman in 1742 conceived the idea of producing a more homogeneous product by melting cementation steel in a crucible and, after skimming off the slaggy material, casting the steel into an ingot, and finally forging it to the desired shape.

Although Huntsman did not have the benefit of modern metallurgical methods wherein fluxing agents, such as ferromanganese, might be added to the steel for its improvement, he did produce a steel superior to that derived from cementation. His procedure, although crude, is the basis of modern steel-making practice.

The open-hearth furnace. About 1857 a German engineer, Siemens, introduced the idea of using a regenerator in connection with the open-hearth furnace, wherein the air for combustion was preheated before entering the furnace. This contribution made the open hearth furnace practical through the economic use of fuels and the maintenence of the necessary temperatures.

Open-hearth furnaces were first employed in the United States in 1868 by Abraham S. Hewitt, who purchased the American rights to their use. Until such time as the basic-type of lining was perfected in American furnaces the process was more or less unsatisfactory, inasmuch as ores found in the United States were comparatively high in phosphorus. Presently, for all except the most select ores, the basic process is used.

Fig. 4–4. The open hearth furnace. (Courtesy Harbison-Walker Refractories Co.)

The basic open-hearth furnace. Since pernicious phosphorus and sulfur are of acidic nature, the basic lining and slag in an open hearth furnace are capable of fixing and neutralizing these elements so that they may be removed from the steel and the furnace before tapping.

The basic open-hearth furnace is a reverberatory-type rectangular brick structure whose ends and sides are supported by the necessary staves, channels, and slabs. In size, these furnaces range from 15 to 550 tons capacity of charge. A common 100-ton furnace is approximately 20 ft wide and 80 ft long. Accessory to the furnace proper are regenerative chambers for preheating the combustion air when coal or oil fuel is used or for preheating the gas-air mixture when gas fired. Figure 4–4 shows a sectional view of an open-hearth furnace. The lining in contact with the metal and slag is a fire brick of basic material.

The metallic charge of the open-hearth furnace is either molten or cold pig iron and scrap. Obviously, pig iron in the molten state transferred directly from the blast furnace to the open hearth requires less fuel for processing. In addition to the metallic charge, other materials, mainly limestone and ore, are charged into the furnace to control the slag and metal composition. The amounts of scrap and pig iron used depend largely upon the relative market price of the two and the ingredients from each needed in the steel being made.

The chemical reactions in the basic open-hearth furnace take place essentially in five (often overlapping) steps. They are called: (1) melting down, (2) ore boil, (3) lime boil, (4) shaping up or working, and (5) deoxidation.

During the melting down period a considerable amount of the iron and some of the silicon, manganese, sulfur, and carbon are oxidized from exposure to the furnace gases. Also the heat calcines the limestone ($CaCO_3$) into lime (CaO) and liberates CO_2, which promotes oxide formation in the manner of $CO_2 + Fe = CO + FeO$.

Gas continues to escape for a long time after the charge has become molten and agitates the melt in the boiling steps. This stirs the metal and distributes the heat. The iron oxide already formed serves the beneficial purpose of carrying oxygen to the carbon, manganese, phosphorus, and silicon in solution. Thus impurities are oxidized and rise to the slag that floats on top of the bath. Some of the iron oxide is reduced but an appreciable amount remains. The lime forms stable compounds, such as calcium phosphate and calcium silicate, that hold the impurities from returning to the metal. The basic lining also reacts with the oxides to help remove impurities.

During the shaping up or working step the carbon content of the metal is decreased to the amount desired by the addition of ore (in effect, an excess of iron oxide to react with the carbon to release CO), and the melt is brought to the temperature to give it the desired fluidity for pouring.

Because this process is fundamentally one of removing unwanted elements by oxidation, considerable iron oxide, oxygen, and other gases are left in the finished bath. Gases are less soluble and tend to evolve from the metal when it cools and form blow holes which weaken the product. Oxygen particularly must be removed, and that is commonly done by adding strong deoxidizers like ferrosilicon, manganese, aluminum, and other alloys to the metal in the furnace or ladle or both.

According to the amount of deoxidation given them, carbon steels are classified as *killed, semi-killed,* and *rimmed.* Killed steel is sufficiently deoxidized in the furnace so no discernible gas is evolved when it is cooled. The product is free from blow holes and inclusions. Semi-killed steel is not left as long in the furnace, and some of the deoxidizing agents may be added in the ladle or mold. Rimmed steel is only partially deoxidized with the intent that some gas will be liberated on cooling. The purpose is to have the escaping gases clean the surface crystals of the solidifying ingot. The interior of the solidified ingot is porous, but the surface is clean, and that results in a good surface on the finished product, a desirable condition for such a product as sheet steel for deep-drawing, for instance.

The open-hearth process is not fast. A typical 200-ton heat takes 135 hr from the start of the charging of the furnace until the finished metal is tapped and the furnace is prepared to accept another charge. Quality can be readily controlled because the process is unhurried. Because a large amount of steel is produced each time, commonly 200 to 300 tons, the unit cost is low. More steel by far is produced in this way than in any other.

The acid open-hearth process. Except for being somewhat smaller, the proportions of construction and shape of the acid open-hearth furnace, is similar to the basic type. The chief difference between the two types is in the nature of the hearth lining. The acid open-hearth lining is entirely acidic, usually silica sand and silicate brick. This lining reacts less with the metal, and less iron oxide is formed, but sulfur and phosphorus are not removed as well. The process requires high grades of pig iron and steel scrap. In the United States castings and ingots for forgings are the most important products of this type of furnace.

The Bessemer process. The invention of the Bessemer process of steel making marked an important turning point in our modern civilization. Up until 1855, steel, as made by the crucible process and other methods, was comparatively expensive and, for that reason, was not widely used. The Bessemer process made possible the production of large quantities of high-quality steel for domestic and industrial applications.

The Bessemer converter. An American Bessemer converter having the approximate proportions shown in Fig. 4–5 consists basically of a refractory-lined container (the bottom of which has air passages or tuyeres) mounted on trunions for the purpose of tipping in operation. By tipping the converter sharply to one side, its characteristic pear-shape provides a basin into which the molten charge of pig iron is poured. An air supply to the bottom tuyeres is then turned on and the converter tipped back to somewhere near the vertical position, causing the air to bubble up through the liquid charge.

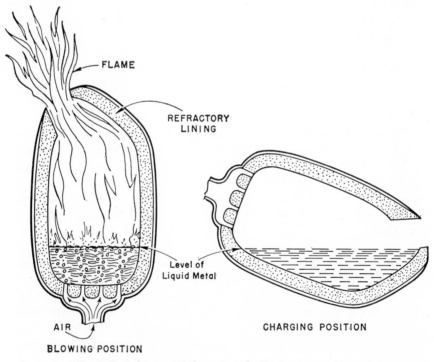

FLAME

REFRACTORY LINING

Level of Liquid Metal

AIR

BLOWING POSITION

CHARGING POSITION

Fig. 4–5. A diagram of the action of a Bessemer converter.

Carbon, silicon, and manganese are burned out by the blown air. During the early stages of the blow considerable amounts of nitrogen, carbon dioxide, oxygen, and hydrogen gases issue from the throat of the converter. The temperature of the charge during this stage increases rapidly, the additional heat being derived from the oxidation of the silicon to silica and the oxidation of slight amounts of iron and manganese. During the initial stages of the blow comparatively little carbon is oxidized. After most of the silicon and manganese have been eliminated, the carbon begins to oxidize rapidly, producing a long yellow flame at the throat of the converter. The success of the operation and the quality of the product depend upon proper control of the temperature during the process. The operator has certain techniques available for temperature control.

Unlike other steel-making processes, because of the short duration of time involved in a Bessemer blow, it is practically impossible to stop the reaction at a specified carbon content. For this reason, the blow is allowed to proceed to completion and the required amounts of carbon and other elements are added back as coke dust, ferroalloys, etc. Generally, if the carbon content of the finished steel is to exceed 0.15%, this is introduced by the addition of molten pig iron rather than by use of coal or coke dust.

Because of the passage of air through the molten steel, the metal will contain considerable amounts of iron oxide and gases which must be removed. This is done by adding ferromanganese for deoxidation during teeming.

Bessemer converters in the United States generally have linings of acidic silicious sandstone or mica schist. Phosphorus and sulfur are not removed from the steel. Basic linings are in use in Europe.

The size of Bessemer converters range from 10 to 40 tons, although this does not represent the highest practical limit of capacity. European converters range up to 60 tons in capacity. The length of time required for a blow will vary from 10 to 20 minutes. This process is the third largest producer of steel in the United States.

The electric furnace. The fundamentals of heating with electricity were discovered early in the nineteenth century, but it was not until about 1879 that Franz Siemens used the electric arc to melt and refine steel. Since then the commercial importance of the electric furnace has grown as electric power has become economical.

In 1900 Hjellin invented the electric induction furnace. It was also in this year that Heroult made the carbon electrode furnace suitable for melting and refining steel. A coreless induction furnace was invented by Dr. Edwin F. Northrup in 1916, in which a high-frequency current was applied to a primary winding contained in the furnace wall. This principle led to rapid and efficient heating and is now used for a multiplicity of purposes.

The advantages offered by electric furnaces are: (1) greater flexibility of operation, (2) higher temperatures, (3) close chemical control, (4) low alloy loss, and (5) no combustion problems. The chief disadvantages of the electric furnace have been the higher cost of operation and low furnace capacity, although both objections have been largely obviated as cheaper power became available and as furnace designs improved.

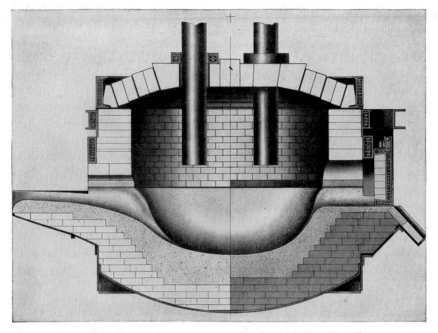

Fig. 4–6. A typical electric arc steel making furnace. For illustrative purpose the left side is shown as acid-lined and the right side as basic-lined. (Courtesy Harbison-Walker Refractories Co.)

The arc furnace. At the present time, the type of furnace most commonly used for metallurgical purposes is the direct-arc type such as the one shown in Fig. 4–6. Two types of direct-arc furnaces are common: one in which a three-phase current is led into the furnace by three separate electrodes, and another in which the hearth becomes a part of the electrical path. In either case the heat transfer is rapid.

The power supply for electric furnaces usually is brought in at service line voltages and transformed down to 90 to 300 v, the current being raised to about 10,000 amperes per phase. Because of the heavy load of furnace melting, power companies often offer attractive power rates for furnace operation in off-peak periods. That is, if the principal load of the power company is a daylight load which peaks somewhere near the middle of the industrial day, rates may be established whereby steel-making concerns may find night-time melting advantageous.

In this country the Heroult furnace that has three direct-arc carbon electrodes is the most popular type. Although built in sizes from less than one to 200 tons, the average units are 40 to 70 tons. The 40-ton capacity furnace is approximately 20 ft in diameter and is encased with 1 in. steel plate. Generally, basic lined furnaces are used for ingot making while the acid lined furnace is used to melt steel for castings. The electrodes are secured with heavy clamp-type arms that are capable of being moved up and down by a hoist arrangement for the regulation of the current and adjustment of the heating effect. Generally the movement of the electrodes is automatically accomplished by electrical apparatus. A small 700 lb capacity arc furnace with all controls, transformers, etc., costs around $45,000.

In the past a great amount of attention has been given to the composition of the scrap materials charged into the arc furnace to keep the phosphorus and sulfur content to a minimum, a means by which the final composition is controlled. At present the basic electric arc furnace practice is similar to that of the basic open-hearth furnace; the scrap composition is less carefully regulated and the final composition is obtained by alloy additions. The charge consists of light and heavy scrap in proper proportions, along with fluxing materials consisting of lime, roll scale, fluorspar, and silica sand. Where reducing or deoxidizing agents are introduced, they are usually in the form of ferroalloys and petroleum coke. The finishing step consists of making the necessary carbon and alloy additions and adjusting the final temperature. In the arc furnace process it is possible to hold carbon values to very low levels if desired. After finishing, the furnace is tipped, the slag is held back with a skimmer until the level of the molten metal is above the tap hole, and tapping is then accomplished. It is considered advisable to obtain as much agitation as possible when tapping into a ladle to mix thoroughly and thus obtain a more homogeneous steel. If the tapped metal is allowed to remain in the ladle undisturbed for a period of time, included material will escape. When the temperature is correct, the metal is teemed into ingot or foundry molds.

High-frequency electric furnace. The induction furnace, the electrical circuit of which is shown in Fig. 4–7, employs frequencies of 20 to 60 kc per sec. Metal in the furnace is melted rapidly by current induced at high frequencies rather than at standard 25, 50 or 60 cps industrial frequencies. Typical electrical apparatus to provide high-frequency current in a furnace of this type consists of a high reactance transformer, a spark gap, and a bank of condensers. A water-cooled coil of copper

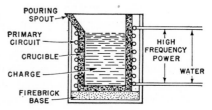

Fig. 4–7. A cross section of an induction furnace.

tubing, which serves as a conductor for high-frequency current, is the primary winding around the crucible and charge. The metallic charge in the crucible acts as the secondary of the transformer.

The lining of the induction type furnace is of the basic type. In average practice the lining will last from 100 to 500 heats, depending on the type of steel made.

Very rapid melting, exclusion of gases, thorough mixing, and high efficiency are the advantages of the induction crucible furnace. Two serious disadvantages are high cost of operation and small capacity. At the present time the largest induction furnace is about five tons. A 50 kw, 4200 cycle induction furnace with a capacity of about 150 lb of steel, complete with motor generator set, costs around $12,000.

The crucible process. The crucible process of steel making essentially uses a refractory container in which the metallic charge and deoxidizing agents are placed and heated by some external source of energy. Although restricted in capacity, the crucible process continues to be used for making of certain types of high grade steels and other alloys. The fuel for heating is ordinarily natural or producer gas. Regenerative chambers similar to those of the blast furnace are employed to improve the combustion efficiency and to obtain adequate temperatures. Electric induction melting is essentially a crucible process.

In modern practice the crucibles are made from natural flake graphite, ball clay, and silica sand, all being mixed together thoroughly, spun into shape, and baked. These pots have a wall thickness of about 1½ in., are 18 in. high, 13 in. in diameter, and each hold about 100 pounds of metal.

Flux consists chiefly of silica sand. Charcoal to adjust the carbon content and ferromanganese for scavenging are placed with the charge. After about three hours of firing the charge will be molten; the lids of the individual pots are removed, and the contents inspected. If no further chemical adjustment is needed, the charge is held for an additional 45 minutes to affect final killing. The melter then removes the pots from the furnace and pours them directly into ingot molds.

EXTRACTION OF NONFERROUS METALS

Extraction of aluminum. Although the earth's crust contains a high percentage of aluminum, the principal source of this metallic element is bauxite ore. The ore is hydrated aluminum oxide, either $Al_2O_3 \cdot 3H_2O$ or $Al_2O_3 \cdot H_2O$ or a mixture of the two, both usually containing impurities such as oxides of silicon, iron, and titanium.

Bauxite deposits are located in Arkansas and other southern states. Also large amounts of the ore are imported from Surinam in South America.

The first step in the extraction of aluminum is the grinding, washing, and calcining of the bauxite. It is then ground to a fine powder and mixed with a hot solution of sodium hydroxide which dissolves the aluminum hydroxide to sodium aluminate:

$$2NaOH + 2Al\ (OH)_3 \underset{\longrightarrow}{\overset{HOT}{\rightleftharpoons}} 2NaAlO_2 + 4H_2O$$

The impurities are essentially unaffected in the reaction and are removed as a sludge. Sodium aluminate, upon being seeded with aluminum hydroxide crystals, forms crystalline aluminum hydroxide which can be segregated. This is the reverse of the first reaction and occurs upon cooling of the solution. The aluminum hydroxide crystals are separated from the caustic solution, washed, and calcined to drive off the combined water. As a result of these refining steps the fine, white powder (Al_2O_3) evolving from the calcining kiln is about one-half the weight of the original ore.

When alumina, Al_2O_3, is dissolved in cryolite, $3NaF \cdot AlF_3$, it can be electrolytically decomposed without affecting the solvent. Electrolytic decomposition of the dissolved Al_2O_3 is accomplished in the Hall-Heroult cell illustrated in Fig. 4–8. The cell is rectangular and constructed of thick steel plate. Immediately inside the steel plate is alumina insulation and inside of the insulation is a 6 to 10 in.-thick carbon lining which serves as the cathode. The carbon anodes are suspended from bus bars above the cell

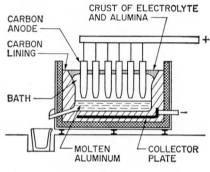

Fig. 4–8. The Hall-Heroult electrolytic cell.

and are in intimate contact with the alumina-cryolite bath. As the electrolytic process proceeds, oxygen escapes from the bath and molten aluminum collects in the bottom (the cathode). Because the bath temperature is maintained at 1800°F (well above the fusion temperature of aluminum) the process is semi-continuous; alumina is added as needed and aluminum is drawn off at intervals and cast into pigs. The pigs weigh about 50 pounds each and have a purity of 97.7% aluminum. Before rolling or drawing is started, the pigs are remelted to remove dross and other impurities.

Each cell or "pot" produces about 1000 lb of aluminum per day. The production of one pound of aluminum is estimated to require 12 kwhr of power, 2 lb of alumina, and ¾ lb of carbon electrode. Aluminum ingot has a market value of about $0.28 per lb.

Extraction of magnesium. Magnesium may be derived from certain natural salt brines, sea water, waste liquors from the potash industry, or ores. The principal ores are dolomite ($MgCO_3 \cdot CaCO_3$ containing about 13.7% Mg), magnasite ($MgCO_3$—about 28% Mg), and carnallite ($MgCl \cdot KCl \cdot 6H_2O$—about 8.7% Mg).

Magnesium has been refined by a number of processes, including chemical and thermal reduction, but almost all is produced today by electrolysis. There are some variations of this process but essentially molten and substantially anhydrous magnesium chloride is electrolyzed in cells. The raw materials must be concentrated carefully before electrolysis. Natural underground brines and byproducts are evaporated in large quantities and dehydrated to yield basically $MgCl_2 \cdot H_2O$ of about 85% purity. Sea water is treated with milk of lime made from oyster shells to precipitate magnesium hydrate $(Mg\,(OH)_3)$. That is filtered out, converted to magnesium chloride by hydrochloric acid, and dried. Dolomite and Magnesite ore may be treated with chlorine to obtain magnesium chloride directly.

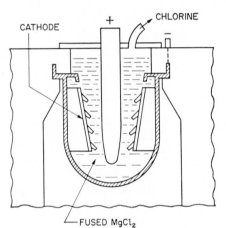

Fig. 4–9. Ward magnesium-chlorine cell.

A typical electrolytic cell capable of producing about 1000 lb of magnesium per day is illustrated in Fig. 4–9. A mixture of magnesium chloride and alkali chloride is heated to about 1300°F in the cell, and current is passed through it. Once the electrolysis is stabilized, the temperature is maintained by the electrical energy consumed. Chlorine (and a small amount of hydrochloric acid from any residual water) collects at the carbon anode, is removed through a duct, and is commonly used for treating the raw materials. The light magnesium floats on top of the bath, is protected from the air, and is ladled out into pigs of about 18 lb each. Around 10 kwhr (at 6 to 9 v) per pound of metal is required. The product is about 99.9% pure. Magnesium alloy ingot sells for about $0.36 per pound.

Extraction of zinc. Zinc may be extracted from its ores by both distillation and electrolysis, their industrial importance being in the ratio of about 3:1.

In the United States the principal zinc ore deposits are located in the Joplin, Missouri, district. Table 4–1 lists the common ores of zinc. Usually they must be concentrated to 50% or more of metal yield for economical processing. This may be done by heavy-solution separation, flotation, or gravity concentration. After concentration, the zinc ores are crushed to a powdery classification.

The sulfide ore is roasted at 1525°F to drive off the sulfur as SO_2. Carbonate ores are calcined to remove excess moisture. The silicate ores usually require no preliminary conditioning between the concentration and extraction steps.

TABLE 4–1. Common Ores of Zinc

Name of ore	Formula	% zinc when ore is pure
Zincite	ZnO	80.3
Sphalerite or Black Jack	ZnS	67.0
Willemite	$2ZnO \cdot SiO_2$	58.6
Calamine	$ZnO \cdot Zn(OH)_2 \cdot SiO_2$	54.2
Smithonite	$ZnCO_3$	52.1
Franklinite	$(ZnO,MnO) \cdot Fe_2O_3$	6–18

In the *distillation process,* concentrated zinc oxide or a mixture of zinc oxide and zinc sulfate is mixed with 40% carbonaceous material and heated to 1400°F or somewhat higher. The fundamental reactions are:

$$ZnO + C \rightleftharpoons Zn + CO,$$

$$ZnSO_4 + 2C \rightleftharpoons Zn + 2CO + SO_2.$$

The zinc appears as a vapor and is collected and condensed.

The flow chart in Fig. 4–10 represents the important steps in the *continuous vertical-retort process.* Compacted briquettes charged into the retort are composed of zinc oxide, carbonaceous reducing agents, and binders. They are dried and then coked by hot gases issuing from the retort.

The retort, where reduction of the briquettes occurs, is about 25 ft high and is 1 ft by 6 ft in cross-sectional dimension, and made of silicon carbide. Producer gas is the heating fuel. The retort is batch-charged at its top but the process proceeds at essentially a continuous rate; zinc vapors are conducted to the condenser where the liquid metal is obtained. Average production for the vertical-retort is about 30 lb of zinc per 24 hr per sq ft of heated space in the long wall.

The *electrolytic production* of zinc consists essentially of dissolving the ground and washed zinc ore in sulfuric acid, purifying the

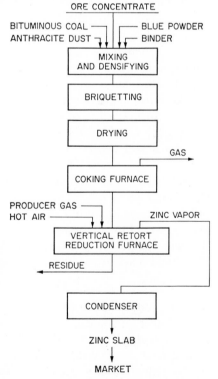

Fig. 4–10. Flow sheet of the vertical retort zinc distillation process.

resulting zinc sulfate, and plating the zinc out of solution by electrolysis. About 3600 kwhr are consumed to produce one ton of zinc. The market on zinc is about $0.12 per lb.

TABLE 4–2. IMPORTANT COPPER-BEARING MINERALS

Name of Mineral	Formula	% copper when mineral is pure
Cuprite	Cu_2O	88.8
Chalcotite	Cu_2S	79.8
Malachite	$CuCO_3 \cdot Cu(OH)_2$	57.3
Bornite	$3Cu_2S \cdot Fe_2S_3$	55.5
Azurite	$2CuCO_3 \cdot Cu(OH)_2$	55.1
Tetrahedrite	$Cu_3SbS_3 + x(Fe,Zn)_6Sb_2S_9$	32–45
Chrysocolla	$CuO \cdot SiO_2 \cdot 2H_2O$	37.9
Chalcopyrite	$CuFeS_2$	34.5

Extraction of copper. The principal copper-bearing ores are listed in Table 4–2. As removed removed from the earth, these ores yield only about 1% of copper metal, but efficient concentration methods increase the copper content to about 30%.

In *pyrometallurgical extraction of copper* the oxide ores of copper may be smelted directly. The smelting of copper oxides is done in the presence of hot CO. Proper fluxing of the furnace charge removes the gangue, although the *black copper* produced contains impurities such as arsenic, antimony, iron, sulfur, and some precious metal. Black copper is 95 to 98% pure.

The *roasting process* for sulfide ores consists of heating the ores to incipient fusion or less to drive off water, CO_2, and sulfur. Roasting may be done in several ways but it is generally accomplished in a rotating cylindrical kiln whose axis is inclined slightly from horizontal to cause continuous movement of the ore.

Both iron sulfide and copper sulfide are contained in the copper sulfide ores; these must be separated. A *matte,* formed from the cuprous sulfide and ferrous sulfide, contains 15 to 65% copper. Because the specific gravity of the matte is higher than that of the iron oxide slag formed, the two separate. Cuprous sulfide and cuprous oxide are heated to above 850°F and react to produce the metallic copper in the matte thus:

$$CuS + 2CuO \rightleftharpoons 3Cu + SO_2$$

The product of roasting is fed into a *reverberatory smelting furnace* about 100 ft long and 20 ft wide and with a hearth that holds a bath of matte and slag 1 to 4 ft deep. The temperatures in the furnace range from 2750°F at the firing end to 2100°F at the flue. This is an oil- or gas-fired melting furnace capable of raising the charge temperature sufficiently high to cause the formation of the matte and slag and to allow their complete gravitational separation.

The fundamental reactions are:

$$2Cu_2S + 2 \begin{Bmatrix} CuO \\ Cu_2O \end{Bmatrix} \rightleftharpoons \begin{Bmatrix} 4Cu \\ 6Cu \end{Bmatrix} + 2SO_2,$$

$$\begin{Bmatrix} 2Cu \\ Cu_2O \end{Bmatrix} + 2FeS \rightleftharpoons 2Cu_2S + \begin{Bmatrix} Fe \\ FeO, \end{Bmatrix}$$

$$3Fe_2O_3 + FeS \rightleftharpoons 7FeO + SO_2,$$

$$FeO + SiO_2 \rightleftharpoons FeO \cdot SiO_2 \quad (slag),$$

$$Cu_2SiO_3 + FeS \rightleftharpoons Cu_2S + FeSiO_3.$$

Part of the iron compounds and nearly all of the sulfur compounds along with the copper, form the matte. The slag discharges continuously at the flue end, and the molten matte is tapped periodically from a side tap-hole.

The matte is transferred to a converter for further oxidation by blowing with air. The converter used is a refractory-lined cylindrical container in which the bath temperature is maintained by the exothermic reactions occurring. An iron sulfide-rich slag is formed and removed; the remaining cuprous sulfide, called *white metal*, is blown further to remove most of the remaining sulfur. The product is *blister copper* and usually contains, in addition to the copper, small amounts of gold, silver, antimony, arsenic, and bismuth. If the percentages of precious metals contained in blister copper are low and, therefore, cannot be profitably recovered, the final step of refining may consist of melting down the charge (blister copper) in a reverberatory furnace with an oxidizing atmosphere. Usually the charge is about 250 tons and requires about 10 to 12 hours to melt. By introducing air to the bath, the desired condition of purity is reached at about 3.5% Cu_2O. Green hardwood poles are then submerged in the bath and the hydrocarbon gases and carbon given off by their combustion agitate the bath and reduce the cuprous oxide. *Tough pitch* is the term applied to the produce of this furnace step. The tough pitch copper containing 0.03 to 0.05% oxygen and 0.27 to 0.45% Cu_2O is cast into such shapes as ingots, billets, bars, etc., for rolling, forging, wire drawing and other processing. Tough pitch copper is generally used for strength or mechanical parts and alloying rather than for electrical conductors.

For the production of electrical conductor and to recover the precious metals contained, electrolytic deposition is employed. The anodes, consisting of partially refined copper cast in slab shapes weighing about 400 to 700 pounds, and the cathodes, consisting of $\frac{1}{16}$ in.-thick sheets of pure copper, are placed in a circulating electrolyte containing about 15%

of sulfuric acid. About one month is required to deposit an anode. Approximately 20 to 25 amp per sq ft and 0.5 v per tank are usual.

The electrically refined copper is remelted and cast into shapes suited to rolling, wire drawing, etc. Electrolytic copper must be 99.9% pure including silver, and its market value is $0.35 per lb.

Elements such as selenium, tellurium, gold, silver, palladium, and platinum are recovered from the slimes which collect under the anodes.

Extraction of nickel. About 90% of the world's supply of nickel comes from ore deposits in Ontario. This ore is nickel-copper sulfide mixed with other minerals. Because the metallic content of sulfide ore is relatively low (2 to 4% nickel, 1 to 4% copper) concentration before smelting is an economic requirement. Ontario nickel ores contain profitable amounts of platinum, silver, and gold, in addition to substantial percentages of iron and lesser amounts of sulfur, alumina, magnesia, and silica.

Roasting of the concentrates reduces the sulfur to about 10%. The calcined material is charged into a reverberatory furnace along with raw ore, flue dust, and flux. About 24 hours is required to smelt 1000 tons of charge to a matte containing 17% nickel plus copper, 50% iron, 32% silica, and minor percentages of magnesia, alumina, lime, and sulfur.

Conversion of the matte is achieved by blowing it with a silicious slag in a horizontal, basic-lined converter, this step requiring about 50 to 60 hours to blow 100 tons of charge. The product is a high grade of matte containing about 80% nickel plus copper, 20% sulfur, and a trace of iron.

To separate the nickel from the copper, the "tops" and "bottoms" process is employed. The converter matte is broken into convenient pieces and charged with sodium sulfate and coke into a blast furnace or cupola. The sulfide tapped from the furnace is allowed to cool about 36 hours and separates into two layers. The top layer is predominately copper sulfide; the bottom nickel sulfide. The separate parts are further treated in stages by resmelting with additives to remove impurities and reseparating in layers. The copper is refined to blister copper. The nickel product is called *washed sulfide* and has a composition of 75% nickel, 0.15% iron, and 1.5% copper, with the remainder sulfur.

Roasting of the washed sulfide reduces its sulfur to a low value. About 15% coarse salt is mixed with the washed sulfide, and the mass is roasted to convert the copper to cuprous chloride. In this chemical form the copper compound can be separated from the nickel by leaching.

Electrolytic nickel is obtained by sintering nickel sulfide to remove most of the sulfur, reducing in a reverberatory furnace, casting to anodes, and electrolyzing. The anode weighs about 400 pounds and the starting sheets about 10 pounds.

The current density required for electrolytic processing of nickel is about 12 amp per sq ft and the potential between electrodes is about 2.5 volts.

Nickel cathodes are usually remelted to ingots for further shape processing or to shot for use in alloying with other metals. Electrolytic nickel sells for $0.79 per lb.

Gold, selenium, platinum, tellurium, and silver are recovered from the anode slimes by further chemical and electrolytic treatments.

Extraction of lead. Missouri, Utah, and Idaho supply most of the lead ores in the United States or about 22% of the world's supply. Other lead-producing countries are Mexico, Australia, Canada, Burma, Germany and USSR.

The most common lead ores are either the oxides or sulfides of lead, both usually containing impurities such as iron, copper, and zinc. Also lead ores ordinarily contain recoverable amounts of silver.

Galena (PbS) is the most common lead ore; it yields 86.6% lead when pure. Cerrussite (PbCO$_3$) and Anglesite (PbSO$_4$) contain 77.5% and 68.3%, respectively, of lead when pure. As found in ore deposits, the latter two ores are of low purity and, for this reason, are usually mixed with roasted galena before being reduced. Concentration is required of all lead ores since they average only 5% of pure metal when they are taken from mines.

For best results in smelting, lead sulfite is ordinarily roasted to agglomerate the particles, to control sulfur content, to minimize the amount of matte formed during the subsequent smelting, and to avoid excessive temperatures from oxidation of the sulfur during smelting. Roasting or sintering is normally achieved by passing the ore, about five inches deep, over an endless belt and under a down-draft air blast. Once started, the sintering temperature is maintained by the combustion of the sulfur. The sintering temperature may attain 1475°F. If properly sintered, the clinker produced will contain about 2% sulfur, 15% FeO, 3% lime, 8% silica, trace amounts of other metals and oxides, and 52% lead.

Charged with properly sintered ore, coke, and flux, the lead-blast furnace employed in the smelting of lead ores reaches a temperature of 1850°F in the tuyere zone; the slag will liquify, and the CO will reduce the oxides of lead.

Tapped periodically into the settler, the slag containing 1.5% lead, matte containing 15% lead, and *speiss* (antimonides and arsenides of iron and copper) are allowed to separate from the lead and are given further recovery treatments. The crucible of the lead-blast furnace is about 30 inches deep and holds 20 to 40 tons of lead. The molten lead is siphoned, also periodically, into the lead well which is outside of the furnace.

Most leads obtained from the lead-blast furnace require further purification before they are commercially usable. The elemental impurities consist of small amounts of arsenic, bismuth, silver, gold, copper, antimony, tin, and zinc. *Drossing* is a purification step in which the lead bullion from the blast furnace is held in a molten state in a reverberatory furnace long enough for the oxides and insolubles to float to the bath surface and be skimmed off. To remove elemental impurities, *softening*, the lead bullion is held at 700°F for about 2 hours, and the dross, containing chiefly sulfur, copper, lead, and arsenic, is removed. Upon raising the temperature to 1400°F, holding for 12 hours while admitting air, the antimony, arsenic, tin, and some lead form a lead-rich slag. By skimming off the slag, the impurities are removed from the lead.

The Parkes process of recovering gold and silver (desilverizing) from lead consists of holding about 100 tons of the lead in a kettle at 900°F and adding zinc to form intermetallic compounds with the noble metals. These compounds have lower specific gravities and higher melting points than lead; consequently, after holding the temperature and agitating for several hours, the noble metals and zinc are removed as a scum. The silver is reduced to below ¼ oz per ton of lead.

Dezincing to purify the lead after desilverization is accomplished by holding the lead 12 hours at about 1400°F in a reveberatory furnace. Air or steam is blown through the bath (or lead oxide is added) to oxidize the zinc, which is removed as a scum. The lead is now of commercial purity and is cast into pigs of convenient size for marketing. Lead pig sells for $0.13 per lb.

High-purity lead is obtained by casting lead bullion into anodes and pure lead into cathodes and suspending these in an electrolyte of lead silica-fluoride and hydrofluorsilic acid; with the electrolyte at 110°F, 15 to 18 amp per sq ft and a potential of 0.5 v are required for deposition. This is the Betts electrolytic process; it is considerably more expensive than the Parkes process of desilverization but recovers bismuth and produces a high-purity lead for the paint industry and other uses.

Extraction of tin. One-third of the world's supply of tin is derived from ores mined in Malaya; the remainder from Bolivia, Siam, East Indies, Nigeria, China, and Belgian Congo.

Cassiterite, SnO_2, is the only important tin ore; it yields 8% tin as an ore but contains 60% tin when concentrated. Compounds of copper, iron, lead, antimony, bismuth, and zinc are usually associated with cassiterite. By roasting the concentrates at 1100°F, most of the sulfur is removed directly and the oxides and chlorides of the remaining elements are removed by leaching with dilute acid.

In blast-furnace smelting, tin oxide is reduced by the hot carbonaceous gases. Unfortunately, tin oxide strongly tends to combine with silica and become part of the slag, the latter containing 10 to 25% tin.

The slag is reprocessed in a reverberatory furnace to recover most of the tin. Upon being tapped from the blast furnace, the tin metal is cast into slabs and pigs for direct use, or refined to a higher purity for more discriminating uses.

A better grade tin is made in the reverberatory furnace than in the blast furnace. In average practice a 10-ton charge consists of concentrates and 15 to 20% of anthracite screenings and fluxing materials. By holding the charge at 2200 to 2400°F for 10 to 12 hours, a high-purity tin is produced. The resulting slag (10 to 25% tin) is reprocessed in the same way, but to a higher temperature, to recover its tin.

Pigs, about 75 pounds in size, are cast for direct use or are given additional refinement. Tin pigs sell for about $1.03 per lb.

To obtain high-purity tin, electrodeposition is employed.

If present in economic amounts, the gold, silver, lead, copper, antimony, arsenic, and bismuth contained in the anode slimes are recovered.

Questions

1. Describe a blast furnace.

2. What reactions take place in the reduction of ore to pig iron?

3. What is wrought iron and what are its advantages and uses?

4. How is wrought iron puddled?

5. What is the Aston process of producing wrought iron and what are its merits?

6. What reactions take place in the basic open-hearth furnace?

7. Define killed, semi-killed, and rimmed steels and state the purpose of each.

8. How does a Bessemer converter refine steel?

9. Compare the open-hearth and Bessemer processes of making steel.

10. What is the principle of operation of the electric induction furnace?

11. How does an electric arc furnace melt metal?

12. What are the advantages and disadvantages of electric furnaces?

13. What is the crucible process of steel making and for what is it used?

14. Describe the process for extraction of aluminum.

15. How is most magnesium extracted?

16. Briefly describe the distillation, retort, and electrolytic process of producing zinc,

17. What are black copper, blister copper, tough pitch, and pure copper and how are they obtained?

18. What are the basic steps in extracting nickel?

19. Describe the process for the extraction of lead.

20. In what two ways is tin extracted?

References

Camp, J. M., and C. R. Francis, *The Making, Shaping, and Treating of Steel,* 5th Edition, Carnegie-Illinois Steel Corporation, Pittsburgh, 1940.

Minerals Yearbook, United States Department of the Interior, Bureau of Mines (published annually).

Transactions, American Institute of Mining and Metallurgical Engineers, Nonferrous Division, AIME, New York (published annually).

5

Heat Treatment of Steels

Although a high percentage of all metals made may be used in the as-formed, as-rolled, or as-cast condition for economic reasons, many metals (steels in particular) and their alloys will not develop their maximum mechanical and physical properties without heat treatment. Severe service conditions often warrant the additional expense of obtaining some special property in a metal—such as high hardness, high tensile strength, or resistance to corrosion—by heat treating.

The object of heat treating a steel is to modify or improve its properties for some later operation or service. Heat treatments may, therefore, serve one or more of the following purposes:

1. Relieve stresses after either hot- or cold-working
2. Improve machinability (discussed in Chap. 17)
3. Increase tensile strength and hardness
4. Improve ductility and shock-resistance
5. Modify electrical and magnetic properties
6. Harden cutting tools
7. Change the grain size (either larger or smaller)
8. Increase resistance to heat and corrosion
9. Change the chemical composition (as in the carburizing of steel)
10. Induce precipitation
11. Remove gases.

All heat treatments of steels are closely related to the temperatures at which their transformations occur. The critical temperatures of steels are shown in Fig. 5–1. This is a more complete iron carbon diagram than that of Fig. 2–13.

On heating and cooling, the crystals of which steel is composed have the ability to change their forms; that is, they have allotropic properties. This type of response makes possible a broad combination of mechanical properties and most heat treatments are given with allotropic behavior in mind. The heat treating of steel is a branch of metallurgy which may be broken down into numerous subdivisions, the more important being:

1. Annealing
   a. Normalizing
   b. Full annealing
   c. Stress relieving
   d. Spheroidizing
   e. Flame softening
2. Hardening
3. Surface treatments
4. Tempering.

ANNEALING PROCESSES

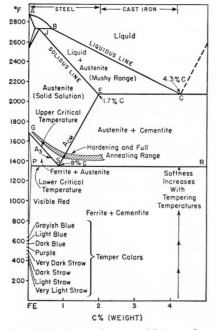

Fig. 5–1. Iron-carbon equilibrium diagram.

Annealing, in its broadest sense, means that some form of heat treatment is applied to a steel which conditions it for further heat treatment or some form of working. Annealing is usually necessary for the ultimate attainment of the highest properties in a finished product.

Softening is the most common purpose of annealing.

Normalizing. This heat-treating process is commonly employed to restore wrought steel to its normal condition after cold-working, hot-working, or overheating. In normalizing steel castings, usually the prime objective is to modify the grain structure and to relieve stresses. Commercially, the process consists of heating to about 100°F above the transformation temperature (Fig. 5–1) and cooling in still air. The final effect of normalizing will depend largely upon the section thickness of the workpiece; thin sections tend to cool rapidly and thus may be appreciably hardened.

Full-annealing. Full-annealing consists of heating the steel to a predetermined temperature, holding the temperature constant for a sufficient length of time to allow uniform heat penetration, and cooling at a controlled rate to room temperature.

The purpose of full-annealing is to obtain one or more of the following effects:

1. Relieve stresses caused by rolling, forging, etc.
2. Soften the steel (as for better machinability)
3. Modify magnetic and electrical properties
4. Create uniform microstructure
5. Change the chemical composition (rectify effects of coring and segregation).

Annealing is almost invariably carried out in a heavily insulated furnace in which there is little or no harmful effects from the atmosphere of combustion. Uniformity of temperature is a prime requirement and, if true annealing is to be realized, the rate of cooling must be held to within fairly close limits. For some types of steels, the period of cooling is 18 hours or more. The workpiece may be cooled in and with the furnace; or it may be removed at high temperature and buried in an insulating material, such as ashes or asbestos. The full-annealing temperature is approximately 50°F above the A_3 line shown in Fig. 5–1.

Stress-relieving. Stresses which are the consequence of a cold-working or welding may be released from steel by heating the workpiece uniformly to a temperature below the critical. The extent to which stresses are relieved is a function of the temperature, usually starting at about 800°F, but not exceeding 1250°F, in commercial practice. In some situations only the peak stresses must be removed, as in welding; but in wire drawing higher temperatures may be necessary to relieve a material more completely for subsequent drawing steps. In low-carbon steels, less than 0.30% carbon, it is the ferrite constituent that is chiefly affected by stress-relieving. Pearlite grains will exist only in small numbers in a low-carbon steel and, therefore, can be disregarded in stress-relieving.

Spheroidizing. Medium- and high-carbon (hypereutectoid) steels have carbides dispersed throughout their microstructures in a host of forms. Carbides may be submicroscopic or microscopic globular, acicular, lamellar, and grain membrane particles. Carbide dispersion and form determine the quality of a finished steel member. The shape of carbides, and hence the properties of a steel in which they are contained, may be controlled by the heat treatments employed.

Carbides are extremely hard. To condition steel for good machinability, it is spheroidized; small carbide particles are caused to coalesce into larger spherical particles. This is done by prolonged heating at just below the lower critical temperature. In commercial practice this is 1250°F (plus or minus 25°) for most steels.

If the hypereutectoid steels are held at spheroidizing temperature, all forms of carbides present have a natural tendency to coalesce into globular particles surrounded by a matrix of ferrite. Where the carbide particles are initially large, such as the membrane or globular types, they may be subdivided quickly and completely by heating to 50°F above the upper critical for the steel and quenching. After that, the carbides can be made to coalesce readily by the spheriodizing heat treatment because of their fineness and distribution.

Lamellar or membrane carbides make steels difficult to cut and, therefore, necessitate low cutting tool speeds. On the other hand, where the cutting tool meets a rounded particle of carbide formed by spheroidizing, the surrounding matrix of soft ferrite permits the carbide particle to be forced aside by the cutting tool edge (see Fig. 17–7). Since machinability is substantially improved by spheroidizing, hypereutectoid or high-carbon steels which are to be machined are customarily heat treated in this way before they are shipped from the rolling mill.

Flame-softening. Flame-softening employs the oxy-acetylene flame, or a similar source of concentrated heat. It is passed at a uniform rate of speed over a surface to be softened. By this method softening may be accomplished either by heating up to the lower critical temperature or above the upper critical temperature, the lower temperature usually being chosen for greater heating economy. This heat treatment may follow the oxygen-cutting of plate that has a high carbon or alloy content and which tends to harden at the severed edges upon cooling. If machining is to follow oxygen cutting as described in Chap. 14, it is necessary that hardened edges be restored to their original state of ductility to avoid difficult machining or cracking. Flame-softening may be applied to the softening of large surfaces that have been quench-hardened previously.

HARDENING OF STEELS

Generally speaking, steels must be heated to their austenitizing temperatures and cooled rapidly to be hardened. The desirable temperature for hardening depends on the amount of carbon in the steel and is shown on the iron-carbon diagram of Fig. 5–1. Too high a temperature coarsens and may burn the steel and should be avoided. The carbon content of the steel must be greater than 0.3% carbon to be hardened appreciably by austenitizing and quenching.

Heating for quenching. In the hardening of steel the primary purpose in heating is to elevate uniformly the temperature of the workpiece through its critical range so that the iron unit cells are changed from body-centered—cubic to the face-centered—cubic type and, as austenite, dissolve the carbon.

The great majority of all pieces heat treated today are heated in hearth-type furnaces whose fuel may be oil, gas, or electricity (see Fig. 5–10). The rate of heating a steel has little metallurgical effect on the final product; although, the rapid heating of a massive piece may cause cracking from uneven expansion. In commercial practice workpieces are usually started in a cold or comparatively cool furnace, and uniform distribution of heat is assured by holding at temperature for a sufficient length of time. To heat satisfactorily for quenching, a furnace should be capable of maintaining uniform and controllable temperatures up to 1800°F for the more common types of steels. A rough rule is to allow one hour of heating time at final temperature per inch of thickness in the heaviest section of a steel workpiece.

Quenching. Quenching is intended to remove heat from workpieces at a controlled rate. Cooling to harden may be accomplished by immersing the austenitized workpiece in water, oil, or heated liquid salt; exposing it to air or gases; or by bringing it into intimate contact with a solid metallic mass. The majority of pieces quenched for hardening are immersed in either water or oil, although the trend is toward the use of air blasts and fused salts.

Rapid removal of heat from the austenitized steel sets up a high state of rigidity before the carbides start to precipitate. Because time is required for the carbides to consolidate after precipitation, rapid quenching and the resulting lack of atomic mobility causes the carbides to be retained in a state of fine dispersion. Apparently, low-carbon steels precipitate their dearth of carbides and transform rapidly, and usually do not reach a high hardness on being quenched. As the carbon content increases, due to the greater abundance of carbides, the hardening effect becomes so intense that slower rates of cooling must be employed to avoid breakage.

In a given steel any degree of hardness may be obtained, within limits, if proper quenching media are employed. On the one extreme, the steel may be buried in asbestos or ashes and cooled over a period of 18 or 20 hours to produce maximum softness. On the other extreme, the same steel may be plunged into a container of cold brine water to produce its maximum hardness.

It has been the practice for a great number of years to heat steel work-pieces to their austenitizing temperatures and quench rapidly to obtain high hardness and subsequently give additional heat treatment to toughen and remove some of the brittleness which attends high hardness. Although still widely practiced, this technique is no longer universally used, since to do so may lead to a high percentage of failures in cracked parts. Interrupted quenching practices described in a later section are less severe and adequate in many cases.

The rate at which heat is withdrawn from a piece, and thus both the effectiveness and severity of a quench, depends on the cooling medium, conduct of the operation, the size and shape of the piece, etc. As an indication, if the cooling rate in a one inch-diameter piece in agitated water is given a value of one, the fastest theoretical cooling rate, approached in chilled brine, has been expressed as 1.23, in agitated oils as 0.48, in an air stream as 0.03, and in still air as 0.02.

Some steels crack if quenched in water. Oil-quenching is less severe but requires a more hardenable steel for equivalent results. Air-hardening steels transform to a high hardness in still air with minimum damage.

Stresses set up by quenching warp workpieces. Slender and thin pieces and those with thin and thick sections together are particularly susceptible to distortion. Quenching measures are practiced to counteract warpage. For example, a long slender shaft is ordinarily suspended from one end when plunged into the quenching tank. Production parts, such as gears with thin webs, are often die-quenched. A heated piece is placed in a special die and gripped firmly against distortion while it is lowered into the quenching medium. In addition to the liquid quench, the surfaces of the die in contact with the workpiece have a quenching effect; and the die is commonly arranged to regulate the rates at which the various sections of the part are quenched.

Quenching involves removing the uniformly heated piece from the furnace, induction coil, fused salt bath, etc., and immersing it into the quench bath. Pieces may be handled singly, but in repetitive heat treating they are usually transported by conveyor, crane, or car. Small pieces are normally handled in wire baskets or on racks. The coolant is ordinarily pumped vigorously to achieve agitation and uniform abstraction of heat from the workpiece.

Hardenability of steel. In several steels of different compositions, but the same thickness, hardened by quenching in exactly the same way, considerable difference will be found both in the intensity of hardening and the depth of hardening among the pieces. The term *hardenability* is indicative of the ease with which martensite is obtained upon quenching a steel. The term *hardness penetration* describes the uniformity of hardness, rather than the intensity. The hardness of a steel increases with the carbon content (up to a point), but its hardness penetration (deep hardness) is increased by alloying to lower the critical cooling rate or the lowest rate of heat removal which will produce martensite (see Chap. 2).

Most of the common alloying elements have a tendency to retard transformation (reduce the critical cooling rate), and thus are valuable to give steel a high hardenability. The curves in Fig. 5–2 show the behavior of steels of different hardenabilities. The configuration of the curves depicts the difference in hardenabilities of steels having different compositions. It is noted that water-quenched plain-carbon steels (SAE 1045 for example) may vary considerably in hardness from surface to interior; whereas the oil-quenched steel (SAE 6140) shows less difference between the surface and interior hardness.

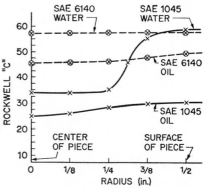

Fig. 5–2. Hardness gradient from center to surface of SAE 1045 and SAE 6140 steel quenched in water and in oil.

The jominy or end-quench. The end-quench test is designed to measure the hardenability of steel by quenching a properly heated piece from one end.

Essentially, the test consists of supporting a 1 in.-diameter by 3⅞ in.-long bar, heated to its austenitizing temperature, in a suitable jig and quenching an end with water spray as shown in Fig. 5–3. The heat is removed entirely via the quenched end surface and is, therefore, withdrawn at different rates along the bar. This results in a decreasing hardness along the bar from the end. After cooling to room temperature, two flats are ground on diametrically opposite sides and Rockwell hardness values are taken at ¹⁄₁₆ in. intervals along the bar. From this data a curve may be plotted; the Rockwell hardness readings representing the ordinate

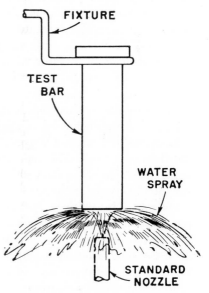

Fig. 5–3. Jominy end-quench.

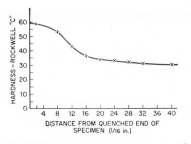

Fig. 5–4. Typical Jominy curve of SAE 8650 steel.

values, and the distances along the bar the abscissa.

Figure 5–4 shows a typical end-quench curve. Although hardness intensity is a function of the carbon content, in a plain-carbon steel the zone of maximum hardness is confined near to the heat-dissipating surfaces; at a short distance inward the hardness drops off rapidly as shown. Steels having small amounts of alloying elements show a less rapid decline.

Interrupted-quench. The interrupted-quench consists of several temperature reductions rather than a single quench to room temperature. The purpose of this quenching technique is to permit temperature equalization of the workpiece and thereby avoid internal stresses (Fig. 5–5(A)). The curves on the left indicate rapid cooling rates from quenching directly into water or oil at a low temperature. As shown, a large difference in temperature exists between the outside and inside of a piece treated in that way. The dashed curves represent placing a heated piece in a liquid, such as a salt bath, at about 500°F for a period of time. The temperature has opportunity to become equalized before transformation starts. The piece is then transferred to a second medium sufficiently low in temperature to start transformation to martensite. After the second temperature equalization, the part may be removed from the bath and reduced to room temperature at any rate.

A *T-T-T* or *S curve,* as idealized in Figs. 5–5(B) through (E), is a convenient diagram to show what transformations take place and what constituents are formed in a steel as temperature and time change on cooling. The curve reflects the fact that austenite is transformed into different compositions if cooled at different temperature levels for various periods of time. Each kind of steel has its own curve.

In *austempering,* steel is quenched in a heated liquid bath ranging in temperature between 300 and 800°F as depicted in Fig. 5–5(B). The temperature is held constant for a sufficient length of time for the transformation to occur (isothermally). The piece is then removed and cooled at any rate. The ultimate hardness of the microstructures will depend upon the temperatures at which they transform and the characteristics of the material. This technique differs from the more conventional one in which the single-quenched part usually requires reheating or tempering to toughen and restore shock-resistance, as depicted in Fig. 5–5(D).

Martempering differs from austempering with respect to bath temperature. After the workpiece is heated uniformly to its austenitizing tem-

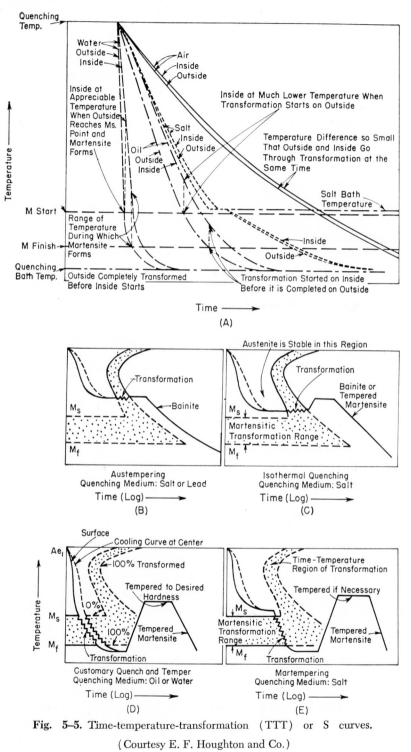

Fig. 5–5. Time-temperature-transformation (TTT) or S curves.

(Courtesy E. F. Houghton and Co.)

perature, it is transferred to a liquid salt bath maintained at a temperature just above where martensite begins to form (M_s temperature, Fig. 5–5(E). The piece is held in the bath at the temperature until the outside and core temperatures are equalized. The part may then be removed and cooled at a moderate rate. If the steel is a deep-hardening type and becomes completely martensitic at the core, the possibility of setting up destructive stresses is always present if the second or final cooling stage is rapid. This results from the core being the last to transform. Martensite is somewhat greater in volume than the austenite from which it transforms, a circumstance that causes virtual heaving (like ice) and often destroys the workpiece. Slow cooling, therefore, is preferred in the second step of martempering so that transformation may be more uniform throughout the section and thus avoid stresses.

In martempering, after the piece is quenched to the M_s point, it may remain at this temperature for an extended period of time for temperature equalization without harmful effects, since martensite will not start to form until after the temperature has been reduced further.

The limitations in the use of austempering and martempering are governed primarily by the mass of the workpiece. Considerable difficulty may be encountered in dissipating heat sufficiently fast from the center of a large workpiece at a low-temperature gradient to produce the necessary hardness.

SURFACE-HARDENING

Surface-hardening may be achieved by austenitizing only the surface of the workpiece and quenching; or by changing the chemical composition of the workpiece surface and then, if necessary, austenitizing and quenching. The following paragraphs describe some of the more common methods employed to surface-harden steels.

Induction-hardening. The principle of induction-hardening introduces no new metallurgical concept. Heating with high-frequency current is an old principle in physics, in which the iron pole piece in an electromagnet is heated because of rapid reversals of polarity. In induction heating for hardening, the workpiece becomes the pole piece, and frequencies of several thousand cycles per second (cps) are used to create heat rapidly and intensely. This greatly simplifies the heating apparatus. After the source of current has been established, the only requirement in the way of equipment is water-cooled copper coils formed to fit the general contours of the workpiece (see Fig. 5–6). These coils are quickly and inexpensively formed, and they lend themselves efficiently to heating for both short runs and mass production. After induction heating, workpieces are quenched conventionally.

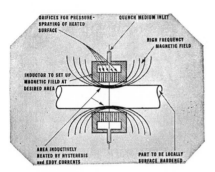

Fig. 5–6. Schematic of induction hardening.

Fig. 5–7. A set-up for induction hardening of gear teeth. (Courtesy The Ohio Crankshaft Co.)

A high-frequency induced current heats the surface or skin of a workpiece; lower frequencies are necessary for deeper heating. The power input determines the intensity and rate of heating. Motor generator sets are the usual sources for frequencies up to 10,000 cps and power to 2500 kw. A popular size of induction heating outfit with a motor generator rated at 50 kw and 10,000 cps costs around $15,000. Spark gap circuits are used for frequencies from 20 to 60 kcps and power up to 30 kw. Electronic tube oscillators serve for frequencies as high as 3000 kcps and power up to 600 kw. Such equipment for 450 kcps and 50 kw costs around $17,000.

Flame-hardening. Instead of heating and quenching the entire member to harden, as in furnace practice, flame-hardening employs the concept of heating and quenching only the portion or area of the member that requires hardening. This is done by suitable high-temperature flames. There is nothing new in this principle, although its refinement and the broadening of its application have come about largely within the past twenty years.

Due to the high temperatures generated and the concentration of heat, the oxy-acetylene flame is preferred for flame-hardening. Figure 5–8 is a sketch of a flame-hardening

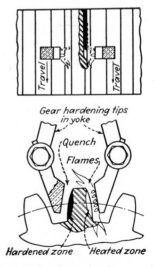

Fig. 5–8. Flame hardening of gear teeth.

operation. The torch apparatus differs from that used for general heating and welding only in shape and number of gas orifices employed. Usually the torch head is given a shape that conforms reasonably closely to the contour of the workpiece being hardened. The head ordinarily has circulating water which carries away radiant heat and then sprays onto the heated workpiece to quench it. In other types of torch apparatus the quenching spray may be a separate unit that follows the heating torch at a distance to quench adequately.

Flame-hardening is limited to surface treatment. The hard, wear-resisting surface supported by a tough, shock-resisting core is a combination eminently suited to numerous industrial applications. Some advantages of flame-hardening are:

1. Treatment of parts that are too large for practical furnace heating and immersion quenching
2. Accurate control of hardness and depth
3. Retention of core ductility
4. Control of distortion
5. Makes possible the greater use of plain-carbon steels.

In general, any plain-carbon steel having 0.40% carbon or greater may be flame hardened, the most usable range being from 0.40 to 0.60% carbon. These steels produce hardness of 40 to 63 Rc.

Depth of hardness is controllable from a few thousandths of an inch to one-fourth inch in usual setups. In commercial practice, some variation of hardness depth is permissible; for example, if $\frac{3}{16}$ in. depth is specified for a job, a deviation of $\frac{1}{64}$ in., plus or minus, will usually make little difference for most purposes. Minimum depth of flame-hardening should always be specified to a fabricator.

Flame-hardening is not as adaptable to production line integration nor is it as rapid in heating as high-frequency current, but the capital investment is much less for similar production capability. Assuming an existing source of gas, equipment to harden small pieces (up to 6 in. diameter) should not exceed $1000 to $2000.

Carburizing to harden. If a workpiece must have a ductile, shock-resisting core and a hard surface to resist wear and abrasion, a steel of low carbon content may be machined to shape and approximate size, carburized to increase the carbon content of the skin, and then heat treated to harden. In such a heat treatment, the core will remain comparatively soft while the skin, having a higher carbon content, will reach a high hardness intensity (Fig. 5–9). The piece is then ground to size after hardening.

Steels for carburizing should have from 0.10 to 0.15% carbon. A steel, when heated to its austenitizing temperature, will absorb carbon rapidly in the presence of CO gas. The solubility of carbon in gamma iron may theoretically reach 1.7% carbon, although in usual carburizing practices the carbon absorption will seldom exceed 1.2%. The infusion of carbon into the surface of the steel at its austenitizing temperature will depend largely upon the temperature, time, and the potency of the medium to which the workpiece is exposed. Thus, the thickness of the case produced may vary through wide limits but usually will be less than ⅛ inch.

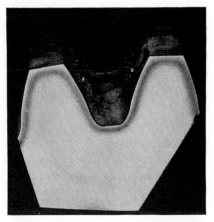

Fig. 5-9. Carburized and hardened case of gear teeth. (From *Republic Alloy Steels* published by Republic Steel Corporation.)

Two methods are in general use for the carburization of steel. *Pack carburizing* consists of completely surrounding the workpiece with carbonaceous material in a closed container, and heating at the carburizing temperature for a period of time. The carbon component of the rich CO gas produced by heating the packing material penetrates the surface of the workpiece and thus increases its carbon content. In *retort carburizing* the carburizing compound is contained in the furnace, but remote from the workpiece, and upon heating gives up CO gas to provide the carbon element. In *gas carburizing* the workpiece is heated to required temperature in a furnace into which a highly carburizing atmosphere is supplied from an outside source. Most of the common hydrocarbon gases may be used for this purpose.

Carburization of low-carbon steel is usually within the temperature range of 1650 to 1740°F. Should the temperature be appreciably less than this, the rate of carbon infusion will be slow, since the ferrite will not be transformed completely to austenite and the carbon solubility in it will be low. At carburizing temperatures the growth of grain will be rapid and, therefore, a carburizing grade of steel should be selected that has less tendency to coarsen. Where grain growth is excessive in carburizing, subsequent heat treatments are given to break down the grain, usually by double annealing.

In heating a carburized part for final quenching, a temperature is chosen that will austenitize only the hypereutectoid case and leave the core essentially unaffected. Water, oil, and fused salts (in that order of quench severity) are common quenchants. It is preferable to follow the hardening operation promptly by reheating to temper and thus reduce the possibility of spoilage from hardening cracks.

Carburizing and hardening are widely applied to such parts as gears, splines, wrist pins, bearing balls, universal joint parts, and a host of other parts.

Cyaniding. This process is similar in some respects to carburizing in that the heated medium which surrounds the workpiece imparts nitrogen and carbon to the steel which is afterwards quenched from its austenitizing temperature to harden. Cyaniding agents consist of fused salts of sodium cyanide, calcium cyanide, and calcium cyanimide. Sodium carbonate usually serves as the base or *inerts* of the cyaniding bath.

The workpiece is immersed in the cyanide bath for a period of time and then quenched in brine, water, or oil.

The depth of the cyanide case is controlled by the potency of the salts, temperature, and the time the steel is held in the fused salt. The nitrides introduced are hard as-formed and do not require quenching, but the cyanided part must be quenched to harden the iron-carbon constituents.

Vessels to contain cyanide salts are usually made of steel, but may be of nickel-chronium alloy. The heat is supplied by any of the common means such as electricity or gas. Cyaniding furnace apparatus should be capable of close temperature regulation.

Appreciable amounts of the cyanide salt will be transferred from the pot bath to the quenching liquid and, because cyanide is poisonous, it should be neutralized before being discharged to the sewer for disposal. In work areas where cyaniding is being done, adequate ventilation should be provided to remove the poisonous process gases.

Nitriding. This process consists of surrounding the workpiece with nitrogen at a furnace temperature of 900 to 1000°F and holding until the necessary thickness of case is produced. About 48 to 90 hours are generally required to produce cases 0.02 to 0.04 in. thick. Ammonia is the most common nitriding agent (the furnace atmosphere). This gas dissociates at the prevailing temperature to supply nascent nitrogen.

If long periods of processing are permissible, nitriding may be done at 950°F, thus making possible the case-treatment of a previously hardened steel. Such a technique provides a combination of high mechanical properties.

A modification of the ammonia nitriding process, referred to as *Chapmanizing*, makes use of anhydrous ammonia. The gas is dissociated and passed through a liquid cyanide bath into which the previously heated workpiece is immersed. By this means the ammonia is considerably activated, the nitriding action requiring only three to four hours to produce a 0.03 in.-thick case at 1400°F.

Nitrided parts do not require quenching, since the nitrides are inherently hard. The process is somewhat more expensive than other methods of surface-hardening. Special steels containing trace amounts of aluminum and chromium for higher hardness and greater nitride stability should be used for nitriding.

Nitriding is applied to such parts as gear teeth, spline shafts, anti-friction bearings, and gun parts.

TEMPERING OF HARDENED STEELS

Generally, quenched steels of high hardnesses tend to be brittle and are unsatisfactory for transmitting shock loads. If shock-resistance is mandatory, the tempering heat treatment is given.

The principle of tempering. As discussed in Chap. 2, martensite resulting from quenching a steel from its austenitizing temperature at a speed equal to or exceeding its critical cooling rate has finely dispersed carbide particles. Shock-resistance is restored to a quenched steel by tempering it to cause coalescence of the particles.

Tempering is a heat-treating process wherein hardened steels are reheated to some temperature below the critical (see Fig. 5–1). Temperatures less than 300°F will not appreciably affect the condition of steel. Where it is desired to release only the peak hardness and stress which follow drastic quenching, the temperature range of 300 to 400°F may be used. In tempering to confer shock-resistance, the hardened parts are reheated within a temperature range of 400 to 750°F. As a result of this treatment the parts are much less brittle than before tempering and the hardness drops only slightly.

To accomplish all purposes of tempering, the temperature range is 400 to 1250°F. The higher the temperature, the softer the product. Time at temperature is of lesser importance, but longer periods give softer steels. The heat treater must select a temperature and length of heating time which will produce the hardness desired in his particular steel. Tempering temperatures, along with other heat-treating information, are usually available from the mill that rolled the steel.

Toughening is a form of tempering used to enhance the toughness of a hardened steel where high hardness is not particularly needed in service. To toughen, the temperature range is usually 1000 to 1250°F.

Quenching to harden before toughening differs somewhat from the method used to produce hardening alone. Since high hardness is not required, quenching at a slow rate, as in oil, before toughening will usually meet the condition of strength and will be less likely to spoil the workpiece by stressing.

The microstructures resulting from tempering and toughening are called secondary troostite and sorbite, respectively (see Chap. 2).

FURNACES AND OTHER HEATING EQUIPMENT

Heating apparatus may be classified as

(1) Hearth furnaces
(2) Molten bath furnaces
(3) Selective area heating apparatus.

Ordinarily, a heat-treating furnace consists of a box-like structure with an access door, a refractory lining, and a means of measuring and controlling the furnace space temperature.

In the past, hearth-type furnaces which used oil and gas as a source of fuel predominated. In recent years with the availability of inexpensive electric power, electrically heated furnaces have gained steadily in popularity. In spite of the relative economy of electric power, gas and oil are still in common use for the heat treatment of large workpieces. The close control of scaling and deoxidation of workpiece surfaces is considerably easier in electrically heated and muffle-type furnaces, since there is no contamination from combustion gases.

Molten-bath furnaces offer the advantages of uniform and rapid heating, exclusion of the deleterious atmosphere, and response to accurate temperature control. The molten bath is of particular importance as a means of quenching at elevated temperatures to avoid cracking and loss of workpieces.

Selective hardening, which employs chiefly the high-frequency induction and flame hardening methods, has in recent years become important industrially. One major application is the heat treatment of tools and production workpieces that require only selected surfaces and portions of the pieces to be heat treated. Heat treatment can be done at lowest cost when applied only to surfaces where needed. Examples of induction and flame-hardened pieces are wrist pins, crank shaft bearing journals, cylinder liners, rail ends, and pump shafts.

Hearth furnaces. The *direct fuel-fired furnace* (Fig. 5–10) is popular in all temperature ranges. The combustion space is also the furnace space, with the burners usually located over the workpieces. This furnace is more adaptable to rough forms of heating such as pieces for forging and pressing, but if fuel is reasonably pure, it may be used at lower temperatures to heat workpieces requiring closer compositional control.

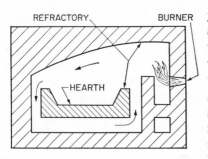

Fig. 5–10. A diagram of a direct fuel-fired furnace.

The *indirect-fired furnace* has a heating chamber and a muffle which separate the combustion space from the work space. The upper temperature limit for this furnace is approximately 2000°F. Reduced scaling and contamination from the fuels are the advantages in its use.

In the *recirculation furnace* the fuel, gas or oil, is burned in a chamber, and the products of combustion are circulated through the furnace work space by a suitably arranged fan and baffling. The hot gases are channeled so that heating will be uniform. The use of recirculation furnaces is most common in temperature ranges below 1300°F, commonly for tempering, toughening, and stress-relieving.

Muffle and *retort furnaces* are used mostly where it is desired to surround the workpiece materials with a protective atmosphere to avoid scaling, decarburization, and other compositional modifications. The muffle, made from suitable refractory, is a permanent part of the furnace and contains all of the work space. It is sufficiently tight to prevent the ingress of combustion gases, and so avoids contaminating the protective atmosphere. Semi-muffle furnaces have a small amount of baffling in the furnace work space to prevent the direct impingement of the combustion flame upon the workpiece. A retort furnace is characterized by a heat-resisting retort that is loaded outside the furnace, properly sealed with a cap, and then placed in the furnace to be heated.

The *radiant-tube furnace* consists of a tightly encased refractory-lined furnace with radiant tubes arranged around the work space.

Electrically-heated hearth furnaces (Fig. 5–11) are usually similar in general configuration to fuel-fired furnaces. The electric resistance heating elements are supported in the furnace wall by the refractory lining.

Movable-hearth furnaces. There are two principal types of movable-hearth furnaces—the car bottom and the rotary type.

In the *car bottom type,* excluding the bottom, the furnace is similar in shape to a fixed-hearth furnace. The car bottom is similar to

Fig. 5–11. Electric resistance heated furnace. The heating elements appear on the refractory wall.

the ordinary flat car but is built of heat-resisting materials and very close to the floor. It travels on two rails and is passed into or withdrawn from the furnace by power. To promote uniformity of heating of the materials on the car, the load is usually stacked on heat-resisting alloy castings or refractory piers to facilitate free under-passage of hot gases. Figure 5–12 shows a car bottom furnace being loaded.

Fig. 5–12. Car bottom furnace.

Rotary-hearth furnaces are discussed under Continuous furnaces.

Continuous furnaces. Where a considerable number of workpieces are to be heat treated, furnaces may be mechanized to expedite the process.

Common forms are the rotary-hearth, roller-hearth, and conveyor-types of furnaces.

Rotary-hearth furnaces are built in a wide range of sizes which will accommodate from a few hundred pounds up to 40 tons per hour. The furnace structure is a round refractory-lined shell that encloses a rotating hearth. The materials are charged as individual pieces, or as small pieces in trays, through the door. The speed of the hearth is adjusted so that the heat-treating cycle will be completed when the hearth turns one time. The materials are removed from the same door through which they were charged.

The *roller-hearth furnace* is a production continuous-type unit that is adapted to the heat treatment of uniformly sized parts. Its hearth consists of numerous rollers mounted on horizontal heat-resisting shafts which are turned by chains and sprockets. The hearth rollers move the workpieces through the furnace at a controlled rate. Small parts are conveyed through the furnace in trays or baskets.

In the *pusher furnace* a hearth mechanism pushes one workpiece against the one immediately ahead of it along suitable guides or rails, the speed of travel being adjusted so that the heat-treating cycle is complete when any given workpiece reaches the discharge end. Trays carrying small pieces may be used in this furnace.

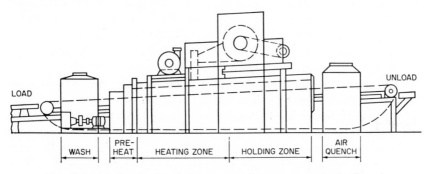

Fig. 5–13. A sketch of a chain conveyor furnace to wash, draw, and cool hardened gears in large quantities.

A common means of mechanizing a furnace is a chain conveyor, the materials of which are of a heat-resisting alloy. The chain carries large workpieces or trays of small pieces into the furnace and extends through an exit door in the opposite side of the furnace, from which it discharges the workpieces. Figure 5–13 is a diagram of a chain conveyor furnace.

TABLE 5–1. Specifications of a Few Typical Industrial Furnaces

Description	Effective work area, ft (width—height—length)	Energy input	Max. rated temp. (°F)	Approx. overall dims., ft (width—height—length)	Approx. cost ($)
Box-type, indirect-fired or recirculation, hearth furnace for toolroom	$2 \times 1\frac{1}{2} \times 3$	32 kw (175,000 btu gas fired)	1,250	$3\frac{1}{2} \times 6 \times 7$	4,000
Box-type, indirect-fired or recirculation, hearth furnace for production	$3 \times 3 \times 8$	107 kw (640,000 btu gas fired)	1,250	$7 \times 12 \times 14$	10,000
Electric rod, conveyor hearth, four zone hardening furnace plus oil quench tank with discharge flight conveyor	$2 \times \frac{2}{3} \times 12$	138 kw	1,650	$6 \times 5 \times 40$	30,000
Electric globar, mesh belt conveyor hearth, five zone brazing furnace	$2 \times \frac{5}{6} \times 8$	130 kw	2,100	$4 \times 5\frac{1}{2} \times 53$	25,000

Furnace atmospheres. In commercial heat treating most ferrous materials are exposed to high temperatures for appreciable periods of time.

As a result, oxide scale forms. The severity of scaling depends upon the nature of the atmosphere present and the length of time the pieces are held in the furnace. Except for the roughest work, the importance of avoiding scaling the parts cannot be overemphasized. Many parts are machined prior to heat treatment. To have their dimensional tolerances changed and their work surfaces oxidized and roughened is often tantamount to ruining the workpieces. To produce unoxidized parts, rather close attention must be given the nature of furnace atmosphere. Gases having the most pernicious effect in heat treating are oxygen, carbon dioxide, and water vapor. These must be avoided.

Oxygen reacts with the carbon in steel and strongly tends to decrease the surface carbon content. The normal reaction of oxygen with iron is to form a dark loose-clinging oxide scale that is about ten times greater in volume than the iron from which it comes. Under some conditions, steel may scale more rapidly than it decarburizes. In either case, the parts will emerge from the furnace with roughened dark surfaces and, if quenched, the decarburized skin will remain soft. In the production of some parts excess material is allowed for finishing by grinding after hardening, but frequently this is not possible.

Nitrogen in the molecular state is satisfactory as a furnace atmosphere for bright annealing of low-carbon steels. Hydrogen, if present at certain temperatures, is absorbed by steel and may cause embrittlement, particularly in the high-carbon steels. Dry hydrogen has no scaling effect on high-carbon steels at elevated temperatures but does cause appreciable decarburization. For bright annealing, an atmosphere consisting of 75% hydrogen and 25% nitrogen is in common use. This is obtained by cracking anhydrous ammonia by passing it over a heated catalyst.

A ratio of 0.6 carbon monoxide to one part carbon dioxide or higher at 1500°F will scale steel readily. Where the ratio is 0.4:1 or lower, the atmosphere will not scale but will decarburize high-carbon steels. For bright annealing of low-carbon sheet steel, a ratio of carbon monoxide to carbon dioxide of about 1:2 is satisfactory.

Gases for furnace protective atmospheres may be generated by passing air over hot charcoal or by partial combustion or cracking of hydrocarbon gases. Various mixtures are made and used. One method of exothermically cracking city or natural gases, propane, or butane with air partially burns the gas to heat a catalyst that causes the formation of hydrogen and carbon monoxide. Water vapor is extracted by cooling, but a high proportion of CO_2 remains from the combustion and tends to decarburize all but low-carbon steel when in a furnace atmosphere. A higher quality atmosphere is produced by the endothermic cracking of natural gas or propane with air in ratios that do not support combustion. In this the water vapor and CO_2 can be controlled to any desired amounts.

The benefits that can be obtained from the major kinds of furnace atmospheres have been described, but their costs must also be considered. Pure gases are the most expensive. Hydrogen from cylinders costs $10 and more per 1000 cu ft. Anhydrous ammonia from cylinders may cost up to $4.50 per 1000 cu ft and less than $1.50 per 1000 cu ft in tank car quantities. In the latter case, equipment for storage and handling may require an investment of $25,000 or more. Equipment for cracking hydrocarbons costs upwards of several thousand dollars, depending on size. Exothermically cracked gases supply the cheapest atmospheres, at $0.08 to $0.12 per 1000 cu ft. Good quality cracked atmospheres run from $0.20 to $0.30 per 1000 cu ft.

Bath furnaces. Bath furnaces are classified as two basic types: gas- or oil-fired and the electrically-heated types.

In the externally heated type of electrically-heated salt bath furnace depicted in Fig. 5–14, the resistance elements are located in the walls of the furnace and heat the external walls of the inserted pot by radiation. Between the resistance elements and the outside metal enclosure of the furnace is insulation to withstand the comparatively high temperatures and prevent rapid loss of heat.

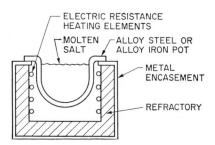

Fig. 5–14. Electric resistance heated salt bath furnace.

The *immersion heating element type* of furnace consists of a heat-resisting alloy pot adequately surrounded by insulation and electric-resistance heating elements immersed directly into the salt bath. Immersion heaters are usually limited to temperatures below 1100°F and, therefore, are normally used for tempering and other low-temperature heat treatments.

The *immersed electrode salt bath* furnace consists of an insulated steel or refractory pot containing the salt into which are immersed two electrodes. These furnaces are restricted to the use of a-c power transformed to low voltages (5 to 25 v), since d-c tends to electrolytically decompose the liquid salt. In this electrical arrangement, relatively high currents flow through the conductive salt medium and give up heat created by its resistance.

Gas- and oil-fired salt bath furnaces are, from the standpoint of first cost, preferred for many heat-treating operations. The temperature of the bath may be regulated in the usual way by use of thermocouple controls. The bath may be heated externally, as in Fig. 5–15, or by immersed radiant tubes.

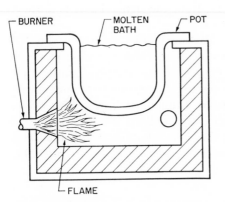

Fig. 5–15. A diagram of an externally heated gas or oil fired salt bath furnace.

Salt baths for heat treating. The use of fused salts, both as a means of heating workpieces and for quenching at elevated temperatures, has become of widespread importance.

When a cold piece of metal is placed in fused salts for the purpose of heating, the salt immediately contacting the piece freezes and clings tightly to the workpiece, thus forming a salt encasement that serves to prevent rapid surface heating and thermal shock.

When the temperature reaches equilibrium, the frozen shell disappears, and further heating occurs by conduction. An additional advantage of this method is that the molten salt in direct contact with the workpiece more efficiently transfers heat (four to seven times faster) than would a gaseous atmosphere. Totally immersed, the materials being heated have no contact with the atmosphere and, therefore, compositional changes are avoided (where the salt bath is neutral). At the end of the heating cycle and when the part is removed, a film of molten salt adheres to the part and protects it against attack of the atmosphere while it is being moved to another bath or to the quenching tank.

Common salts are sodium and potassium chlorides, nitrates, and cyanides. They are mixed in various proportions and with other salts to obtain different melting points for services in various ranges from 325 to 2500°F and for various purposes. Formulas are given in reference- and hand-books.

HEAT TREATING OF STEEL CASTINGS

General. Steel castings are obtained by pouring refined steel (usually from the open-hearth or electric furnace) into properly designed sand molds and allowing it to solidify. No new heat-treating concepts are encountered in the steel castings industry. The usual heat treatments, such as annealing, normalizing, hardening, etc., that relate to wrought steel are also applicable to steel castings in the same compositional range. Some typical properties of cast steels are given in Table 8–5.

Steel castings are ordinarily classified as plain-carbon and alloy steels, with the former division subdivided into low-carbon, medium-carbon, and high-carbon types; and the latter as low- and high-alloy types.

The low-carbon types have 0.2% carbon or less, 0.05 to 0.1% manganese, 0.02 to 0.75% silicon, 0.05% max. phosphorus, and 0.06% max. sulfur.

Medium-carbon cast steels constitute the greater part of steel foundry production. Carbon will be 0.20 to 0.50%, and composition otherwise chemically similar to the low-carbon class.

For severe services, high-carbon cast steels have 0.50% or more of carbon, and are otherwise chemically similar to low-carbon and medium-carbon classes.

Alloy cast steels are multitudinous in type, their heat treatment and uses varying considerably. Generally speaking, constructional type alloy steel castings contain less than 8% total of alloying elements.

In casting, liquid steel is allowed to cool undisturbed within the confines of its mold, the natural consequence of which is coarse dendritic grain and considerable segregation. Since a steel casting will not receive the benefits of hot-work to break up the dendritic grains, heat treating must be employed instead. Generally, heat treating a steel casting improves its machinability and its mechanical properties.

Both full annealing and normalizing are applicable heat treatments, although, unless maximum softness and ductility are desired, normalizing will prove to be more beneficial, since it will provide a finer subdivision of the dendritic grain, higher tensile strength, and is more effective from a standpoint of homogenization.

Where a single homogenizing treatment is given, a temperature of about 200°F above the upper critical range is recommended. This temperature is a compromise between grain growth tendency and rapid diffusion of the segregated elements. In high-carbon steel castings, a second heat treatment at about 1000° to 1200°F is recommended for the purpose of lowering the hardness produced by rapid cooling in normalizing. The holding time at homogenizing temperature will be roughly one hr per in. of thickness in the heaviest section of the casting.

If maximum diffusion of elements and the greatest possible amount of granular refinement are desired, a double treatment is given. This consists of normalizing from 1600 to 2000°F, followed by a refining treatment at slightly above the critical upper temperature.

Immersion-quenching of a steel casting is done to harden and strengthen it. The quenching steps should be preceded by full annealing where the best condition of grain structure is desired. As was true in rolled steels, the casting should be removed from the quenching bath before all the heat is dissipated if difficulty from cracking is anticipated. As an alternative, the casting may be quenched in molten salt.

A hardenable steel casting that has been austenitized and quenched should not be sent into service without tempering. Depending somewhat upon the ultimate mechanical properties desired, the tempering range is usually 800 to 1250°F. This range will dissipate residual stresses.

Questions

1. For what reasons may steel be heat treated?

2. What does annealing do?

3. Describe and distinguish normalizing, full annealing, stress-relieving, spheroidizing, and flame-softening.

4. How is steel hardened by quenching?

5. What can be done in hardening steel to avoid cracking and warping?

6. What does hardenability of steel mean and how is it measured?

7. What is interrupted-quenching and how is it done?

8. Describe how surface-hardening is done by induction-hardening, flame-hardening, carburizing, cyaniding, and nitriding.

9. Why is steel tempered, and how is it done?

10. What are three main classes of heating apparatus for treating metals?

11. Describe and compare the main types of heat-treating furnaces.

12. Why must the atmosphere of a heat-treating furnace be controlled, and how is that done?

13. What are the advantages and disadvantages of salt bath heat treating?

14. Why are steel castings heat treated?

15. What heat-treatment procedures are applicable to steel castings?

References

Grossman, M. A., *Principles of Heat Treatment,* American Society for Metals, Cleveland, 1957.

Metals Handbook, American Society for Metals, Cleveland, 1948 and 1954 and 1955 supplements.

Atlas of Isothermal Transformation Diagrams, United States Steel Co., Pittsburgh, 1951.

Sachs, G., and K. R. Van Horn, *Practical Metallurgy,* American Society for Metals, Cleveland, 1940.

6

Alloy Steels and Irons

General considerations. Plain-carbon steels have, besides iron and carbon, elements such as manganese, silicon, sulfur, and phosphorus. These elements usually appear in carbon steels as a result of a furnace scavenging process and their retention from the parent ores. Steels containing small amounts of these elements are not regarded as alloy steels, inasmuch as not enough elements are present to confer special properties.

Where the mechanical properties of a steel are appreciably modified and improved by the addition of alloying elements, and the amounts added are substantially greater than those found in ordinary plain carbon steel, the steel is of the alloy type. This great family of steels plays a prominent role in modern-day industry. Their use may be conducive to greater fabricating economy, lighter weights in members, better resistance to heat and corrosion, or more durable cutting tool edges.

Alloy steels are of two basic types—the low-alloy and the special-alloy steels.

In the low-alloy steels, elements other than carbon and iron usually do not exceed a total of 5%. The alloys are added mainly for the purpose of improving the mechanical properties of the metal. Tonnagewise, this classification will embrace a high percentage of alloy steels rolled, since they go into such structures as machinery parts, vehicular elements, stills and other refinery equipment, and high-temperature containers. With the advent and perfection of suitable welding procedures, low-alloy steels are used in enormous volume.

Special-alloy steels are those in which alloying elements are added in considerably greater amounts than in the low-alloy types. These serve to resist wear, high temperatures, and corrosive attack, and to provide high impact strength. Metal cutting tools of today made from special steels have a useful life several times greater than their plain carbon steel predecessors as discussed in Chap. 16.

One or more alloying elements may be added to steel. Metallurgical experience has shown that alloying elements tend to intensify the effects of one another and, therefore, for economy several are used—usually two or three.

Where alloys are added to steels, the simplicity of the iron-carbon relationship may no longer exist. In the heat treatment of a plain-carbon steel, reference can be made to the iron-carbon diagram to ascertain critical temperatures for their proper heat treatment. Due to the influence of alloys present, these temperatures and critical zones may be shifted significantly and, consequently, the transformation behavior is quite unlike that of the plain-carbon type.

Alloying elements. The more common elements added to steel for alloying are chromium, nickel, manganese, vanadium, molybdenum, silicon, tungsten, phosphorus, copper, titanium, zirconium, cobalt, columbium, and aluminum. Metallurgists divide these elements into two groups—those that form solutions with ferrite and those that form carbides. Under conditions of slow cooling, complex carbides consisting of iron-carbides and carbides of manganese, chromium, tungsten, vanadium, titanium, columbium, and molybdenum will be present. Elements such as nickel, silicon, and copper remain dissolved in iron (alpha) at room temperature. Generally speaking, carbides tend to dissolve in austenite but precipitate and coalesce at lower temperatures. It is because of the tendency of carbides to precipitate and disperse throughout the steel metallic body that a wide range of mechanical and physical properties are derived through proper heat treatment. No other commercial metal offers this degree of engineering flexibility.

Unit cells of alloying elements. Whether an addition element will dissolve in iron, and so remain at room temperature, depends to a great extent upon the configuration of its unit cell.

If the unit cell of the alloying element is of the face-centered-cubic type (FCC), it strongly resists being removed from solution with gamma iron (also FCC) on a falling temperature, and, therefore, it will tend to stabilize the austenite and retard transformation. Because of the presence of elements that are face-centered-cubic, rapid decomposition of the austenite and early transformation is avoided. This is often an advantage in the treatments of some steels. The more common face-centered-cubic elements are nickel, cobalt, copper and aluminum.

Body-centered-cubic (BCC) elements dissolve in austenite with some reluctance and tend to accelerate transformation on a falling temperature; hence rapid cooling will be required, at least in theory, to obtain hardening. The elements chromium, vanadium, and tungsten are the more common body-centered-cubic types. Carbide-forming elements are chiefly of the body-centered-cubic type.

Cobalt and titanium are the hexagonal-close-packed type (HCP), and have a unit cell configuration closely related to the body-centered-cubic.

With the addition of a sufficient amount of those elements that tend to lower the A_3 temperature, a composition will be obtained in which gamma iron will exist at room temperature. Under these conditions the steel will remain face-centered-cubic and normally no transformation will occur, the 14% manganese steel being typical. Austenite in alloy steels may be retained at room temperature by increasing the severity of quenching, the rate depending primarily upon the amount of carbon and alloying elements present.

Elements such as cobalt, copper and aluminum tend to shift the eutectoid point to the right; almost all other elements shift the eutectoid point to the left. As a consequence of this behavior, the carbon content of eutectoid alloy steel may be more or less than that of the plain-carbon eutectoid steel, depending upon which and how much of the alloy is present.

Retardation of transformation rate by alloying. The stabilization of austenite (the reluctance with which it will transform to ferrite) will, to a great extent, determine the rate of cooling needed to harden a steel completely. Furthermore, the abundance and the nature of the carbides formed on precipitation and their dispersion will govern the intensity of hardening, the overall mechanical properties, and depth of hardening. Except for special properties conferred by alloy additions to steels, carbide dispersion and transformation obstruction distinguishes alloy steels from plain-carbon steels.

Due to the retarded transformation rate from austenite to ferrite, an alloy steel may be cooled to comparatively low temperatures before the transformation actually starts. Consequently, if transformation takes place at all, it must do so under conditions of considerable metallic rigidity. By this metallurgical device, hardening of alloy steels is reasonably easy by quenching in oil or even in air. Oil-quenching is less severe than water-quenching. The use of air-hardening steels provides a convenience in some heat-treating situations where the needed complement of furnaces and quenching baths does not exist. Also, because air-quenching is less severe, it tends to act as a safeguard against the cracking of workpieces which sometimes occur in oil- or water-quenching.

Elements which strongly tend to stabilize austenite and slow up the transformation on a falling temperature are nickel, manganese, nitrogen, carbon, and copper.

Hardenability as affected by alloys. By examining the curves shown in Fig. 5–2, it is seen that when a plain-carbon steel is quenched, the surface where the rate of heat dissipation is highest will attain maximum hardness but will drop off sharply in hardness toward the center where the heat transfer rate is lower. This, of course, means that throughout a considerable portion of the section a cooling rate sufficient to harden completely is not attained. If a similar section of alloyed steel is given appropriate heat treatment, the hardness at the heat dissipating surface will be greatest; the values inward toward the core will drop off slowly and also be minimum at the center of the mass. A typical curve for the alloy steel shown is almost fully hardened at the center. The reason is that the critical cooling speed for full hardening is almost attained because of the sluggish transformation of the alloy. Where it is desired that a section be fully hardened to obtain maximum mechanical properties, alloyed steels are advantageous.

Tempering and toughening of alloy steels. The rate of softening that occurs in tempering a steel is a function of the readiness with which the finely dispersed carbide particles tend to coalesce. Carbide particles in most alloy steels do not consolidate as readily as plain-carbon types on reheating to temper. The stability of cementite made up of complex carbides accounts for alloy steels that remain hard and tough at high temperatures. These properties are evidenced in cutting tools, and high-temperature-operating members such as steam piping and exhaust systems. Martensite, being a highly stressed microconstituent, may be heat treated by tempering so that its peak hardness is lowered only slightly, but the steel is rendered virtually stress-free.

INFLUENCE OF INDIVIDUAL ALLOYING ELEMENTS

Chromium. This element is used widely in the alloying of steel. Except for the making of high-alloy chromium steels, the element is normally employed in conjunction with other alloying elements to obtain the benefits of their mutual intensification.

Chromium (BCC) has lattice dimensions comparing favorably with those of alpha iron (also BCC), and accordingly has high solubility in iron. Chromium is very potent and does not allotropically transform. Consequently, steels having considerable amounts of chromium may be in the body-centered-cubic form at all temperatures and will not be hardened by quenching (no transformation). Since chromium is body-centered-cubic, it tends to stabilize alpha iron, thus causing transformation to come about slowly on heating to the upper critical temperature of the steel. Chromium shifts the S-curve to the right, making possible a comparatively flat cooling curve and high hardenability.

From the standpoint of mechanical properties, chromium, when added to iron-carbon alloys, increases the hardness, decreases the ductility, and increases the tensile strength and elastic limit. It strongly contributes to the stabilization of martensite and, therefore, is nearly always present in cutting tools and steels of similar type.

Nickel. This is a noncarbide-forming element which is soluble in either alpha or gamma iron in all proportions. Being face-centered-cubic, it tends to stabilize austenite and thus lowers transformation temperatures. Nickel appears to have its greatest influence on iron in the presence of carbon, a circumstance which is generally thought to be related to the distribution of carbides. As is characteristic of many other alloying elements, nickel reduces the eutectoid point of steel to about 0.65% carbon when present to the extent of 4 or 5%. Nickel causes a sluggish transformation in steel on cooling which, in effect, is the same as shifting the S-curve to the right and lowering the critical cooling rate.

An important application of nickel steel is in members that are to be placed in service without heat treatment, the alloying element serving the important role of strengthening the ferrite and producing a fine-grain, shock-resistant microstructure. Nickel steels of the structural type have a high tensile strength and elastic limit in combination with high ductility. Where these steels are cold-worked in forming, they are superior to plain-carbon types. Nickel steels are generally regarded as highly workable in hot-forging and rolling.

Manganese. The element manganese has a modified body-centered-cubic unit cell (two forms) and a tetragonal gamma form. It is soluble in both gamma and alpha iron. The manganese carbide probably joins with the iron carbide to form a complex unit. Manganese carbides may be dissolved in gamma iron and are thus retained in solution by rapid cooling. For hard microstructures on quenching, manganese is generally regarded as being twice as potent as nickel.

Aside from forming hard carbides in steel, manganese has a strengthening effect on the ferrite and increases the overall hardenability of the workpiece on quenching. Manganese steels are favored for case-carburizing, since the presence of this element produces larger austenitic grains and thus better hardenability. To form fragile chips in machining, manganese and sulfur are added together to form inclusions of manganese sulfides. Manganese steels have greater impact strength and yield strength (with the same ductility) than plain-carbon steels. Where this alloying element is used alone, care must be observed in heat treating to attain the necessary refinement of grain and to prevent distortion of parts on quenching.

Vanadium. Vanadium forms carbides and is soluble in both gamma and alpha iron. This element is a strong deoxidizer in molten steel but is seldom used for scavenging purposes because of its cost. The potency of vanadium generally limits its use for alloying steel to less than 0.2% — this amount giving refinement of grain; higher elastic limit, strength, resistance to shock, hardness, and fatigue strength; and good wearability. Chromium-vanadium steels are extensively used in tools, drills, and other parts in which high hardness, toughness, and strength are desired in combination.

Molybdenum. This element dissolves both in gamma and alpha iron and, in the presence of carbon, forms complex carbides. Although the element is body-centered-cubic, it, nevertheless, tends to depress the critical points on quenching. As in vanadium, molybdenum finds its greatest use in conjunction with other alloys. It is particularly valuable in increasing the tensile strength and hardenability of a steel. In present-day use of steels for sustaining loads at high temperatures, failures due to creep are avoided or minimized by alloying steel with molybdenum. This element finds wide use in the making of high-speed steels. Most alloy steel specifications call for 0.30% or less of molybdenum and seldom does any exceed 0.65%.

Silicon. Iron combines with silicon to form the compound FeSi which, in turn, forms solid solutions with both gamma and alpha iron. Not only does silicon avoid forming carbides at heat-treating temperatures but often is responsible for decomposition of other carbides by its presence. Silicon has a diamond-cubic unit cell and its presence raises the critical temperatures. Silicon dissolves in ferrite and tends to make a steel ferritic, depending upon the amount of carbon present.

Although silicon does moderately improve the hardenability and strength of ferrite, its biggest role is as a deoxidizing agent and, in high percentages, provides an alloy steel having low magnetic retentivity.

Tungsten. Tungsten is of the body-centered-cubic type, dissolves in both alpha and gamma iron, and is a strong carbide former. Carbon combines with tungsten to produce an abundance of carbides that are hard, stable, and produce good cutting edges. In general, upon cooling, the carbides may precipitate, may remain dissolved in alpha iron to form martensite, or remain dissolved in gamma iron and cool to room temperature as untransformed austenite, all three behaviors being functions of the cooling rate.

In small quantities, say 0.1%, tungsten apparently has little influence upon the mechanical properties and the critical temperatures of a steel in which it is contained. However, the presence of sufficient tungsten in a steel causes sluggishness of transformation, raising the Ac_3 temperature on heating and lowering it on cooling. As is true with a number of other alloying elements, tungsten decreases the eutectoid carbon content of a steel. The complex carbides of tungsten and iron tend to inhibit grain growth and have high thermal stability. Tungsten alloy steels require high heat-treating temperatures and long soaking periods.

Sulfur. In the presence of sufficient manganese, sulfur improves the machinability of steels by the formation of an abundance of brittle manganese sulfides. Sulfur has a great tendency to segregate in the cooling ingot. It decreases the ductility and toughness of steel and, therefore, its specified content in steels (except the free-machining types) is usually 0.04% max. At forging temperatures, liquid iron-sulfides which form at grain boundaries cause "red short" or general disintegration of the forging bar.

Copper. Copper dissolves in both gamma and alpha iron and tends to lower the critical range. Copper is not generally added to steel for any purpose other than to improve its resistance to atmospheric corrosion; this requiring 0.15 to 0.30% of the element.

Titanium. This element is used principally in the making of high-alloy steels. It is a carbon-avid element, uniting with carbon to the exclusion of chromium, manganese, and iron to produce carbides that have high stability. Steels which tend to air-harden because they contain manganese and chromium may have this objection overcome by the addition of titanium. If titanium is added in sufficient amounts, the steels may be rendered pearlitic or even ferritic instead of air-hardening on cooling.

Zirconium. When added to steel, zirconium acts as a deoxidizer and scavenger, combining with nitrogen, sulfur, and oxygen, and either eliminates them from the molten bath or renders them innocuous. This element forms zirconium nitrides, an action which mitigates age-hardening in deep-drawing stock. Its presence in high-sulfur steel leads to the formation of zirconium sulfide and tends to reduce hot shortness. When added in amounts above 0.10%, zirconium will produce fine-grain steels but in smaller amounts, say 0.05%, will function only to cleanse the steel.

Cobalt. Cobalt has a close-packed-hexagonal space lattice and is highly soluble in gamma iron and reasonably soluble in alpha iron. Cobalt will move the S-curve to the left, the result being reduced hardenability. This element is weakly carbide-forming but contributes to red hardness in cutting tool steels by strengthening and hardening the ferrite. Its overall contribution to the hardness of a steel after heat treating is primarily from its retention in solution. The effect of cobalt is often compared to that of nickel; that is, it increases the strength and elastic limit, and there is little loss of ductility if it is added in moderate amounts.

Cobalt is widely used to alloy magnet steels.

Cobalt-base alloys have high stress-to-rupture properties and operate at high temperatures in such applications as jet engine turbine blades. Operating at temperatures as high as 1800°F, cobalt confers metallurgical stability, strength, and resistance to erosion and corrosion.

Columbium. In steel making the use of columbium is more or less restricted to high-alloy steels. In effect it is quite similar to titanium, in that both have a higher affinity for carbon than chromium, manganese, or iron. It is a stabilizing element which renders the quenched product martensitic, pearlitic, or ferritic, depending upon the amounts of the columbium contained. Columbium, as well as titanium, is widely used in the stabilization of austenitic stainless steels. Columbium has the advantage that it does not suffer much loss in passing through the arc stream in welding.

Aluminum. This metal is one of the strongest deoxidizing agents known and is almost universally employed in the United States for deoxidizing molten steel. It will dissolve in all proportions in iron but is seldom used in excess of 0.1% for deoxidation.

Numerous tiny particles of Al_2O_3 remain suspended in the finished steel and seemingly act as nuclei or starting points for nuclei, thus contributing to a fine-grain structure. Aside from cleansing the steel, metallurgists generally believe that aluminum improves the final properties of the finished steel.

CLASSIFICATION OF ALLOY STEELS

For many years steels have been classified by a four-digit number system developed by the Society of Automotive Engineers. Briefly, the system assigns the first digit in the number to the identification of the principal alloying element present. The second digit indicates the approximate amount of the principal alloying elements, and the last two digits denotes the points of carbon in the steel where one point is 0.01%.

After a long period of time the expanded list of alloy steels which appeared on the American market grew beyond the bounds of the SAE numbering system and the problem of clearer identification of the numerous steels became apparent. Through the joint effort of the American Iron and Steel Institute and the Society of Automotive Engineers a new identification system was formed, the AISI–SAE, and is now in general use. The system of number designation is similar to the old SAE system, but, in addition, a letter prefix is employed to show the process by which the steel is produced. The prefix is used as follows:

> *B*–Acid Bessemer carbon steel
> *C*–Basic open-hearth carbon steel
> *CB*–Either Bessemer or open-hearth process at the option of the steel mill
> *E*–Electric furnace alloy steel
> No prefix–Open-hearth alloy steel

The first digit indicates the alloy that characterizes the steel: plain carbon, 1; nickel, 2; nickel-chromium, 3; molybdenum, 4; chromium, 5; chromium-vanadium, 6; tungsten, 7; and silicon-manganese, 9.

As an example, in the AISI–SAE 4340, the first digit, 4, indicates the steel to be of the molybdenum type, the second digit, 3, shows about 3% of the alloying elements present, and the third and fourth digit together means that the steel has about 0.40% carbon. In another example, AISI–SAE 52100, the steel is of the chromium type as indicated by the digit 5, about 2% of the alloying element, and, in this case, the last three digits means that the steel has 1 (1.00)% carbon. Engineering materials handbooks should be consulted for complete tables of AISI–SAE steels.

SPECIAL ALLOY STEELS

Elements may be added to steels for imparting properties over and above those mentioned in connection with low- and medium-alloy types. In general, the alloy additions will range from a low limit of 5 to 10% to as much as 60%. Obviously special alloy steels will be considerably more expensive than the low- and medium-alloy types and, therefore, should not be used if the less costly steels suffice. In service situations where steels must survive high temperatures, corrosion, and shock, special-alloy steels are invaluable.

High manganese steel (above 10% manganese). Where steel products must sustain shock-type loads and be subjected to wear from abrasive materials, austenitic manganese steel has found wide favor. The chemical composition is as follows: carbon, 1 to 1.4%; manganese, 10 to 14%; silicon, 0.3 to 1%; sulfur, 0.5% max.; and phosphorus, 0.10% max. This composition provides a steel that is austenitic at room temperature. When treated to resist shock, it becomes exceptionally hard and tough in service and is superior to other steels for such parts as power shovel dippers, power shovel teeth, rock crushers, and railway crossover parts and frogs.

Austenitic manganese steel in the as-cast, slow-cooled condition tends to precipitate carbides at its grain boundaries, a behavior which causes destructive brittleness and failure of members in service. Annealing of such a casting would promote further carbide precipitation; hence, the proper heat treatment is to completely austenitize the casting, absorbing all existing carbides, and quench to retain the carbides in solution. This is done by heating to a temperature range of 1850 to 1950°F and quenching in water. The result is a uniform austenitic structure which is tough and strong. Following the quench, the tensile strength will be 135,000 to 145,000 psi, and elongation 50 to 60%. In the as-cast condition, the hardness is about 18 Rc, and in the heat-treated condition, 18 to 20 Rc. Even though the hardness as-quenched is not high, when subjected to service impact, such as that obtained from handling rock with a power shovel, the effect of the cold-work increases the hardness to about 45 to 55 Rc. Any type of cold deformation produces hardening of this steel. For service applications where work-hardening is present, manganese steels outlast, 10 to 1, other types of steels having a corresponding initial hardness.

Austenitic manganese steel is cast to shape, inasmuch as it work-hardens and generally makes forming impossible by machine tool cutting or plastic shaping.

Corrosion-resisting (stainless) steels. Under certain conditions all steels corrode to some degree. Corrosion-resisting steels are primarily those containing chromium, their surface oxides being bright or dark depending chiefly upon their environmental temperatures. At their inception, corrosion-resisting steels, usually referred to as stainless steels, were made into such items as knives and other items of cutlery. Even though this steel is yet devoted to cutlery manufacture, the great tonnages today are being used for ornamental purposes and industrial containers. Ornamental items consist of architectural and automobile trim, and some jewelry; industrial containers consist of dairy utensils, piping, processing vats, and petroleum stills. Where used at ordinary temperatures, stainless steel is lustrous. The oxides formed are a result of exposure to the atmosphere or other corroding media, are transparent or the same color as the virgin steel, and quite tenacious, thus preserving the beauty and usefulness of the item. Steels appear to be corrosion-resistant approximately in proportion to the amount of chromium present, the lower limit of the element being about 11%.

Corrosion-resisting steels fall mainly into three basic types: (1) those having less than 16% chromium, (2) those having more than 16%

chromium, and (3) the austenitic types having 17 to 25% chromium, along with 7 to 20% nickel. They are exemplified in the following descriptions of 12% chromium steels, corrosion-resisting irons, and austenitic stainless steels.

Twelve per cent chromium steels. This group of corrosion-resisting steels is used for pump parts, valve seats, turbine blades and similar parts. The carbon content usually ranges from 0.08 to 0.12% and the chromium from 11.5 to 13%.

Cutlery steels having 0.35% carbon and 13.5% chromium are substantially air-hardening and are often heat treated in this way.

Corrosion-resisting irons. Irons of this classification usually have chromium present in excess of 23%, but they may range from 20 to 30%. Their ability to resist corrosion is independent of the carbon present. Wrought chromium irons generally have 0.35% carbon or less. Castings, if they are to survive abrasion as well as oxidation, vary in carbon from 1 to 3%. Since these irons are ferritic at all temperatures, they are not responsive to quench-hardening.

The usual heat treatments given to produce high corrosion-resisting properties in chromium irons is heating to about 1600°F and rapidly quenching in either air or water.

The resistance of this grade of alloy to corrosion is efficient up to 2100°F or possibly higher. A dark tenacious scale is formed which serves as a protection against further metallic loss. A cast alloy of 0.35% carbon and 25% chromium, after being water-quenched, has a tensile strength of 58,000 psi and an elongation of 2%; wrought parts properly heat treated have considerably higher mechanical properties.

Corrosion-resisting irons may be used in parts for heat exchangers, conveyor chains, furnaces, stokers, and other similar high-temperature applications.

Austenitic stainless steel. In this class of steels two ranges of carbon are available—the low-carbon type which is less susceptible to intergranular corrosion and the type having from 0.08 to 0.12% carbon. In the latter, the carbon is definite in its effect upon the mechanical properties of the steel. The tensile and yield strengths increase with the carbon content, the change being greater in the yield property. Exclusive of the carbon content, the compositions of these steels are typically: chromium, 17 to 19%; nickel, 7 to 9%; and manganese, 1.25% max. in the higher-carbon type and 2% max. in the lower-carbon type.

Austenite in these steels is stable at all service temperatures. To obtain maximum softness, the steel is heated to 1800 to 2100°F, held for thorough soaking, and then quenched rapidly in water at room temperature. By this means, all carbides present are in solution at soaking temperature and are thus held by the rapid quench. In the interest of fine-grain structure, it is usually recommended that soaking temperatures in excess of 2000°F be avoided.

A considerable variation in the mechanical properties of austenitic corrosion-resisting steel may be derived by judicious use and control of cold-working. After cold-working, to relieve stresses and to bring about complete softness, austenitic stainless steel may be heated and quenched as mentioned.

Comparatively speaking, austenitic corrosion-resisting steel is a difficult metal to machine. In machining, a continuous chip should be carried if possible, since, in intermittent cutting, the tool has a tendency to work-harden the surface of the material when the cut is lost and some difficulty is encountered when an attempt is made to resume the cut. Carbide cutting tools and coolants are recommended for machining austenitic stainless steel.

Plain carbon tool steels. The medium- and high-carbon grades are employed to make punches, hammers, dies, woodworking tools and a host of other tools which serve at practically room temperature. Plain-carbon cutting tools are discussed in Chap. 16.

Nondeforming tool steels. Since no steel is absolutely nondeforming during heat treatment, certain combinations of alloys in steels tend to lessen the change in shape caused by shrinkage or loss from cracking. Due to the drastic action of water-quenching, steels hardened by water-quenching are not usually included in the nondeforming class.

All steels in this group are of the deep-hardening type. In thinner sections they may be fully hardened to about 63 Rc. Their wear resistance is roughly proportional to the amount of carbides present, or upon the amount of carbon and alloys in the steel.

This group of steels is used in such tools as forming and blanking dies, gages, broaches, and various types of woodworking tools.

Shock-resisting tool steels. Steels formed into tools that resist shock and fatigue should be sufficiently hard to resist upsetting and galling. Chisels, bending dies, and hammers are examples of tools subjected to shock. Chromium-vanadium, low silicon-manganese, high silicon-manganese, tungsten, and tungsten-silicon steels are suited to shock service.

Tool steels for hot-working. Hot-working tool steels are commonly alloys of chromium, molybdenum, and tungsten and have the following characteristics:

1. Red hardness or resistance to wear at elevated temperatures
2. Resistance to heat checking
3. Thermal stability; that is, resistance to softening from repeated or continuous heating
4. Sufficient toughness to prevent breakage.

Tools commonly made from this class of tool steels are hot-heading dies, forging dies, punches, and others.

High-speed steels. The ability of a tungsten alloy steel to hold a keen cutting edge at high operating temperatures rests primarily on the stability of the carbides present. These carbides require comparatively high temperatures for decomposition, a fact clearly evidenced by their slowness in coalescing during the tempering operations subsequent to hardening. Tungsten, being soluble in alpha iron and forming numerous carbides, characterizes high-speed steel as a tough, deep-hardening, high-tensile-strength alloy. High-speed steel cutting tools are discussed in Chap. 16.

High-nickel steel alloys. Nickel, when present in amounts ranging from 20 to 36% and associated with other alloying elements, strongly minimizes the coefficient of thermal expansion of steel, thus making the material quite valuable as parts in dimensional standards and precision measuring instruments. A high-nickel alloy, called Invar, containing 36% nickel and less than 1% altogether of the elements manganese, silicon, and carbon, has a coefficient of thermal expansion of almost zero for ordinary changes in temperature. The high magnetic properties of high-nickel steels make them common as components in communications equipment.

Transformer steels. These are straight silicon steels containing from 0.25 to 4% of silicon; all have very low carbon content. Because this class of alloy steels has high magnetic permeability and low hysteresis loss, they are well suited for transformer and motor laminations and inductor cores.

Questions

1. Why are alloying elements added to steel?

2. What are the differences between low-alloy and special-alloy steels?

3. How does the unit cell structure of an element affect its alloying propensity with iron?

4. How do alloying elements help to make quenching of steel pieces less severe and thus avoid cracking?

5. How does alloying affect hardenability of steel?

6. What effect does alloying have upon tempering and toughening of steels?

7. What is the effect of alloying steel with:
(a) chromium, (b) nickel, (c) manganese, (d) vanadium, (e) molybdenum, (f) silicon, (g) tungsten, (h) sulfur, (j) copper, (k) titanium, (l) zirconium, (m) cobalt, (n) columbium, and (o) aluminum?

8. What is the meaning in the AISI-SAE system of steel identification of:
(a) the prefix, (b) the first digit, (c) the second digit, and (e) the last two digits?

9. What are the composition and merits of high-manganese steel?

10. What are stainless steels and what are their desirable properties?

11. What are the relative constituents, properties and areas of application of (a) 12% chromium steels, (b) corrosion-resisting irons, and (c) austenitic stainless steel?

12. What are the applications for nondeforming tool steels, shock-resisting tool steels, tool steels for hot-working, and high-speed steels?

13. What are the advantages of high-nickel steel alloys?

14. What alloy makes steel particularly suitable for transformer laminations?

References

Bain, E. C., *Alloying Elements in Steel,* American Society for Metals, Cleveland, 1952.

Metals Handbook, American Society for Metals, Cleveland, 1948.

Republic Alloy Steels, Republic Steel Corporation, Cleveland, 1948.

Keyser, Carl A., *Materials of Engineering,* Prentice-Hall, Inc., Englewood Cliffs, N. J., 1956.

Woldman, Norman, *Engineering Alloys,* American Society for Metals, Cleveland, 1954.

7

Nonferrous Metals and Alloys

Nonferrous metals (those metals which do not have allotropic properties), with the exception of lead, aluminum, copper, tin, silver, gold, etc., are seldom used in their pure state. The reason for this is that they are relatively expensive and do not have mechanical and physical properties sufficiently high to warrant their costs except in specific applications. On the other hand, *nonferrous metal alloys* display high mechanical and physical properties and, therefore, have wide acceptance. Typical properties of some nonferrous die cast alloys are given in Table 9–1.

As compared to ferrous metals, nonferrous metals and their alloys may have one or more of the following advantages:

1. Low density
2. Resistance to atmospheric and industrial corrosive attack
3. Exceptionally high thermal and electrical conductivity
4. Relative ease of fabrication
5. Attractive color.

Generally speaking, nonferrous metal alloys are not as high in combined strength, hardness, and modulus of elasticity as steels and irons. Nonferrous metal alloys find their more important applications in engineering practice where a special property of behavior is required. For example, aluminum alloy is used in the aircraft industry because of its high strength-weight ratio, ease of fabrication, and attractiveness. Another example is the application of brasses and bronzes to the manufacture of some items in which good machinability is necessary to achieve low unit cost from rapid production.

ALUMINUM-BASE ALLOYS

Aluminum is used in its commercially pure state as well as in its many alloy forms. The heat-treatable types have the advantage of being relatively easy to fabricate in their soft condition, after which they are heat treated to develop their high strengths. The heat-treatable types account for the high tonnage of aluminum being industrially processed. An example of the properties that can be obtained by heat treating is given by one aluminum alloy, 6061; its tensile strength in the full soft condition is 18,000 psi; and, in the heat-treated condition, 45,000 psi. Another, 7075 alloy may be heat treated to a tensile strength of 88,000 psi. Obviously, these high tensile strengths give a strength-weight ratio advantage over steel and, therefore, account for the wide acceptance of aluminum alloys for the making of articles in which light weight is of prime importance.

Aluminum alloys are machined at high cutting speeds, good finishes are obtained, and, if temperature is controlled, parts can be produced extremely accurately. Forging, extruding, spinning, stretch forming, and deep-drawing are all satisfactorily applicable to the aluminums. Selected alloys may be cast by such methods as sand casting, permanent mold casting, die casting, plaster casting, and others.

The welding processes of joining apply to the aluminum alloys, although their weldabilities vary considerably. Aluminum alloys are particularly well suited to fabrication by pressure welding, such as spot and seam welding; and most of them are quite satisfactorily welded by the inert-gas metal-arc process and other inert-gas or flux-protected processes. Because these alloys are prone to form tenacious aluminum oxides, such welding methods as oxy-acetylene and the conventional metal-arc are not recommended for use where high-quality welded joints are desired.

The first step in the heat treatment of aluminum alloys for high tensile strength and better machinability usually involves heating the workpiece uniformly to a temperature sufficiently high to dissolve the alloying elements. Because of the low or incomplete solubility of the alloying elements at room temperature, heating is followed by rapid cooling to set up a state of rigidity and prevent rapid coalescence of the alloying particles. Aging after quenching is characterized by migration and partial consolidation of the previously dissolved elements. In solution-treated 2024, for example, aging starts immediately at room temperature; whereas in other aluminum alloys this activity is delayed. Particles resulting from the agglomeration are fine and highly dispersed.

These produce a keying effect between the layers of atoms, and, consequently, hardening and strengthening of the alloy.

The aging of aluminum alloys may be accelerated by reheating for a period of time. For example, 2018 is quenched from the 950°F solution treatment and artificially aged or "precipitated" at 340°F for 12 hours. Agglomeration caused either by time-aging or by reheating is a controllable behavior that governs the properties of the ultimate product obtained. A solution-treated alloy, such as 2024 which starts aging rapidly after quenching, may be retained in a soft condition, if desired, by placing the workpiece in a refrigerator. This technique permits fabricating the metal while it is relatively ductile and workable. After that, the shaped workpiece is allowed to age and gain strength at room temperature. Notable of this practice is in aircraft fabrication where rivets are solution treated, held in dry ice until driven, and then aged.

The non-heatable aluminum alloys made into sheet, plate, and wire are cold-worked to harden and strengthen. In the order of increasing hardness the available tempers are −0 (annealed) and −H12 through −H18.

Current base prices for large quantities of aluminum alloys as ingots are about $0.32 per lb, and as sheets and plates around $0.50 per lb.

COPPER-BASE ALLOYS

Except for electrical conductors, statuary, and miscellaneous uses, copper is seldom industrially employed in its pure state. Copper has its most value when alloyed with other elements. It dissolves with elements such as tin, zinc, and silver in rather wide proportions.

Copper-zinc alloys. Copper alloyed with zinc in varying amounts is called *brass*. This alloy is a single phase, solid solution of copper and zinc to the extent of 36% of the latter—called alpha phase brass. Above this amount of zinc a second microconstituent, the beta phase, appears which causes the brass to be more brittle, and thus less amenable to cold-working than the alpha brasses. Since many brasses are fabricated in their cold-worked condition, they usually contain less than 36% of zinc. Whereas beta brasses tend to cold-work rapidly, and consequently are limited in the extent to which they may be formed, they do take shape readily at elevated temperatures. Brasses that are to receive considerable amounts of cutting tool work contain some beta phase to improve machinability.

Common uses and the appearance of brass lead to such names as red brass, cartridge brass, yellow brass, Muntz metal and others.

Red brass has such common uses as architectural trim, light and heavy hardware, heat exchanger tubes, costume jewelry, and miscellaneous badges, compacts, and cosmetic containers. This alloy is easily formed by drawing, blanking, bending, piercing, and chip removal. In joining by the welding processes, soft soldering and silver brazing are preferred.

Cartridge brass containing 30% zinc is used to make deep-drawn cartridge shells, radiator cores, rivets and similar pieces. Almost all of the cold- and hot-forming methods and most welding processes of joining are applicable to cartridge brass.

Muntz metal containing 40% zinc is employed for hot-forging, condensor plates, valve stems, and braze-welding rod.

Admiralty metal containing 71% copper, 28% zinc, and 0.01% tin has good corrosion resistance to sea water and other corrosive liquids and, consequently, finds favorable use as condensor and evaporator tubes.

A brass containing about 45% zinc is commonly found to be acceptable filler material in the braze-welding of carbon steels, cast iron, brasses, copper, and many other alloys.

In general, the extensive industrial application of brasses results from their high thermal and electrical conductivity, resistance to corrosion, their ease of fabrication, and good appearance. Brass shapes in large quantities cost from about $0.50 to $0.60 per lb.

Copper-tin alloys. Disregarding the names applied to some copper-base alloys, a true bronze has, in addition to copper, less than 12% tin. The tensile strength of bronze increases with the addition of tin up to about 20%, and beyond this point an alloy becomes brittle. Because true bronzes are noted for their toughness, wear- and corrosion-resistance, and good strength, they are used for bearings, members carrying heavy compressive loads, gears, and heavy-duty screws. The bronze-bearing metal usually contains up to 10% of lead.

Miscellaneous copper-base alloys. *Phosphor bronze*, grade E, contains 98.75% copper and 1.25% tin. Typical of its uses are flexible hose, electrical contacts and hardware, and trolley wire. It is formed by bending, blanking, upsetting, squeezing, swedging, etc. It is readily joined by soft-soldering and silver-brazing, braze-welding, and fusion-welding.

Cupro-nickel—70% copper, 30% nickel—has good resistance to corrosion and good thermal conductivity and, consequently, is used for condensor components, heat exchanger tubes, and similar applications. The annealed tubular products have 60,000 psi tensile strength. Cupro-nickel may be frabricated by most methods of welding, brazing, and soldering.

Silicon bronze, type A, containing 3% silicon and the remainder copper, is employed for marine hardware, nails, screws, hot water tanks, heat exchanger tubes, kettles, and similar items.

Aluminum bronze—5% aluminum, 95% copper—is particularly suited to cold-forming into corrosion-resisting sheets, strip, tubing, and wire.

Beryllium copper containing 2% beryllium, 0.25% cobalt or 0.35% nickel is a relatively recent development and admirably suited to members requiring high proportional limit, high endurance strength, good corrosion-resistance, and reasonably high electrical conductivity. A wide variety of springs, diaphrams, electrical contactors, and light fastening hardware are made from this alloy. It is heat treatable—requiring a solution treatment at about 1400°F, quench, and precipitation. The temper desired is governed by the time it is held at precipitation temperature.

MAGNESIUM-BASE ALLOYS

Magnesium and its alloys are noted for their lightness. The specific gravity of magnesium is 0.064 lb per cu in.; in comparison, aluminum, steel, and titanium are 0.09, 0.28, and 0.16 lb per cu in., respectively. Because of the low ductility of magnesium alloys at room temperature, shaping, such as drawing, bending and similar kinds of forming, must be done at a temperature of 400 to 600°F. The machinability is high, but careful disposition of fine chips at the machine is necessary to avoid serious fires.

Magnesium alloys lend themselves to welding fabrication if the weld metal and filler are protected by an inert gas. They are relatively easy to cast by most foundry methods, particularly die casting.

From the standpoint of design, the magnesiums are at some disadvantage because of their low modulus of elasticity. The engineer should examine his design parameters with special care where magnesium alloys are being considered, since the advantage of lightness may not be particularly realistic if strength, deflection, or resistance to corrosion are also needed. The proper analysis of a design situation may show that the low density of magnesium alloys is advantageous only if lightness is paramount and strength-ratio or resistance to corrosion is secondary. Common examples of parts made from magnesium alloys are power tool frames, home appliances, and certain aircraft components in which the anticipated stresses are moderate.

An alloy containing 10% aluminum, 0.1% manganese, and the remainder magnesium, is employed for high-quality sand and permanent-mold castings and extruded shapes. For die castings which must have high impact strength and ductility, the alloy containing 1.25% aluminum, 1% manganese, and remainder magnesium is commonly employed. A heat treatable alloy containing 8.5% aluminum, 0.5% zinc, 0.15% manganese, remainder magnesium, serves for forgings, extrusions, and shapes, and has a tensile strength of 30,000 psi or more after heat treating. The heat treatment consists of soaking at 750°F 2 to 4 hours and cooling in air, followed by aging 16 to 24 hours at 350°F and cooling in air.

NICKEL-BASE ALLOYS

Nickel is one of the oldest metals known to man. Currently this metal is almost indispensable in the alloying of steels to confer toughness, uniformity of hardness, and good workability; and as a basic alloy to resist high corrosion and high temperatures. Of the nickel-rich alloys which have been developed, *Monel* is among those which have important industrial distinction. Because of its resistance to strong corrosive agents, such as sea water, caustic solutions, and dilute sulfuric acid, Monel is commonly used in oil refinery piping and stills, laundry equipment, pharmaceutical equipment, marine parts, and others. Monel is not suitable in sulfidizing atmospheres at temperatures above 700°F. Its composition is 67% nickel, 30% copper, 1.4% iron, 1% manganese, 0.15% carbon, 0.1% silicon, and 0.01% sulfur.

Monel may be machined by employing about the same techniques and tooling as in the shaping of steel. The usual methods of forming, such as forging, rolling, drawing, spinning, stretching, and others, apply to the fabrication of this alloy. Monel is joined by both pressure and nonpressure welding, including brazing and soldering. Monel sheets cost around $1.20 per lb in large quantities.

Inconel which has a chemical composition of 80% nickel, 14% chromium, and 6% iron, was developed to resist oxidation and maintain good strength at high temperatures. A typical use of Inconel is for exhaust ducts in aircraft. It is formed by most types of hot- and cold-working. It may be joined by both the pressure and nonpressure welding methods. Hot-rolled Inconel plate has a tensile strength of about 100,000 psi.

Hastelloy A, consisting of about 57% nickel, 20% molybdenum, and iron, was developed to resist hydrochloric acid and other nonoxidizing acids and salts. Hastelloy A may be given shape by all of the usual hot- and cold-forming methods. It is annealed for full softness by quenching in water from 2150°F. Oxy-acetylene, metal-arc, and resistance welding apply to this alloy.

LEAD-TIN ALLOYS

The principal lead-tin alloys consist of solders and bearing materials.

The 70% tin–30% lead soft solder is used mainly in the joining and coating of metals. The 63% tin–37% lead is a eutectic type solder developed primarily for making electrical joints.

A typical tin Babbit bearing material contains 65% tin, 18% lead, 15% antimony, and 2% copper. It is used mainly for bearings and die castings. The compressive yield strength is about 2100 psi at 212°F. The antimony combines with the tin to form hard particles of low-coefficient-of-friction bearing contacts. Under load the soft alloy matrix allows some rearrangement of the hard antimonial particles, and thus the bearing surface accomodates some misfit or misalignment of the mating piece.

ZINC-BASE ALLOYS

Zinc-base alloys predominate as die casting materials. These alloys have high castability and favorable mechanical and chemical properties. Zinc-base alloys can be cast in the range 750 to 800°F, and, therefore, have a low-temperature advantage over other alloys. The American Society for Testing Materials and the Society of Automotive Engineers have standardized requirements for two alloys that correspond to the Zamak alloys of the New Jersey Zinc Company. The zinc used must be of a high purity form (99.99%) to avoid intergranular and surface corrosion. Aluminum is carried in the two alloys to the extent of 4% to improve the workability during casting and to preclude deterioration by solution of the die parts that are in contact with the alloy. Copper ranges from 0.10 to 1.3%, depending upon the alloy, and is used primarily to enhance the tensile strength and hardness. Very limited amounts of magnesium are included to confer alloy stability. Zinc die casting alloys are quoted at $0.17 per lb in large quantities.

LESS COMMON METALS AND ALLOYS

Titanium and its alloys. Because of their high strength-weight ratio, titanium and its alloys have received a great amount of attention from the aircraft and missile industries. These metals were at first considered to be a bridge between steel and aluminum, but they now appear to play a role in their own right. Depending somewhat upon the alloy, the titaniums have a specific gravity of 0.163 lb per cu in. as compared to 0.28 lb per cu in. in steel. The modulus of elasticity varies from 15 to 16.9 $\times$ 10^6. The unalloyed titanium has a tensile strength of 89–100,000 psi and a yield strength of 80–82,000 psi. In the heat-treatable types, such as 6AL–4V, the yield strength may be as high as 150,000 psi. Prices of rolled shapes of various titanium alloys range from $4 to $17 per lb. Although the reports of satisfactory fabrication of titanium alloys vary from different quarters, by the careful selection of an alloy with workability in mind, most of the fabricating processes may be applied. Welding is usually done satisfactorily with the inert-gas metal-arc process.

Molybdenum. This element has long been known for its ability to confer the property of high-temperature stability to steels. Although a small percentage of the total molybdenum produced has been used in the pure form, its greatest value appears when alloyed with aluminum, columbium, silicon, titanium, tungsten, vanadium, and chromium. The addition of these elements improves the strength of molybdenum at both room and elevated temperatures. Molybdenum and its alloys may be processed by forging, drawing, stamping, machining, brazing and welding, but, in general, these operations are relatively difficult. The cost of powdered molybdenum is $3 to $4 per lb.

Molybdenum alloys have a tendency to oxidize rapidly at elevated temperatures if unprotected. With suitable coatings, such as the siliconized coating, nickel, Inconel, and others, they have sustained service temperatures of 2200°F and more for extended periods of time. Their most promising future appears to be in fields where high temperatures are encountered, an example of current application being jet aircraft engine and gas turbine parts.

Zirconium. Zirconium metal has a density of 0.24 lb per cu in. and a melting point of 3355°F. The metal has fair tensile strength, depending somewhat upon its method of manufacture. It fabricates similar to titanium, and is eminently suited to the resistance to corrosion. One of its important uses is in the construction of nuclear reactor components because of its very low thermal neutron absorption cross section. It costs from $20 to $30 per lb.

Questions

1. What are the advantages of nonferrous as compared with ferrous metals?

2. What are the merits and common applications of aluminum alloys?

3. How are aluminum alloys heat treated, and what takes place in the material?

4. In what forms is copper used industrially?

5. Identify several common brasses and their uses.

6. What is bronze and for what is it used?

7. What are the advantages and disadvantages of magnesium and its alloys?

8. What are the principal uses of nickel?

9. What are the principal uses of lead-tin alloys?

10. For what purpose do zinc base alloys predominate?

11. What is the advantage of titanium and its alloys?

References

Samans, Carl H., *Engineering Metals and Their Alloys*, The Macmillan Co., New York, 1949.

Bray, John L., *Non-Ferrous Production Metallurgy*, John Wiley & Sons, Inc., New York, 1941.

CHAPTER | **8**

Foundry Processes

INTRODUCTION

Chapters 8 and 9 will be devoted to the foundry processes and include the common ways of producing castings. The two chapters will not cover the casting of metal in detail but will present and illustrate the principles of the more important aspects of the field.

Founding, or *casting,* is the process of forming objects by putting liquid or viscous material into a prepared mold or form. A *casting* is an object formed by allowing the material to solidify. A *foundry* is a collection of the necessary materials and equipment to produce a casting. Practically all metal is initially cast. The ingot from which a wrought metal is produced is first cast in an ingot mold. A *mold* is the container that has the cavity (or cavities) of the shape to be cast. Liquids may be poured; some liquid and all viscous plastic materials are forced under pressure into molds.

Founding is one of the oldest industries in the metal-working field and dates back to approximately 4000 B.C. Since this early age, many methods have been employed to cast various materials. In this chapter, sand casting and its ramifications will receive first attention because it is the most used of the casting processes. Sand casting is best suited for iron and steel at their high melting temperatures but also predominates for aluminum, brass, bronze, and magnesium. In Chap. 9 other processes of commercial importance will be treated, in most cases those for non-ferrous metals using permanent molds.

The elements necessary for the production of sound castings will be considered throughout this chapter. These include molding materials, molding equipment, tools, patterns, melting equipment, etc. These basic ingredients must be combined in an orderly sequence for the production of a sound casting.

THE PRINCIPLES OF SAND CASTING

Castings have specific important engineering properties; these may be metallurgical, physical, or economic. Castings are often cheaper than forgings or weldments, depending on the quantity, type of material, and cost of patterns as compared to the cost of dies for forging and the cost of jigs and fixtures for weldments. Where this is the case, they are the logical choices for engineering structures and parts.

Some of the characteristics of special interest to be realized from properly designed castings are the following. Properly designed and properly produced castings do not have directional properties. No laminated or segregated structure exists as it does when metal is worked after solidification. This means strength, for instance, is the same in all directions, and this characteristic is especially desirable for some gears, piston rings, engine cylinder liners, etc. The ability of molten metal to flow into thin sections of complicated design is a very desirable characteristic. Cast iron is unique in that it has good damping characteristics which are desirable in producing bases for machine tools, engine frames, and other applications where it is desirable to minimize vibration.

The mold. Good castings cannot be produced without good molds. Because of the importance of the mold, casting processes are often described by the material and method employed for the mold. Thus sand castings may be made in: (1) green sand molds, (2) dry sand molds, (3) core sand molds, (4) loam molds, (5) shell molds, and (6) cement-bonded molds. The major methods of making these molds are called: (1) bench molding, (2) machine molding, (3) floor molding, and (4) pit molding.

In producing a sand mold, the molder's skill is of great value. He must know how to prepare a mold with the following characteristics:

1. The mold must be strong enough to hold the weight of the metal
2. The mold must resist the erosive action of the rapidly flowing metal during pouring
3. The mold must generate a minimum amount of gas when filled with molten metal. Gases contaminate the metal and can disrupt the mold

4. The mold must be constructed so that any gases formed can pass through the body of the mold itself, rather than penetrate the metal
5. The mold must be refractory enough to withstand the high temperature of the metal and strip away cleanly from the casting after cooling
6. The core must collapse enough to permit the casting to contract after solidification.

A *flask* is a wood or metal frame in which a mold is made. It must be strong and rigid so as not to distort when it is handled or when sand is rammed into it. It must also resist the pressure of the molten metal during casting. Pins and fittings align the sections of a flask. They wear in service and must be watched to avoid mismatched or shifted molds.

A flask is made of two principal parts, the *cope* (top section) and the *drag* (bottom section). When more than two sections of a flask are necessary to increase the depth of the cope and/or the drag, intermediate flask sections known as *cheeks* are used.

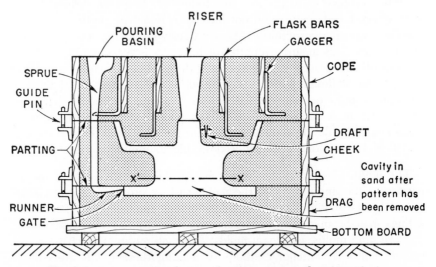

Fig. 8–1. A cross-sectional view of a three part sand mold with the parts labelled. The line x'–x indicates parting in the pattern.

Figure 8–1 is a diagram of a typical mold and its principal parts. The features and functions of the parts will be explained as they are taken up in the text.

The behavior of cast metal. When molten metal is poured into a mold, the casting begins to cool inwardly from all bounding surfaces because the heat can flow only outwardly through the mold. The metal on the surface is more or less chilled because at first the mold is relatively cool. If the chilling is severe, the surface may be appreciably hardened. Under usual conditions a fine, close-grained structure occurs near the surface, and coarser grains towards the center where cooling is slower. If a section is thick, enough metal may be withdrawn by contraction from the center before it cools to leave a void or cavity as indicated for the piece on the left in Fig. 8–2. Such a defect in the casting may be avoided by providing a supplementary mass of metal, called a riser, adjacent to the casting as on the right

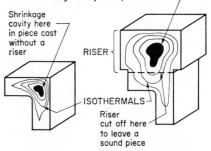

Fig. 8–2. An example to illustrate the purpose of a riser on a casting.

in Fig. 8–2. The purpose of the riser is to feed liquid metal by gravity into the body of the casting to keep it full. The riser is cut off after the casting has cooled.

Thin sections cool more rapidly than thick ones. One result is that thin sections benefit more from a "quench effect" and are likely to be stronger and finer grained. This is brought out for one type of material in Fig. 8–3. At the other extreme, if a section is too thin, metal flowing through the narrow passage may be frozen before it has a chance to fill in the wall completely. The practical lower limit of section thickness depends upon the design of the casting and the fluidity of the metal. Iron can be conveniently handled and cast appreciably above its melting temperature and is commonly cast in sections as thin as $\frac{1}{8}$ in.

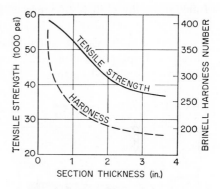

Fig. 8–3. Strength and hardness of different thicknesses of a class 40 gray cast iron.

Steel melts at much higher temperatures than iron, and a minimum thickness of $\frac{3}{16}$ in. is recommended. Phosphorous increases the fluidity but weakens iron, and some foundrymen prefer less phosphorous and higher pouring temperatures. Aluminum may be cast with walls as thin as $\frac{1}{8}$ to $\frac{3}{16}$ in.

Sections of different thicknesses cool at different rates. That leads to difficulty if a casting is not designed with uniform sections throughout. Walls that shrink at different rates pull at each other and set up residual stresses. The situation can be eased by providing gradual tapers or changes in thickness where sections of different sizes must meet.

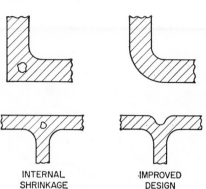

INTERNAL
SHRINKAGE   IMPROVED
DESIGN

Fig. 8–4. Examples of internal shrinkage in castings.

A thick section may be in a casting where it cannot be readily fed by a riser, particularly if it must be fed through thin sections that cool first, and thus develop voids or tears. Metal concentrations or *hot spots* of this kind are indicated in Fig. 8–4. The correction is in the design of the casting to make the sections uniform. A remedy may be to chill the metal at the hot spot to make it freeze before the adjoining sections which can be fed more directly as they cool.

Gates, risers, and chills. Gates, risers and chills are closely related. The function of a gating system of a mold is to deliver the liquid metal to the mold cavity. The function of the riser is to store and supply liquid metal to compensate for solidification shrinkage in heavy sections. The function of the chill is to cause certain sections of a casting to solidify before others, often to help distribute properly the supply of metal from the risers. A good gating system may be nullified by a poor risering application. Improper use of chills can cause the scrapping of well gated and properly risered castings.

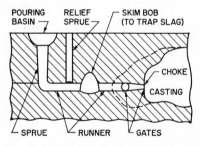

POURING
BASIN   RELIEF
SPRUE   SKIM BOB
(TO TRAP SLAG)

CHOKE

CASTING

SPRUE   RUNNER   GATES

Fig. 8–5. An example of a gating system.

Gating. An example of a gating system in a mold is shown in Fig. 8–5. The gating system must (1) introduce the molten metal into the mold with as little turbulence as possible, (2) regulate the rate of entry of the metal, (3) permit complete filling of the mold cavity, and (4) promote a temperature gradient within the casting to help the metal solidify with the least conflict between sections. The following principles help achieve the goals just listed for good gating.

The sprue should be tapered with the larger end receiving the metal to act as a reservoir. Generally speaking, a round sprue is preferred for diameters up to ¾ in., but larger sprues are often rectangular. There is less turbulence in a rectangular sprue, but a circular sprue has a minimum surface exposed to cooling and offers the lowest resistance to flow.

Gating systems having sudden changes in direction cause slower filling of the mold cavity, are easily eroded, and cause turbulence in the liquid metal resulting in gas pickup. Right angle turns should be avoided particularly.

A definite relationship exists between the sizes of the sprue, runners, and ingates to realize the best conditions for filling the mold. The cross-section of a runner should be reduced in area as each gate is passed, as indicated in Fig. 8–5. This helps keep the runner full throughout its entire length and promotes uniform flow through all of the gates. As another consideration, the rate at which metal can flow into the mold should not exceed the ability of the sprue to keep the entire gating system full of liquid at all times.

The gating system should be formed as part of the pattern whenever possible. This allows the sand to be rammed harder and helps prevent erosion and washing as the metal flows into the mold.

Several ingates rather than one help distribute the metal to the mold and fill the mold quickly, reducing the likelihood of overheating spots in the mold. Ingates should be placed in such positions that they will direct the metal into the mold along natural channels. If metal is directed against the mold surface or cores, burning is likely, and loose sand may be washed into the casting. The opening of an ingate into a mold should have as small an area as possible except in cases where the gates are through side risers. An ingate may be reduced in area or "choked" where it enters a mold cavity. This holds back slag and foreign material but must not leave an area at the entrance so small as to cause a shower effect. That may give rise to turbulence resulting in excessive oxidation of the metal.

Types of gates. The three main types of gates are: (1) parting, (2) top, and (3) bottom gates as illustrated in Fig. 8–6.

The *parting gate* between cope and drag is the easiest and fastest

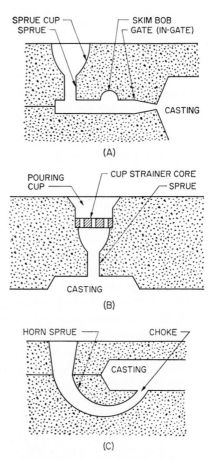

Fig. 8–6. The three main types of gates for molds. (A) Parting gate, (B) top gate, (C) bottom gate.

for the molder to make. Its chief disadvantage is that the metal drops into the drag cavity and may cause erosion or washing of the mold. In the case of nonferrous metals, this drop aggravates the dross and entraps air in the metal, which make for inferior castings.

Top gates are at times used for gray iron castings of simple designs but not for nonferrous alloys since they have a tendency to form excessive dross when agitated. An advantage of top gating is that it is conducive to a favorable temperature gradient, but a big disadvantage is that of mold erosion.

A *bottom gate* offers smooth flow with a minimum of mold and core erosion. Its main disadvantage is that it creates an unfavorable temperature gradient. The metal is introduced into the bottom of the mold cavity and rises quietly and evenly. It cools as it rises, and the result is a condition of cold metal and cold mold near the riser and hot metal and hot mold near the gate. The riser should contain the hottest metal in the hottest part of the mold so it can feed metal into the mold until all the casting has solidified.

Gating through side risers should be done wherever possible. Gating directly into the casting results in hot spots, because all the metal enters the casting through the gate and the sand around the gate becomes hot. Cooling in that area is retarded. Unless risers are provided to feed those localities with molten metal, shrinkage cavities or defects result.

Many types of special gates besides those described are used in foundries.

Risers. In addition to acting as a reservoir, a riser mitigates the hydraulic ram effect of metal entering the mold and vents the mold. It must be last to solidify and to serve efficiently must conform to the following principles. The volume of a riser must be large enough to supply all metal needed. The gating system must be designed to establish a temperature gradient toward the riser. The area of the connection of the riser to the casting must be large enough not to freeze too soon. On the other hand, the connection must not be so large that the solid riser is difficult to remove from the casting.

The shape of a riser is an important consideration. Experience has shown that the most effective height of a riser is one and one half times its diameter to produce maximum feeding with a minimum amount of metal. As the area over volume ratio of a molten mass decreases, less chance is offered for the escape of heat, and the solidification rate decreases. What this means for common shapes is shown in Table 8–1. A sphere stays molten longest but is not ideal as a riser; a cylinder is next best and is practical,

TABLE 8–1. Solidification Time for Various Cast Shapes

(All shapes have volume of 113 cu in. and weight of 32 lb)

Shape	Sphere	Cylinder	Cube	Thick plate	Thin plate
Solidification time (min)	7.2	4.7	3.6	2.7	1.9

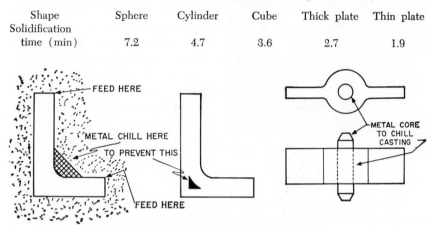

Fig. 8–7. Typical forms of chills for castings.

Chills. *Chills* are metal shapes inserted in molds to speed up the solidification of the metal. Examples are given in Fig. 8–7. Two types are external and internal chills. An internal chill becomes part of and should be made of the same metal as the casting. An external chill should make enough contact and be large enough not to fuse with the casting. The shape, size, and use of a chill must be proportioned with care to avoid too rapid cooling and cracks and defects in a casting.

Vents. *Vents* are small holes made by perforating the sand just short of the pattern in the mold with a wire or vent strip. The function of a vent is to permit escape of gases from the mold cavity to prevent the gases from becoming trapped in the metal or from raising back pressure to oppose the inflow of metal. Vents should serve all high points of the mold and be open to the top. Many small vents are better than a few large ones.

MAKING MOLDS

Hand tools for molding. Some of the basic tools used by the molder are shown in Fig. 8–8. Their uses will be shown in the section that describes how a mold is made.

Riddles are used for sifting the sand over the surface of the pattern when starting a mold. The size of the riddle is given by the number of meshes to the inch; a No. 4 riddle has four meshes per in., etc. Castings with fine surface details require fine sand and a fine riddle.

Fig. 8–8. Common hand tools for molding.

Rammers are used for tamping the sand around the pattern in the flask. There are hand rammers for job work and pneumatic rammers for production work.

A *strike* is a straight edge strip of metal or wood used to scrape the extra sand from the top of the cope or drag after ramming.

Clamps are used for holding together the cope and drag of the completed mold, to prevent the cope from floating or rising when the metal is introduced into the mold.

Bellows are used to blow excess parting material from the pattern and also to blow loose sand and dirt from the mold cavity. Compressed air, when available, is often used to remove the loose sand and dirt.

Trowels are of many different styles and sizes to suit the molders for a particular job. The trowel is used for making joints and for finishing, smoothing and slicking the flat surface of the mold.

Vents are thin rigid steel strips used for piercing vent holes in the sand of a mold.

Swabs are made of flax or camel hair and are used for placing a small amount of water on the sand around the pattern. This moisture strengthens the sand and prevents the edges from crumbling when the pattern is removed.

Draw spikes are screws, eye-bolts, or steel rods inserted into the pattern and used to draw it from the sand.

Spoons and *slicks* are sand-smoothing implements used for patching molds.

A *gate cutter* is a piece of sheet metal bent to a semi-circle on one edge, used to cut a passageway through which the metal flows into the mold.

A *sprue cutter* is a cylindrical metal tube used to cut the sprue in the cope.

Gaggers are mold accessories used to give support to hanging masses of sand which would otherwise break apart under their own weight.

Making a mold. A flask is selected larger than the mold cavity it is to contain to allow for risers and the gating system. There must also be enough mold mass over and under the cavity to prevent any break-out of the metal during pouring. Many castings are lost, or require extra cleaning, and many injuries to personnel are caused by undersized flasks.

A mold cavity may be carved in the sand, but that requires considerable skill for all but the simplest shapes and is seldom done. Normal procedure is to make first an image of the piece to be cast and form the mold around it. That is called the *pattern*. Patterns and pattern making will be discussed more fully latter.

Before use, the pattern is checked for cleanliness and the free action of any loose pieces. When a split pattern is used, the drag part of the flask is turned upside down on the ram-up board. The drag pattern is placed with the parting surface down on the ram-up board along with any pieces used for the gating and risering system (Fig. 8–9). Facing sand is then riddled to a depth of about one inch on the pattern and ram-up board as shown in Fig. 8–10. Riddling is absolutely necessary for good reproduction of the pattern. The riddled sand is then tucked into all pockets and sharp corners and hand packed around the pattern.

Backing sand is then put into the flask to cover the facing sand to a depth of 3 to 4 in. The backing should be carefully rammed into any deep pocket as illustrated in Fig. 8–11. The remainder of the mold is filled and then rammed. Care is taken to avoid hitting or coming too close to the pattern. The mold must be rammed uniformly hard in order to obtain a smooth, easily cleaned casting surface and to avoid metal penetration into the sand, swelling of the mold, break-outs, or other casting defects.

The excess sand is struck off, as in Fig. 8–12, by means of a straight edge, and the bottom board is placed on the drag. Clamps are applied to the ram-up board and the bottom board. The drag is then inverted, the clamps are removed, and ram-up board is removed. The mold surface is cleaned and slicked in preparation for the cope portion of the pattern and flask.

Parting material is dusted over the mold joint or parting surface and the pattern. The parting material prevents the sand in the cope from sticking to the sand in the drag. Parting material for large molds is usually fine silica sand and for medium and small molds is finely ground powders such as talc or silica flour.

The cope of the flask is set on the drag, and seated firmly with the aid of flask pins. The cope pattern, riser form, and parts for the gating system are placed in their proper position. Figure 8–13 shows a mold at this stage.

Facing sand is riddled over the cope pattern and packed firmly as in the drag. At this time, gaggers are set in the cope if needed but not close enough to chill the casting. The cope is then filled with sand and rammed as in the drag. It is necessary to ram the sand a little more firmly around the flask in the cope because the sand must remain intact as the cope is removed from the drag. After the ramming is completed, the mold is struck off and vented as depicted in Fig. 8–14. The cope is then removed

Fig. 8-9. The first step in making a mold. The drag pattern is placed with parting surface down on the ram-up board.

Fig. 8-10. The facing sand is packed carefully around the pattern.

Fig. 8-11. The backing sand is rammed uniformly in the flask around the pattern.

Fig. 8-12. The excess sand is struck off to complete the drag mold.

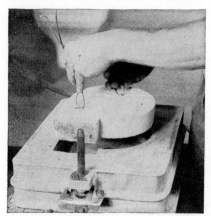

Fig. 8-13. The drag has been inverted, and a core is being placed in the pattern.

Fig. 8-14. The cope is vented.

136

Fig. 8–15. A view of the finished cope and drag with cores in position ready for closing the mold.

Fig. 8–16. The closed and clamped mold is ready for pouring.

Fig. 8–17. Pouring the metal into the mold.

Fig. 8–18 (A). A pump housing casting as it comes from the mold with runners, sprues, etc., attached.

Fig. 8–18 (B). A pump housing casting after cleanup.

137

from the drag, and rolled over to facilitate drawing the cope pattern. All pattern, gate, sprue, and well patterns are removed at this time. The cutting of ingates is usually done before drawing the pattern.

When the cope and drag have been properly finished, the cores should be set into place with care not to damage the mold or core. Figure 8–15 shows the cope, drag and core in position ready for closing.

The mold is closed carefully. Pins guide the cope. After the mold is closed, it is clamped, as shown in Fig. 8–16, and is ready for pouring. Weights are set on top of some molds to keep them from coming apart due to the hydrostatic pressure of the liquid metal. Pouring of the pump housing is shown in Fig. 8–17, and the pump housing casting obtained is seen in Fig. 8–18.

Several kinds of molding procedures depend upon the sizes of the casting. *Bench molding* applies chiefly to molds small enough to be made on a work bench. *Floor molding* involves molds too large for a bench and made in flasks on the floor of the foundry or on machines standing on the floor. Molds too large to be made entirely in flasks are constructed in pits below the foundry floor. This is called *pit molding*.

Molding machines. At one time all molding was done by hand but today's labor costs and competition make machine molding mandatory in industry. Molding machines offer higher production rates and better quality casting in addition to less heavy labor and lower costs.

Molding machines serve in two general capacities: (1) to pack sand firmly and uniformly into the mold, and (2) to manipulate the flasks, mold, and pattern. Properly controlled and applied machine ramming is more uniform and dependable and produces more and better molds than hand ramming. Manipulation is done in various degrees on different machines and may include turning over parts or all of the mold and lifting of patterns and flasks. Molding machines are available in a number of makes, models, and sizes and perform the foregoing functions in various combinations and ways. Generally they fall into one of three classes and will be illustrated by a typical form of each class. These are the jolt-squeeze, jolt-rollover, and sand slinger molding machines.

Jolt-squeeze molding machines. A jolt-squeezer, shown in Fig. 8–19, basically consists of a table actuated by two pistons in air cylinders, one inside the other. The mold on the table is jolted by the action of the inner piston that raises the table repeatedly and drops it down sharply on a bumper pad. Jolting packs the sand in the lower parts of the flask but not at the top. The larger cylinder pushes the table upward to squeeze the sand in the mold against the squeeze head at the top. Squeez-

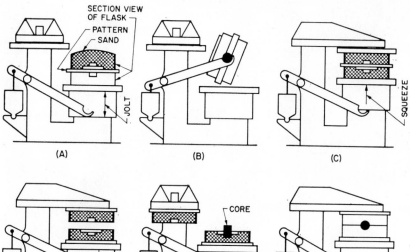

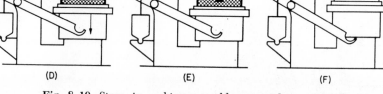

Fig. 8–19. Steps in making a mold on a jolt-squeeze-rollover machine. (A) Jolting the sand on the pattern in the inverted drag. (B) Rolling over the flask to fill the cope. (C) Squeezing to pack the sand in the cope. (D) Raising the cope to remove the pattern. (E) Placing a core. (F) Replacing the cope on the completed mold. A medium size machine like this costs around $2000.

ing compresses the top layers of sand in the mold but sometimes does not penetrate effectively to all areas of a pattern. In the case shown, the cope is squeezed so as not to damage the finished drag by jolting. Some machines do simply jolting; others squeezing alone. For high production, one jolt-squeezer may be set up for the drag portion of a mold and another for the cope. A vibrator may be attached to a machine to loosen the pattern to remove it easily without damaging the mold.

Jolt-rollover pattern-draw machines. The machine illustrated in Fig. 8–20 is designed to mold cope or drag. A flask is set over a pattern on a table, filled with sand, and jolted. Excess sand is struck off, and a bottom board is clamped to the flask. The machine raises the mold and rolls it over onto a car or conveyor. The flask is freed from the machine. The pattern is vibrated, raised from the mold, and returned to loading position. Similar machines squeeze as well as jolt.

The sand slinger. The sand slinger achieves a consistent packing and ramming effect by hurling sand into the mold at a high velocity. Figure

Fig. 8–20. A jolt-rollover pattern-draw foundry molding machine. The pattern has just been drawn after the mold has been jolted and rolled over to the position shown. (Courtesy Davenport Machine & Foundry Co.)

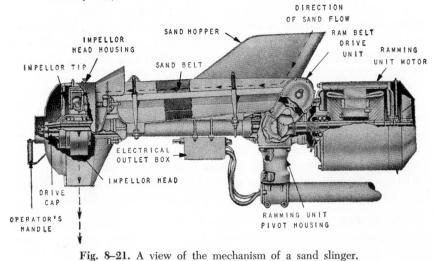

Fig. 8–21. A view of the mechanism of a sand slinger.

8–21 explains the action. Sand from a hopper is fed by a belt to a high-speed impeller in the head. A common arrangement is to suspend the slinger with counterweights and move it about to direct the stream of sand advantageously into a mold. Mold hardness can be controlled by the operator by changing the speed of the impeller.

Sand slingers can deliver large quantities of sand rapidly and are especially beneficial for ramming big molds. Their only function is to pack the sand into molds, and they are often operated together with pattern-drawing equipment.

CORES AND COREMAKING

A core is a body of material, usually sand, used to produce a cavity in or on a casting. An example of a core in a casting is one forming the water jacket in a water-cooled engine block, and an example of a core on a casting is the one forming the air space between the cooling fins of an air-cooled cyinder. A number of properties are essential for good cores. They are mentioned briefly here but will be discussed in more detail later. A core must have: (1) permeability (i.e. the ability to allow steam and gases to escape), (2) refractoriness (i.e. the ability to withstand high temperature), (3) green strength so that it can be formed, (4) dry strength so that it will not wash away or change size when surrounded by molten metal, (5) collapsibility (i.e. the ability to decrease in size as the casting cools and shrinks), (6) friability or the ability to crumble and be easily removed from the casting, and (7) a minimal tendency to generate gas.

Core making. The tools used in the production of cores are much the same as in making a mold, with the addition of the core-box, core driers, and special material and equipment for venting. The core receives its shape from the core-box. Driers are special forms or racks used to support complicated cores during baking. Since core driers are quite expensive, they are used only when large numbers of cores are required. Complicated cores can often be made in parts on flat plates and then assembled with paste.

Core making is much like molding except that the core sand is placed in a core-box. It can be blown into the box, rammed or packed by hand, or jolted into the box. The excess sand is struck off, and a drier plate is placed over the box. The core-box is then inverted, vibrated or rapped, and drawn off the core. The core is then put in a core oven and baked. Cores must be made strong enough to withstand the handling they must endure.

Where the core does not have natural vents, supplementary vents must be provided. For a core made up by pasting parts together, grooves may be cut in the faces to be joined before they are assembled. The vents are continued through to the core prints so molten metal will not reach and plug them. If this method cannot be used, wax venting can be done by placing strips of vent wax in the sand before it is baked. If the core is large and rather complicated, the center of the core may be filled with coke, gravel, or other porous material which will give good permeability, good crushability, and good friability.

Several different kinds of cores can be found in the foundry today. *Baked sand cores* are those that are made, placed in the oven, allowed to bake (time and temperature depending upon the binder), removed from the furnace, allowed to cool, assembled, and used or stored. *Dry sand cores* are those made from a green sand (i.e., sand before it has been dried or baked) mixture to which additional amounts of binder have been added. They are dried in the air or with a torch. Their strength comes from a large amount of binder. Dry sand cores are not as strong as baked sand cores and require more internal support and careful handling.

Core shifting. If a core does not stay in just the right place in its mold, the walls of the cavity it produces will not be of proper thickness. Shifting of cores is a major cause of defective castings. A core may be such a shape that it needs internal support. For that purpose, heavy wire or steel rods may be imbedded in it. *Chaplets* (Fig. 8–22) serve to support cores that tend to sag or sink in inadequate core print seats. A chaplet is usually made of the same metal as, and becomes part of the casting.

A core is subjected to an appreciable buoyant force when immersed in the liquid metal poured into its mold. An anchor, like the one in Fig. 8–22, prevents the core from rising. Chaplets also serve this purpose.

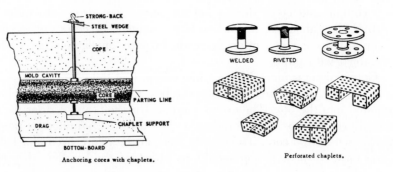

Anchoring cores with chaplets.

Perforated chaplets.

Fig. 8–22. An application of a chaplet and anchor to support a core, and a few examples of chaplets.

A core immersed in heavy metal in a mold is buoyed up by a force equal to the difference between its weight and the weight of the metal displaced. As an example, a sand core with a volume of one cu ft weighs about 100 lb. Molten iron weighs 450 lb per cu ft. A force of 350 lb must be resisted to keep the core submerged. The lifting force is the same at any depth, but the pressure over the surface of the core increases with depth. The ratio of lifting force to the weight of a core, in lb per lb, is about 1.7 in aluminum, 3.5 in cast iron, 3.9 in cast steel, and about 4.5 in copper, brass, and bronze.

Core making machines. Cores of regular shapes and sections may be extruded in a machine like that illustrated in Fig. 8–23 and cut to length. A central vent hole is left by a wire extending from the center of the screw.

Large cores are made like molds in jolt-rollover, sand slinger, and other machines. Small and medium size irregularly shaped cores may be made by hand but in quantities are produced on a *core blowing machine*. This machine blows sand by compressed air through a core plate with holes arranged to pack the sand evenly and firmly in the core-box. Each core-box must be designed properly to release the air but retain the sand in a uniformly dense compact.

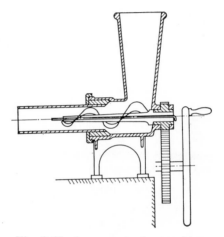

Fig. 8–23. A core extrusion machine.

Core baking. Drying alone is sufficient for many core binders, but most cores are bonded by oils and must be baked for ultimate hardness and strength. The purpose of baking is to drive off moisture, oxidize the oil, and polymerize the binder.

A uniform temperature and controlled heating are necessary for baking an oil-bonded sand core. With linseed oil, a major binder as an example, the temperature is raised at a moderate rate, is held at 400°F for about an hour, and then is allowed to fall slowly to room conditions. If the same core is baked quickly at 500°F, it will be mushy and weak.

The size of a core affects baking. If care is not taken, the outer surface of the core will first bake and attain maximum strength. Then while the inside is curing, the outside will over-bake and lose strength. This can be avoided by making the center of a large core of a porous material such as coke or cinders to allow oxygen to get to the center of the core so that oxidation and polymerization can take place.

PATTERNS

A *pattern* is a form used to prepare and produce a mold cavity. It is another tool in the hands of a foundryman. It has been said that a poor casting may be produced from a good pattern, but a good casting will not be made from a poor pattern.

The designer of a casting must look forward to the pattern to assure economical production. The design should be as simple as possible to make the pattern easy to draw from the sand and avoid more cores than necessary.

Fig. 8–24. Several wood and metal loose patterns.

Types of patterns. Many molds are made from *loose patterns*. Such a pattern has essentially the shape of the casting with perhaps forms for sprues, risers, etc. attached. Several examples are given in Fig. 8–24. This is the cheapest pattern to make but most time consuming to use. A loose pattern may be made in one or more pieces. For instance, a two-piece pattern is normally *split* into cope and drag parts to facilitate molding. For a part difficult to mold, some *loose pieces* may be removable to allow the rest of the pattern to contract for withdrawal from the sand that would otherwise not be possible.

An original casting or an assembly of the pieces of a broken casting may serve in an emergency as a loose pattern. Of course, the part needs to be built up to allow for shrinkage.

Patterns fastened permanently to a board or *match plate* are known as *mounted patterns*. A main advantage is that a mounted pattern is easier than a loose pattern to use and store. Another advantage is that the gating system can be mounted on a match plate, and thus the time to cut the gating system in the mold can be eliminated. Mounted patterns cost more than loose patterns, but when many castings are to be made from a pattern, the time saved in operation warrants the cost of mounting the pattern. Patterns for a number of pieces may be mounted on one match plate like the one in Fig. 8–25.

Fig. 8–25. A match plate pattern.

A *core-box* is essentially a type of pattern into which sand is rammed or packed to form a core as illustrated in Fig. 8–26.

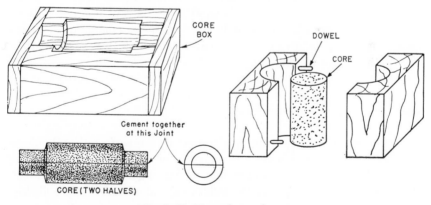

Fig. 8–26. Typical core boxes.

Symmetrical molds and cores, particularly in large sizes, are sometimes shaped by means of *sweeps* like the one in Fig. 8–27. The sweep is a flat board with an outline of the cross section of the part to be made and is revolved around a central axis to clear away excess sand inside the mold.

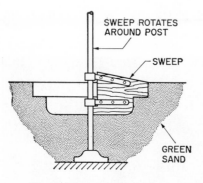

Fig. 8–27. A sweep pattern.

Pattern material. Wood is the most common material for patterns. It is easy to work and readily available. Properly selected and kiln-dried mahogany, walnut, white pine and sugar pine are often used. Sugar pine is most often used because it is easily worked and is generally free from warping and cracking. Moisture in the wood should be about 5 to 6% to avoid warping, shrinking, or expanding of the finished pattern.

Metal patterns may be loose or mounted. If usage warrants a metal pattern, then the pattern probably should be mounted on a plate and include the gating system. Metal is used when a large number of castings are desired from a pattern or when conditions are too severe for wooden patterns. Metal patterns wear well. Another advantage of a metal pattern is freedom from warping in storage. Commonly a metal pattern is itself cast from a master pattern and can be replaced readily if damaged or worn.

Patterns are also made of plaster and plastics. Plaster patterns can be fabricated quickly but are brittle and not suitable for large numbers of castings. Plastics stand in cost and durability between wood and metal for patterns. They are resistant to sand abrasion and are not affected by moisture. Plastics are commonly used to make emergency patterns quickly or salvage worn or broken patterns. A broken machine part or worn pattern may be built up by application of fiber and plastic resin to allow for shrinkage or changes. This may serve as a pattern in the sand for a few pieces or to make a plaster mold in which plastic resin is cast for a more permanent pattern.

Pattern layout. The parting line represents the surface that divides a pattern into the parts that form the cavities of the cope (top) and drag (bottom) of the mold. If at all possible, the parting line should be straight, which means that a simple plane divides the pattern into cope and drag sections. A straight parting line is particularly desirable for a loose piece pattern to enable the sections to lie flat on the molding board. An example is given in Fig. 8–28. A straight parting line is not necessary for a match plate but often makes the pattern easier to fabricate.

Some means are necessary to support and position cores in molds. These are in the forms of extensions, pads, and bosses on the cores and are called *core prints.* A core print must be large enough to support the core. The core weight is carried by the drag, and buoyancy is resisted by the cope.

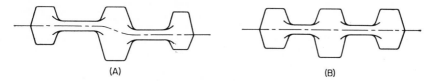

(A)   (B)

Fig. 8–28. The parting line of design (A) is not straight, and the piece is harder to cast than (B).

Pattern shrinkage allowance. As metal solidifies and cools, it shrinks and contracts in size. To compensate for this, a pattern is made larger than the finished casting by means of a *shrinkage allowance.* Although contraction is volumetric, the correction for it is usually expressed linearly. Dimensions are not shown oversized on a part or pattern drawing to allow for shrinkage, but the patternmaker measures to the finished dimensions with *shrink rules.* Such a rule has a scale that is longer than standard by a definite proportion such as $\frac{1}{16}$, $\frac{1}{8}$, or $\frac{3}{16}$ in. per ft. Shrinkage is different for different metals, different shapes of castings of the same metal, and different molding and casting methods. As an example, light- and medium-steel castings of simple design and no cores require an allowance of $\frac{1}{4}$ in. per ft, and a rule for that amount of shrinkage is used to make their patterns. In comparison, an allowance of $\frac{3}{16}$ in. per ft is adequate for pipes and valves of the same metal because their molds and cores offer considerable resistance to contraction. Typical shrinkage allowances are shown in Table 8–2. A master pattern from which metal patterns are cast may have double shrinkage allowance.

TABLE 8–2. TYPICAL PATTERN SHRINKAGE ALLOWANCES

(For simple uncored castings with dimensions of not over 24 inches.)

Metal	Gray cast iron	Cast steel	Aluminum	Brass	Bronze	Magnesium
Shrinkage allowance (in. per ft)	$\frac{1}{8}$	$\frac{1}{4}$	$\frac{5}{32}$	$\frac{3}{16}$	$\frac{1}{8}$ to $\frac{1}{4}$	$\frac{11}{64}$

Other allowances. Machining allowance is an amount dimensions on a casting are made oversize to provide stock for machining. Dimensions on a pattern drawing include machining allowance. The amount of metal left for machining must be no more than necessary but enough to assure that cutters can get an ample bite beneath and completely remove the hard scale and skin on the surface of the casting. What is sufficient depends upon the kind of metal, the shape of the casting, and the methods of casting, cleaning, and machining.

TABLE 8-3. TYPICAL MACHINING ALLOWANCES

(For finishing surfaces of sand castings with dimensions up to 12 in.
Allowance is in inches added to the total dimension.)

Metal	Cast iron	Cast steel	Brass, Bronze and Aluminum
On outside surface	³⁄₃₂	⅛	¹⁄₁₆
On inside diameters	⅛	³⁄₁₆	³⁄₃₂

Distortion allowance may be added to dimsensions of certain objects such as large flat plates and U-shaped castings that are expected to warp on cooling. The purpose of this allowance is to displace the pattern in such a way that the casting will be of the proper shape and size after it distorts in process.

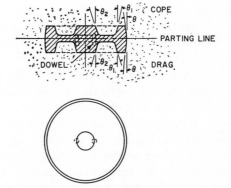

Fig. 8-29. Draft on both pieces of a two piece pattern.

Draft. Draft is the taper or slant placed on the sides of a pattern, outward from the parting line as depicted in Fig. 8-29. This allows the pattern to be removed (drawn) from the mold without damaging the sand surface. Draft may be expressed in inches per foot on a side, or in degrees, and the amount needed in each case depends upon the shape of the casting, the type of pattern, and the process. For example, draft of ⅛ in. per ft on a wood pattern may be required for a certain casting. For the same piece, a metal pattern mounted on a molding machine may need only ¹⁄₁₆ in. per ft.

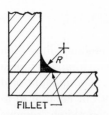

Fig. 8-30. An example of a fillet on a pattern.

Fillets. A fillet is a rounded filling along the convergence of two surfaces of a pattern as indicated in Fig. 8-30. The rounded corner thus produced on the casting is also called a fillet. Fillets may be carved in wood patterns but are usually made more inex-

pensively of wax, plastic, wood coving, or leather. They vary in size from ⅛ in. to 1 in.-radius depending on the size, shape, and material of the casting. Fillets obviate sharp angles and corners and thus strengthen both metal patterns and castings. They provide for easier removal of the pattern from the sand, a cleaner mold, freer flow of metal through the mold, less washing of the sand in the mold, and fewer shrinking strains and hot tears between sections as the casting cools.

Locating pads. Bosses or pads are commonly added to castings to provide definite and controlled spots for location in machining operations. These *locating* or *foundry pads* are gaged and may be cleaned up by filing to a relationship with the major outline of the workpiece. Care must be taken that such pads do not create too heavy sections and hot spots in a casting.

Color coding. All surfaces of a wood pattern are coated with shellac to keep out moisture. Important parts of a pattern may be colored for identification. Some foundries adhere strictly to a color code; others not at all. A widely accepted color code is the latest adopted by The American Foundrymen's Society (Fig. 8–31).

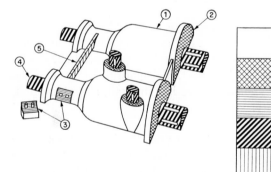

① Unfinished casting surfaces, the face of core boxes and pattern or core box parting faces are to be painted with a clear coating

② Machined surfaces are to be painted red

③ Seats of and for loose pieces are to be painted aluminum

④ Core prints are to be painted black

⑤ Stop-offs are to be indicated by green

Fig. 8–31. An illustration of color coding.

SANDS AND OTHER MOLD INGREDIENTS

The primary function of any molding material is to maintain the shape of the mold cavity until the molten metal solidifies. Silica sand is the most widely used molding material, particularly for metals that melt at high temperatures. It serves well because it is readily available, low in cost, can be formed easily into complicated shapes, and is able to withstand the effects of molten metal.

The three major parts of a molding sand are: (1) the sand grains which have the necessary refractory properties to withstand the intense heat of the molten metal, (2) a bonding material, which may be natural or added clay, cereal, etc. to hold the grains together, and (3) water to coalesce the grains and binder into a plastic molding material.

Molding sand. *Natural sands* contain only the binder mined with them and are used as received with water added. They have the advantages of maintaining moisture content for a long time, having a wide working range for moisture, and permitting easy patching and finishing of molds. Sometimes it is desirable to change the properties of a natural sand by adding bentonite (a clay binder). Such a sand is known as a *semisynthetic sand.*

Synthetic sands are formulated from various ingredients. The base may be a natural sand with some clay content or a washed sand with all clay removed. A binder, such as bentonite, and water are added. The sands have the advantages over natural sands of: (1) more uniform grain size, (2) higher refractoriness, (3) moldability with less moisture, (4) requiring less binder, (5) easier control of properties, and (6) the need of less storage space since one kind of sand may suffice for different kinds of castings.

Loam sand is high in clay, as much as 50% or so, and dries hard. *Loam molding* is done by making the mold, usually for a large casting, of brick cemented and lined with loam sand and then dried.

Properties of sand. The way sand performs in a mold to produce good castings can be tested by and depends largely upon its green permeability, green strength, and dry strength. These properties are determined chiefly by grain fineness, grain shape, clay content, and moisture content of the sand. Other properties of less influence are hot strength, sintering point, deformation, and collapsibility.

Green permeability. *Permeability* is the porosity from the openings between grains. This gives passage for air, gases, and steam to escape when the molten metal is poured in the mold. Permeability is measured in a common test by passing a definite amount of air through a standard test specimen under specified conditions. The result is expressed by a number $P = 501.2/pt$, where p is the pressure in grams per square centimeter and t is time in minutes. Thus the permeability number is larger as the sand is more porous.

Grain fineness is measured by passing sand through standard sieves, each with a certain number of openings per linear inch. Commercial sands are made up of grains of various sizes. Grain size of a sand is designated by a number that indicates the average size as well as the proportions of smaller or larger grains in the mixture. This is determined by a procedure described in handbooks.

Finer grains in a mold impart a smoother finish to a casting. On the other hand, permeability decreases as the grains and thus the voids between grains become smaller. The same condition results from a large proportion of fine grains in a mixture. The best compromise must be reached. For large castings that require coarse sand for high permeability, the surface of the mold cavity may have a thin layer of fine grain facing material.

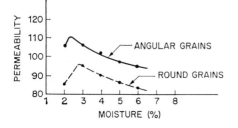

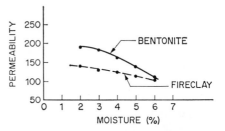

Fig. 8–32. Typical relationships of permeability of molding sand to moisture content and grain shape.

Fig. 8–33. The permeability of two kinds of clay for molding sand with various amounts of moisture.

There are two distinct *shapes of sand grains;* angular and rounded, with many degrees of roundness and angularity between the two extremes. Sharp angular grains cannot pack together as closely and consequently give a higher permeability than rounded grains. This is shown in Fig. 8–32.

Both the *type* and the *amount of binder* have a decided effect on the permeability of sand. An illustration of the permeabilities imparted by two common types of clay is given in Fig. 8–33. Over a wide range of moisture content, bentonite was found to give more permeability than fire clay. Permeability may decrease with an increase in clay content, as depicted by the 2% moisture curve for bentonite in Fig. 8–34. The upper curve for 4% moisture content indicates a fairly constant permeability over a wide range of bentonite content. In general clay content is optimum when present to the extent of coating the sand particles completely without filling the spaces between the grains.

With a low *moisture content,* fine clay particles clog the spaces between the grains, and permeability is low. More moisture softens and agglutinates the clay around the grains for optimum conditions. An excess of moisture fills the voids and decreases permeability. Peaks of maximum permeability are seen in Fig. 8–32. The optimum moisture content is not the same for all molding sands, although it generally lies between 2 and 8%.

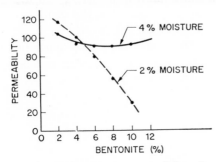

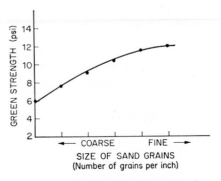

Fig. 8-34. How the permeability of a molding sand varies with bentonite content.

Fig. 8-35. The green strength of a molding sand in relation to the sizes of its grains for one set of conditions.

Green strength. Green strength is the strength of a sand ready for molding, and, if the metal is poured immediately, represents the ability of the sand to hold to the shape of the mold. Green strength is expressed in pounds per square inch required to crush a standard specimen.

The finer the sand grains, the larger the surface area of a given bulk, and the larger the amount of binder needed to cover the area. The contacts and bonds between grains are more numerous, and thus green strength is higher with finer grains. Figure 8-35 shows that as the grain size becomes larger, the green strength decreases under normal conditions.

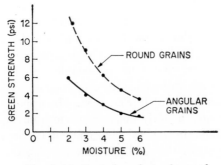

Fig. 8-36. Typical relationship of green strength of a molding sand to moisture content and grain shape.

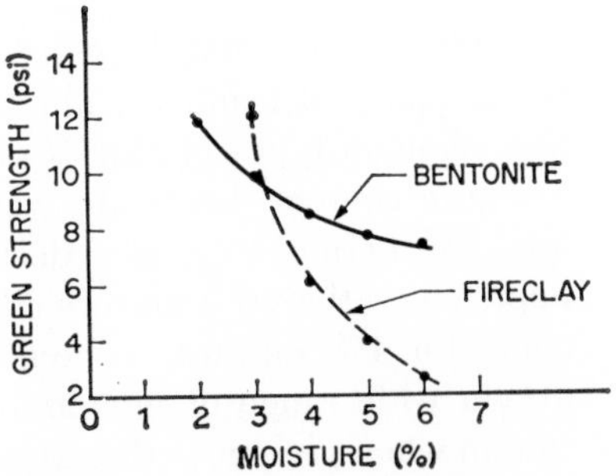

Fig. 8-37. A comparison of the green strengths of two samples of molding sand with different clay binders at different moisture levels.

Round grains pack together much more closely than angular grains and as a result are bonded together with a higher green strength than angular grains. A comparison is given for two types of grains in Fig. 8-36.

Some binders provide a higher green strength than others. Comparison of bentonite and fire clay at different moisture levels is given in Fig. 8–37. The green strength increases in proportion to the amount of binder in a molding sand, but, as pointed out earlier, too much binder is detrimental to permeability, and a compromise must be accepted.

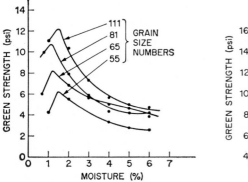

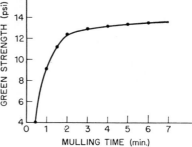

Fig. 8–38. How the green strength of molding sand varies for several sizes of grains.

Fig. 8–39. The increase in green strength of a molding sand with mulling time.

The effect of moisture on green strength is similar to the effect on permeability. Green strength increases with the first additions of moisture, reaches a maximum strength, and then starts to decrease as depicted in Fig. 8–38. Also shown is that an excess of moisture has a weakening effect, even nullifying the influence of grain size.

In addition to other factors, mulling or mixing practice affects green strength as will be explained in the section on the preparation of sand.

Dry strength. *Dry strength* is the strength of sand that has been dried or baked. In general, dry strength varies in the same way as green strength with grain fineness, grain shape, and moisture content. However, different binders can affect dry strength and green strength differently. For example, in contrast to western bentonite, southern bentonite produces a high green strength and a low dry strength, which is conducive to easy shake out of castings.

Sand control. Many substances are added to molding sands to impart certain properties or to change properties. Cereal (such as wheat and corn flour), dextrine, rosin and similar substances are often added to augment or modify the clay binders. It is important to realize that the action of each additive is somewhat different. Corn flour improves green strength slightly but dry strength markedly. Wheat flour improves collapsibility. Dextrine binders are a form of sugar and produce a much higher dry strength than do cereal binders but decrease green strength.

A rosin bonded core has a hard surface when baked but absorbs moisture on standing and should be used as soon as possible.

The binder is burned out and the proportion of fine particles is increased when foundry sand is exposed to the heat of molten metal. As a result, green strength and permeability decrease as the sand is reused. By measuring properties periodically with sand-testing equipment, a sand technician is enabled to make appropriate additions to restore the sand before it deteriorates to the point where it must be discarded. Uniform day to day properties may be maintained by continuous checks and additions of small amounts of binder.

Sand preparation. Under a microscope sand grains are seen to exist in clusters of small particles adhering to large particles. This is thought to be the result largely of previous use. Clusters are less refractory and harder to ram than individual particles and need to be broken up, particularly to prepare sand for cores and for facing patterns to make mold linings. Even so, breaking down of the clustered particles is desirable for all sand and is usually done by stirring and kneading it mechanically. A popular machine for that purpose is a *muller* which kneads, shears, slices through, and stirs the sand in a heavy iron pot by means of several revolving rollers and knives. The time needed for mulling depends upon the type of muller and the type and amount of binder. After the optimum length of mixing time in each case, there is no further increase in green strength as shown by the example in Fig. 8–39.

Mulling sand distributes the binder over the grains. Thus less binder is required for satisfactory green strength and permeability is higher than with hand mixed sand.

Sand is *aerated* to make it fluffy so it flows readily around and takes up the details of the pattern. This is done to some extent in mulling. One device for aeration is a *sand cutter* which hurls the sand from a rapidly moving belt against bars or springs to break the grains apart.

Sands are mixed from the ingredients and by the methods described to many formulas for various metals and purposes. For instance, for steel castings three sands may be prepared: one for the green facing sand, another for the green backing sand, and still another for facing sands that are to be surface dried in the mold by a torch. Formulas for foundry sands are given in reference- and hand-books.

Core sand. Core sand must have much the same properties of permeability, cohesiveness, and refractoriness as molding sand but must also possess collapsibility and friability. *Collapsibility* means that the core gives way easily as the casting cools and shrinks to avoid inducing hot tears and cracks in the metal. *Friability* means that the core crumbles and falls apart when it must be removed from the casting. These properties are imparted by the type and amount of binder, additives to the binder, and by the curing of the cores. For example, if cracks occur in the cored area of a casting, a weaker binder or less binder may be used or a small amount of wood flour may be added to the binder.

Core sand mixes are started with clean dry silica sand. Among various binders used for core sand are corn flour, dextrine, fish oil, raw linseed oil, and commercial core oils. Linseed oil is an ingredient in most proprietary core oils. A long list could be made of binders, each to impart a particular property to the core. Formulas for various purposes are given in reference- and hand-books. As the ingredients are added, the sand is mixed thoroughly in a muller but not excessively, which would cause stickiness.

A development of recent years has been the use of sodium silicate (water glass) as a core binder. After the core is shaped, it is exposed to carbon dioxide gas. This precipitates a silica jell, hardens the core in a fraction of a minute, and eliminates the need for baking. The core can then be used in the mold immediately.

MELTING METALS IN THE FOUNDRY

The reduction and melting of iron and steel in blast furnaces, open-hearth furnaces, Bessemer converters, electric furnaces and crucibles have been discussed in Chap. 4. Most steel is cast from furnaces of the types already described, but the bulk, estimated up to 90%, of gray iron and malleable iron base for castings is melted in the cupola.

The Cupola. The cupola is simple and economical for melting pig and scrap iron. It is essentially a vertical steel shrouded and refractory lined furnace. A view of the construction of a typical cupola is in Fig. 8–40. Cupolas are made in many sizes, commonly about 4 to 7 ft in outside diameter and 30 to 40 ft high. They may turn out from 5 to 25 tons of melted metal per hour. A 4 ft-diameter cupola costs about $25,000 installed with blower and all auxiliary equipment.

A cupola must be prepared and heated carefully to avoid damage. The refractory lining is repaired or replaced as needed, and the bottom doors are propped shut. A layer of sand sloping towards the tap hole is rammed over the bottom. Excelsior, rags, and wood are placed on the sand to protect it from the initial charge of fuel, which is several feet thick, and to ignite the fuel. Materials are charged through a door 15 to 25 ft above the bottom.

After the initial charge has become hot, alternate layers of fuel and metal with flux are added. The fuel may be a good grade of low sulfur coke, anthracite coal, or carbon briquettes. The flux to help form slag to remove impurities and retard oxidation of metal is usually limestone, but sometimes soda ash, fluorspar, and proprietary substances are added. The

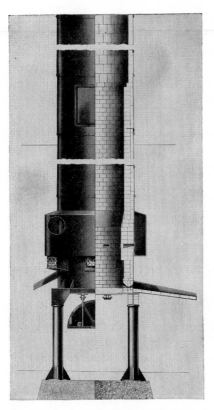

Fig. 8–40. External and internal views of a cupola.

proportion of metal to fuel by weight ranges in various practices from about 6:1 to 12:1. A ratio of 10:1, which is common, means that 200 lb of coke are provided to melt a ton of iron. Fuel cost is lower with a lower proportion of coke, but the melting and output rates are higher with more coke.

After the charge and cupola have had a chance to become heated uniformly, in an hour or two, the forced draft is started. Air is blown through the wind box and tuyeres around the hearth into the furnace. About 30,000 cu ft of air are required to melt one ton of iron. The metal begins to melt. The *tap hole* is plugged with a wad of clay. The molten metal seeps down through the coke and collects at the bottom. Tapping is done by breaking the clay plug in the tap hole. Flow may be permitted at intervals or may be continuous during the melt. For the latter case, the melting rate must be in balance with the capacity of the tap hole. The slag floats on top of the metal. If the molten metal is allowed to accumulate in the hearth, the slag flows off through an opening higher than the tap hole, called the *cinder notch*, in the back of the cupola. Otherwise, the slag may be skimmed off the metal as it flows out of the cupola. When sufficient metal has been melted, the bottom of the cupola is dropped to spill the remaining contents onto the ground to cool.

Cupola calculations. The cupola does little to refine the metal, and the composition of its product depends largely upon what is put into it. The proportions of the metals charged into the cupola must be calculated carefully to assure a uniform and predictable product. These calculations are based upon knowing the amounts of carbon, silicon, manganese, phosphorous, and sulfur in the pig and scrap iron and the nature of the reactions that take place in the cupola. The following example shows how the calculations are made: it is assumed that 3000 lb of iron are needed and will be fed into the cupola. The typical raw materials available in the storage yard of the foundry are listed in Table 8–4 with their analyses. In other foundries still other materials, such as machinery steel scrap and iron of various analyses, may also be stocked depending upon the sources of supply and the desired product.

TABLE 8–4. COMPOSITIONS OF SOME TYPICAL METALS FOR CUPOLA MELTING (%)

Metal	Carbon	Silicon	Manganese	Phosphorous	Sulfur
No. 1 pig iron	3.5	2.50	0.72	0.18	0.016
No. 2 pig iron	3.5	3.00	0.63	0.12	0.018
Cast iron scrap	3.4	2.30	0.50	0.20	0.030
Returns (risers, defective castings, etc.)	3.3	2.50	0.65	0.17	0.035

On the basis of current practices and results in this foundry, it is decided to make up the charge of 10% No. 1 pig iron, 20% No. 2 pig iron, 30% new scrap iron, and 40% returns from previous melts. The amount of each element that may be expected in the product can now be ascertained on the basis of the reactions in the cupola.

(a) The amount of carbon in the iron remains substantially unchanged during the process. Some carbon is oxidized, but about the same amount is picked up from the fuel. The amount contributed by each ingredient is:

$$\begin{aligned}
\text{No. 1 pig iron} &- 3000 \times 0.10 \times 0.035 = 10.5 \text{ lb} \\
\text{No. 2 pig iron} &- 3000 \times 0.20 \times 0.035 = 21.0 \\
\text{New scrap iron} &- 3000 \times 0.30 \times 0.034 = 30.6 \\
\text{Returns} &- 3000 \times 0.40 \times 0.033 = 39.6 \\
\hline
& 101.7 \text{ lb}
\end{aligned}$$

The final percentage of carbon $= \dfrac{101.7}{3000} \times 100 = 3.39\%$.

(b) The silicon content can be expected to be reduced 10% by oxidation. The amount of silicon in the charge is:

$$\begin{aligned}
\text{No. 1 pig iron} &- 3000 \times 0.10 \times 0.025 = 7.5 \text{ lb} \\
\text{No. 2 pig iron} &- 3000 \times 0.20 \times 0.030 = 18.0 \\
\text{New scrap iron} &- 3000 \times 0.30 \times 0.023 = 20.7 \\
\text{Returns} &- 3000 \times 0.40 \times 0.025 = 30.0 \\
\hline
& 76.2 \text{ lb}
\end{aligned}$$

The final percentage of silicon $= \dfrac{76.2 \times 0.9}{3000} \times 100 = 2.29\%$.

(c) The manganese content is expected to be reduced 20% by oxidation. In the same way as for the other elements, the manganese content is estimated to be 18.24 lb, and the final percentage of manganese =

$$\frac{18.24(1.00 - 0.20)}{3000} \times 100 = 0.49\%.$$

(d) Phosphorous losses in the cupola are negligible. In the same way as for the other elements, the amount of phosphorous in the charge is calculated to be 5.10 lb. From this the final percentage of phosphorous =

$$\frac{5.10}{3000} \times 100 = 0.17\%.$$

(e) The iron loses almost no sulfur in melting but picks up about 4% of the sulfur in the coke. The quantity of sulfur in the metal charge is calculated to be 0.846 lb. The iron to coke ratio is to be 8:1, and the sulfur content of the coke is known to be 0.50%. Thus the quantity of sulfur in the coke is $(3000/8)0.005 = 1.875$ lb, and of that 4% or 0.075 lb is added to the iron. The final sulfur content is estimated to be $(0.846 + 0.075) \times 100/3000 = 0.03\%$.

In summary, the composition of the iron from the cupola is estimated to be carbon 3.39, silicon 2.29, manganese 0.49, phosphorous 0.17, and sulfur 0.03%.

If more or less of any of the elements is wanted, the results can be changed by specifying raw materials in different amounts and of different kinds and by adding ferro alloys of elements to the metal in the ladle after melting. These are less expensive than the pure elements. For instance, if in the example 2.50% silicon is desired, about 2 lb of 50% ferrosilicon can be added to each 500 lb of molten iron.

Melting of nonferrous metals. Some nonferrous metal melting is done in almost all types of furnaces. A considerable amount is done in induction furnaces, but most commercial melting of nonferrous metals is in oil and gas fired crucible furnaces. These are of two basic types: stationary and tilting furnaces.

The *stationary type of crucible furnace* requires that the crucible be lifted in and out for pouring. A cross section of this type of furnace is shown in Fig. 8–41. When a stationary furnace is sunk into the floor or deck of a foundry, it is known as a *pit type furnace*.

A *tilting type of crucible furnace*, Fig. 8–42, requires a crucible with a suitable lip for pouring metal when the furnace is tilted.

Most nonferrous metals and alloys oxidize, absorb gases and other substances, and form dross readily when heated. Various practices are followed for each kind of metal to preserve purity and obtain good castings. Space does not permit descriptions of all, and full information may be found in treatises on the subject. The melting of aluminum will be treated in some detail here to point out the nature of the problems and principles.

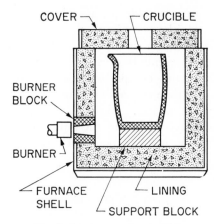

Fig. 8–41. A cross section of a stationary type crucible furnace. A furnace of this kind with auxiliary equipment and a crucible having a capacity of 250 lb of brass or 120 lb of aluminum costs about $1200.

Fig. 8–42. A tilting type crucible furnace. (Courtesy Lindberg Engineering Co.) A furnace of this type with a crucible capacity of about 250 lb of brass or 120 lb of aluminum costs about $1900 with auxiliary equipment.

Aluminum and its alloys have a marked tendency to absorb hydrogen when heated. This gas is released on cooling and causes detrimental pinholes and porosity in castings. Exposure to hydrogen-forming media, such as water vapor, must be avoided. Clean and dry melting stock and crucible are important; a slight excess of air in the furnace atmosphere is desirable.

Molten aluminum reacts readily with oxygen to form a film on the surface. Fortunately the dross serves as a good shield against hydrogen and further oxidation if not broken. Excessive dross may become trapped in the metal, particularly if the metal is agitated, and appear as defects in the final casting. Both the amount of oxidation and the tendency to absorb hydrogen increase with temperature and time. Excessive temperature also causes coarse grains in castings. These considerations dictate the melting procedure for best results. Aluminum should not be heated more than 100°F above the necessary pouring temperature. Temperature is checked with an immersion pyrometer. The melting time should be as short with as little agitation as possible.

Aluminum does not ordinarily require as much flux for protection as some other metals because of its oxide film. However, at times the gas or oxide in the metal must be reduced. Chlorine or nitrogen may be bubbled through the molten metal. Solid fluxes, containing aluminum or zinc chloride, may be added. Various proprietary fluxes are commonly used to help dry the surface dross and facilitate skimming it from the metal.

Vacuum melting. It has become necessary to develop ways of melting and pouring some metals and alloys in the absence of air to make and keep them pure and clean. This is done in a number of ways. A typical installation is depicted in Fig. 8–43 and represents true vacuum melting and pouring. Operating temperatures with this equipment range up to 3000°F. Some such furnaces operate at less than one millionth of normal atmospheric pressure, and most under 10 microns. The metal in the crucible is melted by induction, and the induced field stirs the liquid constantly and aids in the release of gases. The metal is poured by tilting the crucible; in some cases the entire furnace tilts.

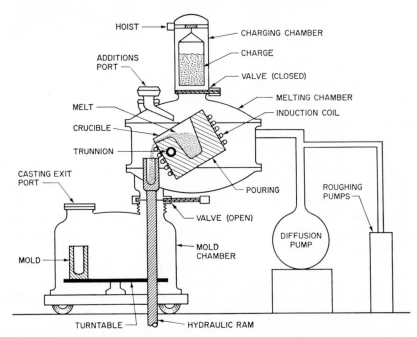

Fig. 8–43. A schematic drawing of a vacuum melting furnace.

Arrangements like that already described eliminate from the casting process the two contaminating media of air and slag. The third source of impurities, the crucible, is neutralized by the *consumable electrode* method. This utilizes an arc in a vacuum, between an initial charge and an electrode of the metal melted, inside a water-cooled copper crucible. As metal is melted off the electrode by the arc, it is quickly solidified, especially in contact with the cooled crucible. Diffusion between crucible and melt is minimized.

A process called *degassing* entails only pouring in a vacuum. The metal is melted by conventional means in air. The vacuum need not be extremely high to draw off substantial proportions of hydrogen and other gases.

Vacuum melting is first of all necessary to cast metals and alloys which are too reactive with oxygen and other gases to be melted at all in air. Uranium and titanium for instance, can be effectively cast only in a vacuum. In addition, vacuum melting improves the properties of metals, such as steel and aluminum, that can be melted by ordinary means. Raw materials of good grade are of course necessary for a superior product. Metals melted and cast in a vacuum can be kept pure because they are not exposed to new contamination and can be further purified because gases are drawn from them. No oxidizers, such as manganese and silicon in steel, are needed, and no slag is formed. In vacuum melting, precise amounts of pure carbon or hydrogen may be added to reduce oxides. As gases are evolved, they are extracted by the pumps, and the reactions driven to completion. The addition of highly reactive elements like zirconium, titanium, and aluminum to an alloy that requires them may be delayed until after the gas content of the melt has been depleted.

Vacuum-melted steel may contain 3 to 20 parts of oxygen per million parts of steel. This is about $\frac{1}{20}$ of the proportion in commercial air-melted steel; and other impurities are reduced to about the same extent. Pure and clean metals are substantially stronger, more ductile, and more resistant to corrosion. For instance, the charpy impact strength at room temperature has been reported to be 220 ft lb for vacuum-melted 430 stainless steel as compared with 8 ft lb for air-melted. The benefits obtained have been found particularly desirable for newer high-temperature alloys, such as nickel and cobalt alloys. Thus vacuum melting is especially in demand for products such as turbine blades, buckets, bearings, and castings, after-burner parts, highest quality tool steels, and all parts which must serve at high temperatures with high strength.

Vacuum melting is inherently more costly than air melting. Operation is impeded by the necessary functions, and the feasible amount of metal obtained at one time is restricted by the size of chamber in which it is practicable to hold a high vacuum. A 5000 lb capacity is considered near the limit for a vacuum-melting furnace, but ingots of 10 tons or more are produced by the consumable electrode method, and up to several hundred tons are poured by degassing. Vacuum-melting equipment is quite expensive. A 2500 lb capacity production unit of the type described in Fig. 8–43 costs about $600,000 with accessories, such as pumps, and over $1,000,000 with building and all adjuncts. An experimental 50 lb capacity vacuum-melting furnace with accessories costs around $25,000.

POURING AND CLEANING CASTINGS

Pouring methods. Common practice is to run the molten metal from the cupola or furnace into a large receiving ladle. From that, metal is distributed to smaller pouring ladles. These range in size from ones that can be handled by one man to huge crane ladles holding hundreds of tons. The bottoms of ladles and the sides of large ladles are lined with fire brick. The bottom and sides of a ladle are daubed with an inner coating of fire sand and clay, which is hardened by baking.

Liquid metal may be delivered to a mold in one or more ladles. The important concern is to have sufficient metal to fill the mold, gates, and risers completely. Pouring must be done continuously and at a uniform rate until the mold is full to keep the slag from settling. The metal temperature must be high enough for the fluid to pour easily and rapidly. Slag is always present on molten iron to some degree and must be kept out of the mold to avoid weak slag pockets in the casting. Figure 8–17 gives a view of a hand-pouring operation.

Foundries are highly systematized for large quantity outputs. An example is given in Fig. 8–44. In common production practice a match plate

Fig. 8–44. A car-type mold conveyor (below) and monorail ladle conveyor (above) for production pouring. (Courtesy Link-Belt Co.)

containing the drag half of a pattern is rigged to a molding machine on which drag halves of a mold are produced continuously. These are placed on an endless conveyor. Cores are set in position as each drag moves along. Cope halves are molded on another machine and placed on the drag halves. The closed molds pass alongside ladles travelling at the same speed on a parallel conveyor and are filled. After the molds cool enough, they are dumped onto a grating to strip out the castings. The flasks return to the molding machines, and the cycle is repeated.

Cleaning castings. After castings have solidified and cooled, they are removed from the sand and cleaned.

A casting may be separated from the sand in various ways. A rudimentary way for a small casting is to dump the mold assembly upside down, remove the bottom board and flask, and then pull the casting from the sand with a hook bar. After being removed from the sand, the casting is rapped with a hammer to dislodge any clinging material. Essentially the same is done mechanically to castings made in large quantities. The flasks are emptied on a vibrating metal grating. The sand falls through, and the castings are pushed or jolted along to fall off, stripped, at the end onto a conveyor. Sand is reprocessed for future use.

Gates are often broken off gray iron castings by hammers. They are removed from steel and nonferrous castings by sawing or flame cutting. Fins, bumps, and other excesses of metal may be ground or chipped away. Finally clean surfaces are obtained by shot or sand blasting or wire brushing. Small castings may be tumbled with scraps of metal. These processes are described in Chap. 30.

SHELL MOLD CASTING

Shell mold casting, developed during and since World War II, makes use of fine sand with a phenolic resin binder for a molding material. This mixture is deposited on a metal pattern heated to about 450°F, a layer around the pattern coalesces, and after a fraction of a minute, the excess is dumped off the pattern. The thickness of the shell depends upon the time the bulk of the material stays on the pattern and is usually from $\frac{3}{16}$ to $\frac{3}{8}$ in. as required for the job. The resin is cured and the shell hardened by baking from 600 to 800°F for a part of a minute or so. The shell is stripped from the pattern, which is then cleaned and sprayed with a silicone parting compound to prepare it for the next shell.

One method of shell molding is to blow the molding material on the pattern. The material can be deposited uniformly, forced into intricate forms, and controlled in amount. A simpler method consists of placing the heated pattern face down on a box partially filled with molding material. The box is turned upside down for the required length of time and then reinverted. The pattern with the green shell is then taken off the box. The *dumping* method does not always produce as accurate shells as the *blowing* method but it is more readily adapted to automatic operation.

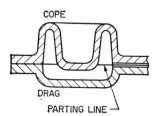

Cope and drag shells are made for a mold and joined together as indicated by Fig. 8–45. They are often glued together in production, but the thickness of the adhesive film may vary 0.010 to 0.020 in., which is not desirable for precision castings. Molds pasted together may be imbedded in sand or shot if reinforcement is necessary to counteract the hydrostatic pressure of the metal. Molds for precision

Fig. 8–45. A section of a shell mold.

casting are clamped together and, in production, are held in metal back-up fixtures, especially for large and heavy castings.

The phenolic resin binder in the shell is mostly burned away, particularly in cores, by the hot metal. The remaining sand is easily stripped from the surface and cleaned from the cavities of the casting by jarring, shaking, and tumbling.

Merits of shell molding. Shell molding is more expensive than green sand molding in most cases. This is because the molding media costs four to five times as much as sand alone. Some of this cost, but usually not all, is saved by certain advantages of shell molding. The savings arise because much less sand needs to be worked and handled; the molds are light, easy to handle, and can be made when convenient and stored; gases escape readily through the thin shells and fewer castings are scrapped because of blowholes or pockets; and the process is readily adaptable to mechanization.

The cost of shell molding is justified for many jobs it can do better than green sand molding. Complex shapes and intricate parts that cannot be cast at all in green sand can be made by shell molding. Usually a better finish is obtained and closer tolerances are held by shell molding. Less stock needs to be left for machining castings made to closer tolerances, and often no machining at all is needed. A thin shell does not have the mass chill effect of a thick sand mold. Thus shell mold castings suffer less from varying cross sections and tend to have softer skins than castings from green sand molds.

METALLURGY OF CASTINGS

Steel castings have low-carbon content and possess essentially the properties attributed to steel in general in Chaps. 2 and 6. With more carbon, the product is cast iron, with or without appreciable quantities of alloys. Cast iron in its common forms will be discussed in this section.

Cast iron. The general product cast iron has several commercial forms called gray irons, white cast irons, malleable irons, and nodular cast irons. Also, pig iron, described in Chap. 4, is a form of cast iron. Cast irons contain usually from 1.7% to about 4.5% carbon, and in general their constituents are those represented in that range of the iron-carbon diagram of Fig. 5–1. The various forms of cast iron represent various combinations of the iron and carbon and their compounds, depending upon how the material is cooled and the presence of silicon and other alloys.

Molten cast iron contains much but not all of the carbon in solution as iron carbide. When the iron is cast and cools, its ability to hold the carbide in solution decreases. At moderate cooling rates common in practice, much of the iron carbide decomposes, and the carbon is precipitated out as graphite flakes. As the metal becomes solid, iron carbide, called cementite, is restrained from further break down and ends up in a pearlitic structure. Pearlite has been defined in Chap. 2. The result is a pearlite matrix with graphite flakes dispersed throughout. A microscopic view of such a structure is shown in Fig. 8–46(A). The edges of the graphite flakes appear as heavy black lines. The flakes have no strength of their own, break up the continuity of the iron, and make the cast iron weak and brittle. The free graphite imparts the nominal coloring to *gray iron*, which usually contains 3 to 4% carbon.

Other forms of cast iron than the gray iron just described result when the metal is cooled at slower or faster rates. Upon slow cooling and particularly with a high-silicon and carbon content, considerable ferrite, as well as pearlite, is formed in the matrix because more of the carbon is released. The graphite becomes coarser. The ferrite is softer and not as wearable as pearlite. The product is sometimes called *open* or *soft cast iron*. When the cooling rate is fast, the iron carbide has less chance to decompose before the metal solidifies. Thus more cementite is deposited in the mass than can be accommodated in the pearlite, which must have a definite composition. The presence of cementite makes cast iron hard. When only part of the available carbon appears as dispersed cementite, the product is called *mottled iron* from its appearance. *White cast iron* has its carbon largely as cementite and consequently is extremely hard and brittle. The absence of free carbon is evident in the photomicrograph of Fig. 8–46(B). This condition is caused by very rapid cooling or by additives that stabilize the carbide. It may be desirable to harden certain areas of a casting for wearability. This is achieved by cooling the areas rapidly by means of metal chills in the mold wall, and the product is called *chilled cast iron* in *chilled castings*.

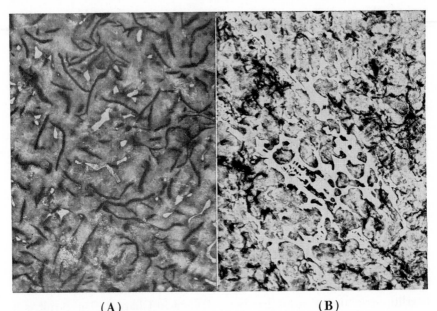

(A)   (B)

Fig. 8–46. Photomicrographs of (A) gray cast iron (X200); (B) white cast iron (X200) (Courtesy R. J. Raudebaugh); and (C) nodular cast iron (X500) (from R. W. Lindsay and J. M. Snook, *American Foundryman*, Nov. 1953.)

(C)

Malleable iron has free carbon in tiny lumps, rather than flakes, in a ferrite matrix, sometimes with pearlite. This makes it ductile, shock-resistant, and easily machinable. The structure is obtained by first producing essentially a white iron casting, reheating the casting above the transformation range, and soaking and slowly cooling it. This separates the graphite from the cementite while the metal is solid and prevents the growth of flakes like those that arise when molten metal hardens.

Nodular cast iron has its graphite in tiny spherulites as depicted by the photomicrograph of Fig. 8–46(C). This form is obtained by adding minute amounts of magnesium, cerium, or other elements to the molten iron just before pouring.

Elements other than iron and carbon are normally present in cast iron as contamination or additional additives. The properties of cast irons can be varied through wide ranges by adding suitable kinds and amounts of alloying elements. The control of graphitization is an important reason for using alloying elements. Other purposes may be to increase strength or resistance to corrosion, heat, or wear. The principal but not the only alloying elements for cast iron and their purposes are discussed in the following section.

Alloying elements in cast iron. The most important effect of *silicon* is to promote the decomposition of cementite into ferrite and carbon. The effect increases with the amount of silicon added. Enough should be used for gray iron to decompose all the massive cementite but not the pearlite. Requirements generally range from 0.50% to 3%.

Sulfur exists to some extent in all irons. It comes from pig iron, scrap, and the coke consumed in cupola melting. Sulfur markedly restrains the decomposition of cementite and combines with iron to form iron sulfide, which has a tendency to weaken the grain structure.

Manganese mitigates the effects of sulfur by forming manganese sulfide, which segregates as harmless inclusions. Most irons from American ores contain only 0.06% to 0.12% sulfur, and 0.50% to 0.80% manganese is sufficient. In such amounts, manganese has little effect on the properties of cast iron other than inhibiting the action of the sulfur. In excess, manganese would tend to combine into carbides and make the iron harder.

Phosphorus in most American irons is from 0.1% to 0.90%. Below about 0.50%, phosphorous has little effect upon the properties of the iron. In larger amounts it tends to form brittle iron phosphide which may add some hardness and wearability but weakens the iron and lowers impact strength appreciably. Phosphorous increases the fluidity of molten iron and improves castability in thin sections. Graphite formation is promoted by the increased fluidity.

Nickel acts as a graphitizer but is only about half as effective as silicon. Small amounts help refine the sizes of grains and graphite flakes. Most additions are from 0.25% to 2.0%. Larger amounts, from 14% to 38%, of nickel are found in austenitic gray irons that resist heat and corrosion and have low expansivity.

Chromium acts as a carbide stabilizer in cast iron and itself forms carbides that are more stable than iron carbide. Thus it intensifies chilling of cast iron, increases strength, hardness, and wear-resistance, and is conducive to fine-grain structure. Most additions of chromium range from 0.15% to 0.90% with or without other alloying elements. Free carbides that appear with chromium of 1% or more make castings hard to machine. With 3% chromium, white cast iron is formed. Special irons to resist corrosion and high temperatures contain as much as 35% chromium.

Molybdenum in amounts from 0.25% to 1.5% is added alone or with other elements to improve tensile strength, hardness, and shock-resistance of castings. It is a mild carbide former but also forms a solid solution with ferrite. The presence of molybdenum in cast iron produces fine and highly dispersed particles of graphite and good structural uniformity. This improves toughness, fatigue strength, machinability, hardenability, and high temperature strength.

Copper, usually from 0.25 to 2.5%, promotes formation of graphite and is a mild strengthener because it helps break up massive cementite and carbide concentrations.

Vanadium is a powerful carbide former and thus stabilizes cementite and restrains graphitization. Its effect in amounts from 0.10 to 0.50% is to increase strength, hardness, and machinability.

Comparison of cast irons. Gray cast iron produces the cheapest castings and should be considered first when its properties suffice. A classic example of an application that requires a bare minimum of strength is a window weight. For it, cast iron serves adequately at the least cost. Common applications for gray cast iron are guards and frames for machinery, motor frames, motor blocks and cylinder heads, bearing housings, valve housings, fire hydrants, pulley sheaves and miscellaneous hardware.

Each class of ferrous castings covers a range of properties. As an example, commercial gray irons are graded in the ASTM specification A48 by tensile strength. The range is from class 20 with a minimum tensile strength of 20,000 psi to class 60 with a minimum tensile strength of 60,000 psi. Strength is not always the major criterion for selection of a material. For instance, gray cast irons of the weaker grades have superior qualities for such applications as resistance to heat checking in clutch plates and brake drums, resistance to heat shock in ingot and pig molds, and dampening of vibrations in machine tool members.

White cast iron is brittle but is found on chilled castings to impart wear resisting surfaces to such products as plowshares, rock crushers, and mining equipment. Malleable iron, nodular iron, and steel castings provide various degrees of strength and shock-resistance for machinery of all kinds.

TABLE 8-5. TYPICAL PROPERTIES OF FERROUS CASTINGS

Kind of metal	Strength (psi)				Resistance to dynamic loading	Hardness (Bhn)	Elongation (%)	Relative sand casting cost ($ per lb(d))
	Ultimate tensile strength	Ultimate compressive strength	Yield strength	Endurance limit				
Cast steel (plain carbon)	50,000 to 100,000	(a)	25,000 to 50,000	(b)	high	110–210	18–27	0.35
Cast steel (low alloy)	90,000 to 200,000	(a)	60,000 to 200,000	(b)	high	170–370	9–20	0.90
Gray cast iron	20,000 to 80,000	80,000 to 190,000	(c)	10,000 to 30,000	low	150–300	0–3	0.18
White cast iron		over 200,000			nil	300–600	nil	
Malleable iron	50,000 to 120,000	(a)	30,000 to 90,000	20,000 to 30,000	medium	110–285	3–25	0.27
Nodular iron	60,000 to 160,000	(a)	45,000 to 135,000	(b)	medium	190–425	3–25	0.32

Notes: (a) Compressive strength about the same as tensile strength.
(b) Endurance limit usually from 0.4 to 0.5 times tensile strength.
(c) Essentially the same as tensile strength.
(d) Costs are relative and can be expected to vary with size and shapes of casting, quality, grade, supplier, market conditions, etc.

Nonferrous cast alloys. Aluminum, magnesium, brasses, and bronzes are important nonferrous alloys cast in sand. Their main properties have been described in Chap. 7. Except for melting and pouring at lower temperatures, the techniques for sand casting nonferrous metals are much the same as for iron founding. However, nonferrous alloys are also commonly cast by other processes and will be considered in that connection more fully in Chap. 9.

DESIGN OF CASTINGS

An engineer must learn how to design castings that do their jobs adequately and can be made economically. Treatment of the casting process in this chapter has explained the principles that must be observed for good casting design. The main ones will be summarized here without further detailed explanation.

Section thickness. The walls and sections of a casting should be as uniform as possible and blend into each other gradually. Thick sections tend to develop shrinkage cavities. On the other hand, metal may not flow fully into and fill sections that are too thin. Contiguous thick and thin sections cool and shrink at different rates and set up high residual stresses. Abrupt changes in sections and sharp corners are points of weakness. Comparisons of good and poor designs are made in Fig. 8–47.

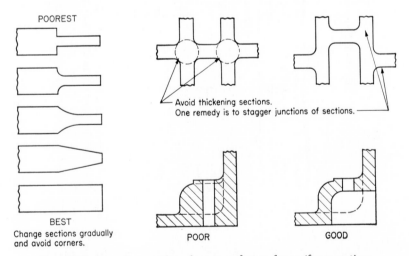

Fig. 8–47. Several examples of casting design for uniform sections.

Draft. A pattern can be drawn satisfactorily from the sand and a good casting made only if its sides are tapered away from the parting line. In addition, projections such as bosses on the sides of a casting away from the parting line, as indicated in Fig. 8–48, cannot be drawn out of the sand and should be avoided. Cores must be provided for them at extra expense.

Allowances. Provision is made for contraction of cast metals by a shrinkage allowance on patterns. Other allowances are those for machining stock for finishing and occasionally to compensate for expected distortions. Typical allowances are specified in Tables 8–2 and 8–3.

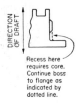

Recess here requires core. Continue boss to flange as indicated by dotted line.

Fig. 8–48. A projection increases the cost of making a casting.

Tolerances. Tolerances of $\pm\frac{1}{16}$ in. for dimensions up to 12 in. are standard commercial practice for sand castings. Tolerances as small as $\pm\frac{1}{32}$ in. are held by some foundries but at extra cost that should not be incurred unless necessary. Shell mold castings are made to tolerances of ±0.020 in. for steel and nonferrous alloys, ±0.015 in. for cast iron, and as small as ±0.003 in. in some cases at extra cost.

The smallest tolerances can be held only on dimensions that lie entirely in one part of a mold. Several times as much tolerance must be given to dimensions that extend from one part of a mold to another. That is because a dimension across a parting line is subject to variations from closing the mold, and cores may shift.

Questions

1. What are the advantages of casting as compared with other processes?

2. What characteristics must a mold have?

3. Draw a sketch of a typical mold and name its principal parts.

4. Explain what happens in a casting when it solidifies and cools.

5. How thick or thin should the sections of a casting be?

6. What elements make a good gating system in a mold?

7. What are the three types of gates and their relative advantages?

8. What principles are conducive to an efficient riser in a mold?

9. What are vents and chills?

10. What are some of the hand tools used by molders?

11. Describe how a typical mold is made.

12. Describe the principles of operation of the three general types of molding machines.

13. What are the seven essential properties of a core?

14. What are chaplets and anchors?

15. Why and how are cores baked?

16. What are the two main types of patterns, and how do they compare?

17. Of what materials are patterns made, and what are the advantages of each material?

18. What is shrinkage allowance, and how is it provided for in a pattern?

19. What is machining allowance, and how is it designated?

20. What is draft on a pattern and what is its purpose?

21. What are fillets and what do they do?

22. Why are patterns colored?

23. Why is sand widely used for molding?

24. Describe the three major parts of a molding sand.

25. What are the differences between and relative merits of natural and synthetic molding sands?

26. What are the green permeability, green strength and dry strength of a molding sand, and how do they determine how the sand performs in a mold?

27. What factors affect the green permeability, green strength, and dry strength of a sand and how?

28. How is sand restored to its best condition and prepared for use?

29. What properties must core sand have?

30. Describe a cupola and the way it operates.

31. Describe the crucible type furnaces for melting nonferrous metals.

32. What are the difficulties in melting and pouring aluminum and how are they overcome?

33. Why and how is vacuum melting done?

34. Discuss foundry procedure from the time the mold is made until a finished casting is obtained.

35. How is shell molding done?

36. What are the advantages and disadvantages of shell molding?

37. What are the constituents of cast iron and how do they vary in gray, white, malleable, and nodular cast irons?

38. What are the effects on cast iron of: (a) silicon, (b) sulfur, (c) phosphorous, (d) manganese, (e) nickel, (f) chromium, (g) molybdenum, (h) copper, and (i) vanadium?

39. How do gray iron, malleable iron, and cast steel compare as to properties, costs, and applications?

40. Summarize the principles of design of castings in regards to section thickness, draft, allowances, and tolerances.

Problems

1. A sand core in a mold has a volume of 100 cu inches. What is the buoyant force on the core if the metal poured in the mold is (a) brass or bronze, (b) aluminum, (c) steel, or (d) cast iron?

2. In addition to the items listed in Table 8–4, a foundry has in its yard ample supplies of steel scrap that averages 0.05 silicon, 0.50 manganese, 0.05 phosphorous, and 0.05 sulfur, all in per cent. Also available is No. 1 machinery scrap that contains 1.9 silicon, 0.6 manganese, 0.405 phosphorous, and 0.085 sulfur in per cent. The carbon is not considered. The iron to coke ratio is 8:1, with 0.5% sulfur in the coke of which 5% is added to the iron. Calculate the composition of the cast iron resulting from the following charges:

    (a) 60% No. 1 machinery scrap, 25% steel scrap and 15% No. 1 pig iron in a 2000 lb charge.

    (b) 20% No. 1 machinery scrap, 5% steel scrap, 15% No. 1 pig iron, 10% No. 2 pig iron, 40% cast iron scrap, and 10% returns in a 10,000 lb charge.

References

Cast Metals Handbook, American Foundrymen's Association, Chicago.

Morris, Joe L., *Metal Castings*, Prentice-Hall, Inc., Englewood Cliffs, N. J., 1957.

Fig. 9–1. An automatic permanent mold casting machine for making pistons. (Courtesy Aluminum Co. of America.)

monly cast in this way are lead, zinc, aluminum, and magnesium alloys, certain bronzes, and cast iron. Typical products are refrigerator compressor cylinder blocks, heads, and connecting rods, flat iron sole plates, and washing machine gear blanks of cast iron and automotive pistons and cylinder heads, kitchenware, and typewriter parts of aluminum. Castings range in weight from a few ounces to 300 lb and even more, with most under 50 lb.

Most permanent molds are made of a close-grain alloy cast iron, such as Meehanite, that is resistant to heat and repeated changes in temperature. Bronze molds are used for lead, tin, and zinc, and wrought alloy steel molds for some bronzes. Cores are usually made of alloy steel but may be sand or plaster for severe service. Molds and cores are washed with an adhesive refractory slurry, basically graphite, clay, or whiting. This helps keep the castings from sticking, promotes easy ejection, and prolongs die life. Mold life may run from 3000 to 10,000 iron castings to as many as 100,000 pieces of softer metal.

With sand cores, the process is called *semi-permanent mold casting*. Sand cores are cheap, but the structure, accuracy, and surface finish of the cored openings are only as good as those of sand castings.

Permanent mold casting is often done manually but is readily adaptable to mechanization. One type of machine is illustrated in Fig. 9–1. A machine generally transfers the molds through several stations for ejection of castings, cleaning and coating the mold, placing of cores, locking, pouring, cooling, and unlocking. Some or all of the functions may be performed automatically as needed.

Slush casting. Molten metal is poured into a metal mold. After the skin has frozen, the mold is turned upside down or slung to remove the metal still liquid. The thin shell that is left is called a slush casting. Toys and ornaments are made in this way from zinc, lead, or tin alloys.

A slush casting is usually bright and well suited for plating but is weaker and takes longer to make than a die casting. Die costs are relatively low for slush castings, and that is an advantage for small quantity production.

Fig. 9–2. A cross section of a die casting operation showing how it is done. (Courtesy New Jersey Zinc Co.)

Die casting. Molten metal is forced under considerable pressure into a steel mold or die in the die casting process. The action that takes place is depicted in a cross section of a die in Fig. 9–2. The molten metal is shot through a runner and gate to fill the die. Vents and overflow wells are provided for escape of air. The metal is pressed into all the crevices of the die, and the pressure is held while the metal freezes to ensure density. Many dies are water cooled to hasten freezing. After the metal has solidified, the die is pulled open, and the part is ejected by pins actuated by a mechanism in the manner indicated in Fig. 9–2. The product is called a *die casting*.

Metals and their alloys that are die cast in the order of their importance are zinc, aluminum, magnesium, copper, lead, and tin. Zinc alloys, described in Chap. 7, are popular because they have good strength and ductility and great resistance to shock at normal temperatures. As shortcomings, they have low creep strength, become increasingly brittle at decreasing temperatures, and corrode appreciably in some environments. Zinc alloys cast well; in thinner sections, with sharper outlines, to closer dimensions, at lower die cost, and more rapidly than other commercial die casting alloys. They can be plated easily for protection as well as decoration. Zinc costs about $75 per cu ft as compared with about $50 per cu ft for aluminum and $40 per cu ft for magnesium. Even so zinc castings can be made with less metal in thinner sections and faster and more cheaply than the others. Other metals are used for properties not furnished by zinc. A comparison of several metals for die casting is made in Table 9–1.

TABLE 9–1. TYPICAL PROPERTIES OF DIE CASTING METALS

Type	Tensile strength (psi)	Yield strength at 0.2% offset (psi)	Elonga- tion (%)	Charpy impact (ft. lb)	Brinnel hardness number	Density (lb/cu in.)
Zinc alloy (1)	40,000 to 45,000	. . .	3 to 5	20	75 to 85	0.26
Aluminum alloy	30,000 to 40,000	14,000 to 24,000	2 to 6	2 to 10	60 to 80	0.098
Magnesium alloy	30,000 to 33,000	21,000	1 to 3	1 to 2	60 to 65	0.063
Brass (2)	45,000 to 60,000	25,000 to 30,000	10 to 15	15	120 to 130	0.30

The strengths indicated are only for standard test specimens and not necessarily for die cast sections.

(1) The properties of the zinc alloy are as cast. Some decrease in tensile and yield strength may be expected after prolonged indoor aging with slight increase in elongation. Impact strength decreases markedly at low temperatures.

(2) Some special brass alloys may have tensile strengths up to 90,000 psi, yield strength of 60,000 psi, and elongation of 8%.

Aluminum offers lightness, service at a wide range of operating temperatures, and good resistance to corrosion in die castings. A number of alloys with a choice of properties are available. They are recommended particularly for contact with food and fruit acids.

Magnesium alloys are particularly light and fairly corrosive resistant but are badly attacked by humid tropical climate and sea water.

Brass alloys have the most strength but are not often die cast because their high melting point is damaging to the dies. Thus the cost of brass die castings is relatively high, and they are used only when die castings of other metals are not suitable and where enough can be saved in production and machining costs over sand or plaster castings to make up for the die costs.

The automobile industry uses a high percentage of all die castings. An average automobile may have from 50 to 150 lb of die cast parts. Typical parts are found in the speedometer, windshield wiper motor, horn, grill work, and decorations. The aircraft industry also utilizes many die castings, mostly of aluminum and magnesium for lightness. Other die cast parts are found in telephone hand sets, household appliances, business machines, bathroom hardware, outboard motors, clocks, jewelry, locks, pulleys, etc.

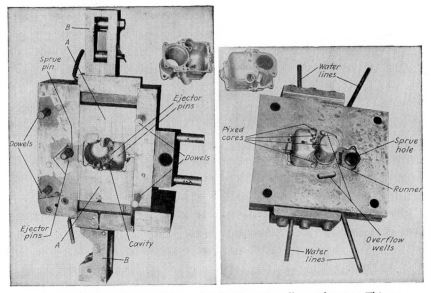

Fig. 9–3. The two halves of a die for a zinc alloy carburetor. This complex die has two slides marked A to form the side walls and undercuts between the flanges of the part. The slide operating and locking mechanisms are marked B. Several movable core pins, not readily discernible, are provided for angular holes. (Courtesy New Jersey Zinc Co.)

Die casting dies. Dies must be massive and strong to withstand the large loads imposed on them by die casting. A die is normally made in two parts like the one in Fig. 9–3. One called the *front cover portion* is mounted on a stationary platen and receives the molten metal from an injection nozzle of the machine. The other is the *ejector portion* and is carried on a movable platen toward and away from the front cover to open and close the die. The two portions are aligned by the machine and by their own dowel pins. The two portions meet at the parting line and are locked together by the machine-locking mechanism when closed.

A die is always made so that the casting shrinks in cooling onto projections and core pins attached to the ejector portion. Thus when the die is opened, the part clings to the movable portion, is drawn away from the cover portion, and can then be ejected into the opening between the die halves. There it falls clear or is picked up by tongs.

Dies for complicated parts with undercuts, recesses, and angular holes are equipped with slides and movable core pins, like the one in Fig. 9–3. Such construction is expensive but frequently makes possible the production of parts that could not otherwise be die cast. Movable cores and slides are arranged to be withdrawn before the die is opened.

Dies are of single-cavity, multiple-cavity, combination, and unit types. A *single-cavity die* turns out only one casting for each cycle of an operation. For large quantity production of small and moderate size pieces, a number of cavities may be sunk in a single die and be gated from a common sprue so that several castings are made at once. This is a *multiple-cavity die*. If the cavities are of two or more different shapes and produce as many different parts at one time, the die is called a *combination die*. A *unit die* consists of a die holder in which several die elements may be placed and filled at the same time. Any of the units may be blocked off to regulate the quantity cast of each part.

The steel needed for a die depends upon the operating conditions such as temperature, metal, etc. For die casting zinc alloys at 750° to 800°F, ordinary low-alloy tool steels are satisfactory. That material may be heat treated. Heat-resistant chromium and/or tungsten steels are recommended for higher temperatures.

The design of die casting dies is largely an art. It is difficult to predict how efficiently a die will function except by comparison with past experience. Commonly dies must be modified after being first made to make them perform properly.

Die casting machines. The two basic types of die casting machines are the *hot chamber,* exemplified here by the *gooseneck machine,* and the *cold chamber machines.*

Figure 9–4(A) shows a typical gooseneck die casting machine mechanism. The gooseneck contains a cylinder and curved passageway immersed in a pot of molten metal. When the plunger is retracted, the gooseneck fills with metal. When the die is closed, the air cylinder actuates the plunger to force the metal through the gooseneck and nozzle into the die. Machines like this are more or less automatic and are fast, but the gooseneck can safely stand only an injection pressure of less than 6000 psi at operating temperatures. Zinc alloys can be injected satisfactorily at 1500 psi but higher pressures for zinc and other metals are desirable for the utmost density, strength, and serviceability in die castings.

A gooseneck machine is at a disadvantage for casting aluminum.

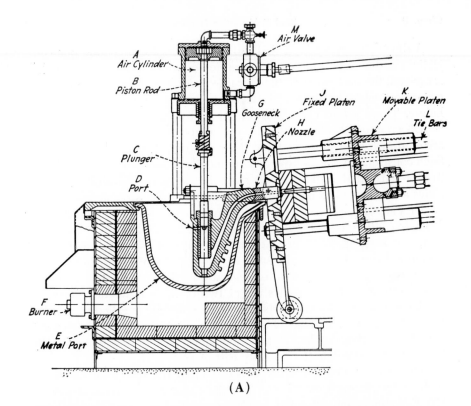

(A)

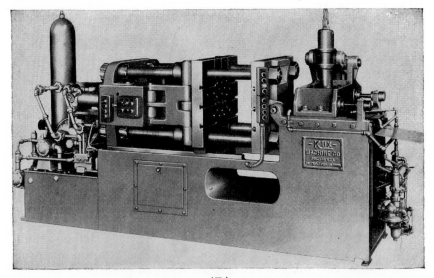

(B)

Fig. 9–4. (A) A diagram of the mechanism of a gooseneck type hot chamber die casting machine. (Courtesy New Jersey Zinc Co.) (B) A picture of a gooseneck type die casting machine without dies. (Courtesy Kux Machine Co.)

180

Aluminum, at melting temperature in constant contact with a ferrous gooseneck, picks up enough iron to impair its properties.

The metal needed for each shot is ladled from a separate furnace or pot into a cold chamber machine as indicated in Fig. 9–5. A plunger is driven by air or hydraulic pressure to force the charge into the die. Injection pressures are available from 4000 to 35,000 psi.

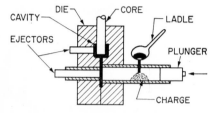

Fig. 9–5. The principle of operation of a cold chamber die casting machine.

High pressures can give, but alone do not assure superior die castings. Selection and control of the material, design of the die, and timing and conduct of the operation must be done expertly to take most advantage of the opportunity.

For safety and efficiency, the operator usually starts a cycle of the machine, and the subsequent steps are carried out automatically. Functions are interlocked to avoid spoiling the part, damaging the machine, or spilling metal. Injection of the metal and ejection of the workpiece are related to the closing and opening of the die. Dies are closed and locked by various mechanisms, but a common device is a toggle, like the one on the machine in Fig. 9–4(B).

One way of rating a machine is by the locking force in tons that keeps the dies closed. Another rating specifies the dimensions of the platens inside the bars. This designates the space to take the die. The cross-sectional area of the die cavity times the injection pressure must have a value less than the locking force of the press.

One manufacturer of die casting machines makes gooseneck models rated from 25 to 750 tons capacity and cold chamber machines from 100 to 1000 tons capacity. As an example, a 600 ton cold chamber machine has a die space of 20½ in. by 26½ in. between the tie rods and takes dies up to 24 in. thick. It can inject a charge of 2¾ lb of aluminum at 20,000 psi and as much as 14 lb at 2000 psi. It is operated by a 25 hp motor, weighs 29,000 lb, and costs over $30,000. A melting furnace and other accessories cost an additional $10,000 or more.

Finishing die castings. Liquid metal forced into a die cavity under high pressure intrudes into parting face joints, around ejector pins, into overflow wells, and through any cracks. Clearances in dies are held as small as practicable, and the metal in the cracks solidifies into thin and fragile extrusions called *flash*. The flash as well as sprues, runners, etc. must be removed to finish a casting. In large scale production of a suitably shaped piece, the flash can be removed quickly in a shaving die in a press. For small production runs, the excess metal may be broken off by hand and the edges cleaned by filing, buffing, etc.

Dimensions can be held closely enough by die casting for most purposes, and only a minimum of machining is usually necessary. Some surfaces, like threads in small holes, may be more easily machined than cast. Machining of die castings is no different from machining other objects of the same materials and is governed by the principles presented in the chapters in this book on metal machining.

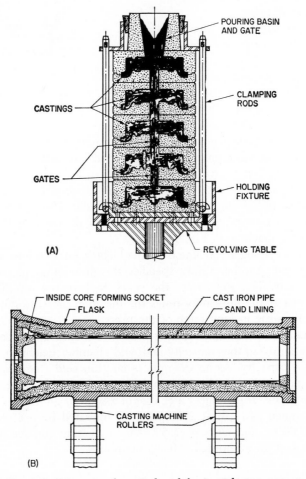

POURING BASIN
AND GATE

CLAMPING
RODS

CASTINGS

GATES

HOLDING
FIXTURE

(A)   REVOLVING TABLE

INSIDE CORE FORMING SOCKET   CAST IRON PIPE
FLASK   SAND LINING

CASTING MACHINE
ROLLERS

(B)

Fig. 9–6. Diagrams of vertical and horizontal arrangements for centrifugal casting. The vertical set-up is for a stack of track wheels; the horizontal for cast iron pipe. (Courtesy American Cast Iron Pipe Co.)

Centrifugal casting. Centrifugal casting is done by pouring molten metal into a revolving mold. Centrifugal force creates pressure far in excess of gravity to cram the metal into the mold. For instance, an aluminum alloy spun at 2600 rpm is subjected to a pressure of 32 psi at about 4 in. diameter and more at larger diameters. This is better than feeding a static casting with a head of 26 ft.

Centrifugal casting produces good quality and accurate castings, drives off impurities, and saves material. The castings are dense and have a fine-grained structure with uniform and high physical properties and are less subject to directional variations than static castings. Metal flows readily into thin sections, and castings come out with fine outside surface detail. Gases and impurities are squeezed out, particularly near the periphery. Inclusions, oxides, and slag are displaced by the heavier metal and dispelled to float on top toward the center. Gates and risers are not needed to supply a pressure head and may be few and stubby. Waste metal in these appendages may be almost eliminated. This has been found to mean a saving of 40% and more in metal poured.

All the common metals may be centrifugally cast in either refractory or metal molds. Rotation about a vertical axis is fast and relatively easy to do. The hole inside fluid metal rotated in that way becomes shaped like a paraboloid small at the bottom. For a straight hole, a long piece is rotated about a horizontal axis as depicted in Fig. 9–6.

True centrifugal casting in which a piece is rotated about an axis is best suited for ring- or tube-shaped pieces with straight walls. The outside surfaces may be round, square, hexagonal, etc. and should be concentric with the hole. Round holes may be formed without cores, and that may save appreciable expense for large holes, but holes of other shapes need to be cored. Sometimes bosses may be cast on the perimeter if not too thin or high. Centrifugal castings without holes, like the track wheels in Fig. 9–6, are apt to be porous and weak and contain inclusions at their centers. In the case shown, a hole is later drilled and bored through the center of each part.

Parts not symmetrical about any axis of rotation may be cast in a group of molds arranged in a circle to balance each other. The set-up is revolved around the center of the circle to induce pressure in the molds. This is called *centrifuge casting.*

Comparison of metal mold casting methods. Almost any metal or shape or size of piece, except intricate pieces, can be sand cast, but some cannot be cast in metal molds. Some compositions are too weak at solidifying temperatures or shrink too much to avoid cracking up around the unyielding projections in a metal mold. Some metals melt at temperatures that are damaging to metal molds. Some parts are too complex for metal molds to be practical.

Parts that can be cast in metal molds are stronger, have better surface appearance, can be held to smaller tolerances, can be made with thinner sections, and require less machining than equivalent sand castings. A comparison of the major casting processes in these respects is made in Table 9–2. In general, properties are best in parts cast in metal molds under pressure. Sometimes only one process gives the required results, but usually a process is selected because it gives the desired results at the lowest costs.

TABLE 9–2. A Comparison of Casting Methods

Factor	Type of Casting Process			
	Sand	Permanent mold	Die	Centrifugal (or Centrifuge)
Metals processed	all	nonferrous and cast iron	nonferrous (low melting point)	all
Commercial sizes, min. max.	largest	½ lb 300 lb	minute 75 lb in aluminum 300 lb in zinc	over 25 tons
Commercial surface finish (rms)	300–600	150–500	20–125	20–300 (d)
Tolerance (first in., per in.)	$\frac{1}{16}$	$\frac{1}{64}$	0.006	0.010 (d)
Porosity (a)	4	3	2	1
Minimum section thickness (in.)	$\frac{1}{8}$–$\frac{3}{16}$	$\frac{1}{8}$	$\frac{1}{32}$–$\frac{1}{16}$	$\frac{1}{16}$
Tensile strength, (psi) (b)	19,000	23,000	28,000	25,000 (d)
Prod. rate (pcs per hr) (c)	10–15	40–60	120–150	30–50
Mold or pattern cost (dollars) (c)	300	2,000	5,000	1,500
Scrap loss	1	2	3	4

(a) 1 is least porous and 4 most porous.
(b) For No. 43 F Aluminum alloy as example.
(c) Production and tool cost figures are for a 3 lb aluminum casting of moderate complexity.
(d) In metal molds.

As shown in Table 9–2, tools cost most for die casting and lesser amounts for the other processes. Also, the rate of production decreases and the scrap loss increases in much the same order. Sand casting is usually cheapest for a few parts; the other processes for larger quantities. The relationships are different for each case. Two examples are illustrated in Fig. 9–7. The part at the top may be made adequately either by die casting or centrifugal permanent mold casting. For both processes, the cost per piece decreases as the quantity increases, but the centrifugal casting process continues to hold the advantage. For the part below, the choice is between permanent mold casting and die casting. The higher cost of tools makes die casting more expensive for small quantities, but the higher production rate more than offsets the tool cost for large quantities, and then die casting is cheaper.

Metal mold castings are even at times competitive with other processes with which sand castings are at a disadvantage. They have been found adequate to replace forgings and at less cost. They may be cheaper than some drawn parts that require multiple operations. Metal mold castings have even been proven more economical than some parts turned out on automatic bar machines where considerable metal was lost in chips.

Designing castings for metal molds. The same principles that point the way to good castings of all kinds apply to metal mold castings. All metals shrink on cooling, and allowance must be made accordingly in the mold dimensions.

The walls and sections of a casting should be as nearly as possible of the same thickness for uniformity in filling of the mold and cooling of the metal. Where differences in thickness of sections are necessary, the transition from thick to thin should be gradual and not abrupt.

Sections generally can be made thinner in metal mold than in sand castings, and the thinnest sections are feasible in the pressure-casting processes. Thin sections often mean a saving in metal.

Metal mold castings must have more draft than sand castings. Inside surfaces must be given about twice as much draft as outside surfaces because they shrink on their cores as they cool.

Generous fillets and adequate ribs add strength and stamina to a casting. Slightly curved surfaces are easier to cast than large flat areas.

Less stock needs to be allowed for finishing metal mold castings than for sand castings. From $\frac{1}{32}$ to $\frac{1}{8}$ in. stock, depending on size, is recommended for permanent mold castings. Die castings require little or no machining for most applications. Stock removal should be avoided or minimized because about $\frac{1}{32}$ in. of the cast surface next to the mold wall is most chilled and thus is the densest part of a metal mold casting.

The parting line is an important factor in the costs of making and operating a metal mold. The line should lie as much as possible in one plane for lowest costs. Flash can be expected to occur along the parting line and can be removed most readily without defacement if the line is

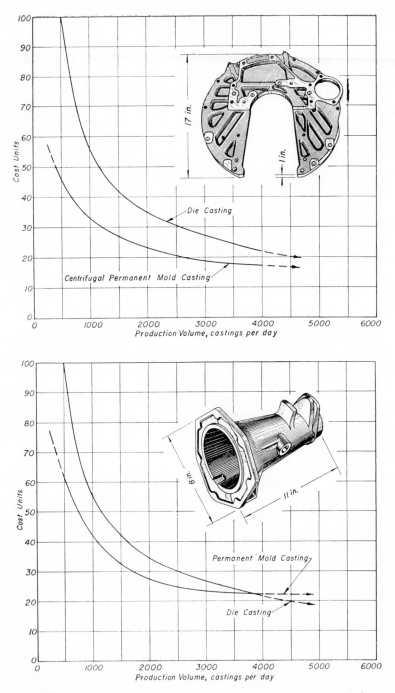

Fig. 9–7. Cost comparisons of casting processes. (From *Metals Handbook, 1955 Supplement,* by permission of the American Society for Metals.)

located on a bead or along the edge of a flange instead of across a flat surface.

Some indication has been given in this text of practicable dimensions such as for section thicknesses, stock allowance, etc. for metal mold castings. Detailed specifications to guide the designer in these respects are furnished in reference- and hand-books.

PLASTER MOLD CASTING

Castings are made from nonferrous metals that melt below 2100°F in disposable or semi-permanent plaster molds or in metal molds with plaster cores. The basic mold material is the hemihydrate calcium sulfate called *plaster of Paris* to which may be added fibrous talc, silica sand, hardening accelerators, substances to deter expansion, and other additives. When calcium sulfate is combined with the proper amount of water, it is converted to the dihydrate compound and sets to a hardened mass. This happens because interlacing crystals are produced by the following reaction:

$$(CaSO_4)_2 \cdot H_2O + 3H_2O \rightarrow 2(CaSO_4 \cdot 2H_2O)$$

The plaster slurry is poured over a pattern in a flask or into a core box and allowed to harden. The mold is dried to remove water and prevent the formation of steam upon exposure to hot metal. Plaster cores are shown in Fig. 9–8 being assembled into a metal mold for a torque converter casting.

Plaster mold casting was at a disadvantage until ways were found to make the plaster permeable so that gases could escape from the mold. The method that gives most porosity is to add the plaster slurry to an agent that is first beaten to a foam. The mold is dried below 400°F. The walls of the bubbles break as the plaster sets.

Metals commonly cast in plaster molds are yellow brass, manganese and aluminum bronzes, aluminum, and magnesium and their alloys. Alloys high in lead are avoided because reaction of that metal with the sulfate has been found detrimental in some cases. Typical products are aircraft parts, plumbing fixture fittings, aluminum pistons, locks, propellers, and ornaments.

Plaster molds have low heat conductivity and provide slow and uniform cooling. Castings can be made in intricate shapes with varying sections and particularly with extremely thin walls. Most satisfactory section thicknesses are from $\frac{1}{16}$ to $\frac{1}{4}$ in. Inherent slow cooling precludes chilling and is conducive to a coarse-grain structure. As a result, some but not all metals cast in plaster molds have less strength than if cast in sand or metal molds. This may amount to as much as a 25% loss in strength for some aluminum alloys, but less in other cases.

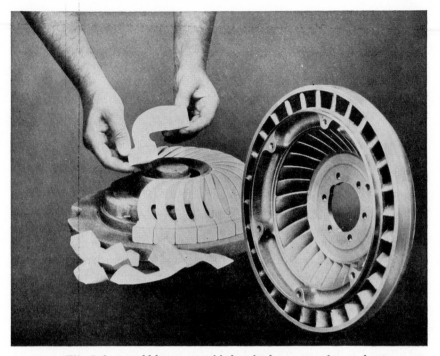

Fig. 9–8. A mold being assembled with plaster cores for an aluminum torque converter casting. (Courtesy Aluminum Company of America.)

Plaster molding material is yielding enough not to restrain the cast metal when it cools and shrinks. The weakness of the plaster limits commercial sizes of castings. Most weigh from a few ounces to around 20 lb, but some of over 100 lb have been cast.

Patterns and core boxes for plaster molds are made of yellow brass and of phenolic resin plastic. The equipment requires more care to achieve the accuracy and finish of which the process is capable and costs about 50% more than corresponding equipment for sand casting. As an average, plaster mold castings have been estimated to cost about three times as much as sand castings. However, plaster mold casting can give more accuracy, smoother surfaces, and more faithful reproduction of detail. In some cases it is the means of eliminating machining or finishing operations required for sand casting. Tolerances may be held to ±0.005 in. per in. on one side and ±0.010 in. across parting lines. Surface finish from 30 to 125 microinches, rms, can be expected.

Under some conditions plaster mold casting is preferable to metal mold casting; in many cases not. Accuracy and finish produced by the two methods are comparable. Operation cost with plaster molds is generally higher than with metal molds. On the other hand, the patterns for plaster molds may cost less than metal molds, and the overall cost then may be lower for plaster mold casting for small quantities. Plaster mold casting is of particular advantage for the nonferrous metals that melt at higher temperatures and are hard on metal molds. Upkeep may be enough less in such cases to give the cost advantage to plaster mold casting, even for large quantities. This explains why metal mold cores, which are even more exposed to heat than the molds, are often made of plaster.

PRECISION INVESTMENT CASTING

Lost wax process. An ancient process for making precision castings utilizes an expendable pattern of wax or plastic material. For duplication of parts the pattern is injected or molded in a die of rubber, plaster, or wood but generally of metal for quantity production. Pieces of a pattern may be joined together by heat or adhesive. In this way gates, risers, etc. are ordinarily added. The patterns for a number of pieces may be joined together in a cluster for economical production. Quite complex parts and even whole assemblies may be fabricated by joining components together in the pattern stage rather than by assembly of finished pieces after casting.

A mold is invested around the pattern in the next step. The molding material is basically a refractory silica, commonly sand. For temperatures not over about 2000°F, a plaster binding agent is adequate. For higher temperatures, the binding agent is usually an organic silica compound. One method is to dip the pattern into a series of slurries to build up a layered shell ⅛ to ¼ in. thick of successively coarser grains. The fine grains at the inside surfaces of the mold impart a fine surface finish to the casting. Another method is to fix the pattern to a plate in a flask and pour molding compound around it. Commonly the mold is vibrated when filled to settle the material and drive out air bubbles. A third method is a combination of the other two; applying several coats to the pattern by dipping and then filling a mold.

After the mold has cured for from minutes to hours, depending on the material, it is placed in a furnace at up to 2000°F to bake and melt or volatize the wax or plastic pattern. Carefully melted metal is poured into the mold and may be subjected to pressure from compressed air or centrifugal force. One technique is to draw a vacuum from beneath a mold to pull out gases and concentrate atmospheric pressure on the metal. After the casting has cooled, the mold is broken, cores are shaken out, and sprues and irregularities are cut off or ground away.

The Mercast process. An important precision investment casting process starts with a pattern of frozen mercury made in the manner depicted

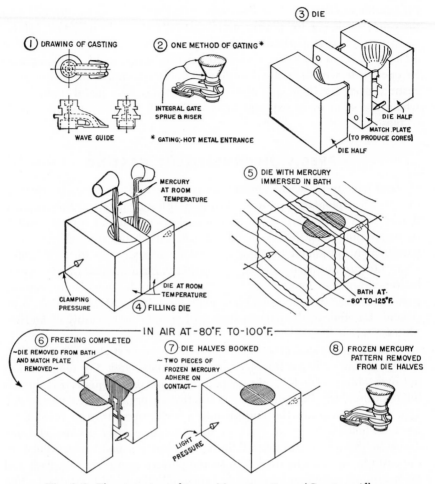

Fig. 9–9. The steps in making a Mercast pattern. (Courtesy Alloys Precision Castings Co.)

by Fig. 9–9. Mercury is a desirable pattern material because its volumetric change on melting is small and it has a high rate of solid diffusion. The low volume change permits fabrication of larger castings and thin shell molds because the pressure to crack the mold is small compared with wax or plastic when the pattern is purged from the mold. A thin shell mold provides for more rapid cooling and better physical properties for the casting. A high rate of solid diffusion is the reason pieces stick together readily on contact as stated in view 7 of Fig. 9–9. By that means cavities difficult to put into a whole piece can be formed easily in the parts of the pattern before they are joined.

In the Mercast process, the mercury pattern is dipped into a series of ceramic slurries maintained well below the freezing point of the mercury to form a shell. After the shell has been built up and dried, the pattern is flushed from the investment by a stream of room temperature mercury. The mold is fired at 1850°F for two hours. It then resembles unglazed porcelain, is porous, and has a smooth finish in the cavity. The ceramic shell is packed in a flask with coarse sand or shot for support. Some molds may be preheated, others are not. Casting may be done by gravity alone or by centrifugal or pneumatic means.

Merits of precision investment casting. All common metals and alloys can be cast by one method or another of precision investment casting. For ages the process has been used for tooth fillings, surgical instruments, and jewelry. Typical products in present day industry include buckets, vanes, and blades for gas turbines, reciprocating slides for cloth-cutting machines, pawls and claws for movie camera projectors, fuel parts for aviation carburetors, and airborne radar wave guides.

Investment casting is too expensive for parts that can be made readily by other processes. It is not competitive with metal mold and die casting for low melting point alloys except for quite small quantities or complex parts. It is economical for metals that melt at temperatures too high for metal or plaster molds and in parts with requirements, such as for small tolerances, that cannot be met by sand casting. Some complicated parts are difficult and expensive to machine, form, cast by other methods, or produce by powder metallurgy, and can be made most cheaply by investment casting. As an example, it is sometimes cheaper to cast a whole assembly by the investment process than to assemble it from a number of parts as would be required if made by other processes.

Investment casting is comparable with shell molding in the variety of metals that it can handle and in tolerances and surface finish. As a rule, shell molding is more economical for simpler parts in larger sizes, and investment casting for complex pieces, particularly in small sizes. Most investment castings weigh from a few ounces to around 5 pounds, although some have been made as heavy as 26 pounds. Sections are limited to about one inch in thickness, but extra-thin or -thick sections should be avoided.

Tolerances as small as 0.002 in. are held by investment casting, but usually at extra cost. Commercial tolerances normally are around ±0.005 in. per in. Investment casting has an advantage tolerance-wise because draft largely may be eliminated and the mold does not have a parting face, across which dimensions vary appreciably in other casting processes. Commercial surface finishes range from 60 to 220 microinches, rms.

CONTINUOUS CASTING

Continuous casting consists of pouring molten metal into one end of a metal mold open at both ends, cooling rapidly, and extracting the solid product in a continuous length from the other end. This is done with copper, brass, bronze, aluminum, and, to a lesser extent, cast iron and steel.

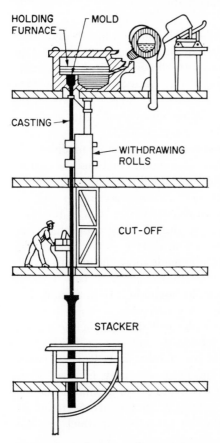

Fig. 9–10. A diagram of a continuous casting process.

A number of processes differing in detail are in operation for continuous casting. The problems are somewhat different for various metals and higher and lower temperatures. A successful and productive method, called the Asarco process, for copper base alloys is depicted in Fig. 9–10. The mold or die extends into the holding furnace. Metal flows into the mold from below the surface of the charge in the furnace to guard against impurities. A tortuous path is provided for the flow of the metal in the furnace to protect the mold from sloshing effects during pouring. The lower part of the mold is jacketed and freezes the metal rapidly. The solidified casting is pulled from the mold at a controlled speed by the withdrawing rolls. Some arrangements employ vibrating or reciprocating molds. Finally the product is cut to desired lengths by saw or torch.

A typical producer casts copper base alloys in diameters from $1\frac{3}{32}$ in. to $9\frac{1}{8}$ in. and in lengths up to 16 ft but standard at 12 ft. Shapes may be round, square, rectangular, hexagonal, fluted, scalloped, gear toothed, and in many other forms of cross section. Castings may be made hollow.

Continuous casting offers definite advantages for some applications. In the case of individual ingots cast for rolling, an appreciable part of the end of each ingot must be cut off and returned to the furnace because it is porous, unsound, and full of impurities. This waste is practically eliminated by the uniformity of continuous castings. The result is a higher yield from a given amount of molten metal and a lower capital cost for each ton-year of production. Also, the uniformity and purity of the product makes it possible to prepare pieces suitable for rolling that are smaller than ingots cast individually for the same purpose. The smaller pieces can be rolled more easily and cheaply.

For some applications, continuously cast shapes can be cut to lengths to produce finished products with few operations. For one example, bronze bushings are cut to standard lengths and finished by light inside and outside cuts. In another case, cast fluted bars are cut to length and pump gears completed by two light cuts on the teeth.

Questions

1. What is permanent mold casting and where does it serve?

2. What is slush casting?

3. How is die casting done? What are its advantages?

4. Describe a typical die casting machine and point out its necessary force relationships.

5. What is centrifugal casting and what does it offer?

6. What is the difference between centrifugal casting and centrifuge casting?

7. Should the axis of revolution for a centrifugal casting be horizontal or vertical?

8. How do die, permanent mold, centrifugal and sand casting compare as to what they can do and as to cost?

9. How much stock should be allowed for finishing metal mold castings?

10. What conditions make satisfactory plaster molds for castings?

11. How does plaster mold casting compare with sand casting?

12. How does plaster mold casting compare with metal mold casting?

13. How is precision investment casting done and what are its advantages?

14. What are the advantages of the Mercast process?

15. What is continuous casting, and what advantages does it offer?

Problems

1. A single gear blank 8 in. in diameter is to be die cast from zinc at 2000 psi pressure. What should be the capacity of the machine in tons of locking force?

2. When a casting is centrifuged at n rpm around a minimum diameter D,

CHAPTER 9

Hard Mold Casting Processes

Casting in sand molds as described in Chap. 8 gives sufficient results at lowest cost in many cases. Other casting processes that produce more uniformly, more precisely, or at lower costs in some cases will be described in this chapter. One group utilizes metal molds that are not destroyed in service as sand molds are, but can be used over and over again. Where metal molds are not adequate, precision casting is done in plaster and ceramic molds. Another group of processes casts metal continuously rather than in individual pieces.

METAL MOLD CASTING PROCESSES

Processes that use metal molds are permanent mold and die casting. Although applied to other kinds of molds also, centrifugal casting is often done with metal molds and will be included in this section.

Casting in metal molds is confined practically to metals with low to moderate melting temperatures. Metals like steel with high melting points are too hard on metal molds.

Permanent mold casting. When fluid metal is poured into metal molds and subjected only to hydrostatic pressure, the process is called *permanent mold casting.* The mold separates into two or more pieces to release the casting when solidified and is held together during the operation by C-clamps, screws, toggles, or other mechanisms. Metals com-

show that the minimum accelerating force in lb per lb imposed on the casting is $A = a/g = 1.42 \times 10^{-5}Dn^2$, where a is the centrifugal acceleration of the casting in ft per sec per sec and g is the accelerator of gravity in the same dimensions.

3. Common practice with iron and copper base alloys is to centrifuge their castings to impose accelerating forces from 40g to 60g lb per lb. This gives good castings without damage to the molds. In one operation the molds are arranged around a 14 in.-diameter. At what speed should the centrifuge be rotated? Refer to the equation in Prob. 2.

4. A full circular disk of unit thickness of molten metal of density γ lb per cu in. is rotated around its axis to make a centrifugal casting. Show that at n rpm the pressure in psi from the centrifugal action at any radius of r in. is $P = 1.42 \times 10^{-5}\gamma \, n^2r^2$.

5. Experience has shown that a good centrifugal casting is obtained from aluminum or magnesium if it is rotated at sufficient speed to create a pressure of 30 to 35 psi on its periphery. It is assumed that casting is continuous from its center of gravity, about which it is rotated, to its periphery. The conditions are those stated in Prob. 4.

    (a) At what speed should a 20 in.-diameter symmetrical aluminum casting be rotated?

    (b) At what speed should a 16 in.-diameter symmetrical magnesium casting be rotated?

6. A cast iron pipe 36 in. in diameter with a one in. wall thickness is centrifugally cast and rotated at sufficient speed to set up an accelerating force of 60 g on its periphery. At what speed is it rotated? Make use of and modify the equations of Probs. 2 and 4 to find what the peripheral pressure is in the casting in psi.

7. A three pound aluminum casting for which data is given in Table 9–2 can be made satisfactorily by any of the processes listed in that table. The cost of labor and overhead is $8.00 per hr. Assume top production rate and the same set-up time for all processes. What process should be selected for each of the following numbers of pieces?

    (a) 1   (b) 100   (c) 1000   (d) 3000   (e) 5000   (f) 10,000
    (g) 20,000   (h) 30,000   (i) 40,000   (j) 50,000   (k) 100,000.

8. For the conditions stated in Prob. 7, what range of production quantities is most economical for each of the following processes?

    (a) sand casting   (b) permanent mold casting   (c) centrifugal casting (with metal mold)   (d) die casting.

References

A.S.T.E., *Tool Engineers Handbook*, McGraw-Hill Book Co., Inc., New York.

Metals Handbook, American Society for Metals, Cleveland.

Morris, Joe L., *Metal Casting*, Prentice-Hall, Inc., Englewood Cliffs, N.J.

10

Powder Metallurgy

Powder metallurgy is the manufacture of products from finely divided metals and metallic compounds. The powders are loose in some applications and pressed into pieces and parts in others.

Loose powders of metals and their compounds are added to some products. Aluminum and bronze powders are mixed into paints for metallic finishes. Metal powders add strength and wear-resistance to plastics. Metals in powder form in fireworks burn with colorful effects.

The most important and growing applications of powder metallurgy in industry are in the manufacture of pieces and parts. As an example, a modern automobile contains about 70 powder metal parts. Powder metallurgy has achieved this status because it excels in several respects, which are explained in the following paragraphs.

Powder metallurgy is the only feasible means of fabricating some materials. The melting points of the refractory metals, such as tungsten (6098°F), tantalum (5162°F), and molybdenum (4748°F), are so high they are hard to work in appreciable quantities with available equipment. Other substances, such as zirconium (mp 3452°F), react strongly with and are contaminated by their surroundings when melted. Powder metallurgy is a practical way of refining and fabricating such metals. It is also the only feasible way to consolidate and form the superhard tool materials, such as cemented carbides and sintered oxides.

Combinations of metals and non-metals not obtainable economically in other ways can be made by powder metallurgy. This is of particular value to the electrical industry. Motor brushes and contact points must have proper conductivity but be resistant to wear and arcing. Brushes are made from powders of copper, graphite, and sometimes tin and lead; points require combinations like tungsten and copper or silver. Permanent magnets can be made of densely packed and finely dispersed particles of suitable substances and be held to small tolerances. Other examples are clad or duplexed parts such as rods and slugs for nuclear reactors, bimetallic units for thermostats, and coated welding rods.

A class of materials of growing importance made possible by powder metallurgy is known as *cermets*. As the name implies, they are combinations of metals and ceramics, with the strengths of the metals or alloys and the abrasion- and heat-resistances of the metallic compounds, which are the ceramics. One example is Al_2O_3–Cr. Cermets were developed in Germany in World War II for possible jet engine use. That usage was never realized because of their brittleness, but they are finding other important applications. A few examples are in corrosion-resistant chemical apparatus, nuclear energy equipment, pumps for severe services, and systems for handling rocket fuels.

Metal can be made porous by powder metallurgy. Practical applications are bronze, nickel, and stainless steel filter elements, more shock-resistant than ceramic, and bearings, gears, pump rotors, etc., impregnated with lubricants for long carefree life.

Some structural parts for machines and other products can be made most cheaply by powder metallurgy. This is true particularly for iron that melts at too high a temperature to be die cast and must be machined to small tolerances. In some cases parts can be made with adequate strength and accuracy by powder metallurgy more cheaply than they can be machined. Examples are bushings, small gears, valve retainers, brackets, and blocks.

Powder metallurgy encompasses the preparation of the powders and their combination into useful articles. Basically, a powder metal is compacted to the shape desired and heated to strengthen the compact. The actual processes are many and differ to suit the materials treated and obtain the properties required in the finished product. The principles of the processes will be discussed.

Metal powders. What a metal powder will produce depends upon its composition and physical characteristics. The most used compositions are the copper base and iron base powders; brass, iron, and steel for structural parts and bronze for bearings. Others of importance, though in lesser amounts, are stainless steel, aluminum, nickel, tin, tungsten, copper, zirconium, graphite, and metallic oxides and carbides.

Substantially pure metal powders are used for some parts; alloys for others. Alloys may be obtained by alloying a metal before it is powdered or by mixing together powders of the desired ingredients. The first method gives a finer and more uniform alloy. The second is easier to compound but must be sintered with care to assure that the ingredients become diffused.

The physical characteristics of a powder metal are influenced by the way it is made. The chief characteristics are particle size and size distribution, purity, grain structure, density, flow rate, and compressibility. These determine how the powder must be processed to get the required properties in the parts.

Most metal powders are obtained by *reduction* of refined ore, mill scale, or prepared oxides by carbon monoxide or hydrogen as described for sponge iron in Chap. 4. Grains tend to be porous. Particle size can be made quite uniform, which contributes to uniformity in the final product. Crude reduced powder called *sponge iron* is quoted at about $0.11 per lb.

Metals with relatively low melting points, such as aluminum and brass, are often *atomized.* Molten metal is forced through a small orifice and dispersed in a stream of air, steam or inert gas. Grains have a fine dendritic cast structure and form irregular to spherical shapes.

Under controlled conditions metal powder may be *deposited electrolytically.* The material may have to be broken up and is milled or ground for fineness, heated to be annealed and to drive off hydrogen, and sorted and blended. Electrodeposited powders are among the purest. Cost is about $0.36 per lb for electrolytic iron powder and $0.44 per lb for copper.

Milling or *grinding* in ball mills, stampers, crushers, etc. is a means of producing powders of almost any degree of fineness from friable or malleable metals. Tungsten carbide grains are pulverized in this way. Some malleable metals are milled with a lubricant to flakes, which are not suitable for molding but are used in paints and pigments.

Nickel or iron can be made to react with carbon monoxide to form *metal carbonyls* such as $Ni(CO)_4$. These are decomposed to powders of high purity with spherical grains, but the process is expensive.

Shotting is the process of dropping molten particles from a small opening through air or an inert gas into water. This produces spherical particles but not the smallest sizes.

Other methods of making metal powders include ordinary *machining, vapor condensation, chemical precipitation,* and *granulation* by stirring vigorously during solidification. These are used occasionally for special purposes.

Fabrication processes. The basic operations of compacting (or pressing) and heating (or sintering) may be combined in a number of ways in processes for fabricating metal powders. Common processes are depicted in Fig. 10–1. In addition, the operations of pressing and sintering are

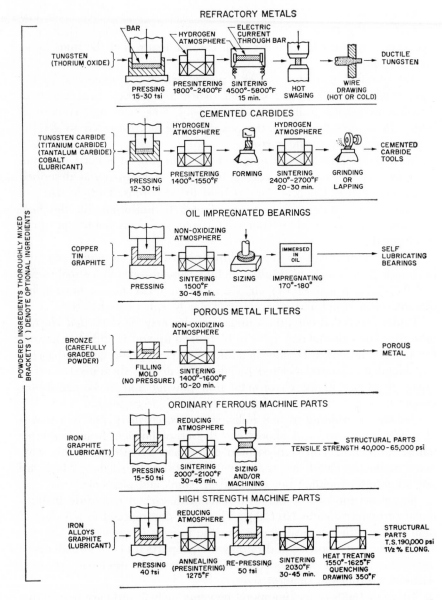

Fig. 10–1. Some typical powder metallurgy processes.

varied and controlled to suit many conditions, and in some cases other operations are added. The basic operations and the principles that govern them will be described in the following sections.

Pressing. The effect of pressure on powder metal is to squeeze the particles together to lock or key them in place, initiate inter-atomic

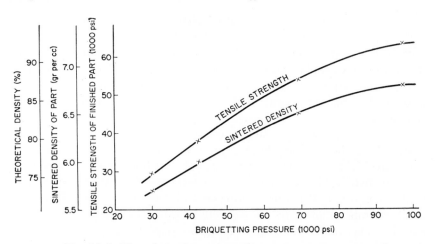

Fig. 10–2. The relationships among briqueting pressure, sintered density, and tensile strength for a carbon-iron powder sintered at 2030° F for 30 min. (as reported by S. R. Crooks.)

bonds, and increase the density of the mass. The pressure applied to a compact determines its ultimate density and strength. A typical case is illustrated in Fig. 10–2. Theoretically if a powder is pressed enough, it will attain 100% of the density and strength of the parent metal, at least on being sintered. This is approached in some parts, in one way by re-pressing after initial pressing and presintering. High pressures, and particularly additional operations, are expensive and not warranted for parts that do not have to have high strength. On the other end of the density scale, little or no pressure is needed for porous parts.

Most parts are pressed cold; only a few hot. Hot-pressing is hard on tools, must be done enclosed in a neutral atmosphere, and is slow.

Suitable particle size and size distribution and careful mixing are prerequisites for obtaining a satisfactory pressed part. A lubricant, such as zinc stearate, is often mixed with the metal powder. It lubricates the compact under pressure but also volatilizes on sintering and helps open and induce continuity among the pores in finished pieces.

Powder metal is commonly compressed in a die cavity of the shape of the part by one or more punches.

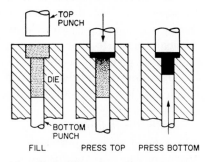

Fig. 10–3. The steps in pressing a simple powder metal part.

Quality depends upon packing the material uniformly. Powder metal does not flow readily around corners and into recesses like a fluid. Friction is high between the particles and walls of the die. Thus, one punch cannot compact any but the simplest parts to a uniform density. Those parts in particular that have steps, thin walls, flanges, etc. must be acted upon by two or more punches to distribute the pressure uniformly through the sections. A simple example is given in Fig. 10–3. The most complex of parts may require as many as two upper and three or four lower punch movements, and even some side core pulling movements. Some parts cannot even be made with available equipment.

Production powder pressing is normally done on presses specifically designed for the purpose. Such a press is rated by the tons of force it can deliver and by the maximum depth of die chamber it can accommodate, in inches. The tonnage rating determines the cross-sectional area of the largest part that can be subjected to a given pressure. The depth of die chamber, called the *die fill*, determines how deep a powder filling may be. This limits the length of a pressed part. The ratio of powder depth to compacted part length is from 2:1 to 3:1 for iron and copper and as high as 8:1 for some materials.

Most presses under 150 tons are mechanical because it is fast. A mechanical press works to uniform size but causes differences in density with variations in conditions such as the amount of charge. A hydraulic press may be set to exert a given pressure for uniform density or to stop at a uniform size. Large powder metal presses are hydraulic, with capacities up to 5000 tons. In intermediate sizes, combination presses are popular for mechanical speed and hydraulic uniformity and high pressure capacity. Presses range from slow single stroke hand-fed models for an output of a few pieces per hour to automatic rotary and multiple punch machines capable of producing hundreds of parts per minute.

Other compacting methods. Powder metal may be *slip cast* in molds. The powder is dispersed in a liquid containing chemicals to wet the particles and keep them from settling non-uniformly. Density is satisfactory for many purposes. Mold cost is low, and the method is economical for parts that are complex or made in small quantities. An example is given by a stainless steel part that would have required a $6000 hardened steel die in a 1200 ton press but was slip cast in a mold which cost less than $30. The method is slow and not justified for large quantities.

In *fiber metallurgy,* a liquid slurry containing metal fibers is poured into a mold with a porous bottom. The liquid is withdrawn, and the fibers are deposited uniformly in a felted mass of the shape of the mold. The mass is then worked to increase density and sintered. The products are used for sound absorption, vibration damping, and as reinforcements for plastics and light metals.

A method for heavy powders, such as tungsten carbide, is *centrifugal compacting*. The powder is twirled in a mold and packed uniformly with pressures up to 400 psi on each particle. Parts must have uniform round sections. Equipment cost is not high.

Continuous strips and rods are compacted by *rolling* copper, brass, bronze, Monel, titanium, or stainless steel powders or fibers. In a typical process, stainless steel powder is fed from a hopper between two rolls in a horizontal plane. The material emerges as a strip with a density of 6 to 6.8 g per cc. It is then sintered, re-rolled three times, and annealed to a tensile strength of 108,000 psi and an elongation of 33%. Another process makes porous sheets for filters; a uniform layer of powder poured on a ceramic tray is sintered and then rolled to the desired density.

Sintering. Sintering augments the bonds between the particles and therefore strengthens a powder metal compact. In all cases this occurs because atoms of the particles in contact become intermingled. Generally speaking, this is brought about in one of two ways. In one way, one of the constituents of the compact melts; in the other way, none melts. An example of the first case is the sintering of cemented carbide, which is done above the melting point of the cobalt constituent. Some of the cobalt dissolves a bit of the tungsten or other carbide, and this becomes an inter-link firmly bonded to adjoining particles.

The second case is characteristic of the sintering of iron, copper, or tungsten powder. It is done usually at 60 to 80% of the melting temperature. The metals are non-volatile, and no fusion occurs. The atoms at the spots of contact intermingle and migrate.

The reason sintering is done below the melting point is that the process would actually be casting if the metals were melted, and powders would not be needed. Still the temperature must be high enough to excite rapid atomic mobility.

If substantially one constituent is present, as in the sintering of iron powder, a single phase is continuous from one particle to the next after sintering. In compacts of two or more different metals, alloys, or compounds, whether one melts or not, intermediate compounds or phases of the constituents are formed at the points of bonding of the particles. As sintering continues in either case, the bonded areas grow larger, and material more or less fills the voids between the particles. This is depicted in an ideal way in Fig. 10–4 in which particles are assumed round, and metal that enters the voids is shown darkened.

When no melting takes place, atoms must migrate from the solid parent particles to form and enlarge the bonds and fill the voids. The mechanisms believed to have roles in transporting the atoms are *surface diffusion, evaporation and condensation, bulk flow,* and *volume diffusion.* All seem to take place individually, successively or simultaneously during the sintering process depending on the metal, powder condition, temperature, time, and atmosphere.

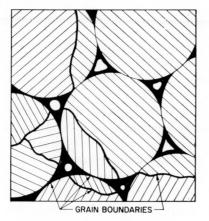

GRAIN BOUNDARIES

Fig. 10–4. An idealized diagram of the arrangement of grains in a metal powder compact. Sections of original particles are depicted as circles.

Diffusion and movement of atoms on the surfaces of the particles have been found to be the main activities in the early stages of sintering. Surface tension is the driving force to reduce the surface area, round and smooth surface irregularities, and segregate the unfilled spaces into fewer but larger pores. The surface area of small particles is large in relation to volume, and the influence of surface diffusion is proportionately great.

Evaporation and condensation can be expected to have more effect with a molten constituent than with non-volatile ones. One definite effect seems to be to spheroidize angular voids.

Bulk flow is the movement of solid material under stress. Some stress may be left in the particles after pressing, but most seems to be induced by enveloping surface tension forces, which appear to cause viscous flow of the material within the particles as well as on their surfaces at sintering temperatures.

Volume diffusion originates in the random movements of atoms induced by thermal vibration. Atoms tend to move from a location of high to one of lower concentration. Within metal crystals, atoms migrate from grain boundaries to voids within the lattice structure. There is strong experimental evidence that the major action in the later stages of sintering is a movement of atoms from the grain boundaries to the voids between the particles. Below the re-crystallization temperature atoms migrate slowly. Above that temperature the atoms move faster, but the grains grow, and the grain boundaries become fewer. It has been shown that atoms do not rapidly enter and shrink voids no longer connected by grain boundaries. The lower left-hand section of Fig. 10–4 depicts the presence of grain boundaries and diminution of voids. The upper right-hand portion indicates a crystal grown to encompass several grains and the isolated pores within it that do not shrink appreciably.

As atoms leave grain boundaries, their space is filled by the grains moving together. This explains volume shrinkage often evident in sintering. After sufficient grain growth, grain boundaries become insignificant. Then atom migration, volume shrinkage, bond growth between particles, and increase of compact strength practically cease. That explains why there is an optimum time of sintering for each case. Up to that time properties are improved, but beyond that there is little benefit.

All parts do not shrink when sintered; some grow. The most widely accepted explanation is that gases caught within many isolated pores in the maze cause expansion which is frozen into the part on cooling.

Because of its relatively large surface area, a powder metal compact is especially susceptible to oxidation and attack and must be kept clean to coalesce on an atomic scale. It usually is sintered in a neutral or reducing atmosphere. The sintering process and its speed can be strongly activated by adding gases to the atmosphere to react with the metals and purge impurities. Solids are often mixed with powder metals to vaporize on sintering and to open pores, but the vapors must not contaminate the main sintering atmosphere. Precise control of atmospheres and temperatures is particularly important for sintering furnaces. Most are semi- or fully-continuous furnaces of mesh-belt, roller-hearth, or mechanical pusher type with several chambers for heating and cooling in separate stages.

Finishing operations. Operations to impart specific properties or conditions to sintered metal parts include infiltration, heat treatment, impregnation, sizing, machining, and extruding.

Infiltration consists of placing a piece of copper on top of a presintered iron part and heating to 2100°F. The copper melts and is drawn into the pores of the part by capillarity. This increases strength 70 to 100%, but the product is relatively brittle.

Iron parts may have *carbon added* to the original mixture or be *carburized* after sintering. They then are heated, quenched, and tempered like any other high-carbon steel product to a high degree of strength and hardness. An example is given at the bottom of Fig. 10–1.

Sintered compacts such as bearings may be saturated with oil, about 20% by volume. This *impregnation* is done by immersion in hot oil or by drawing oil through the part by vacuum. The oil is withdrawn by heat or pressure as needed in service. Some impregnation is done with low melting point alloys such as solder.

Powder metal parts are *sized* or *coined* by being squeezed in presses, as described in Chap. 13. A hole can be sized by pushing a mandrel or balls of the desired size through it. Squeezing also makes the material denser and stronger.

A major purpose of powder metallurgy is to eliminate *machining*. Yet sometimes machining must be done to hold small tolerances or get surfaces, such as small holes or threads, that cannot be molded easily. Porous parts such as bearings can be machined, but care is necessary to avoid closing the pores. Tools must be sharp and with ample angles, speeds high, and feeds fine. Ordinary cutting fluid with water is not desirable because it contaminates oil in impregnated bearings and tends to corrode iron compacts.

Powder metal rods and slugs of uranium and zirconium for nuclear reactors are *clad* with other metals for strength and protection against contamination. This is done by placing the powder metal in a can, which is welded shut, and extruding the combination through a die. For example, uranium powder is enclosed in a copper can, heated to 1100°F, and extruded into 1 in.-diameter rods.

Design of powder metal parts. Four guides to successful production of powder metal are:

1. Design parts to suit the process, especially if they have been made previously in other ways.
2. Design the tools to conform to the principles of powder metal operations, to compress the powder metal uniformly.
3. Standardize parts as much as possible to be able to use the minimum number of tools on the most parts.
4. Control all operations strictly.

What can be done in powder metallurgy is limited largely by the equipment now available and by the behavior of the materials being processed. A number of rules must be observed to design parts and tools to get the most from the process. One rule is that cylinders, squares, and rectangles are the easiest shapes to press. Other rules state that sharp corners, edges, thin ridges, and deep slots should be avoided, since they make tools, preforms, and finished products weak. The length of a part should not exceed 2 to 3 times its diameter. Thin and thick sections expand differently on heating, lead to cracks, and should not be adjacent. Other rules are listed in treatises on the subject for the designer of powder metal parts.

Tolerances as small as 0.001 in. per in. may be held but are expensive. More practical tolerances are 0.005 in. per in. or more.

Comparisons with other processes. Powder metallurgy stands alone as a means to process some materials and parts and for making porous metal parts. In addition, this process competes successfully with others to produce many machine parts. It does so because it offers simple and fast operations at a low cost for the time for each piece.

The unfavorable costs for powder metallurgy are those for raw materials and tools. Iron powders cost $0.11 per lb up in large quantities as compared with carbon steel ingots at $0.04 per lb and shapes or bars at $0.06 per lb. Aluminum powder is quoted at $0.30 per lb and ingots at $0.28 per lb. The simplest of dies cost $150 or so, and many as much as several thousand dollars. However, a die may turn out from 50,000 to

250,000 or more pieces, and the cost per piece is little if many pieces are required.

As a rule, powder metallurgy is not considered competitive for quantities of less than 20,000 pieces. Some cases have been reported where careful designing and planning has made powder metallurgy profitable for lots of as small as 1000 pieces. The capacities of ordinary equipment limit the process to relatively simple parts not over 4 sq in. in area across, but pieces weighing as much as 350 lb have been made.

Questions

1. What advantages does powder metallurgy offer?

2. How may alloys be obtained in powder metals?

3. What are the important physical characteristics of powder metals?

4. What are the principal ways of obtaining metal powders?

5. Describe the basic operations in powder metallurgy to produce ductile tungsten wire, cemented carbide tools, self-lubricating bearings, porous metal filters, ordinary structural parts, and high-strength machine parts.

6. Why is powder metal pressed? Why is uniformity important, and how is it obtained?

7. What kinds of presses are used for powder metallurgy?

8. What are the benefits of slip casting powder metals?

9. What materials may be compacted centrifugally?

10. How are continuous strips made of powder metal?

11. Discuss what takes place to bond powder particles together when they are sintered.

12. What four processes contribute to the movement of atoms to bring about bonding of metal powders?

13. What factors determine the optimum temperature and length of time to sinter a powder metal?

14. Why do some powder metal compacts shrink on sintering? Why do others grow?

15. Why must powder metals be sintered in controlled atmospheres?

16. What is infiltration and what does it do?

17. What is impregnation and what is its purpose?

18. What does coining or sizing do to powder metal parts?

19. What precautions must be taken in machining powder metal parts?

20. How are powder metals clad?

21. State four guides to successful production of powder metal parts.

22. What helps and what hinders powder metallurgy in competition with other processes?

Problems

1. A bushing with 1½ in. outside diameter, 1 in. inside diameter, and 1¼ in. length is to be made from iron and alloying materials in the manner depicted at the bottom of Fig. 10–1. What force in tons and die fill depth in inches must a press be able to provide for the first pressing?

2. The green density of the compact described in Prob. 1 is 7 g per cc. What is the approximate density of the powder metal before pressing?

3. A round piece as depicted in Fig. 10–3 has a head of 2 in.-diameter and ½ in. thickness. The stem is ¾ in. in diameter and ⅝ in. long. The part is to be made from brass powder. Compacting pressure must be 25 tsi. Estimate the force and die fill the press must provide.

References

DeGroat, Geo. H., *Tooling for Metal Powder Parts,* McGraw-Hill Book Co., Inc., New York, 1958.

Metals Handbook, American Society for Metals, Cleveland.

CHAPTER 11

Plastics and Rubber

The term plastic in its original sense applies to a material that can be made to flow so that it can be molded or modeled. That is true of metals, clay, and other materials, but the name has come to designate specifically a group of organic solids that can readily be made to flow by heat or pressure, or both, into valuable commercial shapes.

Plastics are mostly products of this century. Natural shellac and bitumen have been known for ages. Celluloid was discovered by Hyatt in 1868 in a search for a substitute for ivory for billiard balls. The modern plastic industry started with the development of Bakelite by Baekeland in 1909. Since then growth has been rapid, into more than 30 chemically distinct families of plastics, hundreds of compounds, and thousands of products.

Plastics have been increasingly accepted because they offer unique combinations but yet a wide variety of properties and are particularly fitted for many developments of the age. Plastics are light in weight; most weigh less than magnesium. Outside of especially light foamed plastics, an average specific gravity is about 1.4. This has suited them for trim and accessories in commercial aircraft and has helped lighten many implements held by hand. Plastics are good electrical insulators at low and high frequencies and have important uses in the electrical industry. They are good heat insulators also. Some weather well and are highly resistant to corrosion. Mechanical properties vary widely.

Strengths, for instance, of some plastics are only 1000 psi or so but mostly run from about 5000 psi in ordinary objects to 80,000 psi and more in special laminates.

Manufacture is economical because most products can be almost entirely finished by molding or forming.

Probably of most significance, plastics offer a greater range of appeal to the eye than any other class of materials. Molding usually leaves a good surface finish, but a higher luster can be added by a simple solvent treatment or buffing. All colors are available, but not in all plastics. Color is impregnated into an object and is more lasting than paint. Some plastics offer true transparency without the brittleness of glass.

Rubber and synthetic elastomers have some of the same properties as plastics and will be included in this survey.

PLASTIC MATERIALS

The resins. Many kinds of materials are called plastics. Most of them are based on some form of synthetic organic resin that is a compound containing carbon as the central element. Other elements such as hydrogen, oxygen, nitrogen and chlorine are linked to the carbon atoms to form the molecules.

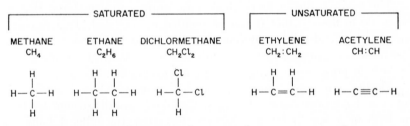

Fig. 11–1. A designation of some simple organic compounds.

An example of an organic compound is methane, one of the simplest. Its formula is written in Fig. 11–1 to designate its structure. Methane is a gas and not a plastic. It is the first of a series of organic chain compounds that are said to be *saturated* because all the valence bonds of the carbon atoms are satisfied. The second compound of the series is ethane, for which the formula is given in Fig. 11–1. A compound in which the valence bonds of the carbon atoms are not satisfied is said to be *unsaturated.* The structures of two simple unsaturated compounds, ethylene and acetylene, are indicated in Fig. 11–1. The double and triple lines in the formulas designate the lack of saturation.

With proper pressure, temperature, and catalysts, a number of ethylene molecules with unsaturated bonds can be joined together into a long

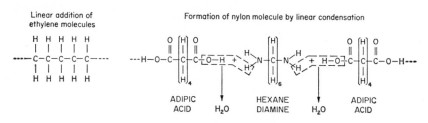

Fig. 11–2. Two examples of polymerization.

molecule as indicated in Fig. 11–2. A substance composed of basic molecules is a *monomer*. The formation of larger molecules from smaller ones is called *polymerization*. The substance thus formed is a *polymer*. As the molecules grow larger, a gas like ethylene becomes a liquid and ultimately a solid. Polymerization leads to an increase in the boiling point of a liquid and the melting point of a solid.

The formation of a long-chain type molecule, as exemplified by the polymerization of ethylene, is known as *linear addition*. Another type of reaction is characterized by the splitting off or condensation of water molecules as illustrated for the formation of nylon in Fig. 11–2. This is called *linear condensation*. When dissimilar monomers are combined, the process is called *copolymerization*, and the product is a *copolymer*.

Most plastics are organic high polymers. One major class of plastics, called the *thermoplastic* materials, is composed of long molecules alongside each other or intertwined. The links between the atoms within a molecule are chemical bonds and are called primary bonds. The physical forces of attraction between individual molecules are known as secondary bonds. When a thermoplastic material is heated, the secondary bonds are loosened, and the plastic becomes soft. The primary bonds are not broken unless the temperature is raised enough to decompose the material. Short of that, the molecules remain unchanged, and the plastic hardens when the secondary bonds become stronger upon cooling.

A second major class of plastics, called the *thermosetting* materials, are composed of long molecules linked to each other with primary bonds. An example is given by the reaction between phenol and formaldehyde to form a phenolic resin as indicated in Fig. 11–3. Under proper conditions of temperature and pressure, some of the formaldehyde molecules form links in linear chains and others form links between the chains of phenol molecules. If such a substance is heated to an excessive temperature, it chars and decomposes, but short of that it does not soften once formed since the primary bonds are not disturbed.

The thermosetting plastics are generally stronger, harder, more resistant to heat and solvents, and lower in material cost. The secondary bonds of the thermoplastic materials allow deformation and flow under stress. This tends to redistribute stress concentrations under load and

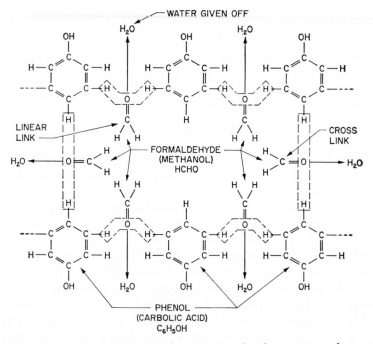

Fig. 11–3. A diagram of the polymerization of a thermosetting phenolic resin.

makes the material tough. In contrast, the thermosetting plastics are brittle. The thermoplastics can usually be molded more rapidly.

Thermoplastics are found commonly in packaging and consumer goods for use at room temperatures. Even so, the distinction between the two classes of plastics has been fading away in some respects. Early thermoplastics softened at 150°F, but some today are serviceable above 300°F, which is top working temperature for most thermosetting materials. It is possible to induce cross-linking in thermoplastic materials and convert them to thermosetting materials by means of high-energy radiation. In some cases this has been found more detrimental than beneficial.

Other constituents. The plastic resin in most cases is mixed with other substances to make the final product. The added constituents are grouped as *fillers, pigments* or *dyes, plasticizers,* and *lubricants.*

Fillers are added to most thermosetting plastics and to some thermoplastics. Their purpose may be to add bulk, increase strength, or give heat or electrical resistance, etc. They may comprise from little or none to a large part of the total mixture. For instance, low-cost and low-strength molded parts may have 80% or more of an inert filler.

Earthy materials such as calcium carbonate at $0.02 per lb provide bulk alone. Wood flour gives bulk cheaply with fair strength and good moldability but tends to absorb moisture. It costs about $0.04 per lb. Macerated cloth and fibers are more expensive but add more strength. Glass fibers and cloth give the most strength at a cost of $0.40 per lb for fibers and $0.50 to $1 per yd for fabric. Asbestos fibers are added for heat-resistance and dimensional stability, and mica for low moisture absorption and good electrical-resistance. Other fillers are used for special purposes.

Normally neither the resins nor fillers have attractive colors by themselves. Pigments are added to impart color by their presence; dyes to color the resins or fillers.

A solid or liquid plasticizer is intended to make the product more flexible or less brittle. It may help the flow of material in the mold.

A lubricant or release agent facilitates removal of parts from the mold. It may be a wax, fatty acid, or metallic soap.

A plastic may be in one or more of three forms in the raw material state. First are powders, flakes or granules for molding plastic pieces. Second are liquids for castings, impregnated laminates, adhesives, and mixed molding compounds. Third are the filaments, films, sheets, rods, and tubes to be fabricated into the finished articles such as by weaving into cloth, cutting and joining into wrappers, or machining.

Full specifications of the properties of plastics are tabulated in handbooks. The outstanding features of the important plastics will be described in this text. For that purpose they are classified as thermosetting, thermoplastic, casein, rubber, elastomer, and silicone materials.

Thermosetting plastics. Thermosetting plastics are polymerized when molded or formed. A primary mixture is subjected to heat, pressure, or a catalyst, singly or in combination, over a time to enforce the links within and between the large molecules. The mixture first softens and can be forced into the shape desired but then hardens permanently.

A survey of the highlights of the major thermosetting plastics is given in Table 11–1. It is important to realize that each type of plastic material may have numerous varieties. The phenolic resins are examples of this. The two main phenolic resins are nominally phenol–formaldehyde and phenol–furfural compounds. Each maker of these resins has his own formulas. For instance, the phenol may be carbolic acid or any one of a number of related substances. In addition, a variety of fillers in various amounts may be added to the resin. The result is that phenolics are available with a wide range of properties; tensile strength is only one example. It may be as low as 3500 to 5000 psi in the ordinary run of molded parts but can be made as high as 12,000 psi in parts intended to have high strength. Exceptional properties, of course, cost more, and the attempt of each supplier is to meet his customers' needs at the lowest cost.

TABLE 11-1. THE MAJOR THERMOSETTING PLASTICS

Classification	Trade names	Tensile strength (1000 psi)	Impact strength (ft lb/in.)	Cost ($/lb)	Advantages	Limitations	Typical uses
Phenol Formaldehyde Phenol Furfural (Phenolics) — Most widely used plastic	Bakelite Textolit Resine	3.5–12	0.24–33	0.20–0.40	Low cost. Good heat- and electrical resistance, rigidity, strength, hardness, and stability. Low moisture absorption. Can be made fairly resistant to chemicals. Easily molded, cast, or laminated.	Colors generally confined to blacks and other dark shades. Severely attacked by strong acids and strong alkalis.	Handles, pulleys, wheels, fuse blocks, plugs, coil forms, milking machine cups, radio cabinets.
Urea-Formaldehyde (Ureas)	Bakelite Plaskon Beetle	5–10	0.34–35	0.20–0.33	Good colorability in light colors. Physical properties comparable to phenolics. Easily molded in large or small sizes.	Not cast. Relatively high molding pressure. Max. temperature for use about 170°F.	Cabinets, toilet seats, electric switches and plugs.
Melamine-formaldehyde (Melamines)	Melmac Catlin	5–10	0.24–12	0.40–0.45	Excellent electrical- and heat-resistance. Good strength. Hardest plastic. Good colorability and stability. Low moisture absorption.	Higher cost. Not cast.	Switch panels, moldings, ornaments, kitchen ware, lighting fixtures.
Polyesters: Alkyds (Glyptal) Allyl cast resins	Thermaflow Mylar Kriston	3–10	0.3 –12	0.32–0.50	Exceptional dielectric properties. Passes H. F. radio waves. Low moisture absorption. Resists heat to 400°F. Good colors. Most used for reinforced plastic moldings.	Higher cost.	Radar domes, ignition, radio, and T.V. parts, aircraft glaze, boat and car bodies.
Epoxides: Epoxy resins Epichlorohydrin bisphenol	Araldite	3–12	0.35–10	0.45–0.80	Good chemical- and electrical resistance. Low shrinkage. Adheres well to metal, glass, etc. Not affected by most organic solvents.	High cost. Mostly available in liquid form for casting, foaming, and reinforced molding and laminating.	Tools and dies, precision castings, high strength laminates, encasing electrical parts.

Aldehydes

Prices are given for plastic materials in this chapter as a basis for comparison. Their purpose is to indicate relative costs. They can be expected to change with economic and other conditions and quantities. Material cost is only part of the cost of the finished product. Processing cost is also a substantial item and is to a large extent based on time. In the case of thermosetting plastics, polymerization takes time, from a fraction of a minute in some molding operations to several days for some castings.

The phenolics are the oldest forms of thermosetting plastics and are used more than any other plastic material because they serve many purposes at low cost. The other materials offer advantages for particular applications as noted in Table 11–1 but at higher cost.

Thermoplastic plastics. The thermoplastic materials are conventionally classified as *cellulosics* and *synthetics* as listed in Table 11–2.

The *cellulosics* include those that are the oldest forms of thermoplastics. They are molded, are available commercially in sheets, rods, tubes, etc., are extruded into textile fibers, go into paints, and have wide usage as film and foil for packaging. A wide range of properties, as indicated in Table 11–2, and moderate cost suit them to many uses. Cellulosics are made by dissolving cotton or wood fibers in acids and then processing with a plasticizer such as camphor.

A variety of materials with a large spread in prices and many uses are included under the heading of *synthetics.* Mostly they are synthesized and polymerized from simple substances and can be modified in many ways by variations in the processes and additives. The polystyrenes are used more than any other thermoplastic for molded articles because of good physical properties and low cost. Polyethylenes cost more, but some can be injection-molded faster and for some applications are more economical than styrenes. Other synthetics have properties preferred for particular applications. For instance, the vinyls are readily produced in sheet form and give flexibility and fluid-resistance desirable for floor and wall covering, etc.

Other plastic compounds in existence at this time are not economically prominent but in the future may receive more acceptance. Still others can be expected to be developed from time to time. The picture of the industry is a changing one.

Caseins. Casein plastic results from the hardening action of formaldehyde upon casein obtained from milk. Scrap material obtained during the molding process can be reworked like a thermoplastic, but the finished product is like a thermosetting material and cannot be resoftened by heat. Casein plastic is resistant to burning and organic solvents and takes color well. It absorbs moisture readily and deteriorates from repeated exposure to dampness. Typical products are buttons, buckles, handles, and small novelties.

TABLE 11-2. MAJOR THERMOPLASTIC PLASTICS

Classification	Trade names	Tensile strength (1000 psi)	Impact strength (ft lb in.)	Cost ($/lb) mold. comp.	Cost ($/lb) sheet	Advantages	Limitations	Typical uses
Cellulosics: Cellulose nitrate	Celluloid Pyralin Nitron	7–8	5–7		1.60–2.73	Tough. Fair chemical-resistance.	Highly flammable. Becomes yellow and brittle with age.	Fountain pens, drawing insts., Ping-pong balls.
Cellulose acetate	Tenite I Lumarith Plastacele	2.7–8.5	0.4–5.2	0.36–0.65	0.92–1.16	Flame- and age-resistant. Easily molded and colored. Clear form passes ultraviolet light. Good insulator.	Absorbs considerable moisture. Parts over 2 lb must be compression molded. 200°F max. temperature.	Glazing, eye shades, packaging, buttons, toilet articles.
Cellulose acetate butyrate	Tenite II	1.9–6.8	0.6–5.4	0.40–0.65	1–1.28	Low moisture absorption. Good stability. Molds easily. Dissolves readily in solvents to make gel. Good wearing qualities.	Distorts from heat. Does not pass ultraviolet light. 200°F max. temperature.	Tool coating, handles, steering wheels, helmets.
Cellulose propionate	Forticel	1.5–7.5	0.8–11	0.51–0.63		Easily molded. Stable. Tough. Low moisture absorption.	Higher cost. 200°F max. temperature.	Telephones, flashlight cases, pens.
Ethyl cellulose	Ethocel Lumareth	3–6.5	1.7–7	0.72		Low temperature toughness. Good chemical resistance. Good wearing qualities.	Higher cost. 200°F max. temperature.	Jigs and fixtures, hose nozzles.
Cellophane (regenerated cellulose)	Cellophane	8–19			1.25	Durable and attractive. Resists fire, tearing, and solvents.	Extruded into sheets only. Not heat sealing.	Packaging and wrapping, curtains and drapes.
Synthetics: Vinyls or polyvinyls	Vinylite Resistoflex Elvanol Chemaco Tygon Saran	1–11	0.25–0.20 when rigid polyvinyl acetate polyvinyl alcohol polyvinyl chloride etc.	0.27–0.43	0.62–0.92	Many varieties (rigid and flexible) and forms (sheets, liquids, pieces). Can be highly resistant to water, chemicals, and especially oils. Good colorability. Elect. resistant. Temp. range from −70° to 175°F.	Some kinds difficult to injection mold.	Floor and wall covering, rainwear, hose and tubing, phono records, safety glass interlayers.

TABLE 11-2. MAJOR THERMOPLASTIC PLASTICS (*Cont.*)

Acrylics methyl methacrylate	Lucite Plexiglass	6–10.5	0.3–2	0.51–0.59	0.49–2.15	Remarkable transparency. Colors well. Can be molded or cast. Good strength, moisture resistance, and dielectric properties.	Easily scratched. Attacked by organic solvents. Somewhat brittle. 200°F max. temperature.	Lenses, sign letters, name plates, decorations, display novelties.
Polyamids	Nylon	6–20	0.6–16+	1.18–2.30	3 rod	May be molded or extruded into rods, tubes, or filaments. Good insulator. Tough. Resistant to organic solvents and wear. Temp. range from −40° to 250°F.	High cost.	Cloth, bristles, sutures, gears, combs, wire insulation.
Polystyrenes	Cerex Lustron Styron Loralin	3.5–14.5	0.25–15	0.25–0.44	0.57–0.61	Excellent moisture- and electrical-resistance. Clear or in all colors. Strong but somewhat brittle. Good heat-resistance. Can be molded, cast, and foamed. Used for most injection molding.		Toys, packaging, H. F. insulation, refrig. parts, battery boxes, dental plates, table ware.
Polyethylenes	Polythene	1.4–5.5	mostly flexible	0.31–0.56	0.85–1	Exceptionally resistant to acids, alkalies, and solvents. Good insulator. Tough and resilient. Can be made quite flexible. Film has a soft smooth feel.	Brittle at low temperatures. Softens at 200°F or below.	Wire insulation, coatings and lacquers, chemical ware, squeeze bottles, pipe.
Fluorocarbons	Fluorothene TFE CFE Polyfluoron	1.5–5.7	2.5–4	4–8	11–23	Exceptional chemical- and electrical-resistance. Low friction. Little adhesion to other substances. Withstands 300°F and above.	Very high cost.	Coating for aircraft skis, greaseless bearings, chemical containers, electrical equipment.

tetrafluoroethylene
chlorotrifluoroethylene

215

Rubber. As a moldable organic substance, rubber can be considered a plastic, but it is different from plastics in two important respects. It can be stretched greatly without harmful effect and it is produced and treated in a whole industry by itself.

Most natural rubber comes from the rubber tree, *Hevea Brasiliensis,* cultivated in plantations in tropical countries mostly in the Far East. The trees are tapped for sap called *latex,* containing about ⅓ rubber. Some liquid latex is brought to this country for adhesives and other uses, but most of it is dried and converted into crude rubber at the plantation. It is then shipped in baled sheets in a number of grades of purity. The properties and quality of the final product depend to a large extent upon the grade of crude used and the amount of reclaimed rubber mixed with it.

Although found by Columbus, rubber was no more than a curio for hundreds of years. It was of little value because in the raw state it is soft and sticky when warm and hard and brittle when cold. In 1839 Charles Goodyear discovered how to vulcanize rubber to make it consistently useful by heating it with sulfur. Today selenium, tellerium, and organic sulfur compounds also serve as vulcanizing agents. Other additives to rubber are substances to accelerate vulcanization, activators for the accelerators, anti-oxidation agents, plasticizers, stiffeners, fillers, and pigments or coloring agents. Reinforcing agents such as carbon black are added to increase strength and resistance to tearing and abrasion. Thus rubber can be made to have a large variety of properties and in most cases is compounded to meet specific service conditions.

Rubber is best known for *stretchability* or elasticity although it does not conform to Hooke's law and does not return exactly to its original size. The amount of stretchability varies; hard rubber has little. Rubber also can take flexion repeatedly. This may be called resilience and makes rubber a preferred material for such applications as gaskets, printing rolls, upholstery, and hose. Other properties are electrical-, water-, and chemical-resistance which make rubber suitable for wire coverings, rainwear, bottle stoppers, etc. The natural stickiness of rubber makes it a good adhesive. For some uses, rubber has been supplanted by plastics and synthetic elastomers.

A weakness of natural rubber is its poor resistance to many oils and solvents. Its tensile strength is not high, only a few thousand psi. For high strength, rubber is coated on fabrics, cords, or wire largely as a flexible insulation against friction. Examples are in automotive tires and conveyor belts. The average current price of the most common grade of raw rubber is $0.35 per lb. A finished product may cost several to many times as much.

Synthetic elastomers. Many materials with rubbery properties have been synthesized. Those few of commercial importance are designated in

Table 11–3. These elastomers are sometimes called *synthetic rubbers*, but they actually are not chemically and physically identical to natural rubber. Butadiene-styrene (SBR) rubber was the synthetic to take most of the burden when natural rubber was not available in time of war. Some of the synthetic elastomers are superior to rubber in certain respects, such as in resistance to oil, heat, and light and in longer life. Each is limited to specific applications because of high cost or some weakness as pointed out in Table 11–3, and natural rubber remains the most widely used elastomer.

Most so-called *hard rubber* is highly vulcanized SBR (formerly GR–S) synthetic rubber. It is a low cost thermosetting compound with properties similar to polyvinyls. Typical uses are salt water valves, battery cases, industrial jars, and X-ray tanks.

Silicones. The *silicones* are compounds built around a basic silicon-oxygen unit in a manner similar to the way the organic compounds are formed from their basic carbon atoms. The silicone compounds can be polymerized in chains and rings to produce a large number of compounds. They are less active chemically than similar organic compounds and more resistant to heat. They stand temperatures in various applications from 300° to 600°F. Some are molded thermosetting plastics, others are varnishes for high-temperature electrical insulation, and still others are in the forms of high-temperature greases and oils. They are found in such products as waxes and polishes, paints, cosmetics, antifoaming agents, and dielectric fluids.

An important group of silicones have rubber-like properties and are called silicone *rubbers*. Their outstanding properties are specified in Table 11–3. The use of silicones is limited by high cost. Various compounds are quoted at $2 to $6 per lb.

PLASTIC PROCESSING

There can be said to be two steps in the manufacture of plastic products. The first is a chemical process to create the resin. The second is to formulate and shape the material into the finished article or product. That is mechanical in all cases but also includes the end of a chemical process for thermosetting plastics, which polymerize in the mold. The second step will be treated in this section.

Plastic objects are formed by compression, transfer, and injection-molding. Other processes are casting, extrusion, laminating, sheet forming, joining, and machining. Some of these and still others are used for rubber. A reason for a variety of processes is that different materials must be worked in different ways. Also, each method is advantageous for certain kinds of products. The principles of operation and merits of the processes will be discussed.

TABLE 11–3. MAJOR SYNTHETIC ELASTOMERS

Classification	Tensile strength (1000 psi)		Elongation (100%)		Cost ($/lb)	Advantages	Limitations	Applications
	Pure gum	Black	Pure gum	Black				
Natural rubber (for comparison)	2.5–3.5	3.5–4.5	7.5–8.5	5.5–6.5	0.30–0.50			
Polyisoprene rubber (Isoprene)					0.30	Properties equal to or superior to natural rubber for some purposes.	Relatively new and prod. and processing facilities limited.	Auto and truck tires.
Butadiene-styrene (SBR) (GR-S)	0.2–0.3	2.5–3.5	4–6	5–6	0.16–0.30	Properties like natural rubber. Ample production facilities.	A little inferior to natural rubber in strength and wear.	Commonly compounded with natural rubber and used in same ways.
Butadiene-acrylonitrile copolymers (Nitrile)	0.5–0.9	3.0–4.5	4.5–7.0	4.5–6.5	0.49–0.68	More oil- and solvent-resistance.	Less strength.	Carburetor diaphragms, self-sealing fuel tanks, gasoline and oil hose.
Chlorobutadiene polymers (Chloroprene) (Neoprene)	3–4	3–4	8–9	5–6	0.39–0.75	High resistance to heat, light, oils, and chemicals.	Fair electrical resistance. Not processed like natural rubber.	Oil hose and gaskets, particularly for high temperatures. Heavy duty tires, oil-resistant footwear.
Isobutylene copolymers (Butyl rubbers)	2.5–3.0	2.5–3.0	7.5–9.5	6.5–8.5	0.23–0.28	Exceptional gas impermeability. Superior resistance to heat, light, and acids. Long life.	Hard when cold. Fair abrasion resistance. Burns readily.	Inner tubes, steam hose and diaphragms, gas masks, electrical insulation.

Classification	Tensile strength (1000 psi)		Elongation (100%)		Cost ($/lb)	Advantages	Limitations	Applications
	Pure gum	Black	Pure gum	Black				
Polysulfides (Thiokol)	> 1		4.5–6.5		0.50–1.25	Excellent oil and solvent resistance. Good chemical resistance.	Poor tear-, abrasion-, and flame-resistance. Low strength.	Refinery and oil field equipment seals, gaskets, diaphragms, valve seat disks.
Polyacrylites (Acrylic rubbers) (Hycar)	1.2		3	5	1.34	Excellent resistance to oils, solvents, and acids. Stands high temperatures.	Poor wear, tear and abrasion resistance. High cost.	Automotive gaskets for hot E.P. oil. Chemical apparatus.
Silicone rubbers (Polysiloxane)	0.6–1.0		0.6–4.0		2–4	Stands working temperatures to 300°F and occasionally to 500°F. Elastic to −100°F.	Low strength. Poor resistance to tear and abrasion. Not compatible with rubber. High cost.	Wire and cable covering, gaskets, tubes, etc. for extreme conditions.

Compression molding. In compression molding a proper amount of material in a cavity of a mold is squeezed by a punch, also called a force. The plastic is heated in most cases between 250° and 500°F, softens, and flows to fill the space between force and mold. The mold is kept closed for enough time to permit the formed piece to harden. This is done in a press capable of exerting 2000 to 8000 psi over the area of the work projected on a plane normal to the ram movement, depending on the design of the part and the material. Semi- and fully-automatic presses are available for large quantity production.

Most thermosetting and a few, particularly large, thermoplastic pieces are compression-molded. The charge into the mold may be a loose molding compound but for rapid production is prepared as a cold-compressed tablet or rough shape called a *preform*. It may be heated just before being put in the die to speed the operation.

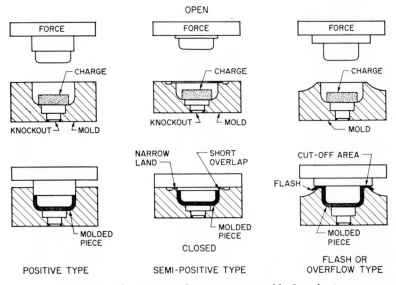

Fig. 11–4. Three types of compression molds for plastics.

The three basic types of compression molds for plastics are shown in Fig. 11–4. The force fits snugly in the *positive-type mold*. The full pressure of the force is exerted to make the material fill out the mold. The amount of charge must be controlled closely to produce a part of accurate size.

The force is a close fit in a *semi-positive type mold* only during about the last $\frac{1}{32}$ in. of travel. Full pressure is exerted at the final closing of the mold, but excess material can escape, and the charge does not have to be controlled so closely. This type is considered best for quantity production of pieces of quality.

The force does not fit closely but closes a *flash-* or *overflow-type mold* by bearing on a narrow flash ridge or cut-off area. The amount of material does not need to be controlled closely, and the excess is squeezed out around the cavity in a thin flash. Some material is wasted, and all pieces must be trimmed. Full pressure is not impressed on the workpiece. A mold of this kind is usually cheapest to make.

Elaborate molds are used for certain purposes. *Multiple-cavity* or *gang molds* are economical for large quantity production, of bottle caps for instance. A *sub-cavity gang mold* has a common loading chamber for a number of cavities. A *split-cavity mold* can be opened to remove a piece with undercuts, etc.

Compression molding is done hot mostly, but some *cold molding* is done, particularly for refractory-type compounds, because it is fast. The material is pressed to shape in the mold and then baked in an oven until cured. This method does not control size as well nor give as good a surface finish as hot molding.

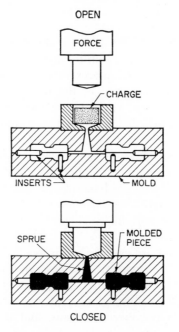

Fig. 11–5. A transfer mold.

Transfer molding. In transfer molding, also called *extrusion* or *gate molding*, the material is heated and compressed in one chamber and forced through a sprue, runner, and orifice into the mold cavity (Fig. 11–5). The mold is costly, but less trouble and better results are experienced in molding pieces with thin sections or inserts because the action in the mold is gentler than in direct molding.

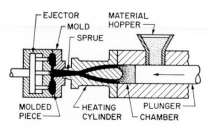

Fig. 11–6. A sketch of an injection molding system.

Injection molding. Injection molding in the manner illustrated in Fig. 11–6 is a rapid means of processing thermoplastic materials. When the plunger is drawn back, raw material falls from the hopper into the chamber. The plunger is driven forward to force the material through the heating cylinder where it is softened and squirts under pressure into the mold. Operating temperature is generally between 300° and 700°F, with final pressures usually over 5000 and up to 50,000 psi. The cool mold sets the plastic. The molded piece and sprue are withdrawn from one side and ejected from the other when the mold is opened. The mold is then closed and clamped to start another cycle. A production rate of three to six shots a minute is common for moderate-size work.

Injection molds for large quantity production of plastic parts cost from $1500 to $30,000. Several pieces may be made at one time in a mold, depending on the capacity of the machine. Some equipment is fully automated, even to the extent of stripping the gates and runners from the pieces, grinding the scrap material, and returning it to the hopper.

Modified injection molding systems have been developed for thermosetting plastics. Only enough material for each shot is heated and all injected so that none becomes polymerized before it is molded. The systems are called *jet flow* and *offset injection molding.* They require careful control and are suitable only for small parts.

Casting. Plastics that are cast are resins available in liquid form such as phenolics, polyesters, epoxies, silicones, and acrylics and thermoplastics that can be softened enough to pour, such as some cellulosics. They are cast in lead, rubber, glass, plaster or composition molds. A catalyst is added to unpolymerized resins, and they are heated in an oven while in the mold for hours or days at about 150° to 200°F to harden.

Plastics can be cast in many shapes. A model is made of wood, plaster, porcelain, metal, etc., and the mold is formed around it. This may be a simple draw, split, cored, or flexible mold depending on the size and shape of the part and the kind of plastic. The equipment is not expensive, but the process is slow. Casting is commonly done to make ornamental objects, jewelry, dies, punches, and jigs.

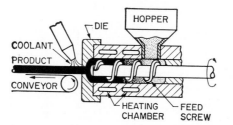

Fig. 11–7. Extrusion of plastic material.

Extrusion. Many plastics are extruded into long shapes by being forced through dies. Sometimes this is done intermittently by a plunger in a cylinder, but a common continuous method is illustrated in Fig. 11–7. The material drops from a hopper into a heated cylinder in which it is pushed along and out through the opening in the die by a screw, like meat in a grinder.

Many thermoplastic materials can be extruded into tube, rod, film, sheet and other shapes. Reinforced thermosetting tube and rod are formed by extruding reinforcing fibers soaked in liquid resin and passing the extruded shape slowly through a heated tube to allow it to polymerize. Extrusion is rapid and more economical than molding for many parts.

Laminates and reinforced plastic moldings. Sheets, rods, tubes, and shells are commonly made by laminating materials impregnated with plastic resin. These may be divided in two classes which are called: (1) *high-pressure laminates*, and (2) *low-pressure* or *reinforced plastic moldings.*

High-pressure laminates are available commercially as sheets, rods, and tubes in standard sizes and are fabricated in special shapes. Several trade names are Formica, Micarta, and Lamicoid. Reinforcement materials include paper, cotton or glass cloth, asbestos, and nylon. The resins ordinarily used for impregnation are phenolics, melamines, silicones, and epoxies. The material is cut to size, arranged in layers, compressed usually at over 1000 psi, and heated to around 300°F to harden the resin. Operations on flat and curved sheets are depicted in Fig. 11–8(A) and (B).

Reinforced plastic moldings usually are curved laminates. The most common reinforcing material is glass as fabric or fibers, but others are cotton, asbestos, and nylon. Mostly thermosetting, but some thermoplastic, resins are used. The simplest method is *contact laminating* or *molding.* Layers of reinforcing material are placed by hand over a low-cost form or mold, and resin is brushed or sprayed on each layer. The resin may be catalyzed to harden without heat or pressure, or it may be baked, or a low pressure may be applied by vacuum bag.

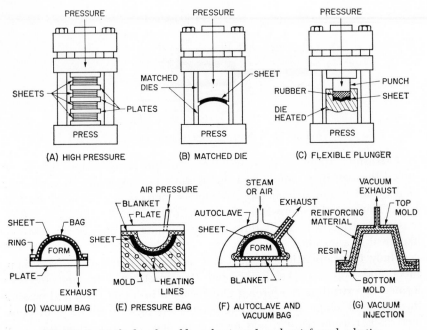

Fig. 11–8. Methods of molding laminated and reinforced plastics.

Layers of reinforcing and resin placed over a form or mold may be subjected to pressure for curing in *vacuum bag* or *pressure bag molding* depicted in Fig. 11–8(D) and (E). This is done by exhausting the air from a bag containing the workpiece on a form or inflating a bag against a sheet in a mold and under a plate. Either arrangement may be put in an autoclave with hot air or steam to augment the pressure and add heat as indicated in Fig. 11–8(F).

In the *vacuum injection process*, illustrated in Fig. 11–8(G), reinforcing material is clamped between two matching nonporous molds. The resin is put in a trough around the bottom and is drawn up through the material by a vacuum drawn through the top mold. The saturated molding is held in position until it sets.

Reinforced plastic moldings may be formed by rigid or flexible punches and dies in presses as indicated in Fig. 11–8(B) and (C). Rigid dies are usually heated by steam or electricity to about 250°F. Rigid steel dies give the lowest cost per piece and fastest rate of production of all methods for large quantities. Cheaper and softer dies of Kirksite serve for moderate quantities.

A general comparison of the processes is made in Table 11–4.

Forming plastic sheets. Thermoplastic sheets are softened by heating and *formed* or *thermoformed* into a large variety of thin-walled articles

TABLE 11-4. RELATIVE MERITS OF LAMINATED AND REINFORCED PLASTIC MOLDINGS

Method	Pressure (psi)	Tool invest.	Tool upkeep	Time per piece	Finish	Overall quality	Size of product	Suitable quantity
Steel plates or molds in press	1000	high	low	low	excellent—two sides	best	up to 60 sq ft	large
Kirksite molds in press	200–400	moderate	moderate	moderate	good—two sides	good	medium to large	few thousand or less
Flexible plunger	1000	moderate	moderate	moderate	good	good	small	medium
Contact or vacuum bag	0–15	low	low	moderate	fair	fair	medium to large	small
Pressure bag	200–300	moderate	moderate	moderate	good—one side	good	medium to large	few hundred or less
Bag in autoclave	50–100	low to moderate	high	high	fair to good—one side	good	medium	few hundred or less

such as display packages, bowls and trays, refrigerator door liners, lighting fixtures, safety helmets, and luggage. The material is held in the desired shape until it cools and becomes rigid. Sheets may be formed by pressing between molds or by mechanical bending as indicated in Fig. 11–9(A). Mechanical pulling or stretching is done in some cases. Another group of methods is based upon blowing or drawing the sheets by air pressure or vacuum. In this way certain shapes may be free-formed as exemplified in Fig. 11–9(B). This avoids marring the surface, which is of advantage in such products as clear windshield canopies for aircraft. Plastic sheets are blown or drawn to shapes against molds in a number of ways basically illustrated by Figs. 11–9(C) and (D).

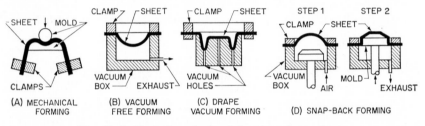

Fig. 11–9. Typical methods of forming plastic sheets.

A major advantage of sheet forming is that the sheets may be pre-decorated, coated, or preprinted for such effects as wood grain, lettered, or metallic finishes. The formed parts may have quite thin walls or large areas difficult to mold. Sheet-forming molds and other equipment usually cost less and can be made up more quickly than molds for injection or compression molding. Most molds for sheet forming cost only a few hundred dollars.

Unit costs for sheet forming for both labor and material are relatively high. A flange required for clamping during the operation must be trimmed from most parts, adding an extra operation. Other operations that may be required are secondary forming of undercuts, laminating, cleaning, cementing, and sealing. Because they are less expensive, ex-truded sheets have largely replaced cast or calendered sheets. Still the raw material in sheet form is relatively expensive.

Except for a limited number of cases, sheet forming is only economical for quantities that are not large, such as for prototypes or to get into production quickly. Generally the higher tooling cost of injection or compression molding is justified by lower operating and material costs for quantities of 100,000 pieces or more.

Joining plastics. The four basic methods of joining plastics are: (1) cementing with solvent, (2) bonding with an adhesive, (3) thermal welding, and (4) mechanical fastening.

Only certain soluble thermoplastic materials can be cemented. Among the most amenable are acrylics, polysterenes, cellulosics, and some vinyls. The strength of the joint is comparable to that of the parent material. Adhesive bonding is suitable for all plastics and is widely used for those not suited for solvent cementing. Plastics may be adhesive bonded to metals and other materials as well as to each other. A large number of solvents and adhesives are available, and the properties of a joint depend upon the materials selected.

All except highly inflammable thermoplastics can be welded by heat softening and pressing together surfaces to be joined. The four common welding methods are by means of: (1) hot gas, (2) a heated tool, (3) induction heating, and (4) friction. Fusion is not always complete, and the strength of the joint may be less than that of the parent material.

Plastic parts may be joined with and like other parts by means of screws, bolts, nuts, rivets, swaging or peening, press or shrink fitting, etc. Allowance must be made for the weakness and localized stress susceptibility of plastics in designing serviceable joints.

Machining plastics. Molding and forming are the usual ways of producing plastic parts, but machining from standard shapes may be cheaper than the cost of a mold when only a few pieces are needed. Some parts can be made most economically by slicing them off of extruded shapes. Hard-to-mold forms, such as threads and dimensions with small tolerances, can often be obtained most economically by machining. Some cutting to remove excess material in flash, runners, sprues, flanges, etc. is done on almost all molded and formed plastic parts.

Most of the techniques and equipment described in this text for machining metal are applicable also for plastics. However, there are some principles of machining that apply to plastics alone because the properties of plastics are different from those of metals. Because there are many plastics, there are many specifications for cutting plastics. This is not the place to list them, but specifications for tool shapes, speeds, feeds, etc. for particular applications are given in reference- and handbooks. What are important are the principles that explain why and how plastics must be treated differently from metals when cut. These will be discussed.

The properties of plastics that determine their machinability are: (1) they do not readily conduct but are easily affected by heat, (2) some contain abrasive fillers, (3) they are mostly soft and yielding, (4) some are quite brittle though soft.

Thermoplastics soften, lose shape, become gummy, and clog cutters; thermosetting plastics deteriorate and char at higher temperatures. The heat generated is not conducted away rapidly by a plastic when it is cut, so good results depend upon practices conducive to cool cutting. This calls for tools with keen cutting edges and smooth polished faces. For sawing, a band saw is preferable to a circular saw because the teeth on a long band have more time to cool. Air-, water-, and oil-coolants are commonly used for cutting plastics.

Hard and wear-resistant nonferrous alloy, cemented carbide, or cemented oxide tools are necessary to cut plastics with abrasive fillers.

Cutting tools stand high speeds well for most plastics because the materials are soft. As for tool shape, a relatively obtuse cutting angle usually is necessary to keep the tool from digging into the plastic, just as for brass and copper. In fact, a common practical rule is to set up to cut a plastic like brass or copper if specific information is not available. Then make adjustments by trial during the operation to reach optimum conditions.

Machine tools can work to as close tolerances in cutting plastics as with any material, but in most cases a small tolerance is futile because the plastic will not retain a size. Many plastics are yielding and change appreciably in size under cut; some absorb moisture and swell. In some cases plastic pieces are chilled to make them rigid for cutting.

Some plastics are brittle and chip readily when cut. For these, tools must be sharp and cuts light. Shearing is commonly done with sharp dinking dies or rule cutters. In some cases, plastics are heated before being cut.

Rubber processing. Raw rubber is composed of long molecules of great molecular weight and is therefore quite springy and resistant to being worked. These molecules must be broken up so the rubber can be molded and formed. For that purpose crude rubber may be extruded in a *plasticator,* masticated by revolving beaters in a *Banbury mixer,* or plasticized between rolls in a *rubber mill.* The last may be done alone or after one or both of the other treatments. In the rubber mill, the rubber is squeezed between two rolls turning toward each other on the entering side. One revolves up to ⅓ faster than the other and induces a severe shearing as well as compressive action in the rubber. The sheet coming out of the rolls is commonly fed back for a time into the entering mixture for thorough blending. In the mixer and mill the rubber is impregnated with the substances added to it for the final product. Much the same processes are used also for some plastics, one example being the calendering of decorative vinyl sheets and films. Most synthetic elastomers do not respond to mastication or working and must be synthesized to an amenable state.

The second step is to mold or form the rubber as desired and vulcanize it to make it elastic, non-sticky, strong, and more resistant to solvents. Forming and molding are done in a number of ways. Many shapes are extruded, in the same way as described for plastics. The extruded strips may be coiled or laid upon trays for vulcanizing in open steam heaters. Rubber is both compression- and injection-molded and heated in the molds for vulcanizing. Rubber is calendered into sheets, vulcanized, and then die cut into shapes. It may be pressed or wiped into the voids of fabric passing between rolls. Some rubber products are made on forms by dipping into, spraying, or electro depositing latex. Foams are made by beating latex into a froth or adding a blowing agent to a mass of rubber to generate gases during vulcanization.

DESIGN OF MOLDED PLASTIC PARTS

The engineer is obligated to design a part that serves its purpose at the lowest possible cost. The design of a plastic part includes the selection of material, the shape of the part and its detailed features, tolerances on dimensions, and finish requirements. Each of these factors influences the costs of the material, the mold, the molding operation, and secondary operations such as finishing, painting, etc.

Material is first of all selected to provide a plastic part with its required properties such as strength, color, atmospheric resistance, dielectric strength, etc. at lowest cost. Moldability of the material into the size and shape required must be considered.

Many objects are made from plastics for appearance sake, and art should have a place in their design. Still in all cases the shape must be not only pleasing but also serviceable and economical to make. The first principle of design for molding is that the part must be as simple and easily removable from the mold as possible. The more complicated the part, the higher are the mold and molding costs.

Whether a part is simple or intricate, its quality and cost depend upon how its detailed features are proportioned. Major considerations are radii and fillets, thickness and uniformity of walls, and draft. These will be discussed to illustrate what the designer must think about when proportioning plastic parts.

Plastic parts should be molded with adequate radii and fillets to eliminate sharp edges and corners wherever possible. This obviates stress concentrations and makes parts stronger and more durable. It is conducive to lower mold cost, longer mold life, better surface finish, better flow of the material into filling out the mold, elimination of trapped air, and less warpage of pieces. One rule is that a radius or fillet should be at least 25% of wall thickness and never less than $\frac{1}{32}$ inch.

Unnecessarily heavy sections in plastic parts waste material and retard molding because they cool slowly. On the other hand, walls must be thick enough for adequate strength, proper material flow in the mold, and minimum warpage. Ribs, beads, etc. properly placed add strength, make parts lighter and cheaper, and provide avenues for flow in the mold. Generally walls should not be thinner than $\frac{1}{16}$ to $\frac{3}{32}$ in. and may be as thick as $\frac{1}{4}$ to $\frac{3}{8}$ in. for large parts. A related rule is that the sections of a part should be of uniform thickness for even cooling and shrinkage throughout. This results in the least distortion and fewest flaws from molding.

Taper and draft are necessary to remove a piece readily from a mold. Taper also provides a wedging action that helps compact the material when a compression mold is closed. Draft of $\frac{1}{2}°$ to $1°$ on a side is considered the least desirable, with $2°$ or more preferred.

Other considerations include the locations of parting lines and gates, the selection and positioning of inserts, arrangements of undercuts and holes, provisions for letters and figures, and finishing. Rules on these points are given in the references cited at the end of this chapter and in similar treatises.

Workable tolerances for most molded plastic parts are of the order of ±0.005 in. per in. Smaller tolerances can be held at higher costs for the mold, operating time, and scrap.

The surface finish and color specified for a plastic part influence all costs. First they enter into the selection of the material. Surface finish dictates the degree of finish and thus the cost of the mold. Combinations of materials and colors can be obtained by various techniques of mold design and operating procedure. Most plastic parts have flash, runners, or sprues that must be removed, usually by secondary operations. Much thought is given to design parts so that this finishing can be done most easily without detracting from the appearance of the product. A typical solution is to mold a bead around a piece at the parting line. Flash can be trimmed from the bead, which serves as a guide, without marring large smooth areas of the piece. Where extra effects are required, masking, buffing, painting, and vapor metal coating operations may become necessary.

The design and production of plastic products is not a simple matter. Even the most experienced of plastics engineers commonly takes the precaution of first building a single-cavity experimental mold to perfect a process before putting a part into production with a multiple-cavity mold. Many viewpoints help, and the designer of plastic products can obtain valuable aid by consulting the supplier of the plastic material and the molder.

Questions

1. What advantages do plastics offer as a class?

2. Describe the differences in chemical composition and physical properties between thermoplastic and thermosetting resins.

3. What kinds of substances are added to plastic resins, and for what purposes?

4. Discuss the relative merits of the major thermosetting plastics.

5. Discuss the relative merits of the major thermoplastic materials.

6. How is rubber obtained and made serviceable?

7. What are the principal advantages and disadvantages of natural rubber?

8. Discuss the relative merits of the principal synthetic elastomers.

9. How do the silicones differ from organic materials and what makes them useful?

10. Describe compression molding of plastics and the three basic types of molds used.

11. How is injection molding done and what are its advantages and disadvantages?

12. How are plastics extruded?

13. What are high pressure laminates and how are they made?

14. Describe the principal ways of making reinforced plastic moldings.

15. What are the relative merits of the various methods of making laminates or reinforced plastic moldings?

16. How may parts be made from plastic sheets and under what conditions is that done?

17. What are the common methods for joining plastics?

18. What are the properties of plastics that affect their machinability? What are some of the resulting practices?

19. How are rubber products made?

20. What are the major considerations in the design of plastic parts?

Problems

1. A case for an electrical instrument can be made from either an urea compound by compression molding or from cellulose acetate butyrate by injection molding. The volume of the article is 9 cu in.

   The urea compound costs 1.89¢ per cu in. It takes 90 sec to mold one piece in a mold that costs $1500.

   The cellulose compound costs 2.87¢ per cu in. A piece can be molded from it in 15 sec, but the injection mold costs $4500.

   Time is worth $8 per hr. When should each material and process be selected?

2. A rectangular plaque 3 in. by 5 in. is to be compression-molded from a phenolic molding compound. A mean pressure is required. What force in tons should the press be able to exert to process four pieces in a gang mold?

References

A.S.T.E., *Tool Engineers Handbook,* McGraw-Hill Book Co., Inc., New York.

Keyser, Carl A., *Materials of Engineering,* Prentice-Hall, Inc., Englewood Cliffs, N.J., 1956.

Plastics Engineering Handbook, Reinhold Publishing Corp., New York, 1954.

CHAPTER | **12**

Primary Metal-working Processes

The processes described in this chapter produce what are known as the *wrought metals*. These are important engineering materials because of their strength and toughness. They are mandatory for many applications, such as critical structural members, for which cast metals do not suffice. Examples of the forms of these products are structural I-beams, channels, and angles; railroad rails; round, square, and hexagonal bar-stock; tubes and pipes; forgings; and extruded shapes.

Common primary metal-working processes included in this chapter are metal rolling, cold-drawing, pipe and tube manufacture, forging, and extrusion. All squeeze metal. Although much of their output is in final form, such as rails, most of it goes to feed secondary processes that make finished products by cutting or forming as will be described later in this book.

Metals are worked by pressure in the primary processes for two reasons. These are: (1) to form desired shapes, and (2) to improve physical properties. The results depend on whether the work is done *hot* or *cold*. Hot-working is done above the recrystallization temperature. This is at or near room temperature for lead, tin, and zinc. It is above the critical temperature for steel, as depicted in Fig. 12–2. Comparisons of the effects of hot- and cold-working are made in Table 2–1. The principles will be illustrated mostly for steel in this discussion for the sake of brevity.

Hot-working. The properties of a metal are different above than below its recrystallization temperature. Above that temperature and up to the melting point, crystals grow larger. If a crystal is broken up, new crystals form out of the pieces. Small crystals tend to combine, and large ones to absorb small ones. Deformed crystals are metamorphosed into undeformed ones. The higher the temperature, the faster the growth. The longer at any temperature, the larger the grains become. At the same time, the higher the temperature, the less strength the metal has and the easier the grains are broken into bits. These conditions help explain the following advantages of pressing or working hot metals.

1. True hot-working does not change the hardness or ductility of the metal. Grains distorted and strained during the process soon change into new undeformed grains.
2. The metal is made tougher because the grain structure is refined. The grains are broken up, and their parts are reformed into smaller and more numerous crystals.
3. The metal is made tougher because its pores are closed and impurities segregated. Slag and other inclusions are squeezed into fibers with definite orientation. A typical wrought structure is shown in Fig. 12–1. Chains of crystals intertwined with the filaments of impurities make the metal particularly strong in one direction. Metal is hot-worked to orient the flow lines as nearly as possible for strength in the direction of largest stress.
4. Less force is required, the process is faster, and smaller machines can be used for a given amount of hot- as compared with cold-working because the metal is weaker.
5. A metal can be pushed into extreme shapes when hot because the continual reformation of crystals obviates ruptures and tears.

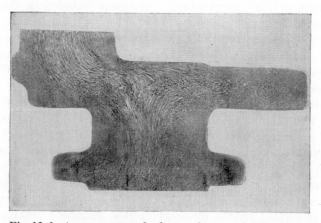

Fig. 12–1. A cross section of a forging for a crankshaft. This shows the fine grained fibrous structure resulting from hot working. (Courtesy Drop Forging Association.)

Hot-working is done well above the critical temperature to gain most of the benefits of the process but not at a temperature high enough to promote extreme grain coarsening. This is exemplified in Fig. 12–2 which shows the range of working temperatures for carbon steels.

Hot-working has several major disadvantages. It requires heat-resistant tools which are relatively expensive. The high temperatures oxidize and form scale on the surface of the metal. Close tolerances cannot be held. Cold-working is necessary to overcome these deficiencies.

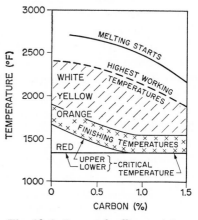

Fig. 12–2. Range of rolling and forging temperatures for carbon steel.

Cold-working. Cold-worked metal is formed to shape by the application of pressure at temperatures below the critical and for the most part nominally at room temperature. It is preceded by hot-working, removal of scale, and cleaning of the surface, usually by pickling. Cold-working is done mostly to hold close tolerances and produce good surface finishes but also to enhance the physical properties of the material.

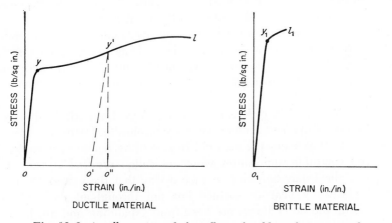

Fig. 12–3. An illustration of the effect of cold working a metal. Typical stress-strain relationships are depicted for room temperature.

When a piece of metal is initially subjected to stress, it is strained in proportion in an elastic manner as depicted by the line *oy* in Fig. 12–3. More stress causes permanent or inelastic deformation, along the line *yl*. The point *y* is called the *yield point*. Stresses and strains beyond it are in the region where cold-working must take place to change the shape of an object. What happens within the metal when it is cold-worked is described in Chap. 2.

The stress-strain diagram of Fig. 12–3 may typify tension, compression, or shear and the resulting strain in any one direction in a material as a basis for illustration. How such a curve is derived is explained in Chap. 3. The diagram at the left is characteristic of a ductile material, one that can stand considerable straining between its yield point, y, and point of rupture, l. That is the kind of material amenable to cold-working. The diagram at the right is indicative of a brittle material that breaks before it is deformed appreciably, like cast iron.

Consider that cold-working applies a stress to a ductile material and causes a plastic strain to point y' in Fig. 12–3. When the stress is released, the strain falls back slightly to point o' at zero stress. This constitutes an elastic return along path $y'o'$, which is parallel to yo, and accounts for the phenomenon called *springback* that always occurs when metal is cold-worked. When a piece is released from the shaping tools, it returns slightly towards its original shape.

Now assume that a material has been cold-worked and released to point o' in Fig. 12–3. If the material is again stressed in the same way, its yield point is then y', and further plastic stress takes place along the path $y'l$. In the cold-worked state, the material exhibits a new stress-strain relationship along $o'y'l$. Thus the material has a higher yield point, is harder, and has less ductility than before the original cold-working. The more the material is cold-worked, the closer its properties approach those of a brittle material illustrated on the right of Fig. 12–3.

The natural effect of most cold-working operations is to apply much more stress in one direction than in others. Thus in one direction the material may be strained to the equivalent of point o' with a yield point y' as in Fig. 12–3, but to points closer to o and yield points closer to y in other directions.

Strains that occur in different or opposite directions within the same piece often react upon each other when the applicable forces and stresses are released. That keeps the material from settling back to a completely unstressed condition and causes what are called *residual stresses*. For example, a sheet may be rolled in such a way that the material is compressed plastically near its surface but not throughout its thickness. After rolling, the outer layers are kept from expanding and are held in compression by tension exerted by the inner material which resists being stretched.

Strain hardening that results in a loss of ductility, in residual stresses, and in directional properties is desirable in some products but not in others.

If a metal is cold-worked along line oyl to a point close to l in Fig. 12–3, further cold-working will lead to failure. This can be averted and the metal returned to or near its original state, depicted by point *o*, by *annealing* or *normalizing* as described in Chap. 5. When a metal is plastically cold-worked, its crystals are deformed internally by forced movements of their atomic planes with respect to each other. The crystals become distorted, disarrayed, and broken. Their resistance to further movement increases. If the metal is heated above its recrystallization temperature, its atoms reform into natural crystals, and the metal reverts towards its original condition.

Relatively large forces must be exerted for cold-working. That means that equipment must be proportionately rugged and powerful, particularly for rapid production. Even so, many products can be finished by cold-working to close limits and with good finishes at lower cost than by other means. Cold-working processes have a major and basic role in most high production industries.

ROLLING

Principles of metal rolling. When metal is rolled, it passes and is squeezed between two revolving rolls in the manner indicated in Fig. 12–4. The crystals are elongated in the direction of rolling, and the material emerges at a faster rate than it enters. In hot-rolling the crystals start to reform after leaving the zone of stress, but in cold-rolling they retain substantially the shape given them by the action of the rolls.

The rolls make contact with the metal over a length of contact depicted by arc *AB* in Fig. 12–4. At some point of contact the surfaces of the material and roll move at the same speed. This is the no-slip point, *C*, in Fig. 12–4. From *C* to the exit at *A* the metal is in effect being extruded and moves faster than the roll surface. In that zone, friction on the surface of the metal is opposed to the direction of travel, and that sets up stresses within the metal that hinder its reduction. Between *C* and *B* the metal is moving slower than the roll, and friction acts in the direction to draw the metal between the rolls. The position of the no-slip point *C* in the length of contact *AB* depends upon the conditions of the operation, such as the diameter of the rolls, the amount of reduction, etc. As the angle of contact increases, *C* tends to move to *A*. When the angle of contact exceeds the angle of friction, the rolls cannot draw the ma-

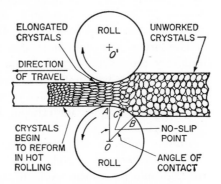

Fig. 12–4. A sketch to show what happens when metal is rolled.

terial spontaneously into the space between them. When the angle of contact is more than twice the angle of friction between roll and work, point *C* coincides with *A*, and the metal cannot be drawn through by the rolls even if placed between them. That is because the horizontal component of the normal pressure of the rolls against the metal equals and nullifies the horizontal component of friction tending to draw the metal along.

As the metal is squeezed together between the rolls, it is elongated because it is incompressible. To accomplish this, the rolls have to apply both normal squeezing and frictional drawing pressures. Normal pressure of the rolls on the work is usually one to several times the amount of the yield stress of the metal. The pressure may rise to several hundred thousand pounds per square inch in severe operations. The frictional force between roll and work in the driving direction approaches the normal force times the coefficient of friction. This friction force times the surface speed of the rolls determines the power.

Both the frictional and normal pressures that the rolls must apply to stretch the work can be reduced appreciably if axial tension is applied to the work either fore or aft or both. For instance, it has been found with a metal having a yield strength of y psi that the maximum normal pressure of $3y$ without tension falls to y when axial tension of $\frac{1}{2}y$ is applied front and back to the strip. This is commonly done in cold-rolling.

The larger the reduction in size of work as it goes through the rolls, the larger the forces, the more the power, and the greater the instantaneous stresses within the material. The power and strength of the equipment and the workability of the metal determine the amount of reduction that may be undertaken at any one time.

Rolling mills. A rolling mill is commonly designated by the number and arrangement of its rolls as indicated in Fig. 12–5. A non-reversing two high mill passes the work in one direction only. The stock may be passed back over the top of the rolls, but that is slow, or it may go through a series of rolls for successive reductions. The latter is faster but requires more investment in equipment. The work may be passed back and forth through a reversing two high mill for successive reductions but extra power is required to overcome inertia in reversing the heavy rolls rapidly. Even so, some time is lost between passes. The work can be passed between the bottom two rolls of a three high mill and then raised by an elevator and passed back between the top two rolls. Large backing rolls support small working rolls in four high and cluster mills. Small rolls are weak by themselves but are cheaper to replace as they wear, make contact with the work over less area, tend to spread the work less sideways, are subject to smaller separating forces, and require less power than large rolls. These common varieties of rolling mills and

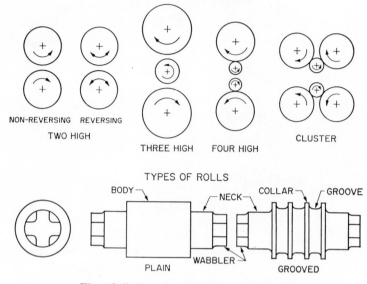

Fig. 12–5. Types of rolls and rolling mills.

their relative advantages and disadvantages illustrate the alternatives that an engineer commonly has in designing equipment. His problem is to ascertain the operating and capital costs of each to find the one which gives the lowest total cost for his particular application.

Plain rolls, as depicted in Fig. 12–5, serve for flat sections, and grooved rolls for bars and shapes. Mostly they are made of cast iron or cast or forged steel. Roll design is a challenging engineering problem. The dimensions and properties of each roll must be selected for optimum conditions of hardness, wear-resistance, strength, rigidity, and shock-resistance. Chilled cast iron rolls are hard but have high residual stresses. Strength, rigidity, and toughness can be obtained in steel rolls, particularly alloy steel, at a price. Stronger materials make possible smaller rolls with their inherent advantages. The material in a roll must not have affinity for the work material. Hot-rolls are commonly rough, even notched, to bite the work, but cold-rolls are highly finished to impart good finish. A brief description of roll grinding is given in Chap. 29.

A set of rolls in their massive housing is called a *stand*. A number of stands may be arranged in a row in a continuous mill like the one in Fig. 12–6. In operation, the metal runs continuously through all the stands at once. For jobbing, the stands may be side by side. When the work is finished in one stand, it is moved to the next, etc. These arrangements have many variations to suit specific conditions. Each mill is designed and operated for a limited range of products. For instance, a huge mill for rolling chunks of steel with a cross-sectional area of almost

Fig. 12–6. A 72 in. continuous sheet strip mill. (Courtesy Bethlehem
Steel Co.)

four square feet is not economical for rolling small pieces of less than a
square foot in area across. The small pieces can be rolled as well on a
less powerful mill that costs only a fraction as much. On the other hand,
each mill can take pieces only so big. Also, to change rolls, particularly
in a large mill, is costly. For that reason, when a mill is set up for some
particular shape or shapes, it is economical to keep it on the same work.

Most rolling mills today have a full complement of equipment to
handle the work, particularly hot-work, mechanically all along the line.

Hot-rolling steels. After being melted and refined as described in
Chap. 4, a metal is cast into a form called an *ingot* in preparation for
rolling. Steel ingots are held and heated in a soaking pit to a uniform
temperature throughout of about the maximum indicated by Fig. 12–2.
A soaking pit is a large furnace lined with refractory silica brick, having
a neutral or reducing atmosphere, and usually loaded from the top. Not
much can be done in the pit to improve the quality of the steel, but care
must be taken not to depreciate it by under-, over-, or unevenly-heating
the ingot.

Ingots are rolled into blooms or slabs as indicated in Fig. 12–7. This

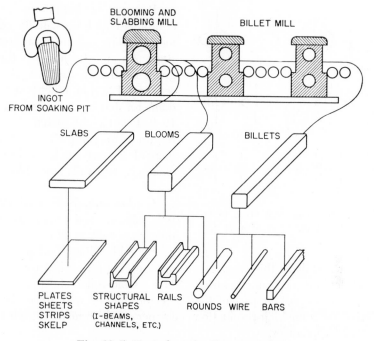

Fig. 12–7. Typical steel rolling procedure.

is done rapidly before the metal cools below the working temperature. A typical performance is to reduce an ingot almost 2 ft square down to a bloom 6 in. square in about 2 minutes, all in about 17 passes through the rolls. Most blooming mills are two high reversible mills. The work is turned 90° between heavy reductions to work it uniformly on all sides. The ends of the blooms are sheared away to remove cavities or pipes carried over from the ingot. At the same time the bloom may be cut to convenient lengths for later operations.

The great bulk of flat plates, sheets and strips are rolled in continuous mills from slabs or directly from ingots. For premium quality products, defects are removed from the surfaces of slabs by pneumatic chipping or oxy-acetylene scarfing. Structural shapes are rolled from blooms. For bars, rods, or wire, the blooms are customarily reduced to billets. If the temperature drops too low during processing, the blooms may be reheated.

Blooms, billets, and slabs are semi-finished shapes with rectangular sections and rounded corners. A bloom generally has a square cross section with an area of 36 sq in. or more. A slab is 1½ in. or more in thickness with a width at least 1½ times its thickness. A billet is 1½ in. or more in both thickness and width and has an area between 2¼ and 36 sq in.

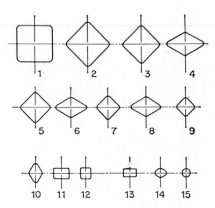

Fig. 12–8. The steps taken to reduce a 4 x 4 in. billet to a ¾ in.-diameter bar.

Because of limitations in the equipment and workability of the metal, rolling is done in progressive steps. An illustration of this is given by the 15 steps required to reduce a 4 × 4 in. billet to a ¾ in.-diameter bar as indicated in Fig. 12–8. From eight to ten steps are required to complete most commercial shapes, such as I-beams, channels, and rails from blooms.

Cold-rolling. Bars of all shapes, rods, sheets, and strips are commonly finished in all common metals by cold-rolling. Foil is made of the softer metals in this way. Steel bars are cold-rolled but usual practice is to cold-draw diameters under 3¾ in. Cold-rolled sheets and strips make up an important part of total steel production and are major raw materials for some high-production consumer goods industries, such as for household appliances.

Two main reasons for cold-rolling metals are to get good surface finishes and improved physical properties, such as springiness in sheets. Sheet steel less than about 0.050 in. thick is cold-rolled as a matter of course because it cools too rapidly for practical hot-rolling. Cold-rolling results in uniform thickness and workability in sheets and close tolerances on bar sizes. Machinability of steel is improved by cold-rolling, and for that reason cold-rolled or -drawn stock is widely used in fast automatic machining operations.

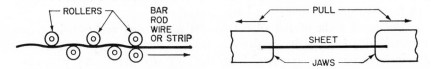

Fig. 12–9. The principles of operation of typical straightening devices.

Material may need to be straightened at any stage of fabrication. Common practice is to pass bar stock, rods, wire, sheets, or strip through a series of rollers as depicted in Fig. 12–9. This is called *roller levelling.* Sheets are *stretcher levelled* or straightened by pulling them between jaws to induce a tensile stress throughout slightly in excess of the yield strength.

Steel is pickled prior to cold-rolling to clean the surface and remove scale. Sheets or strips are often given a light cold-rolling at first to establish a good surface finish and uniform thickness as a basis for good quality from later heavy cold-rolling. Most work is done with small rolls in four high or cluster mills and frequently tension is applied at either end or both ends of the sheet or strip to minimize the effects of the high pressures of cold-rolling. As thickness is reduced by cold-rolling, the metal becomes harder and less ductile for the reasons previously explained and may have to be annealed. If a bright finish but not hardness is desirable, the material may be annealed just before the final rolling pass. Cold-rolling is a practical means of producing the degree of hardness wanted in material. Cold-rolled sheets and strips are classified commercially as skin-rolled, ¼ hard, ½ hard, and full hard to denote amounts of reduction up to 50% without annealing.

Quality and cost. Typical commercial thickness tolerances for cold-rolled carbon steel sheets or strips 20 in. wide are ±0.002, ±0.005, and ±0.007 in. for thicknesses of 0.015, 0.060, and 0.180 in., respectively. Wider sheets are given more tolerance, and narrower ones less. Hot-rolled sheets have tolerances of about ±0.001 more for each size. Alloy steel and aluminum sheet and strip tolerances are about the same as for carbon steel.

Cold-rolled sheets and strips are given surface finishes varying all the way from smooth and bright as a base for chrome plating to a rough matted finish for enamelling.

Hot-rolled round low-carbon steel bars have tolerances for size of from ±0.007 in. for the smallest to ±0.010 in. for 1 in.-diameter, and larger tolerances for larger sizes. Indicative for cold finished bars is a tolerance of +0.000 and −0.002 in. for 1 in.-diameter low-carbon steel. The tolerances are larger for larger sizes, higher carbon content, and alloys of steel. Cold-drawn bars can be expected to be straight within $\frac{1}{32}$ in. in 5 ft. As a rule cold-drawn bars have better precision and finish than cold-rolled bars, but ground bars are the highest in quality.

The values added by working steel into commercial shapes are indicated by the following relative prices. Pig iron was $67 and steel scrap about $35 per ton. Alloy steel in ingot form was $82, bloom or slab $119, plate $150, hot-rolled strip $168, hot-rolled bar $134, and cold-finished bar $180 per ton. For comparison the prices of comparable shapes of plain-carbon steel were bloom or slab $80, hot-rolled sheet or strip about $105, cold-rolled strip $143, hot-rolled bar $114, and cold-finished bar $153 per ton. These were base prices for large quantities at the mill. Any sizes, compositions or requirements other than standard add to the price. Cost may be two to three times as much for small quantities from a distributor.

COLD-DRAWING

Round, rectangular, square, hexagonal and other shapes of bar up to about 4 in. across or in diameter, wire of all sizes, and tubes are commonly finished by cold-drawing. Wire cannot be hot-rolled economically smaller than about 0.2 in. in diameter and is reduced to smaller sizes by cold-drawing. Steel, aluminum, and copper and its alloys are cold-drawn in important quantities.

Cold-drawing operations. Hot-rolled stock is descaled, cleaned, and prepared for drawing. A common way of treating steel is to immerse it in hot sulfuric acid, rinse, coat with lime, and bake. The leading end of a piece is tapered for insertion through the die. The action as the work is pulled through the die is illustrated in Fig. 12–10. A piece is pulled through a hole of smaller size and emerges correspondingly reduced in size. Wire is pulled by being wound on a drum as it comes out of the die. Rods, bars, and tubes are pulled in a straight line by mechanical means. A mandrel is inserted in a tube to control the size of the inside diameter.

Drawing pressure against a die must exceed the yield strength of the work material and commonly is as much as 100,000 to 300,000 psi for steel. Steel is only able to slide through a die if coated by a lubricant that stands up under such tremendous pressures. Soap is commonly applied and is fixed to the surface by the lime coating which in turn is anchored by a soft oxide coating, called the *sull,* left by pickling. A thin copper or tin and copper plate also provides a good bearing surface on steel. It has been aptly said that what actually is drawn is a tenuous cylinder of copper or soap-lime-sull inside of which a steel core is squeezed to a new shape.

Dies must be hard and wear-resistant as well as strong. They are made of chilled iron, hardened alloy steel, cemented carbide, and diamonds. The harder materials last longer but cost more.

The force to pull a wire or bar through a die is transmitted by tensile stress in the material that has just left the die. This stress increases more than proportionately with the amount the area of the wire is reduced by the draw. The stress in the material leaving the die may not exceed the yield stress. Theoretically the yield stress is approached with a reduction in area of 50%. In practice a reduction in area of less than 40% for each pass usually is found desirable. If the wire must be reduced more, it is passed through several dies. After a number of draws, a work-hardening material like steel becomes so brittle it must be annealed if it is to be drawn further.

Coarse low-carbon steel wire for fences, bolts, etc. may be drawn

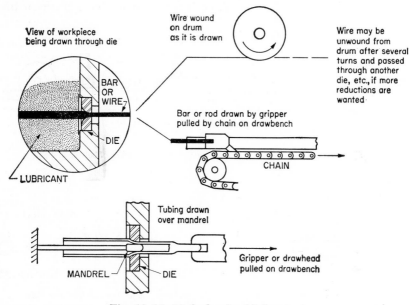

Fig. 12–10. Methods of cold drawing.

just once; hard bright wire is produced by several draws after annealing. Soft wire is annealed after being drawn. A soft bright wire is annealed and then given a final mild draw. Heat-treated steel with a carbon content of 0.3 to 1.2% is made into stiff and high-strength music wire, spring wire, wire for brushes, etc.

Bars are reduced from $\frac{1}{64}$ to $\frac{1}{8}$ in. by cold-drawing from the hot-rolled size. The amount depends on the size and composition of the bar and the extent to which it is desired to change the physical properties.

MANUFACTURE OF PIPE AND TUBING

Butt welded pipe. Pipe with a welded seam is made from a strip, originally flat, called the *skelp*. Its edges are bevelled enough to butt together when the skelp is rounded. The skelp is heated to welding temperature and is gripped at one end by tongs pulled by a draw chain. This pulls the skelp through a welding bell which forces it into a circular shape as depicted in Fig. 12–11(A). The edges of the hot skelp are pressed and welded together.

For continuous butt welding of pipe, the skelp is used in coils, and the ends of the coils are welded together to make a continuous strip. Flames are directed to the edges to heat them to welding temperature as the skelp passes through a furnace. From the furnace, the skelp passes through a series of grooved rolls and is formed into pipe as illustrated in

Fig. 12–11(B). Pipe as large as three inches in diameter is made in this way.

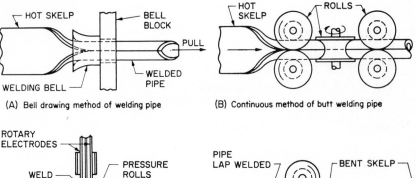

(A) Bell drawing method of welding pipe   (B) Continuous method of butt welding pipe

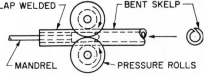

(C) Continuous resistance butt welding pipe   (D) Method of lap welding pipe from bent skelp

Fig. 12–11. Methods of welding pipe.

Continuous steel strip is roll-formed to a circular shape to prepare it for electric-resistance welding. The principles of roll-forming are described in Chap. 13. After being roll-formed, the pipe passes between pressure rolls that hold the edges together and electrode rolls that supply current to create welding heat at the joint. This arrangement, indicated in Fig. 12–11(C), is used for pipe up to 16 in. in diameter and wall thickness of ⅛ to ½ inch. Larger pipes are commonly formed in large presses and welded by the submerged-arc method.

After being formed and welded, pipe is normally passed through sizing and finishing rolls that make it round, bring it to size, and help remove scale. Continuously made pipe is cut to desired lengths. Cutters remove the extruded flash metal from both inside and outside of the larger sizes of pipes.

Lap welded pipe. The edges are bevelled as the skelp comes from the furnace to make lap welded pipe. The skelp is then rounded in one of the ways previously described but with the edges overlapping. It is then reheated and passed over a mandrel between two rolls as illustrated in Fig. 12–11(D) to press and weld the lapped edges together. Lap welded pipe ranges in size from 2 to 16 in. in diameter.

Seamless tubing. Seamless steel tubing is pierced from heated billets passed between tapered rolls and over a mandrel in the manner depicted

in Fig. 12–12. The rolls are shaped so that their surfaces converge on the entering end to a minimum distance apart called the "gorge". From there the surfaces diverge to the exit end. The billet may have a small center hole drilled in the end. It is pushed and guided be-

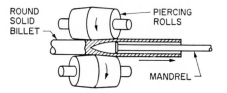

Fig. 12–12. The Mannesmann process of tube piercing.

tween the rolls, which are set to grip it in the entering taper. The rolls revolve with a surface speed of about 1000 fpm in the direction shown. Their axes are crossed, and so they impart axial as well as rolling movement to the billet and force it over the mandrel. The mandrel can revolve, and the material is in effect helically rolled over the mandrel and not extruded. Shells as long as 40 ft and up to 6 in. in diameter are produced in 10 to 30 seconds in this way. A second piercing operation is applied for sizes up to about 14 in., and a third of similar kind for still larger sizes. The pierced shells are given subsequent rolling and sizing operations to make finished tubes.

Seamless steel tubing is available in almost all compositions and alloys of steel and in common nonferrous metals such as aluminum, brass, copper, etc. It is the natural form from which to make many thin-walled round objects. Seamless tubing is a popular and economical raw stock for machining because it saves drilling and boring of many parts.

Tubes from some hard-to-work steel alloys and nonferrous metals are not easily pierced and are produced by other methods. One way is to draw and redraw cups from hot plates in the manner described for drawing in Chap. 13. The bottom of a long cup may be cut off to make a tube. Tubes also are extruded. That process is discussed in a later section in this chapter.

FORGING

Forging is the forming of metal, mostly hot, by individual and inter-mittent applications of pressure instead of applying continuous pressure as in rolling. The products generally are discontinuous also, treated and turned out as discrete pieces rather than as a flowing mass. The forging process may work metal by compressing its cross section and making it longer, by squeezing it lengthwise and increasing its cross section, or by squeezing it within and making it to conform to the shape of a cavity.

Forging may be classified as done in open or closed dies. Open die forgings are generally struck between two flat surfaces, but in practice the dies are sometimes vee shaped, half round and half oval. Closed die forgings are formed in die cavities. Closed dies require less skill to operate and produce faster and to smaller tolerances than open dies.

Forging is done in various ways to suit particular purposes. The common forms to be described here are hammer, drop, press, upset, and roll forging.

Heating the work. It is important that a piece of material be heated uniformly throughout and to the proper temperature for forging. The proper temperature range for steel has been indicated in Fig. 12–2. Heating is done in furnaces of various sizes to suit specific needs and in forms from the open forge fire to refractory lined furnaces with precise atmospheric and temperature controls. A simple and popular type is in the shape of a box lined with fire brick and having a single door through which the pieces are put in and taken out. For production work, furnaces are used with lengthwise conveyors or rotary hearts to hold work for a set heating time and then discharge it. Gas and oil are economical, easily controlled, and mostly used as fuels. A non-oxidizing atmosphere generally is maintained for surface protection. The use of electricity is growing, particularly for induction heating where only a bit of each piece needs to be heated.

Hammer forging. The well known and simple form of hammer forging is that done by the blacksmith. A hot workpiece is placed on an anvil and struck repeatedly by a hammer. That is done mostly by machines today. The blows must be heavy to exert high pressures that penetrate and knead the material deeply and work it uniformly and completely. Light blows are undesirable because they are likely to affect only the material near the surface. On cooling, the inner structure then differs from the outer, and the part lacks the strength of homogeneity and the flow lines of complete forging.

A mechanical hammer raises a heavy weight and drops it on an anvil. Various means have been employed. The *helve hammer* is widely used for light work, particularly to strike blows rapidly. It has a beam with a fulcrum at the middle, a heavy hammer at one end, and a revolving cam applied to the other end to raise and release the hammer repeatedly.

The most common forging hammers are steam or air operated. A single-frame steam forging hammer that gives access to the anvil from three directions is illustrated in Fig. 12–13. A double frame is stronger

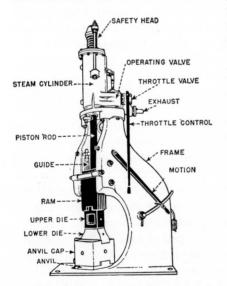

Fig. 12–13. A single-frame steam forging hammer. (Courtesy Drop Forging Association.)

SAFETY HEAD

OPERATING VALVE

STEAM CYLINDER

THROTTLE VALVE

EXHAUST

THROTTLE CONTROL

PISTON ROD

FRAME

GUIDE

MOTION

RAM

UPPER DIE

LOWER DIE

ANVIL CAP

ANVIL

and is in the form of an arch around the hammer and anvil, which can be reached only from two directions. Most steam hammers today are double acting; the hammer is driven down by the steam pressure as well as by gravity. To keep down vibration, the anvil for open die work is mounted on its own foundation separate from the frame. The effective work done by the hammer depends on the weight of the anvil. Ratios of 20:1 or more between anvil and hammer weights are found in standard hammers.

The ability of a hammer to deform metal depends on the energy it is able to deliver on impact. The energy from falling is augmented by the work derived from the steam in a double acting hammer. Steam pressures are commonly from 75 to 125 psi. As an example, a hammer has a falling weight of 2000 lb and a steam cylinder bore, d, equal to 12 in. Mean effective steam pressure, p, is assumed to be 80 psi, and the stroke is 30 in.

The steam force $= \dfrac{\pi d^2}{4} \times p = \dfrac{\pi \times 12^2}{4} \times 80 = 9050$ lb.

Total downward force $= 9050 + 2000 = 11,050$ lb.

Energy in blow $= 11,050 \times 30 = 331,500$ in.-lb.

If the hammer travels ⅛ in. after striking the metal, the average force exerted $= 331,500/0.125 = 2,652,000$ lb $= 1326$ tons.

The amount of energy and force needed for a particular job is a matter of economics. A large hammer is expensive but can concentrate the energy to work the metal deeply and quickly. A small hammer may do the job but works lightly and takes the time for many blows. A starting rule is that a hammer should have at least 50 lb of falling weight for every square inch of cross-sectional area to be worked in the metal.

The size of a hammer is designated by the weight of the reciprocating parts that contribute to the blow. Air hammers range in capacity from 100 to 5000 lb; steam hammers from 600 to 80,000 lb. A single-frame steam forging hammer, rated at 6000 lb, has a total weight of 148,000 lb and costs about $40,000.

Drop forging. Drop forging is the name given to the operation of forming parts hot on a drop hammer with impression or cavity dies. The products are known as *drop forgings, closed-die forgings,* or *impression-die forgings.* They are made from carbon and alloy steels and alloys of aluminum, copper, magnesium, and nickel.

Stock in the form of the heated end of a bar, slug, or individual billet is placed in a cavity in the bottom half of a forging die on the anvil of a drop hammer. An example of a die is shown in Fig. 12–14. The upper half is attached to the hammer or ram and falls on the stock, which is made to flow into and fill the cavity. Generally a finished forging cannot be formed in one blow because the directions and extent to which the

Fig. 12–14. A set of forging dies and illustrations of the successive steps for forging a connecting rod. (Courtesy Drop Forging Association.)

metal can be forced at any one time are limited. Thus most dies have several impressions, each a step toward the final shape. The workpiece is transferred from one impression to another between blows. Excess metal not needed to fill the cavity is squeezed into a thin flange around the forging called the *flash*. This is sheared from the forging in a subsequent trimming operation. Scale collects in the die from the hot workpiece and is removed by blowing with a blast of air or steam.

Most forging dies are made of heavy blocks of forged alloy steel heat treated to less than maximum hardness but to a toughness to resist shock. The cavities are cut or *sunk* to allow for shrinkage in the workpiece when it cools. In addition to size, a die is designed to produce a forging with a minimum of residual stress and the most benefit from the original grain fibers of the bar. This requires enough but not too many stations, as dictated by a careful study of each case. The die is provided with draft to release the workpiece readily and generous fillets, radii, and ribs to prolong die life. At times locking surfaces or pins are provided to make the two halves of a die match the same way each time they come together. The die establishes the efficiency of an operation. Rules and standards for good die design are given in reference- and hand-books on the subject. For large quantity production, a die may have cavities in groups to produce several pieces at a time.

Drop hammers. A drop hammer has a guided falling hammer or ram but differs from a forging hammer by having the anvil attached to the frame. This to keep the upper and lower halves of a die aligned.

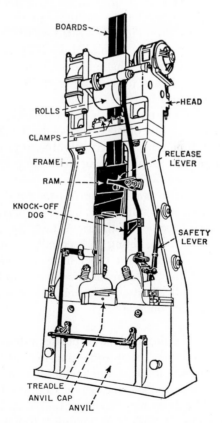

Fig. 12–15. A board drop hammer. (Courtesy Drop Forging Association.)

The board drop hammer illustrated in Fig. 12–15 is suitable for small and moderate size forgings. The ram is fastened to the lower ends of vertical hardwood boards. These pass between powered friction rolls that press from opposite sides against the boards when the ram is down. The revolving rolls raise the boards, which become latched in their uppermost position. Tripping the press releases the boards and allows the ram to drop. Maintenance and down time cost are relatively high. One study showed that boards had to be replaced every week, and about 14% of the work time was lost each year.

The ram is lifted by compressed air acting on a piston in an overhead cylinder on another type of drop hammer. In one design, an air clamp locks the piston rod to hold the ram in its uppermost position. The clamp is released when the press is tripped, and the ram drops. Power may cost several times as much as for a board drop hammer, but repair and down time costs are almost negligible. Because of relatively low total costs, air operated drop hammers have been gaining in favor.

The same factors as explained for forging hammers determine the energy and force delivered by a drop hammer. Direct calculations to determine what capacity is needed are quite complex. An empirical rule of thumb is that a gravity drop hammer's rated size in pounds should be equal to the product of the area of the final die impression and the flash times 45 to 75, depending on the shape and type of material. A double-acting steam drop hammer may have a rating of ⅝ of that of a gravity drop hammer but be suited for the same job.

Board drop hammers are made with ram capacities of 400 to 10,000 lb. One with a rated capacity of 4000 lb weighs 136,800 lb and costs about $50,000. Air drop hammers are comparable in price, not including air compression equipment. Double-acting steam drop hammers for large work have capacities up to 50,000 lb.

An innovation of recent years is the *impact forging machine* that works through two horizontal opposed rams. Two halves of a die held by the rams are driven together at the same time by air cylinders and pound the work between them, acting on it equally from both sides. The impact of each is neutralized by the other instead of being absorbed in an anvil. Energy is not dissipated in the machine foundation, and there is a minimum of noise and vibration. The machine operates rapidly and fits well into high production lines.

Press forging. Press forging is done in presses rather than with hammers. The action is a relatively slow squeezing instead of pounding and penetrates deeply because it gives the metal time to flow. Dies may have less draft, and the forgings come nearer to desired sizes. Vibration and noise are less, and a press may have less bulk than a hammer of the same capacity. The largest and most complex forgings are made in presses. Powerful presses can produce small forgings three to four times faster than hammers because they have to act fewer times upon each piece. Die and press life are relatively long.

A press is rated on the basis of the force in tons it can deliver near the bottom of a stroke. A press usually does not have a number of chances like a hammer but is expected to have sufficient capacity to squeeze a forging to the desired shape in one crack. Pressures in tons per square inch of projected area on the parting plane have been found to be 5 to 20 for brass, 10 to 20 for aluminum, 15 to 30 for steel, and 20 to 40 for titanium. These values are for conventional forgings with adequate draft, fillets, etc. Precision forgings made in dies that confine the metal almost completely may require twice as much pressure. The force the press must deliver is equal to the unit pressure times the projected area.

Fig. 12–16. A 460,000 lb ingot being shaped on a 7500 ton forging press for a magnet yoke of a cyclotron. (Courtesy Bethlehem Steel Co.)

Presses for forging are similar to those described in Chap. 13. Hydraulic presses are often used for steel forging, particularly in large sizes, but mechanical presses are more often applied to nonferrous alloys and forgings under 30 lb in weight. The common mechanical drives for this service utilize eccentric, toggle, and screw mechanisms. Common press sizes are 500 to 6000 tons, but some of the largest presses, up to 50,000 tons capacity, have been built for forging.

Upset forging. Upset forging, also called *hot heading* and *machine forging,* consists of applying lengthwise pressure to a hot bar held between grooved dies to enlarge some section or sections, usually the end. Not only bulging, but piercing can also be done. The workpiece may have any original uniform cross section but is mostly round and may be of steel, aluminum, copper, bronze, or other metal. Upset forgings range in weight from a few ounces to several hundred pounds. Examples are automobile mushroom valves, gear blanks with stems, cluster gear blanks, shafts and levers with knobs or forks on their ends, and artillery shells. Many parts require several steps and a corresponding number of dies, like the example in Fig. 12–17.

Fig. 12–17. A set of four position upset forging dies and punches with an example of the work done at each position. The product is a blank for an automobile cluster gear. (Courtesy The Ajax Manufacturing Co.)

Fig. 12–18. A five inch upset forging machine. (Courtesy The Ajax Manufacturing Co.)

Upset forging is done on a machine similar to the one in Fig. 12–18. A piece of hot stock is placed in the cavity on one side of the die. The machine is tripped, closes the two halves of the die to grip the stock, pushes the punch in to upset the stock, retracts the punch and opens the die. The stock is moved to the next die station, and the cycle is repeated.

Although used for many other parts, an upset forging machine is rated by the largest diameter bolt it is capable of heading. Some take bolts up to 8 in.-diameter and exert 2000 tons of force. A medium size

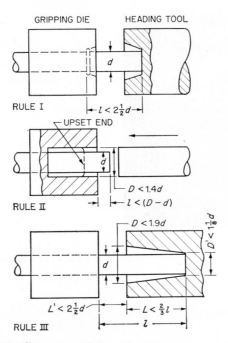

Fig. 12–19. Illustrations of the rules governing upset forging.

machine for 2 in.-diameter bolts weighs 47,000 lb and costs about $45,000.

Enough material must be gathered from the original stock to fill out ultimately the volume of an upset forging. The amount of stock that may be extended safely from the dies in any one stroke to be gathered into the upset is indicated by the rules depicted in Fig. 12–19. Experience has proven that if an attempt is made to gather too much at once, the stock bends out of control, and damage may result. The rules given here may be exceeded somewhat, but only on the authority of an expert. Repeated applications of these rules make it possible to gather large amounts of stock by a series of steps.

Roll forging. Two half rolls are arranged on parallel shafts for roll forging as shown in the end views of Fig. 12–20. These roll segments have one or more sets of grooves. A piece of stock is placed between the rolls, which then turn and squeeze the stock in one set of grooves. The stock is transferred to a second set of grooves, the rolls turn again, and so on until the piece is finished. Each set of grooved segments is made to do a specific job. By this method bar stock can be increased in length, reduced in diameter, and changed in section as desired. Because it is rapid, roll forging is of advantage in preparing some shapes for forging machines and hammers and also for completely forging parts like levers, leaf springs, and axles.

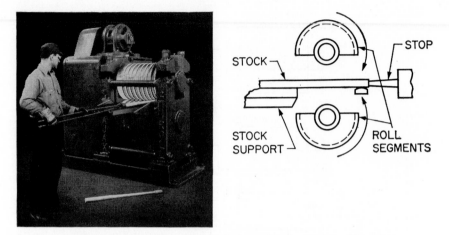

Fig. 12–20. A roll forging machine with 25 in. wide rolls and a sketch to illustrate its method of operation. (Photo courtesy Ajax Manufacturing Co.)

Another kind of rolling and forging, called *die rolling,* is a continuous high production operation for simple parts like shafts, axles, and levers. Heated bars are passed through a set of rolls with die sunk imprints around their peripheries. Formed pieces emerge in a line with flash to be trimmed from them later.

Quality and cost. The dimensions of a series of forgings from a die vary because of differences in the behavior of the material, temperatures, and closing of the die, mismatch of the die halves, and enlargement of the cavities as they wear. A tolerance of $\pm\frac{1}{32}$ in. is considered good for small forgings and may be as large as ¼ in. in all for large pieces. Tolerances of 0.010 in. and less have been held on precision press forgings, but at costs that can be justified only in exceptional cases, such as some aircraft work. Tables of commercial tolerances for various sizes and kinds of forgings are available in reference- and hand-books.

Many forgings are finished by machining to close tolerances and must have enough stock on the surfaces to be machined. The least stock is about 0.060 in. per surface on small forgings, and may be as much as 0.250 in. on large ones.

Parts made from forgings may be made also as castings, cut from standard shapes, fabricated by welding pieces together, or made in other ways. For a particular size, a forging may be selected because it has more strength, shock- and fatigue-resistance, and durability. It may provide the needed qualities with less weight. On the other hand, a forging may offer the cheapest means for producing a part.

Forgings are economical in some cases because less material has to be removed from them than from bar stock. An example is given by a brass

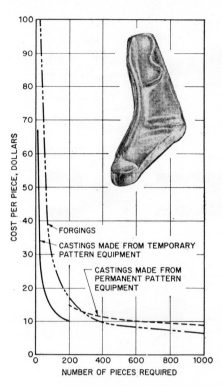

COST PER PIECE, DOLLARS

NUMBER OF PIECES REQUIRED

FORGINGS

CASTINGS MADE FROM TEMPORARY
PATTERN EQUIPMENT

CASTINGS MADE FROM
PERMANENT PATTERN
EQUIPMENT

Fig. 12–21. The unit cost of a 3½ lb brace for various quantities and two methods of manufacture. (From *Metals Handbook, 1955 Supplement,* by permission of the American Society for Metals.)

compression fitting originally machined from 1¾ in.-diameter hexagonal rod. Each lot of 5000 pieces required 1580 lb of brass at $0.1492 per lb, a total of $235.74. A forging was made from round stock and cost $0.1376 per lb. Each lot required 932 lb at a total cost of $128.24. In addition to the material savings of $107.50, or $0.0215 per piece, shortening of machining time raised the total savings to about $0.03 per piece. A forging die costing about $400 was paid for by the savings from three lots.

Dies are expensive and usually rule out forgings for small quantities. This is illustrated by Fig. 12–21 which shows a casting to be cheaper for less than about 300 pieces in one case. In this instance the forging dies cost about 3½ times as much as the temporary pattern equipment and 15% more than the permanent pattern equipment. The scrap loss is much less for the forging, which is more economical in large quantities.

EXTRUSION

Principles. When metal is extruded, it is compressed above its elastic limit in a chamber and is forced to flow through and take on the shape of an opening. An everyday analogy is the dispensing of toothpaste from a collapsible tube. Metal is extruded in a number of basic ways as depicted in Fig. 12–22. The metal is normally compressed by a ram and may be pushed forward or backward. The product may be solid or hollow. The process may be done hot or cold. The problems and results of hot and cold extrusion are somewhat different, and the two methods will be discussed separately.

Hot extrusion. Forward hot extrusion of solid or hollow shapes enables the metal to be easily supported, handled, and freed from the equipment. When a piece is forward extruded, it is cut off, and the butt end is removed from the chamber.

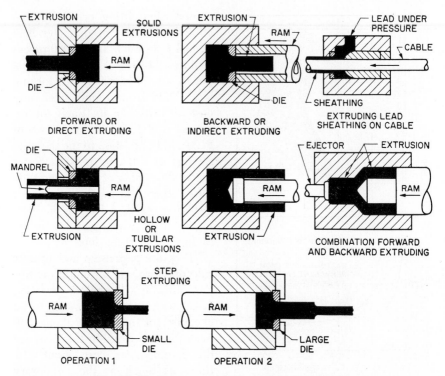

Fig. 12-22. Common methods of extruding metal.

Preservation of the equipment subjected to high temperatures and pressures, as it is, is the major problem of hot extrusion. Temperatures are 650° to 800°F for magnesium, 800° to 900°F for aluminum, 1200° to 1650°F for copper alloys, and 2200° to 2400°F for steel. Pressures normally are from 80,000 to 100,000 psi. Lubrication and protection of the chamber, ram, and die are necessary. Mopping these parts with an oil and graphite mixture may be sufficient at the lower temperatures. Glass, which becomes a molten lubricant, has made possible the extrusion of steel at high temperatures. Components like the ram and mandrel may be sprayed with cooling water while idle. A dummy block is used between the ram and hot metal. For extruding steel, the die is changed and allowed to cool for each piece. The best safeguard for equipment is to extrude the metal as rapidly as possible. A steel tube 6 in. in diameter and 50 ft long is extruded in 9 seconds.

Most hot extrusion is done on horizontal hydraulic presses especially constructed for the purpose. Common sizes are rated from 250 to 5500 tons, but some designs in recent years have reached as high as 25,000 tons. One with 12,000 tons capacity is illustrated in Fig. 12-23.

Applications of hot extrusion. Most hot extrusions are long pieces of uniform cross section, but tapered and stepped pieces are also producible.

Fig. 12–23. A 12,000 ton extrusion press for seamless steel tubing. The press is 126 ft long, 22 ft high, and cost $7,500,000 installed. It is capable of turning out alloy and stainless steel tubes up to 20 in. diameter and 50 ft long. (Courtesy Curtiss Wright Corp.)

Fig. 12–24. A few shapes extruded from aluminum for aircraft. Millions of pounds of aluminum extruded shapes are used each year in the aircraft industry to put the greatest strength where it is needed with the least weight and at the lowest cost. (Courtesy Aluminum Company of America.)

Examples of commercial extruded products are trim and molding strips of aluminum and brass and structural shapes, rods, bars, and tubes of all forms of aluminum and steel. A few aluminum sections are shown in Fig. 12–24. Sections that can be contained within a 17 in.-diameter circle are available for aluminum and within a 6 in.-diameter circle for steel. Usual lengths are about 20 ft, but some are as long as 50 ft. Examples of other kinds of hot extrusions are poppet valves, gear blanks, projectile shells, and propeller and turbine blades.

A common workable tolerance for hot extrusions is ±0.005 in. Surface finishes of 150 microinches are obtainable economically.

Shapes that can be rolled are more expensive to extrude, but extrusion can produce many shapes, such as those with re-entrant angles, that cannot be rolled or produced in other ways. In some cases, extrusion offers an economical way to make small parts in large quantities. A simple pump gear is an example. A long gear is extruded and then sliced into a number of individual gears. In other cases, extrusion may be the cheapest way of making parts even in small quantities. Extrusion dies are not expensive, for most shapes they cost less than $150, and tools for other processes often cost much more.

Cold extrusion. The names of *impact extrusion, cold pressing, cold forging,* and *extrusion pressing* have been given to and are descriptive of various forms of cold extrusion. Although nominally done at room temperature, cold extrusion is quick, and the heat liberated can be expected to raise the temperature of the metal several hundred degrees for an instant. Also the slugs of some metals such as magnesium and zirconium are heated a few hundred degrees before cold extrusion. Even at room temperature, lead and tin are in the recrystallization range.

An old and until recent years the main cold extrusion operation was the manufacture of toothpaste and other collapsible tubes from soft aluminum, lead, tin, and zinc. To perform this operation, a slug of metal is placed at the bottom of a closed cavity. A punch strikes it sharply, and the metal squirts up around the punch to form the tube. The tube is blown off as the punch retracts. Production rates of 40 to 80 tubes a minute are reported. Copper tubes are forward extruded by similar operation. Because of the fast impulsive action, operations like these are called *impact extrusion.*

In recent years the extrusion of functional parts for aircraft, automobiles, appliances, etc. from high-strength aluminum alloys, copper alloys, steel and titanium has been developed. Cold extrusion of this sort is like precision press forging except that the metal is not hot. Pressures range from one to three times the finished yield strength of the metal; in tons per square inch from 25 to 50 for softer metals to 200 for some carbon steel and higher for alloy steel and titanium. Adequate lubrication is mandatory for flow at such high pressures. Oils and greases, some saponified, are the main lubricants. To extrude steel and other high-strength alloys cold, it was discovered necessary to apply a zinc phosphate or copper coating. This is not the lubricant but acts to hold the lubricant to the surface.

Cold extrusion is done mostly on vertical mechanical presses because they are fast and simple. Hydraulic presses are used for large work and where long strokes are necessary.

Applications of cold extrusion. Cold extrusion is done both to improve physical properties of a metal and to produce specific shapes. For example, an aluminum alloy with a yield strength of 6000 psi and tensile strength of 16,000 psi may acquire upon cold extrusion a yield strength of 30,000 psi and a tensile strength of 39,000 psi. Examples of cold extruded parts are cans, fire extinguisher cases, trimmer condensers, aircraft shear tie fittings and brackets, and automotive pistons from aluminum; also projectile shells, rocket motors and heads, hydraulic and shock-absorber cylinders, wrist pins, and gear blanks from steel.

Advantages of cold extrusion are that it is fast, can finish parts in few steps, can produce parts in large quantities with a low unit cost, causes little waste of material, can make parts with small radii and no draft, may save heat treatment in some cases, and requires relatively cheap tooling in many cases. Walls of parts have been held to ±0.010 in. tolerance when about $\frac{1}{8}$ thick and ±0.020 in. when thicker. Diameter tolerances normally are ±0.010 in., and length tolerances $\pm\frac{3}{16}$ in. Surface finishes of the order of 20 to 70 microinches are obtainable.

The limitations of cold extrusion are that only softer metals and simple shapes can be economically worked, equipment is available with capacity for only small and medium sizes of work, powerful and expensive presses must be used, and length to diameter ratio of a part is restricted to 10:1 for aluminum and 3:1 for steel.

Cold extrusion is competitive with deep-drawing from sheet metal, described in Chap. 13, for making cups and deep shells. Extrusion has the advantage of requiring fewer steps and cheaper tooling. For example, a round can 2 in.-diameter and 16 in. deep can be extruded in one operation but must be drawn in more than six operations. Tooling for this extrusion was estimated to cost one third as much as for drawing, even though an individual compressive die costs upwards of 50% more than a drawing die.

Cold extrusion is competitive with casting and forging for some parts. Extruded parts are commonly lighter and stronger than comparable cast parts. Tolerances are closer and less machining is required for extruded pieces. Because the physical properties of the metal are improved, cheaper metals can sometimes be used for extruded parts.

An illustration of the competitive situation of cold extrusion for making an aircraft aileron nose rib is given by Fig. 12–25. Little tooling investment was required to machine the part from barstock, and the cost

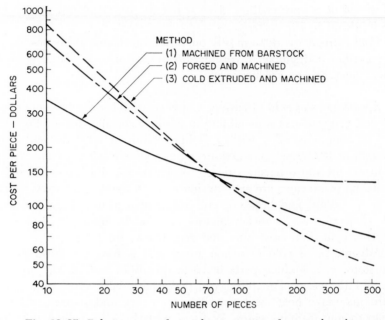

Fig. 12–25. Relative costs for making an aircraft part by three methods in various quantities.

per piece was the lowest by that method when few pieces were to be made. A forging required a little less tooling but more machining than an extrusion, which proved to be cheapest for more than 70 pieces.

Questions

1. How does a metal act above its recrystallization temperature?

2. What are five advantages of hot-working metal?

3. What are the disadvantages of hot-working metal?

4. Why is metal cold-worked?

5. Explain what happens to a metal when it is cold-worked.

6. What are residual stresses, and why do they occur?

7. Why is cold-worked metal annealed?

8. Describe what occurs in metal when it is rolled.

9. What advantage is gained by applying lengthwise tension to a piece being rolled?

10. Describe and specify the merits of the different kinds of rolling mills.

11. What are the forms through which steel goes when rolled into sheets or plates, structural shapes, and bars or rods?

12. Why are a number of passes required to roll a steel bar?

13. What benefits are obtained from cold-rolling metal?

14. How are metal wires or sheets straightened?

15. How is cold-rolling done?

16. How is metal cold-drawn? Why is it done?

17. What determines how much the area of a bar may be reduced when drawn through a single die and how much altogether when drawn through a series of dies?

18. Describe three ways of making butt welded pipe.

19. How is seamless tubing pierced?

20. What is important in heating the work for forging and how is it accomplished?

21. Compare open and closed die forging.

22. Why are heavy blows necessary for good forgings?

23. Describe the common kinds of forging hammers.

24. What determines how large a forging hammer should be?

25. How are drop forgings made?

26. How are a forging hammer and drop hammer alike and how do they differ?

27. What is press forging and how does it differ from drop forging?

28. What is upset forging and how is it done?

29. What are the limitations of upset forging?

30. What is roll forging and how is it done?

31. What is the order of tolerances that can be held by forging?

32. Under what conditions may forgings be selected for manufactured parts?

33. Describe the common ways of extruding metals.

34. What is done to help preserve equipment for hot extrusion?

35. What are the main applications for hot extrusion?

36. What is impact extrusion?

37. What are some of the applications of cold extrusion?

Problems

1. A 1 in. × 36 in. slab enters a hot-rolling mill at 500 fpm. It passes through seven stands and emerges as a strip ¼ in. × 36 in. What is the exit speed of the strip from the last set of rolls?

2. Draw a diagram of the resultant forces of a set of rolls on an entering bar of metal and show the state of equilibrium that is reached when the rolls are not able to draw the metal spontaneously into the space between them. That is when the angle of contact is approximately equal to the angle of friction. Show why that is so. Depict the limiting conditions after the bar has been fully introduced between the rolls.

3. A hot steel bar 3 in. × 16 in. is to be reduced in one pass to 2½ in. thick. It is assumed width does not change appreciably. Rolls are 25 in. in diameter. The yield stress of the hot steel is 20,000 psi, and the average pressure between the rolls and work is 1½ times the yield stress. The coefficient of friction is 0.50. What is the force tending to spread the rolls apart? How much torque must be applied to drive the rolls? What power must be delivered to the stand for a rolling speed of 25 fpm?

4. A carbon steel wire has a yield strength of 80,000 psi. It is to be drawn from 0.218 in.-diameter to 0.189 in.-diameter, which is expected to stress the small size near its yield point. What is the per cent reduction in area? What is the expected drawing force? What power must be applied to draw the wire at a speed of 80 fpm?

5. A low-carbon steel has a yield strength of 60,000 psi. What is the maximum force that may be exerted to cold-draw a bar to 1½ in.-diameter? What horsepower is required for a drawing speed of 20 fpm?

6. Wire of 0.063 in.-diameter is to be drawn from stock 0.218 in.-diameter. The material will stand a 60% reduction in area between annealing operations. It can be reduced 30% in area in any one draw. How many drawing operations and how many annealing operations are necessary? When must annealing be done?

7. A forging can be made in 15 minutes by means of standard open dies and smith tools. The skilled operator's rate is $3.50 per hr. A set of closed dies to make the same forging costs $700. The operator using these dies has a rate of $2 per hr and can turn out a piece every three minutes. Overhead is the same in both cases. Interest and related charges on the dies may be neglected. For how many pieces is a set of closed dies justified?

8. The actual falling weight of a steam hammer is 1200 lb, the cylinder is 10 in. in diameter, and the stroke is 27 in. The mean average steam pressure is 80 psi.
   (a) What is the energy of the hammer blow?

(b) What is the average force exerted by the hammer if it travels ⅛ in. after striking the workpiece?

9. A free falling drop hammer weighs 1500 lb and drops 36 in.
   (a) With what velocity does it strike?
   (b) What is the energy of the blow?
   (c) What average force is exerted if the ram travels ¹⁄₁₆ in. after striking the workpiece?
   (d) What diameter cylinder for steam at an average pressure of 100 psi is required to quadruple the working capacity of this hammer?

10. A forging has a face projected area of 23 sq in. What size press must be selected if the material is: (a) steel, (b) aluminum, or (c) brass?

11. A cluster gear 3¾ in. on the largest diameter and 7 in. long can be machined from bar stock 4 in.-diameter by 7¼ in. long. Machining time by this method is 26 min. An upset forging can be made from round bar stock 1⅞ in.-diameter × 9 in. long, and 17 min are required to machine the forging. The material costs $0.45 per lb, forging costs $0.30 per lb, and machining $8 per hr. The forging die can be made for $900.
   (a) Which method would you select for 100 pieces? Why?
   (b) For how many pieces is the forging warranted?

References

Metals Handbook, American Society for Metals, Cleveland, 1948, and Sups.

Rusinoff, S. E., "Forging and Forming Metals," American Technical Society, Chicago, 1952.

CHAPTER 13

Metal Shearing and Forming

Introduction. A large proportion of the products of industry are manufactured by processes that shear and form standard shapes, largely sheet metal, into finished parts. The common forms of these processes and their principles of operation will be described in this chapter. A few examples of products from these processes are pots and pans, metal cabinets, door and window hardware, and automobile bodies. Other examples can be seen in almost any manufactured product because these processes are versatile, fast, and naturally adaptable to large quantity production. These processes mostly work metal cold and produce the effects of cold-working described in Chap. 12.

The operations that make up the processes being considered may be classified as those for shearing, bending, drawing and stretching, and squeezing and will be described under those headings. The machines and tools used for most of those operations are presses and dies. They will be taken up in the last section of this chapter.

METAL SHEARING OPERATIONS

Types of operations. Operations that cut sheet metal, and even bar-stock and other shapes, have various purposes. Common operations and the work they do are depicted in Fig. 13–1. *Shearing* in one sense designates a cut in a straight line completely across a strip, sheet, or bar.

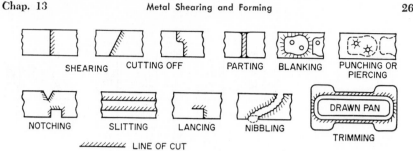

Fig. 13–1. Typical patterns of common sheet metal cutting operations.

Cutting off means severing a piece from a strip with a cut along a single line. *Parting* signifies that scrap is removed between the two pieces to part them.

Blanking cuts a whole piece from sheet metal. Just enough scrap is left all around the opening to assure that the punch has metal to cut along its entire edge. If the object is to cut a hole and the material removed is scrap, the operation is called *punching* or *piercing*. *Slotting* refers to the cutting of elongated holes. *Perforating* designates the cutting of a group of holes, by implication small and evenly spaced in a regular pattern. *Notching* removes material from the side of a sheet or strip. *Lancing* makes a cut part way across a strip. *Trimming* is cutting away of excess metal in a flange or flash from a piece.

The operations described so far usually are done in dies, which will be described later. *Slitting* cuts sheet metal coiled stock lengthwise by passing the stock through spaced and contiguous rolls as indicated in Fig. 13–2. Sheet steel is rolled in widths of 50 to 80 in. and usually is slit into narrower strips. Widths are held within $\frac{1}{16}$ in. Pieces are made in quantities by cutting off or blanking one after another from a strip.

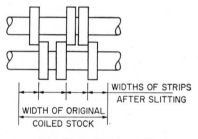

Fig. 13–2. Slitting rolls.

Nibbling is an operation for cutting any shape from sheet metal without special tools. It is done on a *nibbler,* which is a machine that has a small round or triangular punch that oscillates rapidly in and out of a mating die. The sheet of metal is guided so that a series of overlapping holes are punched along the path desired. This is a slow operation but is economical where only a few pieces of each kind are needed because it saves costly special dies.

Principles of metal shearing. Sheet metal is sheared between a *punch* and *die block* in the manner indicated in Fig. 13–3(A). The punch has the same shape all the way around as the opening in the die block, except

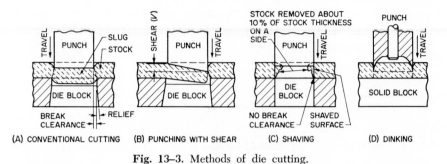

Fig. 13–3. Methods of die cutting.

it is smaller on each side by an amount called the *break clearance*. As the punch enters the stock, it pushes material down into the opening. Stresses in the material become highest at the edges of punch and die, and the material starts to crack there. If the break clearance is correct, the cracks meet and the break is complete. If the clearance is too large or too small, the cracks do not meet, further work must be done to cut the metal between them, and a jagged break results. The proper amount of break clearance depends on the kind, hardness, and thickness of the material. For steel it usually is from 5% to 8% of the thickness of the stock.

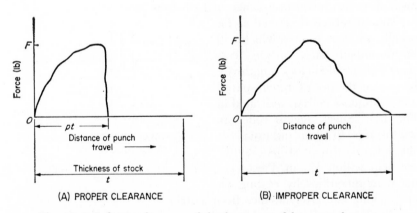

Fig. 13–4. Indicator diagrams of the force exerted by a punch penetrating sheet metal.

As the punch in its downward course enters the material, the force exerted builds up as indicated in Fig. 13–4. If the clearance is correct, the material breaks suddenly when the punch reaches a definite penetration, and the force vanishes as shown in Fig. 13–4(A). This distance is the percent penetration, p, times the thickness of the stock, t, in inches. The maximum force, F, in lb is equal to the product of the length of cut in inches times the thickness of the stock times the shearing strength, S, in psi. If the piece is round and has a diameter, D, in inches, $F = \pi DtS$. The shearing strength and percent penetration are properties of the material and are 8000 psi and 60% for soft aluminum, 48,000 psi and 38% for 0.15% carbon steel annealed, and 71,000 psi and 24% for 0.5% carbon steel annealed. Values for other metals are given in reference- and hand-books.

If the break clearance is not correct, the force does not fall off suddenly, and the curve is something like that of Fig. 13–4(B). In any case, the theoretical amount of energy needed for the operation is represented by the area under the curve. In practice, the situation is not always ideal, and energy is also needed to overcome friction. Experience has indicated that the energy, E, in ft-lb for almost all cases can be estimated from the empirical relationship that $E = 1.16 \times F \times p \times t/12$. If the punch makes N strokes per minute, the power in horsepower required is $P = E \times N/33,000$.

It has been assumed in the discussion so far that the end of the punch and the top of the die block lie in substantially parallel planes. If they do not, they are said to have *shear*, which can be put on either the punch or die block in a number of ways. One way of putting shear on the punch is shown in Fig. 13–3(B). With shear, only part of the cut is made at any one instant, and the maximum force is much less. The energy expended to take a cut is not changed. Shear distorts the material being cut and consequently cannot be applied in many cases. An effect similar to shear can be obtained by *staggering* two or more punches that all work in one stroke. For staggering no shear is put on the individual punches, but they are arranged so that one does not enter the material until the one before it has broken through. Then the most force that must be exerted during the stroke is that needed for the largest punch.

Practical tolerances in punching range from ±0.002 in. for the smallest parts to ±0.015 in. for dimensions over 6 inches. Tolerances as small as desired can be held at extra cost.

An initial cut in sheet metal is a more or less jagged break and is not perpendicular to the surface of the stock. *Shaving* is a secondary operation to produce a smooth cut square with the surface of the stock. Shaving of a hole is illustrated in Fig. 13–3(C).

Paper, rubber, and other soft and fibrous materials are cut with a sharp edged punch against a wood or soft metal block in a *dinking* operation as illustrated in Fig. 13–3(D).

BENDING

Punch and die bending. Bars, rods, wire, tubing, and structural shapes as well as sheet metal are bent to many shapes in dies. Several common kinds of sheet metal bends are shown in Fig. 13–5. All metal bending is characterized by the condition depicted in Fig. 13–6, with the metal stressed beyond the elastic limit in tension on the outside and in compression on the inside of the bend. Stretching of the metal on the outside makes the stock thinner.

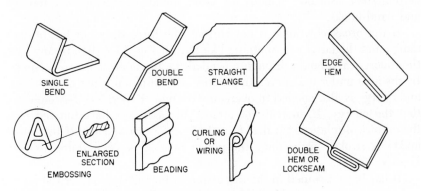

Fig. 13–5. Some kinds of sheet metal bends.

The stretching of a bend causes the neutral axis along which the stock is not strained to move to a distance of 0.3t to 0.5t from the inside of the bend in most cases. An average figure of 0.4t is often used for calculations. If the inside radius of the bend is r, the original length of the stock in the bend is estimated to be $L = 2 \times \pi\ (r + 0.4t) \times \alpha/360$, where α is the angle of the bend in degrees and t is the original stock thickness in inches.

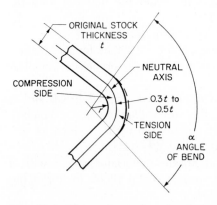

Fig. 13–6. The nature of a bend in metal.

As has been explained, even metal that has been stressed beyond the elastic limit is prone to a certain amount of elastic recovery. If a bend is made to a certain angle, it can be expected to spring back to a slightly smaller angle when released. This *springback* is larger for smaller bend radii, thicker stock, larger bend angles, and hardened materials. Average values are 1° to 2° for low- and 3° to 4° for medium-carbon soft steels. The usual remedy for springback is to bend beyond the angle desired.

Certain limitations must be observed to avoid breaking metal when bending it. In general, soft metal can be bent 180° with a bend radius equal to the stock thickness or less. The radius must be larger and the angle less for metals of hard temper,

The amount depends upon the metal and its condition. Working values are given in hand-books. A bend should be made not less than 45° and as close as possible to 90° with the grain direction of rolled sheet metal because it cracks most easily along the grain. A bend should not be closer to an edge than 1½ times the metal thickness plus the bend radius.

The derivation of a formula for the force, F in lb to make a bend will be explained for the case of a single bend in a vee die illustrated in Fig. 13–7. A basic formula of mechanics of materials for the stress in the outer fibers of a beam of thickness $2c$ and moment of inertia I, subjected to a moment M is $S = Mc/I$. This applies when the stress in the beam nowhere exceeds the elastic limit. For the case illustrated by Fig. 13–7,

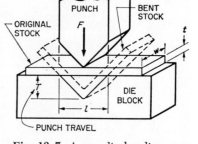

Fig. 13–7. A vee die bending operation.

$M = F_E l/4$; $c = t/2$; and $I = wt^3/12$. If the formula has these values substituted in it and is rearranged, it becomes $F_E = 0.67Swt^2/l$ for elastic deformation. Experiments have shown that for plastic bending the maximum force is about twice as much as indicated for elastic flexure by the formula. On this basis, $F = 1.33Swt^2/l$, in which S is the ultimate tensile strength of the material. The same approach leads to variations of this formula for other types of bending operations, such as single flange bending and for dies with pressure pads. Such formulas are given in texts devoted to a detailed treatment of bending.

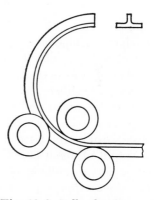

Fig. 13–8. Roll bending a structural shape.

Roll forming. Bending of plates, bar, and structural shapes into curves is commonly done between rolls in the manner depicted in Fig. 13–8. The rolls are held in a heavy frame, the center one is adjustable to set the curvature, and usually the other two are revolved by power to feed the stock.

Cold-roll forming is the name given to a high-production process whereby a flat strip of metal is passed through a series of rolls and is progressively formed to a desired uniform shape in cross section. Among its many products are metal window and screen frame members, bicycle wheel rims, furnace jacket rings, garage door trolley rails, metal molding,

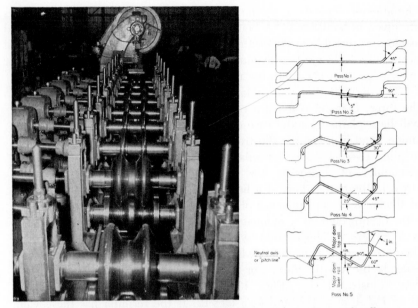

Fig. 13–9. At left, a view of a cold roll forming machine with rolls in place for a job. At right, drawings to show how a shape is evolved from a strip passing through a series of rolls. (Courtesy The Yoder Co.)

trim, and siding. A set of rolls is made for each job and mounted on a standard machine of adequate size. A set-up is shown in Fig. 13–9. Each pair of rolls can only bend the metal properly a certain amount so the number of rolls needed for a job depends on how much bending must be done altogether.

Both hot-rolled and cold-rolled stock in all thicknesses up to about ¾ in. and with polished, galvanized, electroplated, and even painted finishes can be roll formed. Speeds average about 100 ft per min, giving an output of about 30,000 lin ft in a productive day. In a few months out of a year, millions of feet of a shape can be cold-roll formed, and that alone often is profitable. Machines with standard equipment cost from $10,000 to over $60,000, depending on size. Rolls, cut off die, and other tools cost an extra amount for each job. As an example on a small size machine, tooling for a venetian blind cornice section would be about $2700, and for the bottom rail section about $8000.

Cold-roll forming is competitive with two major types of operations. One is the hot-rolling and extrusion group described in Chap. 12. The equipment costs much less for cold-roll forming, but the raw material is more expensive. The other type of operation is the bending of shapes in discrete lengths on presses or press brakes. That equipment cost is much less but the operation is much slower than cold-roll forming. A molding, for example, would be bent in press brake dies for quantities up to thousands of linear feet. Cold-roll forming would be desirable for millions of feet, but extrusion might be economical for even larger quantities.

DRAWING AND STRETCHING

The operations in this category produce thin wall hollow or vessel shaped parts from sheet metal. Examples are seamless pots, pans, tubs, cans, and covers; automobile panels, fenders, tops, and hoods; cartridge and shell cases; and parabolic reflectors. The sheet metal is stretched in at least one direction but is often compressed also in other directions in these operations. The work is mostly done cold but sometimes is done hot.

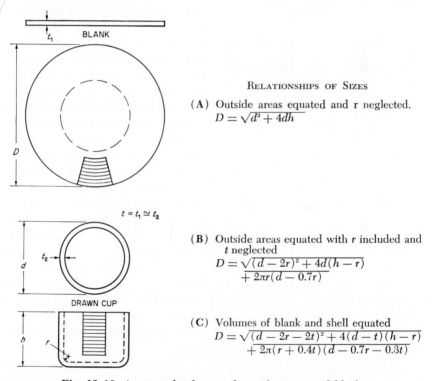

RELATIONSHIPS OF SIZES

(A) Outside areas equated and r neglected.
$$D = \sqrt{d^2 + 4dh}$$

(B) Outside areas equated with r included and t neglected
$$D = \sqrt{(d - 2r)^2 + 4d(h - r)} + 2\pi r(d - 0.7r)$$

(C) Volumes of blank and shell equated
$$D = \sqrt{(d - 2r - 2t)^2 + 4(d - t)(h - r)} + 2\pi(r + 0.4t)(d - 0.7r - 0.3t)$$

Fig. 13–10. An example of a cup drawn from a round blank.

Rigid die drawing. A great variety of shapes is drawn from sheet metal. The action basic to all is found in the drawing of a round cup, and that will be posed to illustrate the principles. The cup depicted in Fig. 13–10 is formed by being drawn from the blank shown above it. Shaded segments of the blank and cup indicate what is done to the metal. A trapezoid in the blank is stretched in one direction by tension and compressed in another direction into a rectangle. Metal must be stressed above the elastic limit to form the walls of the cup, but not for the bottom. Because the volume of the metal cannot be changed, the size of blank to make a cup can be ascertained by equating the expressions for blank and cup metal contents. The change in thickness of the metal is small during drawing. Except for thick metal, the outside surface areas of the cup and blank may be equated. The solutions for the blank diameter are given in Fig. 13–10.

A cup with an even edge is an ideal. In most cases the edge comes out uneven because of the anisotropy of the metal, and the cup is made higher than needed. The excess is trimmed away.

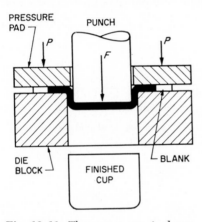

Fig. 13–11. The way a cup is drawn.

The way a cup is drawn is shown in Fig. 13–11. The blank is placed on the top of a die block. The punch pushes the bottom of the cup into the hole in the block and draws the remaining metal over the edge of the hole to form the sides. The edges of punch and die must be rounded to avoid cutting or tearing the metal. The clearance between punch and die block is a little larger than the stock thickness. As has been explained, compressive stresses are set up around the flange as it is drawn into smaller and smaller circles. If the flange is thin (less than about 2% of the cup diameter), it can be expected to buckle like any thin piece of metal compressed in its weakest direction. To avoid wrinkling, pressure is applied to the flange by a *pressure pad* or *blank holder*. In practice pressure is obtained from springs, rubber pads, compressed air cylinders, or an auxilary ram on a double-action press. The force required is normally less than 40% of the drawing force. Usually the blank is lubricated to help it slide under the pressure pad and over the edge of the die.

The force applied by the punch is transmitted solely through the tensile stress in the wall of the cup to draw the metal against friction over the edge of the hole from under the pressure pad and set up the necessary stresses in the flange. Only as much force can be applied as the wall of the cup can support. Otherwise the cup will be torn. This limits the amount of stress that can be set up in the flange and the amount of reduction possible. Theoretically it can be shown that from a blank of diameter D in. to a cup of diameter d in. a reduction $(D - d)/D$ of 50 to 70% is possible, depending upon the behavior of the material.

Actually friction from the hold-down pressure and bending forces detract from this, and in practice a reduction in diameter of only 35 to 47% is feasible for an initial draw. Generally thinner blanks require more hold-down pressure to prevent wrinkling and can be reduced less than thicker blanks.

A drawn cup may be redrawn in another operation into a longer cup of smaller diameter. Practical reductions in diameter for 1st, 2nd, 3rd, and 4th redraws are reported by E. V. Crane to be 30, 25, 16, and 13%. Metal becomes work-hardened as it is drawn and redrawn and must be annealed to prevent failure before it reaches its limit. The reduction in area during a tensile test is an indication of the total reduction in diameter to which a metal can be subjected. For instance, if a metal shows a reduction in area of 60% in tensile tests, indications are that a blank of diameter D in. can be reduced to a cup of diameter d in., such that $(D - d)/D = 0.6$. This probably will have to be done in several operations with rigid dies.

The most force that can be applied to draw a cup is $F = \pi dtS_t$; where S_t is the tensile strength, d the diameter, and t the wall thickness of the cup. More exact formulas have been derived, but this one always specifies enough force. The necessary force may be appreciably less for small reductions in diameters. The energy for a draw is estimated from the formula that energy $E = CFh$; where h is the height of the cup, and C is a constant with an average value of 0.7.

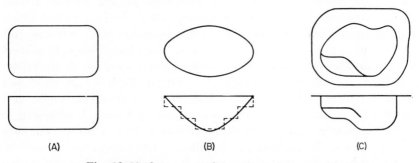

(A) (B) (C)

Fig. 13–12. Some parts drawn from sheet metal.

Several hypothetical parts drawn from sheet metal are sketched in Fig. 13–12 to point out some of the considerations in drawing parts more complex than round cups. Often two or more basic actions occur at once. In the case of the rectangular pan at A, the sides and ends are formed mostly by bending while the corners are drawn. Parts like B and C represent problems in control of parts which do not take the same shape as the punch until just about done. That means the punch and die cannot hold contact with enough of the metal during most of the operation to have full control. Out of control metal tends to wrinkle or become misshapen. A part like *B* may have to be formed in steps as indicated by the dotted lines before the final shape is struck. In some cases blanks must be preformed before drawing. A flange is required on some drawn parts, like *C*, to hold the metal while it is stretched to its final shape. The flange may ultimately be trimmed away.

Flexible die drawing and forming. Several drawing and forming methods use either a punch or die but not both. The ways they operate are illustrated in Fig. 13–13 and will be described in this section.

Rubber pad forming, also known as the *Guerin process,* forms the work over an inverted punch by the action of a pad of rubber in a container attached to the ram of a standard hydraulic press as indicated in Fig. 13–13(A). The operation is limited to shallow drawing, simple bending and forming, and shearing of sheet metal against sharp edges because there are no pressure pads around the punch. Typical jobs are forming flanges around flat pieces, raising ridges and beads to add rigidity to flat pieces, embossing, and trimming. Tolerances are not close.

In rubber forming, several punches and pieces may be placed under one pad. Loading tables that can be filled alternately are helpful to keep a press fully occupied. Lubricants are commonly used. The force applied must be sufficient to build up a pressure of 1000 to 2000 psi over the entire bottom face of the pad, not just on the workpiece.

The *Marform process* utilizes a rubber pad to envelope the part and also a blank holder or pressure pad around the punch. A blank is laid on the punch and blank holder as shown in Fig. 13–13(B). The blank is drawn from between the rubber pad and blank holder as it is wrapped around the punch while the press closes. The blank holder is pushed down against hydraulic pressure. Forming pressures are mostly from 5500 to 8000 psi, but sometimes as high as 12,000 psi. Typical parts produced are flanged cups, spherical domes, conical and rectangular shells, and unsymmetrical shapes with embossed or recessed area. Marforming is slower but is more suitable for deep-drawing and gives better definition to shallow forms than rubber pad forming.

Special hydraulic presses are made for Marforming, but the necessary equipment may be added to standard ones. Capacities up to 13,000 tons are reported. Speeds of operation range from 60 to 240 cycles per hr.

Hydroforming employs a punch and a flexible die in the form of a diaphragm backed up by oil pressure. The piece is laid on a blank holder and over the punch as depicted in Fig. 13–13(C). First the dome is lowered until the diaphragm covers the blank, and initial oil pressure is applied. Then the punch is raised, and the oil pressure augmented to draw and form the metal to the desired shape. Hydroforming produces the same kinds of parts as Marforming with a little sharper detail particularly in external radii.

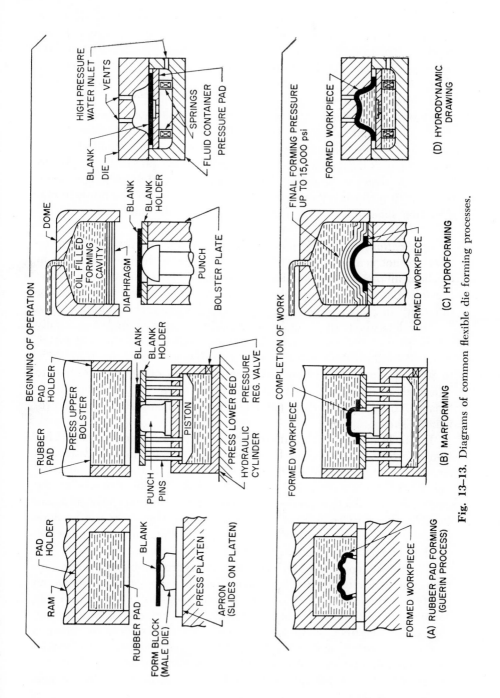

Fig. 13–13. Diagrams of common flexible die forming processes.

BEGINNING OF OPERATION

RAM
PAD HOLDER
RUBBER PAD
BLANK
FORM BLOCK (MALE DIE)
PRESS PLATEN
APRON (SLIDES ON PLATEN)

RUBBER PAD
PRESS UPPER BOLSTER
PAD HOLDER
BLANK
BLANK HOLDER
PUNCH PINS
PISTON
PRESS LOWER BED
PRESSURE REG. VALVE
HYDRAULIC CYLINDER

DOME
OIL FILLED FORMING CAVITY
DIAPHRAGM
BLANK
BLANK HOLDER
PUNCH
BOLSTER PLATE

HIGH PRESSURE WATER INLET
VENTS
BLANK
DIE
SPRINGS
FLUID CONTAINER
PRESSURE PAD

COMPLETION OF WORK

FORMED WORKPIECE

(A) RUBBER PAD FORMING (GUERIN PROCESS)

FORMED WORKPIECE
FORMED WORKPIECE

(B) MARFORMING

FINAL FORMING PRESSURE UP TO 15,000 psi
FORMED WORKPIECE
FORMED WORKPIECE

(C) HYDROFORMING

FORMED WORKPIECE

(D) HYDRODYNAMIC DRAWING

277

Hydroform presses and equipment are available in 8 to 32 in. sizes, which designate the diameter of the blank that can be drawn. Draw depths range from 5 in. to 12 in. and operating rates from 90 to 200 cycles per hr. The small presses are fastest. A complete outfit may cost as much as a quarter of a million dollars. Both Hydroforming and Marforming are patented processes.

Flexible punch forming is exemplified by the patented *Hydrodynamic process* illustrated in Fig. 13–13(D). The blank is pressed between the die and a spring loaded pressure plate. Water or oil admitted under pressure passes through an opening in the plate and pushes the work into conformity with the die cavity. The process is limited to forming shallow pieces with inclined rather than vertical sides but is able to finish in one operation some pieces that require several steps by other methods.

Applications of flexible die forming. As a rule the flexible die processes are not nearly as fast and cannot compete with rigid steel dies in mechanical presses for drawing or forming large quantities of pieces. Flexible dies have an advantage for quantities up to several hundreds or thousands of pieces, depending on the part, because their tool costs are low and lead times short. Only one member is needed, and it generally can be made from easily machined material such as a plastic, soft metal, or wood because the service is not harsh. Tooling costs run from 30% to 80% of those for hard steel dies, with savings of several hundred to thousands of dollars for each job. The mild forming action keeps maintenance costs low and does not mar the work material, not even prepainted sheets.

In Marforming and Hydroforming, the stresses in the material being formed are low. The pressure locks the metal to the punch and prevents stress concentrations. When the metal is drawn off the blank onto the punch, the rubber does not force it to bend sharply. Because of the easier action, reductions in diameters up to and sometimes over 60% are feasible, almost twice as much as with steel dies. Many jobs can be done in fewer operations than with rigid dies, and that sometimes gives the flexible die methods the advantage for large quantities.

Equipment costs for Marforming and Hydroforming especially are high, and considerable work in small quantities must be available to justify the investment. A number of jobbing shops have come into being to do work on these forms of equipment for manufacturers who cannot justify the investments individually. Stock as thick as ¼ in. to ⅜ in. is commonly worked, and even much thicker material has been formed from aluminum alloys. Tolerances of ±0.002 in. are possible and ±0.005 in. are practical. These are comparable to performances with the best quality rigid dies.

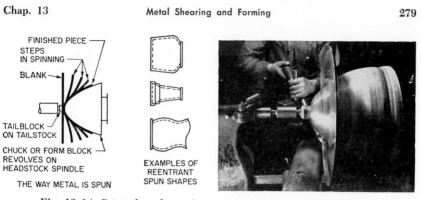

FINISHED PIECE
STEPS
IN SPINNING
BLANK
TAILBLOCK
ON TAILSTOCK
CHUCK OR FORM BLOCK
REVOLVES ON
HEADSTOCK SPINDLE
THE WAY METAL IS SPUN

EXAMPLES OF
REENTRANT
SPUN SHAPES

Fig. 13–14. Principles of metal spinning. (Photo courtesy of Spin-craft, Inc.)

Metal spinning. Parts that have circular cross sections can be made by spinning them from sheet metal (Fig. 13–14). A blank of sheet metal is clamped on center against a chuck or form block. This block may be plaster, wood, or metal and is revolved on the spindle of a lathe. A rounded stick or roller is pressed against the revolving piece and moved in a series of sweeps. This displaces the metal in several steps to conform to the shape of the chuck. The pressure may be applied by hand or mechanically. The latter requires less skill and gives more uniform results.

In addition to flaring parts like reflectors, re-entrant shapes required in such products as kettles and pitchers can be spun as indicated in Fig. 13–14. These are spun on sectional chucks or with internal rollers in hollow chucks. Pieces may be as small as ¼ in. in diameter to as large as 20 ft in diameter and one in. thick or more. Spinning is done both hot and cold. Metal thickness usually is not changed substantially, but it can be if desired. A practical tolerance on dimensions of hand spun articles is ±1/32 in.; about half as much is quoted for mechanical spinning, and even less at extra cost. All ductile metals that can be drawn can be spun. Metal can be trimmed, curled, beaded, and burnished in the spinning operation.

Spinning is both supplementary and competitive with drawing in presses. For straightforward parts, spinning is usually slower but offers a lower tool cost and is economical for small quantities. In one case tools cost about $1000 for drawing, redrawing, ironing, trimming, and beading operations to make a pan. These produced 200 pieces per hr in presses at a unit cost of $0.04 per piece, not including tool cost. Tools for spinning in two operations cost $150; output was 18 pieces per hr; and unit cost $0.42 per piece. Spinning was more economical up to about 2200 pieces. For any amount over that, the lower unit cost of drawing more than offset the extra cost of tools. In this case the spinning tools could be obtained in two weeks, but the press tools in seven weeks. After getting started, the press output could overtake the spinning in about half a week, at about 4000 pieces. Thus spinning has an advantage in getting production underway in a short time and sometimes is done while preparations are made for drawing.

Spinning may be just about as fast as drawing for some parts. As an example, a conical shell required eight drawing operations as against one operation on an automatic spinning machine. Some shapes can most economically be made partly by spinning and partly by drawing. Parts that are too large for available presses can be spun.

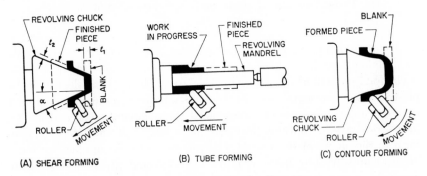

Fig. 13–15. Three kinds of roll turning.

Roll turning. Roll turning, also called *roll forming, Hydrospinning, Floturning, flow forming, power spinning,* and *power roll forming,* uses some of the techniques of spinning but is a more drastic squeezing and extruding process. Three recognized kinds are illustrated in Fig. 13–15.

Shear forming basically extends a thick blank into a cone in such proportion that $t_2 = t_1 \sin \alpha$, as designated in Fig. 13–15(A). *Tube forming* continuously extrudes a thin-walled tube along a mandrel from a short and thick-walled ring. Reductions in thickness up to 90% in low-carbon alloy steel have been accomplished. *Contour forming* acts like the other two kinds but produces parts with curved instead of straight profiles.

Roll turning is done on heavy lathes especially designed to move the tools and exert the large forces required. Work is commonly done from blanks up to ¾ in. thick. Reduction in thickness may be substantial with consequent cold-working and changing of some properties of the metal. Parts with shapes favored by the process can be produced more rapidly than by other means. Parts that have been made in this way are television cones, cream separator bowls, missile noses, thin-walled seamless tubing, and pressure vessel components. Carbon steel, stainless steel, and aluminum alloys are roll turned cold, but magnesium, molybdenum, and titanium must be heated.

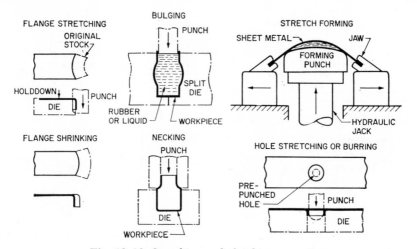

Fig. 13–16. Stretching and shrinking operations.

Stretching and shrinking. Several common operations in which sheet metal is formed by being stretched or shrunk are depicted in Fig. 13–16. Although straight flanging is bending, the forming of curved flanges involves drawing. That may be done with solid or rubber dies.

Bulging is done by placing a cup in a die cavity of the desired shape and filling the cup with rubber or liquid. A punch is applied to create hydrostatic pressure to bulge the walls of the cup to the limits of the die cavity. The die must be split so it can be opened to remove the finished piece.

Shallow shapes of large areas are difficult to draw from thin sheet metal because drawing alone does not strain the metal enough to stress it beyond its elastic limit and give it a permanent set. This difficulty is overcome by *stretch forming* the metal beyond its elastic limit while it is forced by a punch into the desired shape. That can be done in a drawing die by gripping the flange around the part tightly while the drawing punch hits home. Stretch forming presses that do the job in the manner illustrated in Fig. 13–16 have been developed in the aircraft industry. Two and sometimes four sides of the sheet are gripped in jaws that move apart at the same time the forming punch is forced into the metal. Dies may be of easily worked soft materials.

Explosive forming. Forces applied at high velocities to cut or form metal give exceptional results in some cases. This is called *explosive forming, high-energy-rate forming, aeroforming,* and *dynaforming.* It is done in a number of ways, and some are indicated in Fig. 13–17. An explosive shock may be transmitted through a liquid or through air. In the arrangement depicted by Fig. 13–17(D), gas is compressed in a

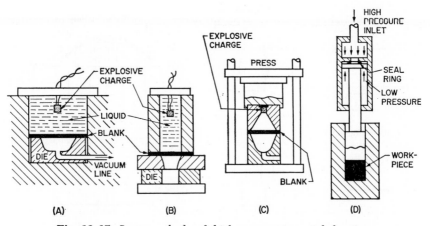

Fig. 13–17. Some methods of high-energy-rate metal forming.

cylinder to 2000 psi and suddenly released against a piston that then slams a ram against the work. Another method, called *hydrospark forming,* utilizes the sudden energy of an electric spark immersed in a liquid.

The relationship of high-energy-rate forming to other methods can be seen from the fact that the energy applied to form a piece of material is $E = Fd = WV^2/2g$. Energy of 50,000 ft lbs may be supplied by a massive press delivering an average force (F) of 50 tons over a distance (d) of 6 inches. The same results may be obtained from a falling drop hammer weighing 10,000 lbs, (W), and striking the workpiece with a velocity (V) of 18 fps. The same effect is found in explosive forming with a moving water front (W) of 6 lbs and an impact velocity (V) of about 730 fps. Velocity is even much higher in some operations.

It is possible to cram enough energy into high-energy-rate forming operations almost to eliminate springback. This occurs in explosive forming when a piece is squeezed against a die cavity surface by a momentary and uniform pressure much in excess of the flow stress of the material, which induces a permanent set.

Explosive forming was developed for and has proven successful in forming aircraft material difficult to work by older methods. These include alloy steels and titanium, but is not confined to them. Almost all the common metals have been formed to advantage, except magnesium, and the process has been spreading to other industries. Among the operations done are forming of hemispheres, hollow inlet vanes, fan hubs, and dished parts. Also flattening, embossing, dimpling, bulging, swaging, forging, notching, perforating, piercing, and lancing are done.

Tremendous pressures can be exerted with relatively simple and light equipment. Thus it is possible to form huge shapes beyond the capacity of available presses and unusual shapes in quantities too small to justify conventional equipment. Another advantage of the equipment is the low tool cost. Only one member, usually the die, is needed for a form. That can often be of soft and easy to machine material for a few pieces. However, explosive forming takes care, skill, and time. It has not been found economical for run-of-the-mill materials and shapes that can be handled routinely in commonplace ways and is not expected to displace older methods but to supplement them.

SQUEEZING

Squeezing is a quick and widely used way of forming ductile metals. Its applications in primary metal working in the processes of rolling, forging, wire drawing, and extrusion are described in Chap. 12. Other applications are cited in thread rolling in Chap. 33 and gear burnishing in Chap. 34. The squeezing operations of cold heading, swaging, sizing, coining, ironing, riveting, staking, and hobbing discussed in this section come under the heading of presswork.

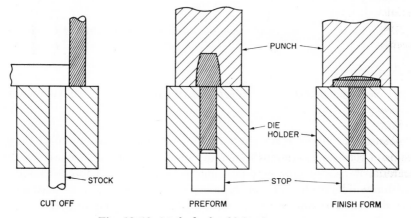

Fig. 13–18. Method of cold heading a part.

Cold heading. Cold heading is a method of forcing metal to flow cold into enlarged sections by endwise squeezing. It is similar to upset forging, which does much the same work hot on larger pieces and harder to work materials. Typical cold headed parts are standard tacks, nails, rivets, screws, and bolts under one inch diameter and a large variety of machine parts such as small gears with stems.

Cold heading is done from wire in machines specifically designed for the process. A typical series of operations is depicted in Fig. 13–18. The stock is cut off at one station and transferred by mechanical fingers to the die holder, where it is struck by one or more punches as needed to give it the shape desired. Some parts are expanded in the middle in addition to or instead of the end. In the case of nails, the points are formed at

cut off. Usually cold heading is limited to an increase in diameter of 4½ times, but larger amounts have been obtained in some cases.

Cold headed parts may be heat treated, but otherwise have a bright and finished appearance. As a rule shank diameters are held to ±0.003 in., head diameters to ±0.005 in., and lengths to ±$\frac{1}{32}$ in. Subsequent operations such as thread rolling may be done to complete the parts. The strength of cold headed parts is improved by the cold-working and the directional flow of the metal. Little or no material is wasted. The process is fast, with outputs of perhaps 50 pieces per minute for large sizes to several hundred per minute of small sizes.

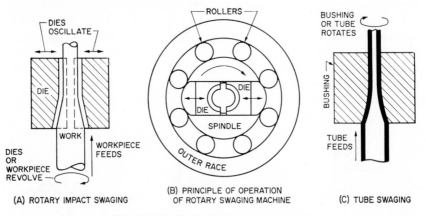

Fig. 13–19. Methods of rotary swaging.

Swaging. The term swaging is used quite loosely to designate many kinds of forming operations, often any squeezing operation in which the material is free to flow perpendicularly to the applied force. This discussion will be confined to one type of operation. This is sometimes more exactly called *rotary swaging* and consists of reducing the size of the diameter, usually over part of the length, of a rod, bar, or tube. One way that rotary swaging is done is by a pair of tapered dies as indicated by Fig. 13–19(A). The dies are opened and shut rapidly. This may be done in a press, while the workpiece is rotated and fed lengthwise. One type of swaging machine makes use of the mechanical device illustrated in Fig. 13–19(B). The jaws are inserted in slots in a spindle, rotated, and forced together repeatedly by the rollers around the periphery, as much as several thousand times a minute. The workpiece can be fed into the jaws mechanically or by hand. All is shielded, so there is no danger. Another form of rotary swaging depicted in Fig. 13–19(C) for tubing is commonly done on engine or turret lathes. The bushing is revolved in the headstock spindle and the tube pushed into it from the tailstock, or vice versa.

Rotary swaging is usually done cold but may be performed on hot metal. When cold, the metal is work-hardened and may have to be annealed after several passes. Reduction in diameter usually should not exceed 30% in one pass. The angle of taper in the reduction should not be over 10° or 12°. Tolerance from ±0.005 in. for 1 in.-diameter to as little as ±0.0005 in. for small sizes have been held. A piece elongates as it is swaged to keep its volume unchanged. The elongation is only about 10% for tubing because the walls thicken. Practical feed rates vary from 1 to 5 ft per sec. The force in lb necessary to cold swage a bar to an average diameter of D in. and with a length of contact in swaging dies of L in. can be estimated from the empirical formula that $F = 1.75\ DLS$, where S is the compressive strength of the material.

Sizing, coining, and hobbing. Parts of malleable iron, forged steel, powdered metals, aluminum, and other ductile nonferrous metals are commonly finished to thickness by squeezing in an operation called *sizing*. An example is given by the sizing of the bosses of a connecting rod depicted in Fig. 13–20(A). Dimensions x and y can be obtained between hardened blocks with a tolerance of ±0.001 inch. Surface finish is comparable to that of milling. About $\frac{1}{32}$ in. stock is provided for sizing. A special die is needed for almost every job, but each piece can be sized in a fraction of the time of machining. Thus, sizing is economical wherever applicable in high-production industries.

Operations like sizing have been called coining, but *coining* more truly involves the impression and raising of images or characters from a punch and die into metal. This is illustrated in Fig. 13–20(B). The metal is made to flow, and the designs on opposite sides of a coined piece are not necessarily related as in embossing. Hard money is probably the best known product of coining.

Hobbing or *hubbing* is a method of making molds for the plastic and die-casting industries. A punch called the hob or hub is machined from tool steel to the shape of the cavity, heat treated for hardness, and polished. It is then pressed into a blank of soft steel to form the mold; slowly and carefully and sometimes in several stages between annealing operations for the blank. A retaining ring keeps the mold from spreading out of shape. A prime advantage of this method is that one hob properly applied can make a number of cavities in one mold or in a series of molds.

Ironing. Ironing is a name given to an operation for sizing and thinning the walls of drawn cups. As indicated in Fig. 13–20(C), the cup is squeezed between a punch and hole in a die as it is pushed through the hole. This is sometimes done at the same time as a redrawing operation. The action is similar to that of wire drawing. The maximum possible theoretical reduction in wall thickness in one pass is 50%, but more has been reported in some cases.

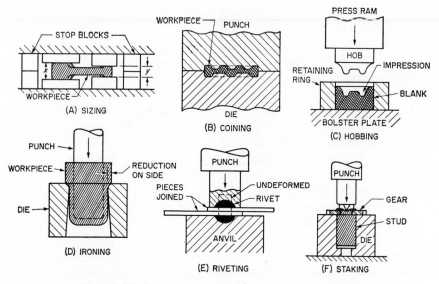

Fig. 13–20. Some common metal squeezing operations.

Riveting and staking. Riveting and staking are two mechanical means of permanently fastening parts together. To rivet two parts as depicted in Fig. 13–20(E), a rivet is put through a hole, and its head placed on an anvil. A punch with a hollowed end mashes the stem to close the rivet. Some rivets are hollow, and their edges are curled outward.

Staking is not done with a separate fastener, but a projection on one of the mating pieces is mashed, curled over, or indented and spread by a punch with sharp edges or points as illustrated in Fig. 13–20(F).

PRESSES

Presses are the machines that perform metal-forming operations. The capacity of a press depends on the following factors.

1. Dimensional size that includes:
   (a) enough space to accommodate the tools,
   (b) a length of stroke to drive a punch the distance required,
   (c) openings to get the stock, finished pieces, and scrap readily in and out of the press.
2. Strength to deliver the force required for each stroke.
3. An energy supply to sustain the force through the working stroke.
4. Speed to deliver the required number of strokes per minute.
5. Power to maintain the energy output at the operating speed.
6. Strength and stamina to maintain alignments, hold tolerances, and produce economically for a long time.

Every press is made up of certain basic units, as indicated in Fig. 13–21. These are a frame and bed, a ram or slide (or rams or slides), a drive for the ram, and a power source and transmission. Each unit can be made in a number of forms, and each form has certain advantages and some disadvantages. By combining various kinds and sizes of units, a large variety of presses are constructed to suit many purposes. Each unit determines part of the physical capacity of the press. Typical units and ways of putting them together will be described and their principles explained to give a comprehensive picture of presses.

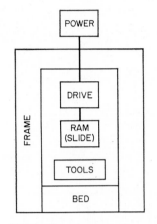

Fig. 13–21. The elements of a press.

Frame and bed. The lower part of a press frame on which the die is placed is called the bed. The bed is heavily ribbed for strength and hollow to accommodate accessories such as scrap chutes and pressure springs. A thick *bolster plate* on top of the bed gives full support to the die which is bolted to it. Important dimensions of the bed are the distances front to back and right to left available to contain a die.

The frame contains the drive mechanism and ways to guide the reciprocating ram in a fixed path. Press frames are made of both iron and steel. They are subject to the same design considerations as other machine tool frames as described in Chap. 21.

A press is rated first in tons of force it is able to exert. Its frame must be strong enough to avoid permanent distortion and rigid enough to resist excessive deflection under the rated load. However, the tonnage rating tells only part of the story as shown by the presses of Figs. 13–24, 13–26, 13–28, and 13–29. All have about the same force rating but differ markedly in other respects.

Most presses from a fraction to over a hundred tons capacity have C-type frames. Common forms are shown in Fig. 13–22. This type of frame is convenient because it allows full access to the die space from three sides. The backs of most such frames are also open. An inherent disadvantage of the C-type frame is that the top and bottom swing at an angle under load. Even if the front is tied by rods, deflection impairs the alignments of the press. This is detrimental to accuracy and tool life and is not tolerable for the largest presses.

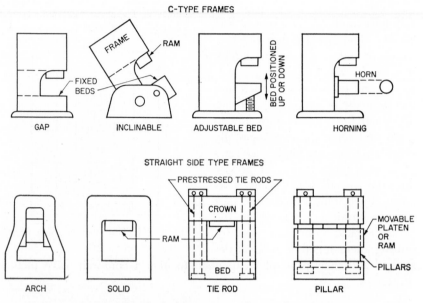

Fig. 13–22. Common types of press frames.

Fig. 13–23. A 60-ton open back inclinable press. Its weight is about 9000 lbs. (Courtesy Clearing Machine Corp.)

The most common press in industry is the *open back inclinable C-type frame press* illustrated in Fig. 13–23. It is inclined backwards to discharge scrap or parts by gravity through the open back. This kind of press is not as rigid as the *gap type,* which has a C-type frame on an integral base and is held in one position; usually vertically. Gap-type presses are often made with wider beds and rams.

An *adjustable bed press* or *knee press* has the lower projection of the C-type frame in the form of an adjustable bed, table, or knee. This press can be adjusted for different sizes of dies and work but loses some in rigidity.

A *horning press* has a large round post projecting out front instead of a bed. This post is called a horn and supports round pieces upon which the press is intended to work. Sometimes the knee is taken off an adjustable bed press and a horn is put in its place to make the press serve double duty.

Press frames that have two or more columns like straight side types in Fig. 13–22 are more balanced and rigid than C-type frames. The design is appropriate for wide beds and long strokes. Access to the die on the bed may be somewhat restricted. Straight side frames are found on the medium to largest sizes of presses.

The larger sizes of presses are constructed of bed, columns, and crown as separate pieces but keyed and bound together by the tie rods as in Fig. 13–24. The rods are heated and shrunk in place to help overcome stretching of the press under load.

The *pillar* or *open frame press* is usually a hydraulic press and has four pillars like the one in Fig. 13–25. The pillars hold the crown to the bed but are not pre-stressed like tie rods. Extension under load does not matter appreciably for a hydraulic press which does not work to a fixed stop. The pillars ordinarily act as guides or ways for the ram.

Fig. 13–24. A 250-ton general purpose straight side press with tie rods. This press has a 12 in. stroke, a 5 in. working stroke, and weighs about 24,000 lbs. The mechanism shown here is covered on late models. A modern press like this costs about $35,000. (Courtesy E. W. Bliss Co.)

Press ram. The ram of a press drives the punch in an operation. The ram on a mechanical press has a fixed length of stroke, but the position of the stroke can be varied by an adjusting nut and screw just above the ram.

Shut height is an important dimension of a press because it limits the height of the punch and die that can be used in it. *Shut height* of a mechanical press is defined as *the distance from the top of the bed to the bottom of the ram when the ram is at the bottom of its stroke and the adjustment is all the way up.*

The *action* of a press refers to the number of rams. A single-action press has one ram, like those in Figs. 13–23 and 13–24. A double-action press has one ram inside another, as in Fig. 13–26. The outer ram is used to apply pressure to the flange of a piece drawn by the inner ram. A triple-action press has a double action above and a third ram that moves upward in the bed soon after the upper rams descend. This may be used to combine drawing and redrawing operations.

Fig. 13–25. This 50,000-ton hydraulic closed die forging press is one of the largest single machines in the world. It weighs about 16,000,-000 lb and is 87 ft in overall height, with 36 ft below floor level and 51 ft above. Its longest stroke is 6 feet. (Courtesy Aluminum Company of America.)

Press drives. The drive of a press as meant here is the means of applying force to the ram. Two kinds of drives are mechanical and hydraulic. The mechanical devices in use today are the crank, eccentric, cam, toggle, knuckle joint, screw, and rack and pinion as depicted in Fig. 13–27.

Most mechanical presses derive the movement of the ram from the throw of a crank or eccentric. These may be on a crankshaft or eccentric shaft running from right to left or from front to back in the press, usually at the top. An eccentric provides more bearing area but has to be excessively large for long strokes. A press may have one crank, as do those in Figs. 13–23 and 13–24, and is said to have a single point of connection or suspension. Better backing is given to large rams by two points of connection from a double crank, as on the press in Fig. 13–28, and even by four points from a pair of double cranks for the largest rams.

Cam and toggle mechanisms are used to drive the outer rams of double action presses. The purpose is to make the outer ram dwell to hold the stock during part of the stroke. Many toggle arrangements

Fig. 13–26. A 250-ton double action toggle press with a 36-in. stroke and a 16-in. drawing stroke. The drive mechanism is visible on this older model press. The press weighs 145,000 lbs. The cost of a press of this type is about $75,000. (Courtesy E. W. Bliss Co.)

have been designed to achieve good holding actions. One is shown in Fig. 13–26.

Knuckle joint and screw drives are used for impact and squeezing operations, such as coining. The *screw-driven press*, often called a *percussion press*, has a long stroke and delivers a blow upon the work, without the shock of a drop hammer. Operation is relatively slow. A knuckle joint is a form of toggle. *Knuckle joint presses* are rugged, like the one in Fig. 13–29, and have a steady squeezing action. The length of stroke is limited. A common application is for sizing operations.

The strength of the mechanism that drives the ram is a determinant of the tonnage rating of a press. Mechanical presses are rated at or near the bottom of the stroke. A crank or eccentric is subject to more torque and cannot stand as heavy a load at higher positions of the ram. This is an important consideration for operations such as drawing in which a near maximum force must be applied during a large part of the stroke. With a given rating at the bottom, the actual capacity at higher points of the stroke is hard to calculate, but press manufacturers specify the capacities in tables and charts in their catalogs.

A double-action press is rated on the basis of the capacity of the inner

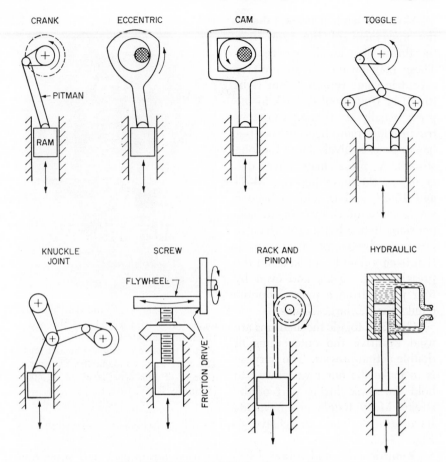

Fig. 13–27. Principal kinds of press drives.

ram. The outer ram usually has a corresponding capacity, and its amount is specified in the press catalog.

With a crank or eccentric type of drive, the ram speed is a maximum at midstroke and decreases to zero at the bottom. A formula for the ram speed is given in Fig. 13–30. This is important for long stroke operations like drawing for which the speed may not exceed 50 to 90 fpm for mild steel, 75 to 150 fpm for aluminum, and 150 to 200 fpm for brass. The proper speed for any case depends upon the condition of the metal, the dies, and the severity of the draw. Too much speed causes the metal to stick to the die.

It is often not desirable for a punch to make contact with the workpiece above midstroke to provide adequate clearance for placing and removing workpieces. On the other hand, the shorter the stroke, the faster the press speed can be in strokes per minute for an allowable

Fig. 13–28. A 200-ton single action straight side press with two point suspension. This press has a 25 hp motor. Its cost is around $60,000. (Courtesy Danly Machine Specialties, Inc.)

Fig. 13–29. A 250-ton knuckle joint press. Its stroke is 2-in. with a working distance of about ⅛ in. for maximum capacity. Its weight is about 12,000 lb, and cost about $25,000. (Courtesy E. W. Bliss Co.)

drawing speed, as can be deduced from Fig. 13–30. To approach this, a press should have as short a stroke as possible for a high rate of production.

Hydraulic presses. A *hydraulic press* ram is actuated by oil pressure on a piston in a cylinder. The principles of hydraulic circuits discussed in Chap. 21 are applicable to presses. Hydraulic presses are more versatile and easier to operate

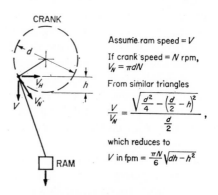

CRANK

Assume ram speed = V

If crank speed = N rpm,
$V_N = \pi d N$

From similar triangles

$$\frac{V}{V_N} = \frac{\sqrt{\dfrac{d^2}{4} - \left(\dfrac{d}{2} - h\right)^2}}{\dfrac{d}{2}},$$

which reduces to

V in fpm $= \dfrac{\pi N}{6}\sqrt{dh - h^2}$

RAM

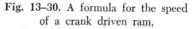

Fig. 13–30. A formula for the speed of a crank driven ram.

than mechanical presses. A hydraulic press usually has a long stroke and can deliver full rated force over the entire length of stroke. The length of stroke and the force can be quickly changed. The force and speed can be held uniform or varied readily throughout the stroke. For example, a rapid approach and return can be combined with a slow steady working stroke. Pressure and distances can be recorded and readily repeated when a job is rerun. A hydraulic press is safer because it will stop at a pressure setting, whereas a mechanical press must plunge through its stroke, even to destruction if it has no safety release.

To offset their merits, hydraulic presses have several disadvantages. Their maintenance costs are reported somewhat higher than for mechanical presses. Some are slow and cannot stand the shocks of heavy punching. These difficulties have been overcome in modern design with locked hydraulic circuits and high-speed pumps. Hydraulic presses are now available that operate as fast as mechanical presses and are more easily controlled, but they are costly. An exact comparison is difficult, but it might be said in a general way that a mechanical press can be purchased for $25,000 that for most production purposes is comparable to a hydraulic press costing $40,000. In some cases, the extra cost is justified because the advantages offered by the hydraulic press are needed.

Power transmission. A crank or other mechanical means of driving a press ram is actuated by a flywheel through a clutch that is engaged by tripping the starting lever. If the lever is released during the stroke, the clutch is disengaged, and the crankshaft is grabbed at its uppermost position by a brake, shown on the left of the crankshaft in Fig. 13–23 and on the right in Fig. 13–29. If the lever is held down, the press operates continuously.

Most small presses have positive mechanical clutches, but some small presses and all of over about 100 tons have friction clutches. Some quite large presses have electric eddy current clutches. A typical form of mechanical clutch has one pin, sometimes more, in a collar on the crankshaft. The pin is made to engage a hole or slot in the hub of the flywheel. Friction clutches are of the disk type, like those found on some automobiles and other machinery, and usually are air operated.

A mechanical clutch acts with a sudden shock that becomes more unendurable the larger the drive; a friction clutch is smoother. Once engaged, a positive clutch cannot be released until the end of the stroke, but a friction clutch promotes safety because it can be disengaged at any time. A friction clutch can be set to slip under overload. A friction clutch costs more to make, to operate because it uses compressed air, and to maintain. A 60-ton open back inclinable geared press like the one in Fig. 13–23 costs about $5000 with a positive clutch and $6000 with a friction clutch.

The flywheel runs all the time a press is in operation and slows down to furnish the energy for each stroke. A flywheel, running with a velocity of V ft per sec at its radius of gyration and having a weight of W lb, has a kinetic energy $E = WV^2/2g$. The more the flywheel slows down, the more energy it gives up, but more time is lost in the stroke. An economic balance must be found between the cost of the press and rapid production. Experience has indicated that this is realized if the flywheel slows down less than 10% during continuous operation, with a press stroke for every revolution, and as much as 20% for intermittent operation, with the operator loading each piece and then tripping the press.

For 10% slowdown, the energy given up by a flywheel is $E_{10} = 0.19WV^2/2g$, and for 20% slowdown, $E_{20} = 0.36\ WV^2/2g$. Most of the weight of an ordinary flywheel is in a heavy rim, and for practical purposes, V may be taken as the speed at the mean radius of the rim. It is necessary when selecting a press to ascertain whether it will supply sufficient energy without slowing down excessively. That may have to be calculated in some cases. In other cases, the energy capacity is tied to the rating of the press. For instance, some manufacturers design their presses for an energy capacity in inch-tons for 15% slowdown to be approximately equal to the tonnage rating. Thus such a 500-ton press is able to deliver a little over 500 in.-tons of energy on 15% slowdown.

Modern presses have individual motor drives. Standard motors made for constant speed applications such as most machine tools, pumps, and generators resist slowdown over about 5% by increasing torque and are called *stiff* motors. Such a motor is satisfactory for a press running continuously at over say 40 spm but is likely to be badly overloaded on a press operated intermittently with a slowdown of as much as 20%. *Soft* motors are made for such purposes. They permit the flywheel to do most of the work and restore energy to the wheel in the relatively long period between strokes. A stiff motor would have to have a much higher rating to supply a major part of the work in part of one stroke. Space does not permit a discussion of motor design, but this points out some basic problems.

Various forms of power transmission between motor and crank- or eccentric-shaft are used on presses. The flywheel is usually mounted on the crankshaft of a small high-speed press and driven directly by the motor through gear teeth or belts. This is called a *direct drive* or *flywheel drive*. A large and slow press ordinarily has gear reductions between flywheel and crankshaft. A *single-geared press* has one reduction; a *double-geared press* has two. A short crankshaft may have one drive gear on it, and that is called a *single drive*. A long crankshaft has a drive gear at both ends to reduce twist, and that is a *double drive*.

Applications of presses. Most presses are mechanical because such drives are simple, durable, and fast but certain applications require other types. Hydraulic presses provide long strokes for drawing and easy action for rubber pad forming and difficult forming and drawing. Drawing and forming have been done as a makeshift on drop hammers when presses have not been available, but that is too crude and slow for production.

Some squeezing operations, such as forging, are done on drop hammers, but mostly eccentric, knuckle joint, screw and hydraulic presses are used. The last are finding favor because through control of speeds a large part of the time cycle of an operation can be devoted to the actual squeezing. This gives the metal time to flow.

Specialized presses. Some presses have features for certain kinds of work but operate on the same principles as other presses. One of these is a *trimming press* that is a crank operated single action press for dies to trim forgings and die castings. It has an auxiliary ram on the side of the frame for light punching, sprue cutting, etc.

Some huge presses have the power transmission and drive mechanism under the bed where it is more accessible than on top. The ram on top is pulled from below. Such an *underdrive press* is mounted in a factory with the top of the bed near floor level and the mechanism extending into the basement.

A *dieing machine* is a small to medium size press with most of its mechanism below the die surface. The ram is above the working surface, is carried on four posts, and is pulled rather than pushed down. That helps to stabilize the ram under load, maintain alignments, and preserve the tools. Access to the working area can be had from all four directions. A low center of gravity is favorable to high-speed operation.

A *forcing press* is usually a hydraulic press capable of exerting large forces to press car wheels, gears, bushings, etc. on or off of mating parts. Some are horizontal; others vertical.

Press brakes and shears. A press brake is a wide press with a relatively thin bed and ram as shown in Fig. 13–31. It can handle wide sheets and plates or accommodate several dies to bend a number of small pieces at once. Almost any kind of bend can be made with suitable dies.

Among other parts, lengths of uniform sections, such as channel, Z, U, S, and I shapes, are commonly bent on press brakes. This method is only economical for a total length up to several hundred feet. An aircraft manufacturer has found that when 1000 or 2000 ft of such sections are needed, they can more economically be drawn through dies on a drawbench, in the manner described in Chap. 12 for making pipe. For larger quantities continuous cold-roll forming is most economical.

Press brakes are rated in terms of the widest and thickest metal that can be formed. An 8 ft by ⅜ in. capacity brake has a 20 hp motor, weighs about 42,000 lb, and costs around $19,000. Small sizes are eccentric

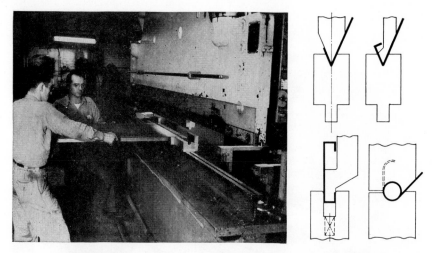

Fig. 13–31. A press brake corrugating sheet metal, and a few of the many bending operations done on a press brake. (Courtesy Verson Allsteel Press Co.)

mechanical types, and some large sizes are hydraulic presses, in capacities up to 24 ft wide and 2 in. thick.

A *shearing press* is like a press brake but is adapted to cutting wide sheets. The ram carries a long blade at an angle to make a gradual cut across a sheet of metal. A plate with holddown fingers in front of the shearing blade presses down on the work as it is cut.

Turret press. A turret press is a modified gap type press with a turret holding a circle of punches on top and another with a circle of dies below. The two index in unison to make it easy to position punches and dies under the ram to pierce a variety of shapes of holes. This is handy for general-purpose work in small quantities. The turret is visible in Fig. 13–32 over a material positioning table. The table has leadscrews for positioning the stock accurately under the punches from hole to hole. Some machines and tables of this type are arranged with a numerical control system, explained in principle in Chap. 35, so that the selection, positioning, and punching of the holes is done automatically in accordance with instructions on punched cards.

High-production presses. Small sheet metal and wire objects such as clips, lugs, brackets, eyelets, fasteners, and many more are turned out in large quantities on moderate size fast presses of which there are several makes. All embody one or both of two principles. One is that there is a series of stations, each an individual press unit with one or more slides. Each station is tooled to perform one or more operations on the work, which is carried automatically from station to station. In some presses

13–32. A turret punch press with a workpiece positioned on a direct measuring table by means of which all holes are located by the operator. The operator is tripping the press by the electrical foot switch to actuate the punch in the selected position. This machine weighs 50,000 lb and costs around $55,000. (Courtesy Wiedemann Machine Co.)

the pieces go through individually; in other presses they are kept in a strip and cut off at the end. The other principle is to provide several slides at one station. The slides converge in timed order on a workpiece to make intricate bends or forms.

The *Verti-slide press* in Fig. 13–33 utilizes both principles just cited to form strip and wire. At the left where the stock enters is a feeding mechanism. To the left of center are two small press units. To the right of center is a station with three main slides and a total of six actions. Capacity in a single station is 12 tons.

Transfer presses for products like ice cube and refrigerator trays, metal shelves, oil pans and headlight housings for automobiles, and stove pans have capacities from 60 to 10,000 tons. A typical example is the *Transmat press* of Fig. 13–34. All the punches are carried on a single ram and descend at once to work on the parts in the stations. On the upstroke, a synchronized mechanism transfers each part to its next position, and so on. The press runs continuously. Transfer presses produce

Fig. 13–33. A high production Verti-slide automatic press for stock up to 4 in. wide by 0.054 in. thick. Output is 40 to 200 pieces per minute. The machine has a 3 H.P. motor and weighs 4500 lb. Cost is from $14,000 to $18,000, depending on equipment selected. (Courtesy The Torrington Mfg. Co.)

Fig. 13–34. A close up view of the die area of a 300-ton Transmat press tooled with eight stations for forming 14 in. automobile wheels. About 900 complete wheels are produced each hour. (Courtesy Verson Allsteel Press Co.)

up to 1500 pieces per hr but are only economical if production requirements are high. One manufacturer has found transfer presses justified
only for parts with five or more operations and outputs of over 4000
pieces per day.

PRESS TOOLS AND ACCESSORIES

Dies. As has been shown, all sheet metal working and forming operations are done by two impinging tools, a punch and die block. They may
be made of soft metal, plaster, or plastic, particularly for forming, to
produce only a few pieces but are of hardened tool steel and even
cemented carbides for larger quantities.

A punch may be fastened to the ram, and a die block to the bolster
plate of a press and used that way. In fact, that is commonly done to
save die cost when very few pieces are to be made, but it is slow and
difficult to set up and operate. Additional details are added for production to facilitate operations. The assembly of all the details is called a
die, and the same name is also given to the die block at times.

Fig. 13–35. A die for piercing six
holes in the ends of the piece shown. This
simple die cost about $300 and is of lit-
tle use except for the specific job for
which it was built. If the job is discon-
tinued, the major items that might be salvaged are the die set that originally cost
about $75 and punches worth perhaps
$25. (Courtesy Punch Products Corp.)

Production dies have the
punches and die block mounted in
a *die set,* as in Fig. 13–35. The die
set consists of a *punch holder* on
top and a *die shoe* on the bottom
to facilitate attachment to the press.
Heavy *leader pins* between top and
bottom maintain alignment between punches and die block.

When sheet metal is blanked or
pierced, it grips the punch after
the breakthrough. Pieces drawn or
bent also tend to cling to punches
and stick in die openings. One variety of details added to dies has
the purpose of stripping pieces
from punches or knocking pieces
from die openings to help remove
work and scrap and speed up oper-
ations. They are called by descriptive names of stripper plate, knockout
pad, etc. Also pressure plates or pads of similar construction are found
in drawing dies to prevent wrinkling.

A third class of details in dies is for locating workpieces. They may
be in the forms of stops, nest, pins, etc. They help to speed up operations.
Examples of the types of details cited can be seen in the illustrations.

Most dies are special tools, made specifically for one job. Many standard details such as die sets, stops, and punches for common shapes are

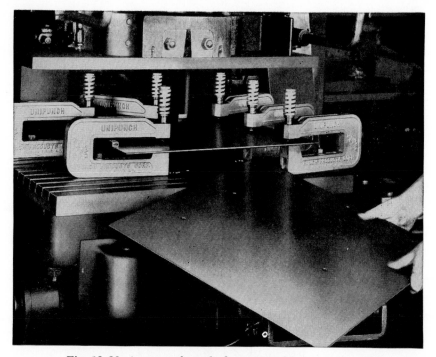

Fig. 13–36. A set up of standard commercial hole punching units on a press bed. These are quickly positioned from the template shown and then fastened in place. The punching units are actuated by the press ram when it descends. The template is estimated to cost about $75 and the punching units about $275. The punching units can be reused on a variety of jobs for holes in many locations. (Courtesy Punch Products Corp.)

available and widely used for economical construction. Even so costs are high and run from several hundred dollars for even a simple die to tens of thousands of dollars for large automobile body dies. Several commercial systems are available for constructing dies from standard units for blanking, piercing, and notching simple common shapes. One of these is illustrated in Fig. 13–36.

Many dies are made to do single operations. Such a die may be designated as a blanking die, piercing die, drawing die, etc. according to its purpose. When the quantity of pieces to be made warrants the cost, a die is constructed to perform a number of operations on a piece. One such type is called a *progressive die,* like the one illustrated in Fig. 13–37. A progressive die has a series of stations, each performing an operation on a piece during a stroke of the press. Between strokes, the pieces, usually in a strip, are transferred to their next stations, and one piece is finished for each stroke. Combination and compound dies do two or more operations in a single station. A *combination die,* like the one in Fig. 13–38 does simultaneous operations of different kinds, such as cutting

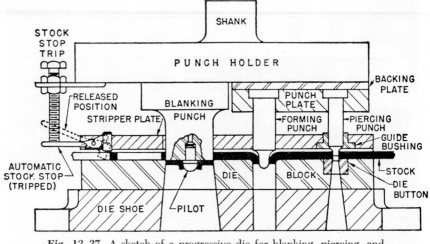

Fig. 13–37. A sketch of a progressive die for blanking, piercing, and forming a piece made in a strip.

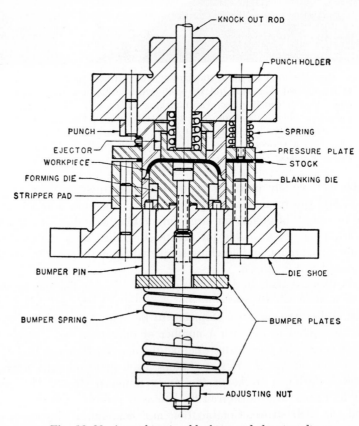

Fig. 13–38. A combination blanking and drawing die.

and drawing. A *compound die* is like a combination die but does operations of the same kind, such as blanking and piercing.

Stock feeding devices. A variety of commercial devices are available
for feeding presses. One usually is economical on any job of more than
a few thousand pieces. Two general classes are devices for feeding strips
and devices for feeding individual pieces.

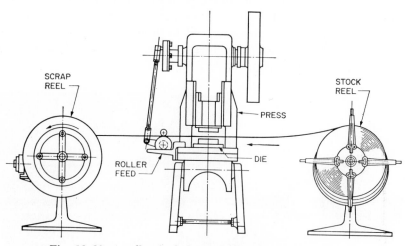

SCRAP
REEL

STOCK
REEL

PRESS

ROLLER
FEED

DIE

Fig. 13–39. A roller feed device pulling strip stock off a stock
reel and through a die. The scrap is wound on a power scrap winder.
The parts being made are punched out of the strip as it passes
through the die. (Courtesy F. J. Littell Machine Co.)

A typical attachment for feeding strips and coiled stock is the *roller
feed unit* typified in Fig. 13–39. The rolls are actuated through a linkage
from an eccentric on the crankshaft. They release the stock when the ram
descends but grip and draw the stock along as the ram rises. Adjustments
can be made for the amount of feed and length and thickness of stock.
Sometimes two sets of rolls are used; one to push the stock into and the
other to pull it out of the die. Coiled stock is held in reels or cradles and
may be passed through a straightener. A device similar to the roller feed
is the *hitch feed* that grips and pulls the stock along by shoes.

A device for feeding pieces one at a time is the *dial station feed*. A
round table with several equally spaced stations around it is indexed
through an eccentric on the crankshaft. For each stroke, a station holding a piece is positioned under the punch. The stations are unloaded and
loaded on the side away from the punch. A few among many other devices are mechanical hands, arms with suction cups, and magazines from
which one piece at a time is pushed mechanically into the die.

Safety devices. A noted authority once said that: "When one con-
siders that 97% of all press accidents can be traced to man failure and

only 3% can be attributed to any mechanical failure, it is evident that by eliminating the human element you have gone a long way towards a solution of the problem." That places the responsibility on the engineer to provide the means to make notoriously dangerous press operations as safe as possible.

One of the best safeguards is to take the operator from the dangerous task, and that is an important benefit from the use of automatic feeding devices just described. However, many operations must have an operator, and two types of devices are used to protect him. One type keeps him out of the danger zone; the other assures that he is out of the way before the press can be tripped.

Fig. 13–40. A stationary barrier guard on a punch press. (Courtesy Junkin Safety Appliance.)

The barrier guard of Fig. 13–40 is a typical means of keeping the human being out of the danger zone. It is interlocked with the starting lever so that the press becomes inoperative if the guard is not in place. Other guards swing in front of the die to sweep the arms of a person out of the way and prevent the press from starting if the path is not clear. Among the devices that assure that the operator is out of the way are two hand starting buttons, a harness attached to the operator's wrists to jerk them back when the ram descends, electronic eyes and light beams, and a sliding die that is loaded away from the punch and slid through a barrier into working position under the punch.

Questions

1. Name and describe 10 common sheet metal cutting operations.

2. What is slitting and why is it done?

3. What is nibbling and what is its advantage?

4. Describe what happens when sheet metal is sheared.

5. What is shear on a punch or die? What are its disadvantages?

6. What is metal shaving?

7. What happens to metal when it is bent? Why does it spring back?

8. What limitations must be observed to avoid cracking sheet metal when bending it?

9. How are heavy plates, bars, and shapes bent?

10. What is cold-roll forming and when is it profitable?

11. What takes place when a cup is drawn from sheet metal?

12. What is the purpose of a pressure pad in drawing a cup?

13. What limits the amount a cup can be drawn in one operation and altogether before annealing? What is the difference between these two circumstances?

14. Describe rubber pad forming and its limitations.

15. Describe the Marform process and its advantages.

16. Describe the Hydroform process and its advantages.

17. Compare the major flexible die forming processes with each other and with rigid die forming.

18. How is flexible punch forming done?

19. How is metal spinning done? How does it compare with drawing?

20. Describe three kinds of roll turning.

21. Describe flanging, bulging, and stretch forming operations.

22. What is high-energy-rate forming and how is it done? What are its advantages?

23. What is cold heading? What are its uses and advantages?

24. Tell how rotary swaging is done.

25. What does hubbing do?

26. When is ironing done?

27. What is the difference between riveting and staking?

28. What are the features of a press that determine its capacity?

29. What are the basic units of a press and what does each do?

30. What is the most common press frame type, and what are its advantages and disadvantages?

31. What are the design principles and advantages of straight side type frames for presses?

32. What is the difference between a double crank and double action press, and what is the purpose of each?

33. What is the difference between a knuckle joint and toggle press, and what is the purpose of each?

34. What determines the actual tonnage capacity of a press?

35. How should a press be selected to obtain the most production from a drawing operation? Why?

36. How do hydraulic drives compare with mechanical drives for presses?

37. Explain quantitatively how the energy is obtained during a stroke of a mechanical press.

38. What kinds of motors are used on presses and why?

39. What are the features of a trimming press, underdrive press, and dieing machine?

40. In what way does a press brake compete with other machines able to do bending?

41. Describe a turret press and state its advantages.

42. What are the principles of operation of high-production presses?

43. What kinds of details do dies have and what is the purpose of each kind?

44. How can standard details be used for economy in die construction?

45. Describe a progressive, a combination, and a compound die.

46. Describe the common ways of feeding stock mechanically into presses.

47. What two types of devices protect press operations?

Problems

1. A round disc 6 in. in diameter is to be blanked without shear from 0.06 in.-thick stock of annealed 0.15% carbon steel. What blanking force and energy are required per stroke?

2. A blank has a perimeter of 12.5 in. The metal is 0.038 in. thick cold-worked 0.15% carbon steel with a shear strength of 60,000 psi and per cent penetration of 25%. Two holes of ½ in.-diameter each are to be pierced in the same stroke the piece is blanked. What are the forces required for blanking and for piercing? What is the maximum force the press must exert at any one time without shear? What energy is required per stroke?

3. (a) Explain why the force in lb required to punch with shear is $F_s = F \times p \times t/(pt + v)$, where F is the force required without shear, p is per cent penetration, t is thickness of stock, and v is amount of shear as designated in Fig. 13–3(B).

   (b) What force is required to blank the disc described in Prob. 1 with 0.12 in. shear?

4. A piece of stock 0.093 in. thick is bent to an angle $\alpha = 120°$ (Fig. 13–6) with an inside radius of ¼ in. What is the original length of the stock that goes into the bend?

5. How much should a medium-carbon soft steel piece be bent for a finished 90° angle bend?

6. A section has been bent in experimental quantities and 6 ft lengths on a press brake. It takes 1 min to bend each length, at a charge of $1 per hr for use of the brake and $2.50 per hr for labor. The section is going into production, and purchase of a roll forming machine costing $15,000 plus tooling at $5000 is being considered. This must be paid off in one year with a 25% charge for interest, insurance, and taxes. Labor on the roll forming machine costs $2.50 per hr. The machine will produce the section at the rate of 60 ft per min but is not expected to have any other use.

   What must be the least expected amount of production in linear feet of section to justify purchase of the roll forming machine and equipment? How many working days of eight hours each does this represent?

7. Derive from Fig. 13–10, (a) equation A, (b) equation B, and (c) equation C.

8. A cup 2 in. in diameter and 3 in. deep is to be drawn from 0.06 in.-thick drawing steel with a tensile strength of 45,000 psi. The corner radius is negligible.
   (a) What must be the diameter of the blank?
   (b) What must be the least number of drawing operations?
   (c) What force and energy must be applied for the first draw with a 40% reduction?
   (d) The reduction in area in a tensile test is 70%. Is an annealing operation necessary?

9. A fluted cup 2¾ in. in diameter by 2¼ deep is to be drawn from 0.04 in.-thick soft aluminum. It can be drawn in one operation by Marforming at the rate of 0.40 min per piece. Marform tooling with a soft steel punch costs $112.50 and with a hardened steel punch $327.32.

   Two operations are needed with conventional steel dies, but each can produce 10 pieces per minute. Soft steel dies cost $504.00, and hardened steel dies $609.00.

Soft steel tools are not expected to last for more than about 5000 pieces, but the hardened steel tools will serve for as many as will be needed. Set up time is about the same for either alternative. Manufacturing time costs $3.76 per hr.

Which type of operation should be selected for each of the following quantities of pieces:
(a) 1000   (b) 5000   (c) 10,000   (d) 25,000   (e) 100,000?

10. A bar of carbon steel with a compressive strength of 90,000 lb per sq in. and a 1 in.-diameter is to be rotary cold swaged to ½ in. diameter. The overall length of the finished piece is 10 in., and the length from the 1 in.-diameter to the small end is 3 in. Average feed rate is 3 in. per min. The dies contact the workpiece over the 10° taper and ½ in. beyond.
(a) How long must the original piece of stock be?
(b) How many passes are needed?
(c) What is the maximum force required?
(d) How much machining time is required for each piece?

11. The disc described in Prob. 1 is to be blanked and then drawn into a cup 2¼ in. deep in one stroke on a single action mechanical press with a 6 in. stroke. If the blanking is done 2¼ in. from the bottom of the stroke, what is the highest speed at which the crankshaft may turn and what power is required for continuous operation?

12. For the conditions given by Prob. 8, specify the kind of press needed, its tonnage requirements, stroke, speed, and power.

13. Show that: (a) for 10% slowdown the energy given up by a press flywheel is $E_{10} = 0.19 \, WV^2/2g$, and (b) for 20% slowdown $E_{20} = 0.36 \, WV^2/2g$ as stated in the text.

14. A 60 ton open back inclinable press has a 1210 lb flywheel that revolves at 90 rpm. The wheel has a 42 in. outside diameter and a rim thickness of 6 in. What energy is it able to furnish when it slows down (a) 10%, and (b) 20%?

References

Crane, E. V., *Plastic Working in Presses*, N. Y.: John Wiley and Sons, Inc., 1944.

Eary, Donald F. and Edw. A. Reed, *Techniques of Pressworking Sheet Metal*, Prentice-Hall, Inc., Englewood Cliffs, N. J., 1958.

Metals Handbook, American Society for Metals, Cleveland, 1948.

CHAPTER 14

Welding and Allied Processes

Welding is a means of joining metals by concentrating heat or pressure or both at the joint to cause coalescence of the adjoining areas. A good weld is as strong as the parent metal. Welding is done in a number of ways. The common processes of commercial importance are listed in Fig. 14–1. In one major class of processes, base metal is melted at the joint, and other metal is usually added to fill the joint. *Fusion* takes place, and no pressure is needed. Another class of processes depends on pressure to push the pieces together at the joint. The metal is usually heated locally to a plastic state, but adherence of metal can be enforced with pressure alone under favorable conditions and is done in some cases.

Electric-arc, gas torch, and Thermit welding are fusion processes wherein the filler metal is essentially the same as the parent metal in the parts being joined. Braze welding, brazing, and soldering use filler metals different from and melting at lower temperatures than the base metal, which is not melted. Two main types of the plastic metal and pressure class are electric-resistance and forge welding.

Although known and practiced in some forms before then, welding has mostly grown to its present vast importance in industry since World War I. It has supplanted riveting almost entirely for boilers, pressure vessels, and tanks; it is the chief means of fastening panels and members together into automobile bodies; it has taken the place of castings for a large

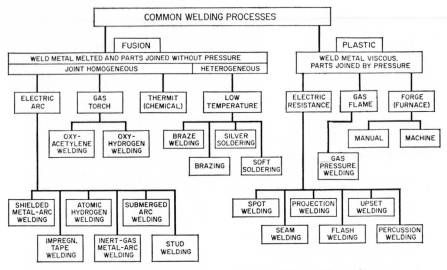

Fig. 14–1. Common welding processes and their relationships.

proportion of machine, jig, and fixture bases, bodies, and frames; and it has become the means of joining at least some of the parts in most products manufactured today. A survey showed that among metal-working plants, 90% used welding for maintenance and 72% for production.

ELECTRIC-ARC WELDING

Principles. The basis for electric-arc welding is an electric arc between an electrode and the workpiece or between two electrodes. The temperature in the arc may be as high as 10,000°F but less than half that just outside the arc. Heat from the arc melts the adjacent base metal. The arc is moved along a joint, and the edges are progressively melted and flow together. Additional metal is commonly added. The electrode is *nonconsumable* for *carbon-arc welding,* and *consumable* for *metal-arc welding.*

Carbon-arc welding, with a carbon electrode, is of secondary importance. It is used in some automatic operations and to weld cast iron, copper, and thin galvanized steel. Filler metal and shielding material must be put into the heated zone as needed. Sometimes the arc is carried between two carbon electrodes and is held next to the workpiece.

The metal electrode in metal-arc welding is melted progressively by the arc and supplies filler metal as shown in Fig. 14–2. The coating on the electrode furnishes the protective gaseous shield and slag that floats on top of the melt. When cooled, the slag is easily chipped away.

Parent metal under a metal-arc is melted and forms the molten pool

to which the filler metal is added to
build up the weld. The size of the
pool is a measure of the *penetration* of the weld into the base
metal. Sufficient penetration is desirable to assure thorough inter-
mingling of filler and base metal
and a sound and homogeneous
weld. The amount of penetration
depends upon the current density,
type of electrode, composition of
base metal, speed of welding and
other factors.

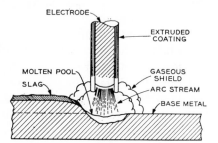

Fig. 14–2. The shielded metallic arc
electrode, arc stream and its shield, deposited metal, and protective slag.

Under a given set of conditions, more heat is put into the weld and
correspondingly more metal is deposited as the current is increased from
a small amount up to a certain point. Above that point welding becomes
less efficient because a large part of the heat is wasted and losses occur
like burning through the metal. Thus for each set of conditions, a certain
current is best. In the same way, a particular voltage is optimum. As
the conditions change, current conditions do likewise. For instance if
the speed of arc traverse along the joint is increased or if a larger size
of electrode is used, metal can be deposited faster, and more current
must be supplied for an optimum welding operation. Thin and fragile
work can withstand less intense welding than thick and heavy pieces.

The radiation from a welding arc is intense and harmful to the eyes.
Anyone within 50 ft should wear a protective shield over face and eyes.
Spatter occurs and makes protective clothing necessary. To protect others
in the vicinity, welding is commonly done in booths or behind opaque
screens.

If d-c (direct current) is used for arc welding, a positive workpiece
(anode) and negative electrode (cathode) constitute *straight polarity*.
This is desirable for bare and some coated electrodes. Manual welding
with a bare electrode is difficult at best because the arc is unstable and
must be kept short to avoid excessive burning of the metal. Straight
polarity is conducive to a stable arc. Some coated electrodes perform
better with the opposite or *reverse polarity*. Generally, straight polarity
melts the electrode faster, and reverse polarity gives deeper penetration
into the work.

Most welding is done with d-c because it can handle all situations
and jobs, usually provides a stable arc, is known to most operators, and
is preferred for difficult tasks like overhead welding. Sometimes a distorted magnetic field will deflect a d-c arc. This is called *arc blow* and
can be avoided with a-c (alternating current). Although all work cannot
be done, about 90% of all jobs can be handled by a-c, which has been

growing in favor because its equipment is simpler and costs only about 60% as much as for d-c.

Open circuit potential is usually from 50 to 90 volts. The electrode tip is touched to the base metal and withdrawn slightly to *strike* the arc. As the electrode melts, it must be adjusted towards the workpiece to maintain the arc. Voltage increases with the arc length. The arc is extinguished when its length exceeds the capacity of the available voltage. Metal-arc voltages range from almost zero on short circuit to a minimum of 17 v to sustain an arc and to around 40 v for an optimum operating arc. Carbon-arc voltages may be 20% higher.

Shielded electrodes. Practically all stick electrodes are of the shielded type, having an extruded coating over the wire. The coating may contain ingredients like SiO_2, TiO_2, FeO, MgO, Al_2O_3, and cellulose in various proportions. Over 100 formulations of electrode coatings are made. The ingredients are intended to perform all or a number of the following functions in various degrees to suit different purposes.

1. Help stabilize and direct the arc for effective penetration.
2. Provide a gaseous shield to prevent atmospheric contamination.
3. Control surface tension in the pool to influence the shape of the bead formed when the metal freezes.
4. Act as scavengers to reduce oxides.
5. Add alloying elements to the weld.
6. Form a slag to carry off impurities, protect the hot metal, and slow the cooling rate.
7. Electrically insulate the electrode.
8. Minimize splatter of weld metal.

One type of electrode has a thick coating containing a substantial amount of iron powder. The coating forms a shell around and helps concentrate the arc. The iron powder adds extra metal to the weld and increases the speed of welding.

A coating with a lower melting point than the electrode metal is usually favored to avoid losing the arc. However, relatively new *drag* or *contact electrodes* are being accepted. Their coating melts enough more slowly than the metal so that the electrode can be positioned in touch with the workpiece. The proper arc length is maintained, and welding is easier.

The core of a typical electrode for welding steel is rimmed steel with 0.1 to 0.15% carbon, 0.4 to 0.5% manganese, and small amounts of sulfur, lead, and silicon. Some cores are of killed steel, and some of alloy steel, although it is cheaper to add alloying elements through the coating.

A standard classification for electrodes, known as the AWS–ASTM classification, designates the characteristics of steel electrodes by a letter and series of numbers such as E 6010, E 7016, E 9030. The prefix "E" indicates the filler material to be a conducting electrode. The *first two,* sometimes *three, digits* specify the minimum tensile strength in 1000 psi units as welded. The examples stand for 60,000, 70,000, and 90,000 psi. Strengths range from 60,000 psi in the low-carbon steel class to 100,000 psi in the alloy steel class. The *third digit* indicates the welding position for which the electrode is suited, viz.: (1) all positions, (2) horizontal and flat, and (3) flat positions only. The position is determined by ingredients that control the surface tension of the molten metal. The *fourth digit* indicates conditions for which the electrode is intended including type of current, polarity, and quality of weld deposited. Full specifications of the properties and applications of standard electrodes are tabulated in reference- and hand-books. Some electrodes are marketed under brand names.

Plain-carbon electrodes cost about $0.15 per lb in 50 lb lots; less in larger quantities. Special and alloy types may cost up to twice as much.

Applications of arc welding. Arc welding has the advantages of being quite versatile and able to make welds under many conditions, of producing high quality welds, of depositing metal rapidly, and of being competitive costwise for many situations. As a result it is used more than any other welding process. Examples of structures arc welded are tanks, bridges, boilers, buildings, piping, machinery, furniture, and ships. Most all metals can be welded by one or more of the forms of arc welding.

Manual-arc welding equipment. The basic units for manual-arc welding are: (1) a source of current called a *welder* or *welding machine,* (2) conductor cords, wires, or leads (one to the ground and one to the electrode), (3) an electrode holder, (4) an electrode, and (5) a workpiece. A typical outfit is shown in Fig. 14–3. A complete outfit for general-purpose work can be obtained for less than $1000.

Welding is commonly done on a metal table to which the ground lead is attached and on which the workpieces are laid or fastened. The operator manipulates the electrode. Tables that tilt and turn to present joints to be welded in the most accessible and advantageous positions are called *welding positioners.* They make welding much faster. For instance, downhand welding in the most convenient position can be as much as four times as fast as welding in vertical or overhead positions. The positioner in Fig. 14–4 is manually adjusted, and ones like it may cost only a few hundred dollars. Some are motor operated for quick and easy adjustment and may cost many thousands of dollars in the larger sizes.

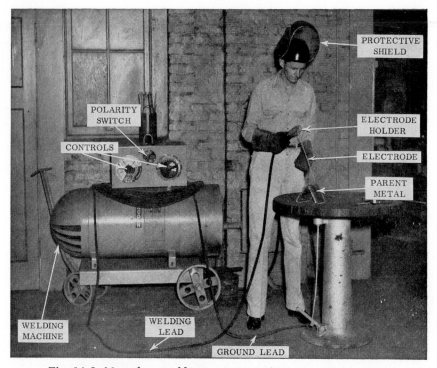

Fig. 14-3. Manual-arc welding equipment. (Courtesy Georgia Institute of Technology.)

Fig. 14-4. A 1200 lb. capacity manually adjusted weld positioner. (Courtesy Cullen Friestedt Co., Chicago.)

Automatic-arc welding. An automatic metal-arc welding machine like the typical one in Fig. 14-5 feeds an electrode wire continuously from a reel through motor driven rollers. Either the welding head or the work table moves to traverse the weld along a joint, depending on the design of the machine. The continuous wire electrode is normally not coated, and one of the protective processes described later, such as submerged-arc welding or inert-gas metal-arc welding, is necessary to protect the arc and metal. Automatic carbon-arc welding is rapid for lap- and edge-welds that do not require the addition of filler metal.

A major drawback of automatic welding is that it is difficult to do in other than a flat position. It is applicable for long seams, say on welded

Fig. 14–5. An automatic welding machine. (Courtesy The Linde Air Products Co.)

pipes, in large quantities and can save appreciable time and labor cost on that kind of work. Operation is continuous, and metal can be deposited rapidly because it is always under control. Results are uniform and cleaning time short. Machines may cost from about $2000 for small semi-automatic models to $10,000 and more for fully-automatic models for heavy production.

Sources of welding current. An electrical generator was long the only source and is still a major source of d-c for welding. It may be driven by an electric motor or by an internal combustion engine for portability. Another means is to reduce the voltage of a-c through a transformer and convert it to d-c through a selenium or silicon rectifier. A-c is obtained directly from a transformer. Combination sources that supply both a-c and d-c are popular. A transformer source has no moving parts but a fan. Thus it operates with less maintenance cost and a higher operating efficiency than a generator. One study with a 60% duty cycle and a welding current of 300 amp for a 9 hr shift showed electric power cost at 1.5 cents per kwh to be $1.71 for a d-c motor generator, $1.28 for a d-c rectifier, and $1.05 for an a-c transformer unit.

Arc welder sizes are designated in amperes. A 100 to 200 amp machine is small but portable and satisfactory for light manual welding. A 300 or 400 amp size is suitable for manual welding of average work like ships, structures, and piping. Automatic welding requires capacities between 800 and 2000 amp either in a single unit or a number of smaller units in parallel. Controls are provided on the best machine for varying both open circuit voltage and welding current in amperes. Some have adjustments only for current. Some machines have an *arc booster* that gives a momentary surge of current to give an arc a good start when it is struck.

The *duty cycle* of a welder specifies the part of a 10 min period in per cent that the rated current can be drawn from the machine without overheating. For example, if a welder is rated at 300 amp at a 60% duty cycle, the machine can be operated safely at 300 amp welding current for 6 out of every 10 minutes. A welder must be operated for a smaller portion of time at a higher than rated current, and the current output must be reduced if the rated duty cycle is exceeded.

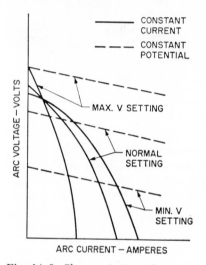

Fig. 14–6. Characteristics of constant current and constant potential welders.

A *constant current or drooping power source* with characteristics typified by the solid curves of Fig. 14–6 is necessary for all manual-arc welding. For any one setting of the welder, the current varies little over a wide range of voltages resulting from variations in the arc lengths. Thus, although the operator cannot hold a constant arc length by hand, he is given the benefit of stable melting of the electrode and easy control of the arc. The settings on the welder for the volts and amperes give the effect of a large number of curves, some steep and some more flat, to meet a variety of situations. Thus a uniformly low current is desirable for a small electrode to weld thin sheet metal without burn-through. A flatter curve would be desirable for overhead welding. In that case the electrode is brought close to the work to control the metal, the voltage decreases, and a heavy current is beneficial to melt and drive an adequate amount of metal into the weld.

Semi- or fully-automatic equipment may be powered by a constant current source or by a *constant potential power source*, which acts as indicated by the broken lines in Fig. 14–6. For any open voltage setting, a small change in arc voltage causes a large increase in current and metal deposition rate.

For automatic welding with a constant current power source, the welding rate is established by setting the welder for a certain current flow. An electrical circuit responds to changes in the arc voltage and controls the speed of the wire-feed motor to keep the arc length, and thus the voltage, constant. The arrangement is simpler with a constant potential power source. The filler wire is fed at a predetermined rate by an adjustable-speed motor. A suitable arc voltage is selected. The wire is melted as fast as it is fed, up to the full capacity of the system, and a constant arc length and arc voltage are maintained.

A *multi-operator power source* is essentially a large capacity d-c constant potential unit with output modified by resistance grids to supply welding current to a number of operators.

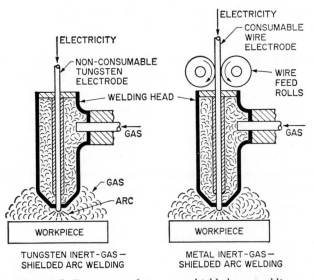

Fig. 14-7. Two types of inert-gas-shielded arc welding.

Inert-gas-shielded arc welding. Inert-gas-shielded arc welding is done by surrounding the arc and metal pool with a protective atmosphere of an inert or semi-inert gas. Two forms of the process are depicted in Fig. 14-7. Carbon dioxide is inexpensive and satisfactory for carbon steel. Nitrogen serves for copper and copper alloys. Helium and argon alone, together, or mixed with various amounts of nitrogen, carbon dioxide, and small amounts of oxygen give good protection for aluminum, magnesium, and alloy and stainless steels.

Tungsten inert-gas-shielded arc welding (called Tig) utilizes a tungsten electrode that does not deteriorate appreciably at arc temperatures in the inert-gas atmosphere. Filler metal is supplied by a separate rod as needed. This process is expensive but is warranted to make clean welds in metals that are easily burned or contaminated, such as magnesium, tantalum, columbium, and molybdenum. No foreign substances need touch the weld. Usually the arc is initiated by an auxiliary high-frequency discharge to obviate even touching the electrode to the work-pieces.

Metal inert-gas-shielded arc welding (called Mig) is done with a wire electrode fed through the welding head to act as the electrode and supply the filler metal. This type of welding may be done by a manual gun or an automatic welding machine. D-c is used mostly because the gas conducts better in one direction than the other.

The weld is clearly exposed and can be fully observed with an inert-gas. No slag needs to be cleaned up after the operation. The weld is clean and neat. On the other hand, spatter must be expected and shielding must be provided against radiation.

Atomic hydrogen arc welding. The arc is maintained between two tungsten electrodes in the atomic hydrogen welding process and the stream of hydrogen gas is passed through the arc and around the electrodes. The molecules of hydrogen split into atoms in the heat of the arc. Outside the arc and particularly near the cooler work surface, the hydrogen atoms recombine into molecules, and some combine with oxygen to form water. These reactions liberate intense heat near the workpiece. Filler metal is supplied by a separate rod as needed. The metal is made to solidify from center to surface to expel absorbed hydrogen.

The hydrogen gas serves as a protective atmosphere and adds to the effective heat from the arc. Metal can be heated to higher temperature in this way than by any other common welding process. Atomic hydrogen arc welding can be used for general welding of steel and iron alloys and some nonferrous alloys but is relatively expensive and is not applied much except for welding some alloys that must be fused deeply and are hard to weld otherwise, such as in the maintenance and repair of die blocks.

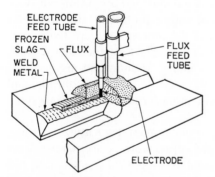

Fig. 14–8. A cut-away view of a sub-merged-arc weld.

Submerged-arc welding. In submerged-arc welding granular flux is poured on the weld area in advance of the moving arc. The electrode is bare wire automatically fed into the flux blanket. Flux around the arc is melted, protects the arc and weld, and is deposited as slag on top of the weld on freezing. The effect is shown in Fig. 14–8. The flux may be neutral or contain alloying elements to enrich the weld. The protection affords a good quality weld and eliminates arc spatter. The unmelted flux may be poured back in the bin for reuse. The slag is easily chipped away.

Submerged-arc welding is used mostly for automatic operations. Some manual welding is done with the process, but it is difficult because the flux conceals the weld.

A variant process called *magnetic flux welding* utilizes a flux that is attracted magnetically to the electrode wire carrying a heavy current. The wire passes through flux in a hopper on the way to the welding zone. Particles of flux adhere in a layer to the wire and are fed to the welding zone as needed.

Impregnated-tape metal-arc welding. Some types of automatic welding machines wind a tape around the electrode wire as it is fed into the arc. The tape is impregnated with substances that volatilize and melt in the heat of the arc and have a shielding effect at the weld. Welds are obtained comparable to those from heavily coated electrodes.

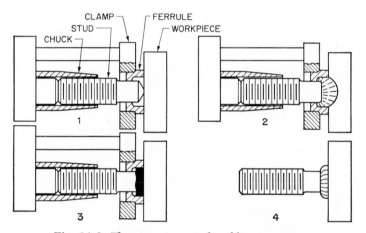

Fig. 14–9. The steps in a stud welding operation.

Stud welding. Studs are attached to steel by means of a variation of the arc welding process called stud welding. The work is done by a special gun that automatically controls the length of arc, length of welding time, and final attachment of the stud. The sequence is depicted in Fig. 14–9. Some studs have a hole in the end filled with flux. The stud is held in a chuck, and a porcelain ferrule around one end is clamped against the workpiece. This shields and confines the arc and the molten metal. The stud is pressed against the workpiece and then is drawn away, after the current is turned on, to strike an arc. The arc melts the end of the stud and some of the workpiece. After a predetermined time, the current is turned off, and the stud is pushed against the workpiece to complete the joint. After the metal solidifies, the gun and ferrule are pulled away.

Stud welding is a fast method of attaching studs, pins, lashing hooks, etc. up to 1 in.-diameter. Common performance is to end weld 5 to 10 studs per min. The gun weighs about 5 lb and can easily be carried to heavy workpieces. Common manual applications are those for installation of conduit, pipe hangars, plank decking, corrugated roofing, plywood, and felt on buildings. Machines are built with up to six stud welding heads for attaching studs to parts produced in large quantities.

Stud welding is not only faster than older methods of attaching studs, like drilling and tapping, but gives more freedom in design. Bosses may be eliminated. Fasteners need not be kept as far from the edge of a part as is necessary for tapped holes. A welded stud affects mostly only one side of a section and usually does not interfere with what may be on the other side.

Comparison of arc welding processes. Automatic welding must be shielded from the atmosphere, and that is done by submerged-arc or inert-gas welding. Equipment and operating costs and attainable traversing speeds along a weld are about the same for both. Submerged-arc welding has a slight advantage in that it has no loss from spatter; whereas the loss of metal may be as much as 10% for inert-gas welding. Its disadvantages are that slag must be chipped and cleaned away and flux must be handled, which is not necessary with inert-gas welding. Also there is less chance of entrapment of slag and voids with inert-gas welding.

Hand welding guns are available for the submerged-arc and inert-gas metal-arc welding processes that are in reality semi-automatic welding machines. They feed the wire and apply the flux or gas automatically. They are somewhat bulky but can be manuevered in most places accessible to manual metal-arc welding. These machines and their accessories cost about four times as much as manual metal-arc welding equipment. However, an operator with one of these machines can control molten metal and the arc more readily, can make use of more current, and is capable of welding two to ten times faster than an operator with only a coated electrode.

The relative unit costs of the common manual-arc welding processes for typical conditions are compared in Table 14–1. Common for all processes are a labor cost of $2.50 per hr, overhead cost of $5 per hr, a weld deposit amount of 0.106 lb per lin ft of weld, a power cost of $0.02 per kwh, and a power source efficiency of 50%. For the submerged-arc process the flux usage ratio is 1.5 lb of flux per lb of metal and the flux cost is $0.095 per lb. For the CO_2 gas process, the gas flow is 30 cu ft per hr and the gas cost is $0.01 per cu ft.

TABLE 14–1. Relative Unit Welding Costs for Several Manual Processes

Type of Operation

Factor of Cost	Conventional metal-arc with coated electrode	Metal-arc with powder-metal electrode	Manual submerged-arc	Manual CO$_2$ gas-shielded
Electrode diam (in.)	$\frac{3}{16}$	$\frac{5}{32}$	$\frac{5}{64}$	$\frac{3}{64}$
Travel speed (ipm)	10	15	30	30
Duty cycle (%)	30	35	45	60
Electrode cost ($/lb)	0.14	0.185	0.135	0.26
Deposition eff (%)	68	70	100	92
Welding current (amp)	175	200	350	350
Nominal arc potential (v)	30	30	35	32
Unit weld cost ($/ft)	0.526	0.317	0.144	0.118

Figures reported by R. W. Tuthill in *The Tool Engineer*, Jan., 1958.

In Table 14–1, the *duty cycle* is the percentage that arc time is of the total operation time. Other than arc or active welding time is that required to change electrodes, chip slag, handle flux, make adjustments, etc. The manual CO$_2$ gas-shielded process has the least lost time largely because it has no flux or slag to handle. The *deposition efficiency* is the percentage that the usable metal deposited in the weld is of the total weight of electrode used. Some of the loss is from stub ends with stick electrodes. Submerged-arc welding has practically 100% deposition efficiency because it does not spatter.

Table 14–1 applies to a particular situation and is presented to show how costs are compared. Under other circumstances the data might very well show the conventional metal-arc process with coated electrode or with iron powder electrode to be most economical. Such a case could occur in a job shop where the costs of adapting the semi-automatic methods to a large variety of jobs would be excessive. Another case could be that of welding the framework of a high structure on which the semi-automatic equipment would be too difficult if not impossible to manipulate.

RESISTANCE WELDING

Principles. Resistance welding is done by passing an electric current through two pieces of metal pressed together. The pieces coalesce at the surfaces of contact because more resistance and heat are concentrated there. The heat is localized where needed, the action is rapid, no filler metal is needed, the operation requires little skill and can easily be automated, and these advantages make the process suitable for large quantity production. All the common metals and dissimilar metals can be resistance welded although special precautions are necessary for some. The parent metal is normally not harmed, and none is lost. Many difficult shapes and sections can be processed.

The main disadvantage of resistance welding is that equipment cost is high. Ample work must be ready to justify the investment. Some jobs call for special equipment, such as fixtures, which add appreciably to the investment. A high order of skill is required to set up and maintain the apparatus.

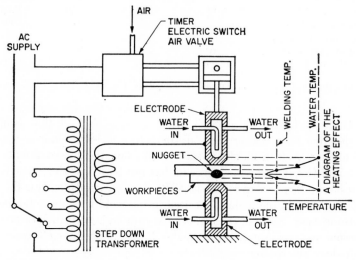

Fig. 14–10. An illustration of the principles of resistance welding.

Resistance welding is usually done with a-c from the line stepped down through a transformer and applied for a length of time controlled by a timer. A typical circuit is depicted in Fig. 14–10. The heat generated in a circuit is $H = I^2RTK$, where I is the current in amperes, R the resistance in ohms, T the time of duration of the current flow in seconds, and K a conversion factor from kw to the unit of heat desired.

The electrodes that carry the electricity to the work also press the pieces together. The current meets resistance in the metal but more so at the surfaces of contact. The most heat is generated where the resistance is highest. Thus the aim is to put the most resistance and heat at the *faying surfaces* between the workpieces to make a sure weld without harming the electrodes. Under pressure, melting of the metal is not always necessary for coalescence. The heat distribution that occurs in a satisfactory operation is indicated by the diagram of Fig. 14–10.

Outside of the zone to be welded the temperature should be low to conserve the electrodes. This is done by conducting away as much heat as possible and generating as little heat as possible where it is not needed. The electrodes are normally water-cooled to carry away heat. The heat generated at any point is proportional to the resistance. Electrodes are made of copper to conduct electricity and heat well but are alloyed and faced with other elements for good bearing strength and endurance. Clean and smooth workpiece surfaces promote low resistance and help preserve electrodes.

An intense shot of electrical current is necessary to concentrate the energy peak to make the weld before the heat is dissipated through the workpiece and into the electrodes. If less current were used, it might generate enough heat in a longer time, but the heat distribution would be much broader and not peaked as shown by the diagram of Fig. 14–10 because the heat would have time to diffuse from the center. On the other hand, the heat is proportional to the square of the current. If the current is doubled, say, the time must be reduced 75% for the same energy. With an intense current, the time must be short enough to keep heat generation and temperatures at all points within bounds and avoid burning the workpieces and electrodes.

When the work and electrode materials have nearly the same resistance, they tend to weld together. Low-resistance metals like copper and silver are hard to weld. Aluminum with a conductivity about ⅔ that of copper requires an intense heat, from a high current, of short duration so that the weld zone is brought to welding temperature before the heat spreads. Special copper-tungsten alloy electrodes are recommended for aluminum.

Metals of medium and high resistance, such as steel, stainless steel, Monel metal, and silicon bronze, are easy to weld. When heat-treatable steel is welded, heat sinks rapidly into the surrounding metal mass, and the weld is more or less quenched to a hard and brittle state. This can be corrected by annealing or tempering in a separate furnace or on the welding machine. In the latter case, a second surge of metered current is put through the workpiece to reheat it to a drawing temperature before it is released.

High-frequency resistance welding may be done at over 100,000 cps when its extra cost is warranted. A source of high-frequency energy, such as a vacuum tube oscillator, is necessary in addition to the usual welding transformer, contacts, etc. The high-frequency current readily breaks through oxide film barriers under little pressure and concentrates on the surface of the work. Thus heating can be localized and can be controlled for best results with thin sheets and tubes, and welding is fast.

The principles that have been discussed are applied in several processes to suit various purposes. These are spot, projection, seam, upset- and flash-butt, and percussion welding. The features of each will be discussed.

Resistance welding equipment. There is no universal machine to do all kinds of resistance welding, but several basic features are common to the various forms of equipment. Common to all machines are a power supply, a system of controls, a mechanical drive, and a structure.

Most resistance welders operate on a-c from a single phase transformer as indicated in Fig. 14–10. This causes a low power factor and a serious unbalance in three phase power systems. Improved circuits are applied, particularly on large machines, to reduce the load on the power source. One type of system continuously rectifies three phase a-c to d-c and stores it in a capacitor, solenoid transformer, or even batteries. Then high-density discharges are drawn from storage as needed.

One capacity of a resistance welding machine is designated in kilovolt-amperes (kva). The rating is based on a 50% duty cycle and means the welder will carry that kva at 50% duty cycle and not exceed a safe specified temperature rise. The kva rating is the product of the welding current times the secondary voltage. Actually, a machine can do a job with a higher kva demand than its rating but at a lower duty cycle, or vice versa.

Any resistance welding machine must have means to adjust the amount and duration of current flow to suit various jobs and conditions. Early machines had manual or mechanical controls, as do some low cost ones today, but these do not give accurate results and are not sufficient for large currents. A simple control for the amount of current consists of taps on the transformer primary. Another is an auto transformer that varies the voltage impressed on the primary of the welding transformer. A common method that gives current adjustment in infinite steps is phase-shift control. This is done by altering the magnitude and wave shape of the current to the transformer primary by means of Thyratron or Ignitron tubes. By still another method, called slope control, the starting current is allowed to rise gradually to reach a peak in 3 to 25 cycles as desired.

Modern high-grade controls for switching the current on and off are electronic. They start or stop the current to the welding transformer at or just after the power factor angle in the phase relationship when the voltage is low. This eliminates transient currents which may occur when the current is switched at random in relation to its cycle. Such transients could reach several times the size of the steady current and burn electrodes and work.

Welding currents must be switched on and off in very short lengths of time and often repeatedly for modern applications. Pulsating currents with definite on and off time are often needed. A typical welding schedule might be 6 cycles on and 4 cycles off, repeated 10 times. Complex electronic controls are used to provide a large variety of pulsation schedules with times of ½ cycle ($\frac{1}{120}$ sec) or less to as long as desired with exact duplication over any time period desired.

Resistance welders use several kinds of mechanical drives to exert forces on the welds. Small machines may be foot operated. One system consists of a motor driving a cam through a speed adjusting transmission. The electrodes are forced together by the cam acting through a spring or air cushion to regulate the force. Air operation is used with many types and combinations of air cylinders, and hydraulic operation on large and some special machines. A common demand is for delivery of the force in steps. A typical condition is to apply a moderate force during passage of the welding current to assure proper contact resistance. Then when welding temperature is attained and the current shut off, the force is increased considerably to complete the weld and forge the metal to help refine the grain structure. On most modern welders, the mechanical schedule is automatically controlled and synchronized with the electrical program.

Many welding machines have their electrodes on the ends of two long arms or horns to accommodate the work. The leads to the electrodes constitute a loop of the secondary circuit in which a heavy current flows. A metal workpiece in the throat between the horns may add considerably to the impedance of the loop and reduce appreciably the a-c that can flow at a given voltage. The loss goes into heat generated throughout the workpiece by induction. The amount of impedance increase depends upon the magnetic properties of the material and how much of the workpiece extends into the loop.

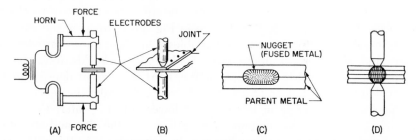

Fig. 14–11. (A) A typical spot welding circuit; (B) a spot welded joint; (C) an enlarged cross section through a spot weld; (D) an indication of the way the current spreads out when passed through several sheets.

Spot welding. Spot welding is the most common form of resistance welding and the simplest. The essentials are shown in Fig. 14–11. Electrodes with reduced ends are pressed against the work, the current is turned on and off, and the pressure is held or increased to forge the weld while it solidifies. This is commonly repeated in a series of spots along a joint.

If a welded spot between two sheets is sectioned, a small mass or nugget of metal is found imbedded in and joining the sheets together as indicated by Fig. 14–11(C). If a good weld is pulled apart, the nugget remains intact, and the sheets tear around it.

If an attempt is made to weld several thicknesses of metal, the current tends to spread out between the electrodes as indicated by Fig. 14–11(D). Thus the current density is less at the inner than at the outer faying surfaces, and it may be difficult to generate enough heat to get good welds at the inner surfaces without burning near and at the electrodes.

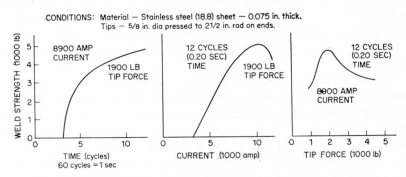

CONDITIONS: Material — Stainless steel (18.8) sheet — 0.075 in. thick.
Tips — 5/8 in. dia pressed to 2½ in. rad on ends.

Fig. 14–12. Curves showing how the strength of a spot weld varies with time, current, and tip force. (After Herbert Van Sciver.)

Sound welds are obtained consistently by applying the proper current density, timing, and electrode pressure uniformly in each case to clean surfaces. The results of tests are given in Fig. 14–12 to show the effects, in terms of weld strength, of the variables. One factor was varied at a time, and all other conditions were held constant. Welds were made with time values of 1 to 12 cycles, at 60 cps. At the current density used, no coalescence took place at less than 4 cycles. At higher currents, weld incipience would occur in less time; at lower currents, later. For time periods larger than the minimum for coalescence, the size and strength of the weld increases with time but at a decreasing rate. Little additional benefit can be expected from still longer time periods, and long time periods give the heat a chance to spread and harm the workpiece and electrodes.

As welding current was increased above 3100 amp with other conditions constant, the size and strength of the weld rose to about 10,000 amp and then fell. The two high tests at 10,600 and 11,800 amp showed considerable electrode indentation into the workpieces and squeezing of the metal out of the weld at the electrode pressure applied. Under a given set of conditions, usable current is limited.

As the electrode force is increased, the resistance decreases at the faying surfaces between the metal sheets. The heat generated is proportional to the resistance. Under the conditions of the tests reported in Fig. 14–12, large amounts of metal melted and were squeezed out of the weld at low pressures because the resistance and heat were high. The workpiece showed large indentations below but not above 1000 lb tip force. A maximum strength was reached at a test with 1900 lb tip force. For larger forces, the resistance at the faying faces was less, the heat less, the weld smaller, and the well strength less. Thus, for a given set of conditions an optimum electrode pressure is indicated. Usually the correct amount for any case is found from experience or trial in practice.

The tests showed excessive indentations for too much current or too little tip force. It is commonly held that one sign of a good spot weld is little or no indentation from the electrode tips.

Both current and time are increased to spot weld thicker pieces because more heat is needed. Electrode tip size is also increased to carry the heavier current. The electrode force is increased even more, so that more pressure is applied to thicker pieces. Operating specifications for various materials and sizes are given in hand-books.

Heat balance. Two pieces to be resistance welded together should be heated the same amount so the weld becomes attached equally well to both. The principles will be explained for the simple case of spot welding but apply to other forms, too. If a thin and thick piece of the same metal are welded between electrodes as indicated in Fig. 14–13, the thick one has more resistance and receives more heat. One solution is to make the electrode tip on the thinner piece of smaller diameter than the other. This raises the current density in the thin piece. Another solution is to face one electrode with a highly resistant material such as tungsten or molybdenum. The same problem exists for two metals of different conductivity. The one of higher conductivity may be made thicker to realize a heat balance.

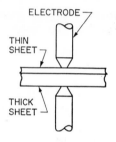

Fig. 14–13. An illustration of the problem of heat balance.

Spot welding machines. Spot welders may be classified as standard machines, special multiple-electrode machines and portable welders.

A standard spot welding machine, like the one in Fig. 14–14, has an upper and lower horn carrying the electrodes and extending from an upright frame. Two types are the rocker arm spot welders and the press type spot or projection welders. The upper horn on the rocker arm type is pivoted in the frame and is tilted upward to open the gap and downward to apply the electrodes. The press type has a ram on the end of the upper horn that moves the electrode straight up and down. The

Fig. 14–14. A view of a spot welding machine in operation. (Courtesy Sciaky Bros., Inc.)

various kinds of power sources, electrical circuits, controls, and mechanical drives described for resistance welders in general are found in spot welders.

Standard spot welders are available in sizes ranging from ½ kva foot- or motor-operated units to 2000 kva capacity air or hydraulic machines. Most sizes for manufacturing are from 5 to 500 kva. Spot welders are also rated by depth of throat, which designates the largest size of workpiece that may be accommodated. Common sizes are from 8 to 36 in. A moderate size standard machine rated at 50 kva with a 27 in. throat capacity costs around $5000. If certain power sources or controls are used, the cost may be much higher.

It is difficult to make multiple welds by using two or more electrodes in parallel on a standard welding machine because of the uncertain current distribution. Special spot welding machines with many combinations of electrodes are found on high-production jobs. One system uses one common welding transformer and a hydraulic cylinder for each electrode assembly. The electrodes are brought in contact with the work one at a time. In another system, all electrodes are pressed against the work at one time, and the current from the transformer secondary is commutated to one electrode at a time. Some machines have a separate transformer and controls for each electrode set. Special machines are built in many sizes and shapes, each to suit its own job. Some have been built to weld hundreds of spots in a single operation. They are rapid, obviate handling the work between welds, and are economical for large quantity production. Some of the largest special spot welders, such as one to weld the panels and top of an automobile body together, may cost as much as $1 million.

Semi-portable spot welders or spot welding guns are convenient for work, such as trucks or railroad cars, too heavy to be put on machines. A gun does not take the place of a machine because it is not as efficient. It consists of a transformer and controls in a case, usually hung from the ceiling, with leads and an air line to a pair of jaws. The jaws carry the electrodes and can be moved about in the work area. The jaws are closed by an air cylinder, and the electrodes bite like teeth on the work and pass the current to make the weld.

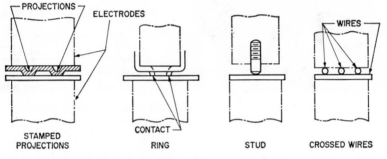

Fig. 14–15. Types of projection welds.

Projection welding. Projection welding is done like spot welding, but the current is concentrated at the spots to be welded by projections preformed on the work as indicated in Fig. 14–15. The electrodes are relatively large and are subject to a low current density, so they stand up well. The process is fast because a number of spots can be welded in one closure of the press.

Projections for welding may be stamped on sheet metal parts. A variation is called *stud welding*, also. A stud with its ends rounded is held in one electrode and pressed against its mating part while current flows to heat the weld. The effect of projection welding is obtained with crossed wires, such as might be welded together into a grill.

A metal must have sufficient hot strength to be projection welded successfully. For this reason aluminum is seldom welded by this process, and copper and some brasses not at all. Free cutting steels high in phosphorous and sulfur must not be projection welded because the welds are porous and brittle. Most other steels are readily projection welded. The projections should be in the heavier of two mating parts so they will not be burned off before the weld is completed.

Spot welding machines may be used for projection welding with the proper electrodes. Machines specifically for projection welding are like press type spot welders and are rigidly built to hold parts in alignment during an operation. Projection welds usually require more current over shorter lengths of time and more pressure than spot welds.

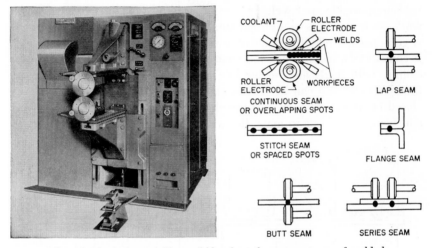

Fig. 14–16. A seam welder and sketches of common types of welded seams. (Photo courtesy Taylor-Winfield Corp.)

Seam welding. A *seam weld* is a series of spot welds either overlapping or spaced at short intervals. The latter is called a *roll spot weld* or *stitch weld.* Seam welding is done by passing the work between revolving roller electrodes as shown in Fig. 14–16. A coolant is applied to conserve the electrodes and cool the work rapidly to speed the operation. Commonly the rollers run continuously along a seam, and the current is interrupted. Another method utilizes a steady current with intermittent motion of the rollers or with notched rollers. Surfaces to be seam welded must be thoroughly cleaned, descaled, and deoxidized for satisfactory results. Pickling is a preferred method of preparing surfaces. Most seam welding is done at 60 ipm to 60 fpm depending on the capacities of the metal and equipment.

Both lap and butt joints may be seam welded. Continuous seams are gas and liquid tight. Seam welding is done on metal sheets and plates from 0.003 to 0.187 in. thick with standard equipment and up to ⅜ in. thick with special machines. Seam welding is done mostly on low-carbon, alloy, and stainless steels but also on many other metals including aluminum, brass, titanium, and tantalum. Typical seam welded products are mufflers, barrels, and tanks. Specifications for proper seam proportions and designs for various materials and applications are tabulated in handbooks. A good seam is stronger than the parent metal.

A seam welding machine may be made to do either flat (horizontal) or circular work or both. Seam welders have much the same elements as spot welding machines and also are classed as rocker arm and press types. In addition, a seam welder must have a drive for turning the rollers and supply heavy currents and forces. Current must be strong because much of it is lost through spots near the weld of the moment. An ordinary duty cycle for seam welding may be as high as 80% while spot welding is seldom over 10%. A recommended pressure for low-carbon steel is 15,000 psi. A sturdy construction is necessary for the heavy forces. Good quality controls are necessary for precise timing. A fully equipped seam welder rated at 50 kva with a 24 in. throat for stainless steel and titanium stock up to 0.051 in. thick is quoted in the $30,000 to $40,000 range.

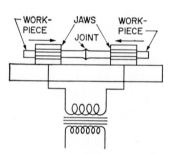

Fig. 14–17. A diagram of upset butt welding.

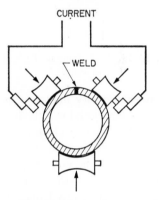

Fig. 14–18. A diagram of the method for upset butt welding pipe.

Upset-butt welding. Upset-butt welding consists of pressing two pieces of metal together end to end and passing a current through them. Current densities range from 2000 to 5000 amp per sq in. The resistance of the contiguous surfaces under light pressure heats the joint. Then the pressure is increased. This helps metal from the two parts to coalesce and squeeze some metal out into a *flash* or *upset* as depicted in Fig. 14–17. The current may be interrupted one or more times for large areas. Final pressures range from 2500 to 8000 psi depending on the material. Too little pressure leaves a porous and low-strength joint; too much squeezes out an excess of plastic metal and makes a joint of low impact strength.

Metal is not melted when upset-butt welded, and there is no spatter. The upset is smooth, symmetrical, and not ragged, but the ends of the pieces usually must be machined before welding. Most metals can be upset welded. Common applications are the joining of wires and bars end to end, welding of a projection to a piece, and welding together the ends of a loop to make a wheel rim. A method for upset-butt welding pipe is shown in Fig. 14–18.

Wire as small as 0.004 in. and up to 1 in.-diameter has been upset welded in manually operated machines with springs to hold the pieces together. Machines motor driven through gear or cam mechanisms are made for large work.

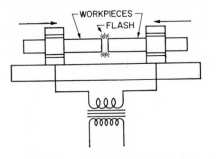

Fig. 14–19. A diagram of flash butt welding.

Flash-butt welding. Two pieces to be flash welded are clamped with their ends not quite touching. A current with a density of 2000 to 5000 amp per sq in. is applied to the pieces and arcs across the joint in a flash that melts the metal at the ends of the pieces as indicated in Fig. 14–19. A pressure of 5000 to 20,000 psi is applied suddenly to close the joint, clear out voids, and extrude impurities. On upsetting, the current density may rise as high as 50,000 amp per sq in.

Most commercial metals may be flash welded. Pieces welded together in this way should each have about the same area at the joint. Common applications are the end welding of sheets, strips, and bars. An example is flash welding the end of one coil of stock to the next for uninterrupted passage of material through a continuous rolling mill. A flash weld has a small amount of upset material around the joint, but the flash is sharp and ragged. Because the metal is melted, a weld of full strength may be obtained even with dissimilar metals. The ends of the pieces need no preparation. Flash welding requires less power, is faster, and heats the whole piece less than upset welding.

Both upset- and flash-butt welding have the advantages in comparison with other joining operations of giving reliable joints, being fast and of low cost, handling dissimilar metals and shapes not suitable for other processes, and requiring little operating skill on readily available equipment.

Both upset- and flash-butt welding can be done on the same welding machines by changing the method of operation or on different kinds of machines. Mechanically operated flash welders are preferred over manual ones. Drives may be cam operated or hydraulic, the latter for the largest machines. Butt welding machines of over about 300 kva rating are the flash type, some as large as 15,000 kva with capacity to weld together areas of over 500 sq in.

Percussion welding. Two parts to be percussion welded are clamped end to end but some distance apart. One is on a spring loaded slide.

When the machine is tripped, the one part is hurled into contact with the other. The parts are connected to the terminals of a high voltage charged condenser that flashes an arc between them for about 0.001 sec before they touch. The arc fuses a layer about 0.003 in. thick on the end of each part. The molten and softened metal is forged into a weld as the parts slam together.

Percussion welding is a fast method of joining and gives very little splatter and flash. It can handle dissimilar metals. The process is limited to welding areas of less than ½ sq in.; the pieces must be concentric; and the surfaces must be smooth.

THERMIT WELDING

Principles. Thermit welding is done by filling a joint with molten metal that is obtained by reducing its oxide by aluminum. Aluminum reduces any oxide but that of magnesium, but Thermit welding is done with iron and its alloys. Finely divided aluminum and magnetic iron oxide, in proportion of 1 lb to 3.lb, are mixed and ignited and react as follows:

$$8Al + 3Fe_3O_4 \rightarrow 9Fe + 4Al_2O_3.$$

The reaction raises the temperature to 4500° to 5000°F. The metal produced is about ½ of the original mixture by weight or ⅓ by volume.

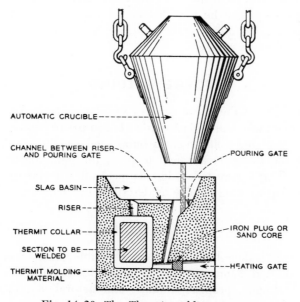

AUTOMATIC CRUCIBLE

CHANNEL BETWEEN RISER
AND POURING GATE

POURING GATE

SLAG BASIN

RISER

THERMIT COLLAR

IRON PLUG OR
SAND CORE

SECTION TO BE
WELDED

THERMIT MOLDING
MATERIAL

HEATING GATE

Fig. 14–20. The Thermit welding process.

Procedure. The first step in making a Thermit weld is to prepare a mold for the metal. The pieces to be welded are positioned and fastened in place. A wax pattern of the weld desired is made around the joint, and a sand mold is rammed around the zone to be welded. A typical set-up is illustrated in Fig. 14–20. A torch is inserted into the mold to melt out the wax and heat the workpieces to cherry red.

The Thermit mixture is placed in a crucible and ignited by a welding torch or by the addition of a small amount of barium peroxide and magnesium ribbon. The reaction takes about 30 seconds to produce up to a ton or more of metal, which flows into the mold around the parts to be welded. The superheated weld metal fuses appreciable amounts of the parent metal, and all solidifies on cooling into a strong and homogeneous weld. Later the mold is torn down, gates and risers are removed, and the weld is chipped and cleaned.

Applications. Thermit welding is largely, but not entirely, applied to joining heavy sections. It is able to supply a large quantity of heat rapidly to parts that have large heat capacities. Typical jobs are the joining of rails, shafts, and broken machinery frames and rebuilding of large gears. Forgings and flame cut sections may be joined in this way to make huge parts. Sometimes this is the only feasible method and often it is the fastest method of welding large pieces. The composition of the weld metal may be controlled by the addition of steel scrap or various alloys in oxide form in the original mixture. Tensile strengths from 50,000 to 110,000 psi and elongations of 20% to 40% in 2 in. are commonly obtained. Thermit welds are considered better than cast steel, and test specimens can be bent flat on themselves. Complete deoxidation occurs, slag has ample egress, and air is excluded from the weld. Slow cooling relieves stresses.

FORGE WELDING

Forge welding is the oldest form of welding; practiced from ancient times by armor makers and blacksmiths. It consists of heating two pieces to red heat, applying a flux such as borax, and completing the weld by hammering the metal on an anvil to press the joint together. Practice of the manual art is rare today, but its mechanical counterpart is found in butt- and lap-welding of pipe as described in Chap. 12.

GAS WELDING

Gas welding is done by burning a combustible gas with air or oxygen in a concentrated flame of high temperature. Commercial gases are acetylene, hydrogen, propane, butane, and natural and manufactured

illuminating gas. Also, chlorine is burned with hydrogen for welding high temperature materials.

As with other welding methods, the purpose of the flame is to heat and melt the parent and filler metal of a joint. Much gas welding has been replaced by faster electric-arc and resistance welding, but gas welding still has important uses. Its temperatures are lower and controllable, which is necessary for delicate work. It can weld most materials. The equipment is inexpensive, versatile, and serves well in many job and general repair shops. It is also adaptable to flame cutting, braze welding, brazing, and soldering described later.

Acetylene gas. Acetylene is the most important hydrocarbon in the welding industry. It contains more carbon available for combustion than any other gas used for welding. It is colorless and has a sweetish but to many an obnoxious odor. It burns with a flame temperature as high as 6300°F, the hottest of all welding gases.

Industrial acetylene comes from the reaction of water and calcium carbide. That is a gray stonelike substance made by fusing limestone and coke together in an electric furnace. The reaction to release the gas is $CaC_2 + 2H_2O \rightarrow C_2H_2 + Ca(OH)_2$. The gas may be generated in a central plant and compressed into cylinders for distribution or generated as needed by the consumer. The most common type of generator feeds carbide into water in a closed container to liberate the gas as illustrated in Fig. 14–21. The water absorbs the heat of the reaction. Carbide is metered as needed through a pressure-regulated mechanism. Lime dust, sulfur, and phosphorus compounds, ammonia, and water vapor are impurities in the raw gas and are detrimental to welding, so they are removed by filtering and chemical reagents. Acetylene generators are low-pressure types, delivering gas at 1 psi or less, and medium-pressure types, for pressures of 1 to 15 psi.

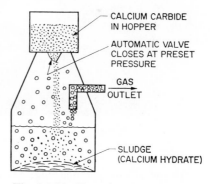

CALCIUM CARBIDE IN HOPPER

AUTOMATIC VALVE CLOSES AT PRESET PRESSURE

GAS OUTLET

SLUDGE (CALCIUM HYDRATE)

Fig. 14–21. The scheme of an acetylene generator.

Acetylene gas is confined in tanks and pipes only at normal temperatures and low pressures. By law free acetylene is limited to pressures of 15 to 20 psi because it dissociates quite readily and explodes violently at pressures over about 25 psi. However, it can be stored safely at about 200 psi if dissolved in acetone. A steel tank or cylinder for storing acetylene is packed with 80% porous material such as asbestos, balsa wood, charcoal, infusorial earth, silk fiber, or kapok. The packing is saturated thoroughly with acetone which is capable of absorbing acetylene to the extent of 25 times its volume per atmosphere of pressure. Gas is forced in to charge the cylinder and withdrawn for use through a valve on top of the cylinder. Safety fuse plugs are provided to relieve the pressure upon exposure to fire. As a safety measure, tanks are emptied in use at a rate not exceeding ⅕ tank per hr.

Oxygen. Oxygen is used commercially pure for welding because it supports more rapid combustion and provides higher temperatures than air. For industrial purposes, oxygen is extracted by the liquefaction of air because that is cheapest. It is distributed commercially in steel cylinders at about 2000 psi pressure.

Fig. 14–22. An oxy-acetylene welding operation. (Courtesy Air Reduction Sales Co.)

Oxy-acetylene gas welding. Much oxy-acetylene gas welding is done manually in the manner illustrated in Fig. 14–22. Gas coming from either the acetylene or oxygen tank is first reduced in pressure through a *regulator*. This is a diaphragm-operated valve that can be adjusted to let only enough gas out of the tank to maintain a desired pressure on the outlet side. Gages on each regulator show the tank and the hose pressures.

Hoses conduct the gases to the torch or blowpipe held by the operator. The torch mixes the two gases properly and emits them into the flame. It consists basically of regulating valves, body, mixing head, and a tip. A number of sizes of tips are available to give different sizes and intensities of flames for various purposes.

Torches are classified as *low-pressure* and *medium-pressure* types, depending upon whether they operate on acetylene pressures up to 1 psi or from 1 to 15 psi. In the low-pressure type, high-pressure oxygen is injected through a venturi and draws the necessary amount of acetylene along through the mixing chamber and out through the tip. Both gases pass through the medium-pressure torch at about the same pressure.

The flame at the tip of the torch is the crux of the whole operation. The reaction that supports the flame is

$$C_2H_2 = 2C + H_2 + \quad 86{,}600 \text{ Btu}$$
$$2C + 2O_2 = \quad 2CO_2 + 352{,}000 \text{ Btu}$$
$$H_2 + \tfrac{1}{2}O_2 = \quad H_2O + 104{,}100 \text{ Btu}$$

$$\text{Total heat per mole} = \overline{542{,}700 \text{ Btu.}}$$

Three distinct types of flames (Fig. 14–23), can be obtained from different mixtures of the gases. The *neutral flame* has no tendency to react with materials being welded. The highest temperature is at the tip of the inner cone and is capable of melting all commercial metals and many refractories. The *carburizing flame* is distinguished by a reddish feather at the tip of the inner cone. It is capable of reducing certain oxides. Some metals welded with a reducing flame absorb a large amount of the excess carbon. An *oxidizing flame* assures complete combustion and the highest temperature but has a strong tendency to oxidize metals being welded, which may be detrimental. Actually, heating is done with the inner cone, and the envelope of a flame shields and protects the weld zone from the atmosphere.

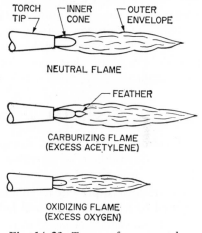

Fig. 14–23. Types of oxy-acetylene flames.

The operator in Fig. 14–22 is applying a welding rod to the weld with his right hand. Such rods supply filler metal, help control the impact of the flame, and restore elements lost from the parent metal. Flux is also employed in the welding of such metals as cast iron, some alloy steels, and nonferrous metals to dissolve and remove impurities, control surface tension, and give protection from the atmosphere. It is usually a paste in which the rod is dipped.

Two hundred dollars will provide the manual equipment for gas welding and flame-cutting operations. Automatic oxy-acetylene welding machines are used for some production operations, but they operate on the same principles discussed for manual welding. They may cost several thousand dollars or more. Generally they employ a number of small flames to obtain large amounts of heat. Equipment and accessories are proportionately large.

Oxy-acetylene pressure welding. Butt welding can be done with heat from the oxy-acetylene flame in ways similar to electrical upset- and flash-butt welding. By one method, two pieces to be joined are pressed together, and the joint is heated by a torch until plastic. More pressure may then be applied and the torch removed to solidify the joint. By a second method, the ends of the two pieces are heated separately and then quickly pressed together. A piece of alloy steel may be put on the end of a soft steel shank by either of these methods to make a tool. Other applications include joining pipeline sections and rails.

Oxy-hydrogen gas welding. Hydrogen instead of acetylene is burned with oxygen to get a milder flame of lower temperature, below 3600°F. This is of advantage for thin sheets and materials that must not be overheated. The hydrogen is stored in cylinders at up to 2000 psi. The same equipment as for oxy-acetylene welding is used. Adjustment is more difficult because the flame does not have distinctive phases. The flame is made slightly reducing and makes a good-quality weld, free of oxides.

SPECIAL WELDING PROCESSES

Electron beam welding. Equipment has been developed in recent years to do welding by directing a concentrated high-energy beam of electrons on the workpieces in a high vacuum. No filler metal, gases, or electrodes are present to contaminate the work. The heating can be confined to a narrow zone and held to a shallow depth or extended to extreme thicknesses of metal to provide a high depth-to-width ratio.

Electron beam welding equipment is costly and not competitive for most work but can do some jobs enough more economically to be worth while. It gives best results on some metals for atomic reactors that must not be contaminated by welding. Heat concentration minimizes warpage. Welds can be made exceptionally close together where necessary without overlapping. In contrast, a joint can be welded deeply in one pass, and thus other passes eliminated.

Plasma-arc process. A plasma jet is produced by forcing gas to flow along an arc restricted electro-magnetically as it passes through a nozzle. The resistance, and thus the temperature, of the arc is increased by the restriction of its cross-sectional area. The gas forced into the arc stream is heated to ionization temperature and is torn apart into free electrons and positively charged ions called a *plasma*. The jet appears as a brilliant beam of flame. When the excited particles return to atomic form, say upon contact with a surface, they give up large amounts of energy and create temperatures reported as high as 30,000°F.

Any known material can be melted, even vaporized, by the plasma jet process and thus becomes subject to welding. Two particular areas in which the obtainable high temperatures have been found useful are metal spraying, of hard carbides for instance, and flame cutting. The advantages of the process are not needed for most applications. Operating costs are not high but equipment is expensive, ranging upward from $4000 per unit.

Ultrasonic welding. Two thin pieces of metal may be bonded if pressed together under pressure vibrating at ultrasonic frequency. Heat is not needed in most cases. The metals are made to adhere by the close contact and friction developed by the passage of high-frequency energy. Temperature is kept well below the melting point of the metals, no cast structure is formed, little alloying takes place, there is no arcing or sparking to contaminate neighboring areas, no filler metal is needed, and no oxidation or deterioration of the metals occurs. Sound- and leak-proof junctions can be obtained, even in production. The process is particularly beneficial for welding thin foil and can be applied to most metals. Joints must overlap, and the material must be thin for this process. Equipment and operating costs are relatively high, and the process is not considered competitive in cases where other methods serve satisfactorily.

FUNDAMENTALS OF WELDING

Welded joints and symbols. Common arc- and gas-welded joints are illustrated in Fig. 14–24. Each joint has several elements. These are the type of joint, the type of weld, and the preparation for the weld. The elements can be put together in many ways. For example, a lap joint may be held by a fillet, plug or slot weld; a tee joint by a fillet or groove weld. The nature of the joint depends upon what the design calculations show to be necessary. A joint may be given no particular preparation, such as a square butt joint. That joint requires no filler metal and may be as much as 80% faster to weld than one that does but depends on penetration into the edges of the piece and is not strong except for thin material. On the other hand, a grooved joint leads to a stronger weld but requires preparation, and that adds cost. A joint is selected in each case to fulfill requirements at lowest cost.

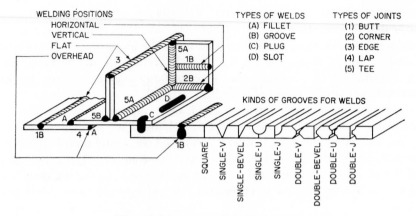

Fig. 14–24. Types of welded joints.

Proportions of welded joints have been standardized. Preferred sizes, dimensions, and charts for calculating the strengths of welded joints are given in reference- and hand-books.

Position, as defined in Fig. 14–24, is an important consideration for any welded joint. Gravity aids in putting down the weld metal into a flat position, which is the easiest and fastest to execute.

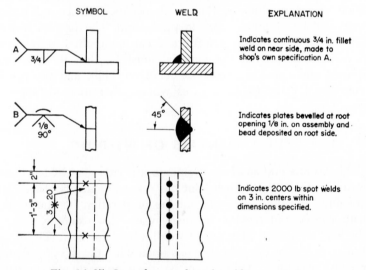

Fig. 14–25. Several examples of welding symbols.

Precise instructions for any welded joint can be given on a drawing by a system of symbols and conventions. This is a language and is governed by definite rules, like the rules of grammar. A full list of symbols and their meanings is given in reference-books. Several illustrations are presented in Fig. 14–25.

Metallurgy of welding. The heat of welding affects the microstructure and composition of weld and base metal, causes expansion and contraction, and leaves stresses in the metal. A knowledge of what happens in metal when it is welded is necessary for an understanding of the welding operation, and will be explained here. For the sake of brevity the discussion will be directed mainly to steel, but some important considerations for other metals will be included.

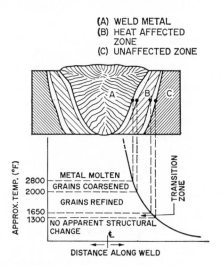

Fig. 14–26. A diagram of the temperatures attained and the resulting structure in a typical weld in steel.

A cross section of a typical cooled weld is shown in Fig. 14–26. The central mass, designated by *A*, represents metal that has been melted. It has the characteristic dendritic structure of a casting, which it essentially is. When the metal solidifies, it cools from the outside inward, and the crystals grow toward the center. Some segregation of constituents occurs with an alloy. The juncture of the dendrites in the center is weak, not so much in a ductile metal like steel as in a brittle one like cast iron. Slow cooling or subsequent annealing improve homogeneity and strength.

Parent metal adjacent to the molten metal in a weld is heated above the critical temperature. This is in zone *B* of Fig. 14–26. Steel so heated recrystallizes to austenite around many nuclei to form small grains. The grains grow at higher temperatures, and the structure becomes coarse. The metal nearest the molten pool almost reaches the melting point and becomes quite coarse. Farther from the center the structure is finer. Beyond that, in zone *C*, the parent metal is unchanged.

Coarse-grained steel hardens more readily than a finer structure of the same composition. A fine structure is tougher and stronger than a coarse one in most nonferrous metals because fine grains offer more points of resistance to slip.

Welding hardens some steels. The principles of hardening of steel have been explained in Chap. 5, and their role in welding will be elaborated upon here. The welding zone is often a small spot within a large mass of cooler metal. Heat flows off rapidly into the surrounding metal. When the heat source is removed, what is called a *mass quench* results. This causes hard martensite to form in hardenable steel in part or all of the zone heated above the critical temperature. The degree of hardness that ensues depends on the hardenability of the steel as well as the cooling rate. The hardenability of a steel must be known to predict how difficult it is to weld and how it must be treated. A high cooling rate is likely to occur when a small bead is deposited at high speed or when a weld is made in a thick section. A large bead is preferred, except on thin pieces. Preheating a workpiece helps retard cooling.

Some aluminum and other nonferrous alloys are hardened by keying agents that are dissolved on heating. The structure of such metals may be altered in the vicinity of a weld, and subsequent heat treatment may be necessary to obtain properties desired throughout the material.

Control of welding quality. What has been shown to happen in a weld explains the faults the weld may have and their remedies. Faults from welding are distortion and shrinkage, voids and inclusions, cracks, and corrosion. They may be remedied by heat treatment, proper welding techniques, or choice of method.

Heating and cooling cause expansion and contraction in various and different places as a weld is made along a joint. The metal in the joint is hotter and tends to shrink more on cooling than the bulk of the pieces on either side. However, lengthwise shrinkage is restrained by the metal adjacent to the joint, and that induces a residual tensile stress along the joint that may exceed the yield point of the material. This pulls some parallel fibers of base metal into light compression. If pieces being welded are restrained in a fixture or by the structure to which they are attached, reaction stresses may be induced in any direction by resistance to contraction of the metal in the welded zone when it cools and cause cracking. Residual stresses do not seem to impair the strengths of most weldments much but do cause warpage, particularly when they are unbalanced by later machining.

Annealing is a means of relieving stresses but is not always desirable because it affects the properties of the base metal of the parts. Much can be done by design and welding practice to enable members of a weldment to flow and move slightly to alleviate stresses and warping. Effective ways are to use as thin material and as little filler metal as possible, preheat, and proceed to weld from the inside or confined portion of a structure to the outside or points of most freedom.

Cracks and voids. A cracked weld is a defective weld and usually is rejected. The causes and cures of cracks are among the most important topics of welding. Major causes are hardened zones in steel, hot short-ness or weakness at high temperature, inclusions and segregations, and gases. Cracks may occur in the weld metal or in the parent metal.

The formation of martensite is a leading cause of cracking in welding steel. The martensite is brittle and does not yield but breaks when the stresses in the weld become high enough. Moreover, the martensite adds to the strains and resulting stresses. It has a lower density and occupies more volume than the softer steel from which it is formed. It is more likely to be formed where grains are coarse or enriched with carbon or alloys from inclusions and segregated elements. Thus spots of different hardness work against each other. High-carbon and alloy steels that harden readily are difficult to weld because of susceptibility to cracking.

The formation of martensite can be suppressed by preheating, and martensite can be transformed by heating after welding. In some cases, oxy-acetylene gas welding helps control martensite formation. It is not as intense at the weld and heats the whole workpiece more than arc welding. The temperature gradient and quenching effect are likely to be less with gas welding.

Cracking may occur in the crater left by the welding pool. This happens if the crater cools more rapidly than its surroundings, which then tend to pull it apart when they shrink. The remedy is to fill the crater fully with molten metal while welding. A similar condition results from use of filler metal different from the base metal. The difference in ex-pansion rates may lead to cracking. This is prone to happen, for in-stance, if steel filler is used to weld cast iron.

Some alloys weaken and crack at welding temperatures. As an ex-ample, magnesium alloys with more than about 0.15% calcium have a grain boundary constituent with a low melting point. This causes fre-quent cracking upon welding. The remedy is to change and control the raw material.

Tests have shown that voids up to about 7% of cross section do not materially change the tensile or impact strength and ductility of a weld. In excess of that amount, inclusions of foreign matter and blow holes or gas pockets weaken welds appreciably and act as stress risers from which cracks spread. Clean surfaces are necessary to avoid dirt and voids. In-clusions are usually slag but sometimes scale and dirt. Grease, oil, or paint left on surfaces liberate gases upon being heated. Shielding keeps out atmospheric gases. Much can be done with welding techniques that keep the welding pool at sufficient temperature for a long enough time to liberate gases and float out slag and other contaminators. Free-cutting sulfur steels are particularly difficult to weld because of the copious release of hydrogen sulfide and sulfur dioxide gases.

Hydrogen is a major cause of cracking in steel. It is highly soluble in hot steel but is largely expelled on cooling. If the gas cannot escape, it exerts pressure to crack the metal. This is likely to happen under the same conditions that form brittle martensite and aggravate the cracking of the martensite. Some welding rods, such as those with cellulose coatings, liberate hydrogen, but low-hydrogen rods are available.

Corrosion. Welding makes metals more susceptible to corrosion in a number of ways. Actually, corrosion occurs from the attack of the air on the hot metal in the welding operation if shielding is not adequate. The intense heat of welding effaces conversion and other protective coatings from metal surfaces. Clad metals should be welded with the same composition as the surface metal, at least on top of the weld. From the standpoint of design, the inner surfaces of a lap joint are difficult to protect from corrosion. Notches and cracks that come from welding are foci for corrosion.

The heat of welding causes changes in some metals to make them more susceptible to corrosion. Chromium in stainless steel forms clinging oxides that give the metal its resistance to corrosion. At welding temperatures the chromium seeks to form carbides that precipitate into the grain boundaries, leaving the metal deficient in resistance. This may be counteracted by adding stabilizers such as columbium and titanium to the alloy. They have even more affinity for carbon and keep it away from the chromium. When some aluminum alloys are heated by welding, parts become overaged and subject to corrosion.

Heat treatment of weldments. References have been made in the preceding discussion to heat treatment as a means of correcting welding faults. This may be done before or after welding, or both. Steel is commonly heated, locally or all over, to between 200° and 1100°F. The more the carbon and alloy content, and therefore the higher the hardenability and the more difficult the steel is to weld, the higher the preheat temperature. The temperature differential between the weld and base metal is smaller with than without preheating. That reduces distortion, relative shrinkage, stresses, the cooling rate, hardening around the weld, and the danger of cracking.

Any of the forms of annealing described in Chap. 5 may be applied to a weldment, depending on the ultimate properties desired. Annealing after welding helps to drive off gases, to unify grain size and obtain a fine structure, to relieve internal stresses, and to eliminate hard spots harmful to cutting tools.

Design for welding. A product to be fabricated by welding must meet two requirements. First it must have adequate strength, rigidity, endurance, etc. Second, it must be producible at the lowest possible cost. The first of these considerations is in the realm of mechanics of materials and is largely outside the scope of this book. For the second, the designer must understand the principles and practices of welding to utilize them most effectively. Several such points will be reviewed here to indicate how they influence welded designs.

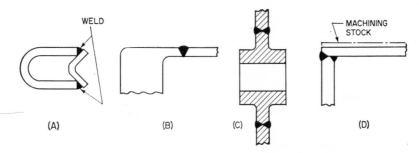

Fig. 14–27. A few examples of good welding design.

The examples in Fig. 14–27 represent ways of coping with some of the aspects of welding. The bent closure welded on two ends in view (A) is easy to fit to the assembly and provides welding grooves without preparation of the edges. View (B) illustrates the rule that sections welded together should be about the same size for the least amount of heat distortion. In this case, the heavy piece has a ledge comparable in thickness to the piece joined to it. The same principle is illustrated by the flanged hub in view (C). If a standard shape without a flange were available for a hub, it might be most economical even if some extra care in welding were necessary, but if a hub must be machined anyway, the flange should be added to match the spokes. View (D) illustrates how a joint should be welded if subsequent machining is to be done on one of the pieces. With the weld in the position shown, there is no need to machine it. Hard spots in the weld can damage the cutting tools.

With the nature of the process in mind, a designer specifies welds in the easiest positions and provides ample accessibility to them. The principles of welding explain why high-carbon and alloy steel and cast iron are hard to weld. Low-carbon steel is used for welding wherever possible. For each weldment, thought should be given to choosing the most suitable welding process. Often times several may be selected for one product for the best results. As an example, a bicycle frame is made with seven resistance welds, four spot welds, four electric-arc welds, and four oxy-acetylene brazed joints, each where it serves most economically.

Many weldments are designed to replace castings for machine frames or bases, jig and fixture bodies, etc. A proven rule is that such a design should not just follow the lines of the casting but should be a complete revision that takes full advantage of the benefits of welding. Each process has its limitaitons, but welding has just about the least. It is a matter of joining pieces together, and the number of pieces available and their possible combinations are practically unlimited.

Normally no effort is made to hold small tolerances on raw weldments. The tolerances that can be held depend upon those of the component pieces, the errors in fabrication and fitting, and the distortions from welding and heat treatment. Tolerances on weldments are commonly in fractions of an inch; $\frac{1}{16}$ in. is feasible in many cases. Surfaces that need to be held to smaller tolerances are left with stock and are machined after welding and annealing.

Inspection of welded joints. Welded joints may be subjected to de- structive or non-destructive testing, using the methods described in Chap. 3. Small weldments may be inspected by taking a piece now and then for destructive tests. Another procedure is to weld test specimens in the same ways as the product and subject the specimens to destructive tests.

Visual inspection is often the only way welds are checked. Much can be judged in this way because good workmanship shows itself in uniform, properly shaped and filled, and attractive welds and is often the best assurance of quality.

Some procedures for economical but adequate inspection are:

1. Inspection should start on the welding floor to detect faulty methods and operations that may cause defective welds.
2. Some consider it worthwhile to specify higher weld efficiency and quality and more thorough heat treatment than absolutely neces- sary to provide a margin of safety and permit less inspection.
3. Weldments should be designed so that welds are as accessible as possible for inspection.

Welding costs. The cost of a weldment includes a number of items. Among these may be the costs of material, machining before and after welding, forging, forming, finishing, fitting up, positioning, welding, in- specting, heat treatment, and flash removal. Most of these are treated else- where in this book, and the present discussion is confined to the actual welding costs.

The elements of cost in welding operations are those for: (1) labor and overhead, (2) electrodes, flux or gas, or rods, (3) power or fuel, and (4) equipment depreciation and maintenance. All are not pertinent to all operations, and they appear in different proportions. A leading equip- ment manufacturer has estimated that for manual metal-arc welding about 80% to 86% of the cost is for labor and overhead, something like 8% to 15% for electrodes, and as little as 2% for power and equipment costs. In contrast, the cost of a projection welding operation may be mostly for power and equipment and little for labor and none for consumable electrodes.

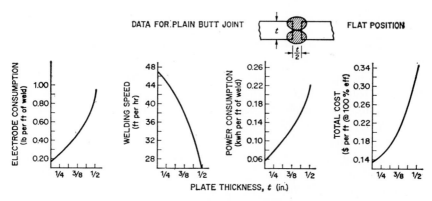

Fig. 14–28. A chart of manual arc welding performance. The curve for total welding cost in dollars per ft at 100% efficiency assumes power cost of $0.02 per kwh, electrode cost of $0.15 per lb, labor of $2 per hr, and overhead of $3 per hour.

The curves in Fig. 14–28 show typical amounts of unit electrode and power consumption, welding speeds, and costs for several sizes of plain butt joints. Basic data of this sort have been compiled for many kinds of welds and conditions and are given in charts and tables in reference- and hand-books for welding. The rates and costs are different in the same shop for different kinds of welds and positions of welding.

The following are the detailed calculations for the cost of a plain butt weld in a ⅜ in.-thick plate to illustrate how the cost curve is obtained in Fig. 14–28.

$$\text{Cost of labor and overhead} = \frac{5}{38} \qquad\qquad = \$0.132$$

$$\text{Cost of electrodes} \qquad = 0.48 \ \times 0.15 = \ 0.072$$

$$\text{Cost of electricity} \qquad = 0.127 \times 0.02 = \ \underline{0.003}$$

$$\$0.207 \text{ per ft}$$

The cost of electricity is negligible and is commonly ignored. The cost of labor and overhead does not allow for the time in which the operator is not engaged in laying down metal on the weld. The lost time may be as much as 80% and must be determined from the performance in each shop. If a 40% efficiency is assumed, the cost of labor and overhead in this case is $5/(38 \times 0.40) = \$0.329$, and the total cost is $0.404 per ft of weld. This unit cost is multiplied by the number of feet in a particular weld to find its cost.

A welder's pay rate is usually based on the position in which he can make a satisfactory weld. For instance, one who can do overhead welding properly receives more pay than another who can do only flat welding. Welds in different positions are subject to different labor rates as well as speeds of welding.

Comparison of welding with casting. Many products, such as machine frames and other members, can be either cast or fabricated by welding. The advantage of welding is that steel structures can be made stronger, stiffer, and lighter than those of cast iron. As a general rule, machine steel can safely be subjected to stresses about four times as high as those for cast iron. Stiffness may be illustrated by the deflection of a simple beam as shown in Fig. 14–29 with the fundamental equation for the amount of deflection. The deflection, d, is inversely proportional to the modulus of elasticity, E, of the material, which is 12,000,000 for cast iron and 30,000,000 for steel. For the same deflection, the width, b, of a steel beam needs to be only 40% of that of a cast iron beam. Approximately the same ratio applies for all kinds of bending and torsion. Good welded steel designs have about half the weight of cast iron structures that are no stronger or stiffer.

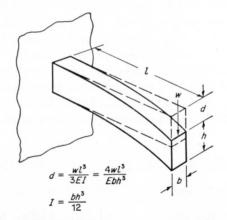

$$d = \frac{wl^3}{3EI} = \frac{4wl^3}{Ebh^3}$$

$$I = \frac{bh^3}{12}$$

Fig. 14–29. The deflection of a cantilever beam.

Some consider cast iron better than steel for dampening vibrations in machine members. This is true only if the two materials are stressed the same amount. If the steel is subjected to higher stresses, as it should be, its dampening capacity is as good or better than that of cast iron. This topic is discussed more fully as a principle of machine tool design in Chap. 21.

Steel costs about ⅓ as much per lb as does cast iron. In a well designed steel product that weighs about half as much, the material cost is about ⅙ as much as for cast iron. In addition the steel must be cut, shaped, fitted, and welded, and the structure annealed. The casting needs only to be cleaned and chipped, but each different casting needs a pattern, which is expensive. In practically all cases a single unit, and particularly large units, can be made by welding more cheaply than by casting. In some cases welding is cheaper no matter how many units are made; in other cases castings are cheaper for larger quantities. Casting is well adapted to automatic production of large quantities, especially of complex pieces. For example, a number of attempts have been made to weld fabricate automobile engine blocks, but none has ever displaced casting generally.

An example of a cast or welded base for a machine tool is illustrated by Fig. 14–30. The casting weighs 800 lb and can be obtained for $0.15 per lb for one unit and at a declining unit cost to $0.10 per lb for 100 units. Cleaning costs $10 for each unit. A pattern costs $450 and serves for any number of units from 1 to 100. The total cost for a single unit is $580. If a lot of 20 is made, the distributed pattern cost is $22.50 per unit, cast iron costs $0.14 per lb, and each unit costs $144.50. A welded machine base for the

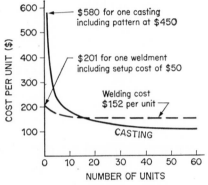

Fig. 14–30. Cost versus quantity for a machine tool base made by casting or welding.

same machine weighs 375 lb. Steel costs $0.05 per lb and heat treatment $0.02 per lb, making the total material cost $26.25 per unit. Fabrication takes 25 hours at $5 pr hr but initial preparation and set-up amounts to 10 hours at the same rate. By welding, one unit costs $201.25. The set-up charge can be distributed over a lot of 20 units, and the cost per unit then is $153.75. As seen by Fig. 14–30, casting is cheaper for 17 or more units; welding for any lot of 16 or less.

Some additional advantages of welding are that it is an easier method than casting to join unlike materials in one structure, to make sections quite thin when that is sufficient or needed, to join thin and thick sections, and to change designs. The storage of patterns for castings may be an appreciable added expense; if anything, less bulky templates are all that are needed for weldments.

Comparison of welding and riveting. An analysis of a joint made by ¾ in.-diameter rivets showed a cost of $0.37 for each 10,000 lb capacity as against $0.07 for a welded joint of equal capacity. At one time all joints in structural steel buildings, boilers, tanks, automobile chassis, etc. were riveted. Welding has largely replaced riveting for such applications.

Sometimes one method, sometimes the other, is economical for pieces joined in large quantities on automatic machinery, depending on circumstances. Some products may be riveted when the quantity does not justify the investment in welding equipment.

Riveting always requires lap joints. The holes and the rivets subtract from strength, and a riveted joint at best can only be about 85% as strong, whereas a good welded joint is fully as strong as the parent metal. Joints can be made gas and liquid tight by welding but must be caulked when riveted. Welded joints are easier to inspect because it is difficult to ascertain whether a rivet has been drawn up fully. The inspector must depend on the ability and integrity of the maker of manually riveted joints.

GAS AND ELECTRIC ARC CUTTING

Principles of gas cutting. Gas or *flame cutting* is done by preheating a spot on a ferrous metal to its ignition temperature and then burning it with a stream of oxygen in the manner illustrated in Fig. 14–31. The reaction that takes place at about 1600°F is

$$3Fe + 2O_2 \rightarrow Fe_3O_4 + 48{,}000 \text{ Btu per mole.}$$

Theoretically 1 cu ft of oxygen is required to oxidize about ¾ cu in. of iron. Actually, about 30% to 40% of the metal is melted and blown away without being oxidized, and removal of 1 cu in. or more of iron per cu ft of oxygen is not uncommon performance.

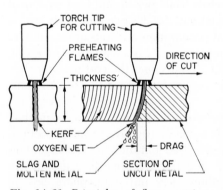

Fig. 14–31. Principles of flame cutting.

The oxygen jet spurts out of a hole in the center of the tip of the cutting torch. Around that, gas flames issue from several holes and heat the top of the metal piece to keep it at the ignition temperature. Acetylene is widely used as fuel because of its hot and adjustable flame, but among other fuels are hydrogen and illuminating gas. As the metal is burnt and eroded away, the torch is moved steadily along the path of cut. A uniformly wide slot, called the *kerf*, is cut by the jet of oxygen. The faster the rate of traverse, the more the bottom lags behind the top of the cut. The amount is called the *drag* and is evidenced by a series of curved lines on the sides of the kerf. Fine lines characterize a quality cut; coarse one a fast or heavy cut. The drag must be kept small to cut a surface with a straight side around a curve.

Flame-cutting equipment and procedures. Flame-cutting equipment
is similar to that for gas welding. A cutting torch mixes the fuel gas with
oxygen and emits it separately from the pure oxygen jet. Tips of various
sizes and designs are used for various purposes. Valves are provided to
regulate the rate of flow and pressures of the gases.

Fig. 14–32. Multiple flame cutting of die shoes from 2 in.-thick
steel plate from a master template. (Courtesy Danly Machine Specialties, Inc.)

A cutting torch may be manipulated by hand for rough work, but
steadier, faster, and more economical results are obtained from mechanized cutting. A flame-cutting machine consists of a table to hold the

work and a framework to carry and move the torch or torches. The workpiece commonly rests on a series of disposable bars on an open top table. A typical production machine with four torches on an arm controlled from a master template to cut out four pieces at a time is shown in Fig. 14–32. This is called *multiple-torch cutting.*

A high degree of skill is required to get best performance in flame cutting. The gas and oxygen pressure, position of torch, intensity of preheat, cutting speed, and type of tip must all be selected and regulated to suit the kind of material cut, the thickness of the work, the shape of the path of the cut, and the finish and accuracy required at the lowest possible cost for gases and time.

In addition to movement in a line, a torch may be moved intermittently forward and backward or from side to side as it is traversed along a cut. Initial preheat tends to burn a spot in the metal, so a cut is started away from the line of cut and usually at an outside edge of the plate where ignition is quick.

Flame cutting usually implies cutting all the way through the metal. The slot may be vertical or at an angle. A principal use of flame cutting is to cut off and prepare plates for welding. The various types of grooves can be cut readily in this way. For instance, a plate may be cut off and bevelled at the same time by means of two torches, one vertical and the other inclined at the bevel angle, traversed along the cut together.

If a cutting torch is inclined at an angle and proper adjustments are made, the stream of oxygen will not penetrate through the piece but will curve around and return to the top. By moving the torch properly, a groove, cavity, hole, or even the entire top to a certain depth may be removed or cut from the piece. This is called flame machining, and specific applications of it are termed flame-planing, -milling, -turning, -drilling, and -boring like the analogous machining operations.

One variation of flame cutting, called *oxygen-lance cutting,* is done with a long iron pipe of small diameter with oxygen flowing through it. The end of the pipe is set aflame and furnishes preheat for the oxygen stream. This torch is able to pierce holes in all kinds of metal. One example of its use is to burn holes in a hunk of metal frozen in a ladle. Dynamite is then put in the hole to break up the chunk and remove it.

Applications of flame cutting. Most ferrous metals are flame cut. Thicknesses up to 60 inches can be cut in the ordinary way, and virtually any thickness by the oxygen-lance method. A number of plates may be piled on top of each other and cut at one time in what is called *stack cutting.*

In addition to cutting out sections for weldments and parts, such as gears, sprockets, and cams, from steel plates, flame cutting is used to cut off structural shapes and barstock, cut up steel scrap, cut off rivet heads, and remove butt ends and seamed, cracked, or defective sections from billets, slabs, and rounds, and for many other purposes. Rough flame cutting is done just to cut off pieces; precision flame cutting to produce fairly accurate shapes.

The metal on the sides of the kerf is heated above its critical temperature but the effect seldom penetrates more than ⅛ in. below the surface. In steel of less than about 0.30% carbon and little alloy content, the result is normally confined to changes in grain size and structure near the surface. That may improve surface strength and toughness. A thin layer is likely to be hardened on high-carbon and alloy steel surfaces and cause high internal stresses and cracks. Heating before or annealing after cutting or both are often done to relieve this situation.

Flame cutting can be done at moderate cost and still leave drag lines negligible with edges sharp, kerf uniform in thickness, and surfaces square with tolerances satisfactory for many purposes. Good flame cut surfaces compare favorably with machined surfaces. Thick pieces do not warp as a rule, but plates ½ in. or less thick may require careful treatment, such as staggering of cuts, to avoid excessive warpage.

Ordinarily a tolerance of ±¹⁄₃₂ in. is considered practical in cutting plate up to 6 in. thick. Closer tolerances are held but at higher than usual commercial costs. In one case of cutting gears about 8 ft in diameter in segments from 5 in.-thick steel plate, the tooth contours were reported held to ±0.006 in. In precision work, cross-sectional squareness is held at from 0.003 in. for 1 in.-thick to 0.030 in. for 6 in.-thick sections. For the most precise results, a piece may be flame cut oversize to remove most of the stock and finish machined to the degree of accuracy required.

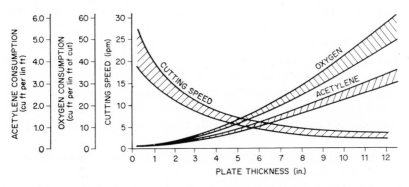

Fig. 14–33. Performance data for machine flame cutting mild steel not preheated.

Costs of flame cutting. The main elements of operating cost for flame cutting are: (1) for labor and overhead and (2) for gas. Labor and overhead costs are based upon the time required to do a job. This usually includes time for preparation, set-up, and tear-down. The cutting time is calculated by dividing the length of cut by the cutting speed. Typical values for cutting speeds and rates of gas consumption, which vary with plate thickness, are given by the curves of Fig. 14–33. Ranges of values apply for any one thickness depending on the skill of the operator, the operating conditions, and the results required. For instance, the cutting speed must be slow to hold small tolerances. Similar tables and charts for various conditions can be found in reference- and hand-books as a guide for cost estimating.

In addition to operating cost, the cutting of a shape may call for a special template chargeable to the job.

An example for estimating the cost of a flame-cutting operation is furnished by a job that requires a cut 237 in. long in 3 in.-thick mild steel. No special template is needed. Set-up time is 35 min. The labor and overhead rate in the shops is $6 per hr, oxygen costs 0.65¢ per cu ft, and acetylene 2.74¢ per cu ft. The conditions are those given by Fig. 14–33.

The cost of labor and overhead $= (35 + 237/8)6/60$ $= \$6.46$
The cost of oxygen $= 6 \times (237/12) \times 0.0065$ $= 0.77$
The cost of acetylene $= 0.5 \times (237/12) \times 0.0274 = 0.27$
Total operating cost $=$ $\$7.50$

Comparison with other methods. Flame cutting is directly competitive with shearing for cutting off plates, bars, rails, etc. Shearing generally is faster for work within the capacity of and readily movable to available equipment. Flame-cutting equipment is relatively portable and easily applied to large pieces and structures to which heavy shears cannot economically be carried.

Friction sawing is comparable in speed and does not use gases. It is more economical than flame cutting for some applications but not as versatile. For instance, rails are cut to desired lengths by friction sawing when they come out of a rolling mill. Occasionally a rail going through the mill runs afoul and becomes twisted in the mechanism. Flame-cutting equipment is then brought up to slice the rail into pieces to free it from the mill.

Flame cutting is generally faster but not as accurate as machining for cutting parts from thick steel plate and shapes. It is usually not as fast as shearing or die cutting for pieces ½ in. or less in thickness and tends to warp thin pieces.

Powder cutting of high alloys. Flame cutting of some high-alloy steels, such as stainless steel, and many nonferrous alloys is difficult, because the alloying elements, such as chromium and nickel, oxidize along with the base metal. Many of these oxides do not melt at attainable temperatures and form an insulating coating on the work that hinders progress of the cut. Free carbon forms a like barrier in cast iron. Also the combustion of some alloys does not add enough heat to the operation.

The same kind of work done on low-carbon steel by flame cutting can be done successfully on stainless steel, cast iron, copper, Monel metal, and others by the *powder-cutting and scarfing process.* In addition to the usual procedure of flame cutting, a fine iron-rich powder is injected into the flame and oxygen stream. This burns and raises the temperature considerably, and cutting can be accomplished mainly by melting in those cases where oxidation is not adequate. The powder is blown by compressed air from a dispenser through a hose and an extra passage in the torch.

A somewhat larger torch tip to accommodate the extra ingredient must be used for powder cutting, and the cut is rougher and wider than for straight flame cutting. Otherwise the results are comparable. Stainless steel can be powder cut about as fast as low-carbon steel can be flame cut but at about twice the cost. Most of the additional cost is for powder.

In *flux injection,* a fine stream of flux powder is injected into the oxygen stream to increase the fluidity of refractory oxides so they can be blown easily from the kerf.

Electric-arc cutting. Cutting with an electric arc alone to melt the metal may be done with either a carbon or metal electrode. In *carbon-arc cutting,* the arc is drawn between the workpiece and a carbon or graphite electrode. *Metal-arc cutting* is arc cutting with a coated electrode. The coating insulates the electrode so it can be inserted deep into the cut and helps control the arc and form fluid slag.

The methods that use an electric arc alone do not depend on oxidation. Direct current with straight polarity (electrode negative) puts most of the heat from the arc into the cut. Alternating current does not serve as well. Ordinarily the molten metal falls by gravity out of the kerf, and the electrode is commonly applied from below to aid the flow. A variant method applies a compressed air jet just behind the arc to blow metal away as it melts.

Good surface finish and accuracy are not obtained by plain-arc cutting, and it is mostly confined to rough work like cutting up scrap and removing risers from castings. It does have the advantage of being able to cut any metal and has some use for work not readily done by other methods, such as cutting large iron castings, manganese steel, and highly refractory nonferrous metals.

For *oxygen-arc cutting,* the electrode is a coated steel tube through which oxygen is blown. The action is similar to that of gas cutting, except that the preheat is supplied by an arc instead of a flame. Electrodes are consumable. About the same finish is obtained on low-carbon steel, a rougher finish on alloy steel and nonferrous metals, and a better finish on cast iron than from flame cutting. The method has not nearly the wide acceptance of flame cutting.

Underwater cutting. Flame cutting is possible in depths up to 300 ft under water by maintaining a bubble of compressed air and gases around the point of operation. This supports combustion and keeps the water from quenching the reaction. Some torches have a skirt around the tip to hold the bubble. The necessary pressure increases with depth, and hydrogen is used when the pressure is too high for acetylene, over about 15 psi. Working time is limited by the ability of the operator to manipulate the equipment and withstand the pressure.

Oxygen-arc cutting may be done under water, in fact it was developed for that purpose. It saves the load of a fuel hose but adds the necessity of thorough electrical insulation.

METAL SPRAYING

Principles and procedures. Metal spraying is done by melting a metal in an oxy-gas flame and blowing it from the nozzle of a spray gun in the manner illustrated in Fig. 14–34. The molten metal is accelerated to a high speed by a jet of compressed air, atomized, and hurled against the workpiece surface. Upon contact with the cool surface, the tiny particles flatten out and freeze quickly. In most guns the metal is in the form of wire and is fed by powered rollers to the flame, but some guns utilize powder or granulated metal.

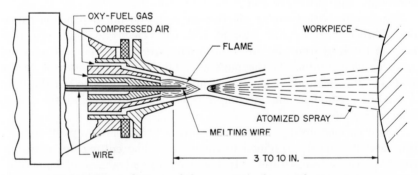

Fig. 14–34. A diagram of the operation of a metal spray gun.

A metal spray gun may be directed by hand or mounted on a machine. A typical application is to spray a round piece turning between centers on a lathe with the gun mounted on the carriage for a uniform feed.

Sprayed metal adheres to a surface essentially through mechanical bonding, so the surface must be roughened first and be free of dirt, oil, and grease. One way to roughen the surface is to machine coarse grooves in it and break these up with a knurling tool. A coarse thread may be put on a round piece. Screws and studs may be inserted in a surface as anchors. Another method is to spray a base coat with a high-temperature melting alloy like molybdenum that welds to steel, aluminum, and zinc. An arc-welding method attaches small and irregular particles of nickel from a vibrating electrode. Large flat surfaces may be blasted with steel grit.

Applications. Any commercial metal may be sprayed, but it must be of good quality. Even some non-metals, such as hard metallic oxides, are sprayed. Spraying may be done on metallic or non-metallic surfaces, such as fabrics, ceramics, and plastics. Spraying is basically done to confer some physical property on a surface. Examples are corrosion-resistance, with a coat of stainless steel; abrasion-resistance, with a coat of high-carbon steel; heat-resistance, with a coat of zirconium oxide in the combustion chamber of a jet engine; or wear-resistance, with a coat of aluminum oxide in an extrusion die. Different properties can be given to different parts of one surface. The original and main use of metal spraying is to restore to correct size parts that have been machined too small or have become worn or eroded. The appearance of poor surfaces on castings can be improved by metal spraying. Sprayed metal can be decorative, like aluminum or bronze on cast iron. Some can even be colored.

Sprayed metal can be expected to oxidize somewhat. The coating is around 10% to 15% less dense than the original metal and somewhat porous, which may impair corrosion protection but provides desirable oil pockets for a bearing or journal. The tensile strength and ductility of a coating usually are poor, but compressive strength is satisfactory. Coatings may be made quite hard with suitable materials. Hardenable steel is quenched rapidly when applied and forms a hard coating. A coating may be as thin as 0.002 to 0.003 in. and there is no upper limit to its thickness if applied properly.

Metal spraying is not by itself a precision process. If a small tolerance is required for a surface, it is coated oversize and then machined or ground to the desired size. Metal spraying is not a rapid method with standard commercial equipment. Typical outfits using wire cost between $500 and $1000, depending on their elaborateness. Adequate means for ventilation must be provided to spray some metals, such as lead and zinc, that give off toxic fumes.

SURFACING AND HARD FACING

Principles. Hard facing or surfacing is a process of welding wear- or corrosion-resistant metal on a part to make it serviceable or to rebuild or repair it. It is commonly done on metal-working dies and tools, oil well drilling tools, parts of earth-moving and excavation equipment, rolling mill rolls, and tractor parts. As an example, it has been found that parts for heavy tractors can be rebuilt by surfacing at about 40% of the cost of replacement parts and last about 50% longer. On the other hand, new forming dies for sheet metal are commonly hard faced at critical spots to make them run longer before they have to be repaired.

All but a few hard facing materials consist of hard particles of carbides of chromium, tungsten, molybdenum, etc. uniformly distributed in a soft matrix. The hardness of an alloy depends on the types and amounts of carbides it contains. No one surfacing material can serve all purposes. The many materials used are classified in the following groups:

Group A: Less than 20% alloy content. These are iron-base alloys with chromium, tungsten, manganese, and silicon for the most part in addition to carbon. They are much more wear-resistant than carbon steel but not as hard as higher priced alloys. They have superior toughness and shock-resistance. Typical applications are for facing the teeth of power-shovel buckets and the jaws of rock crushers.

Group B: More than 20% alloy content. These are iron-base alloys with chromium, tungsten, manganese, silicon, carbon, and sometimes cobalt, nickel, boron, vanadium, and zirconium. They are harder and more expensive than Group A alloys. Their shock-resistance is not as great, but they are valuable as long wearing final coats on top of built-up sections of high-strength metals. They can be highly polished and have a low coefficient of friction. They excel for plowshares and some sliding bearings on machines.

Group C: Nonferrous alloys. One main class includes the cobalt-chromium-tungsten alloys, with carbon and other elements and available in several grades, that are highly resistant to wear and corrosion. A well known trade name is Stellite. Such alloys retain hardness even at red heat. Typical uses are for hot-working dies and mechanical parts in furnaces.

In another class are the nickel-base alloys which are not only hard but have exceptional resistance to atmospheric and chemical corrosion. Some are known as Hastelloys. Their mechanical strength is high, and they have gained favor in chemical and process industries.

Group D: Diamond substitutes. These are pieces of cemented carbides, sintered carbides or sintered oxides fastened to oil well drilling tools, metal-cutting tools, centerless grinder rest blades, etc. The most common are the cemented carbides described in Chaps. 10 and 16. Bits or inserts of these materials are commonly fastened in place by welding or brazing them to the cutter bodies or parts on which they are used.

Group E: Imbedded hard particles. Crushed tungsten carbide particles of various sizes are imbedded in a matrix of steel. They are obtainable packed in steel tubes, fused in steel strips, or bonded with steel in rods. These are used as electrodes to deposit a coating. Loose grains may also be applied to steel welding.

Procedures. Low- and high-carbon, low alloy, stainless, and manganese steels and cast iron can be hard faced with some differences in methods for each. Except as stated in the preceding paragraphs, the surfacing metals are available commercially as welding rods and are deposited as filler metal by welding. This is done mostly by gas- or metal-arc welding, but high-quality deposits and fast facing are obtained from atomic hydrogen arc welding, although at higher cost. Most surfacing is done manually on diverse repair, rebuilding, and maintenance jobs. For enough work of the same kind, facing is done on automatic welding machines by the submerged-arc method. Surface preparation and preheating are helpful and necessary for hard facing, the same as for welding.

BRAZE WELDING, BRAZING, AND SOLDERING

Braze welding. Braze welding, also called *bronze welding,* is like fusion welding, in that a filler is melted and deposited in a groove, fillet, plug, or slot between two pieces to make a joint. In this case the filler metal is a copper alloy with a melting point below that of the base metal but above 800°F. The filler metal is puddled into and not distributed in the joint by capillarity, as in plain brazing described later.

Metals with high melting points, such as steel, cast iron, copper, brass, and bronze, are braze welded. The base metal does not melt, but a bond is formed, sometimes stronger than the base metal alone. Studies of the bonds between copper alloys and cast iron have shown three sources of the forces that bind braze welded joints. One is in the atomic forces between metals at their interfaces in close contact. A second is alloying which arises from diffusion of the metals in a narrow zone at the interface. The third is intergranular penetration.

Braze welding may be done by oxy-acetylene, metallic-arc, or carbon-arc welding. The filler metal is applied by a rod or electrode together with a suitable flux. Most metals require little, if any, preheat, with the exception of cast iron, in which localized heating may set up enough stresses to cause cracking.

The main advantages of braze welding result from the low temperature of the operation. Less heat is needed and a joint can be made faster than by fusion welding. The filler metal yields substantially on cooling to 500°F, and even some below, without weakening, and residual stresses are small. Dissimilar metals not amenable to fusion welding may be joined by braze welding.

Braze welded joints are not satisfactory for service at over about 500°F nor for dynamic loads of 15,000 psi or more.

Brazing. Brazing is the name given a group of welding operations in which a nonferrous filler metal melts at a temperature below that of the metal joined but is heated above 800°F. The molten filler metal flows by capillarity between the heated but unmelted adjacent or overlapping joint members or is melted in place between those members. Examples of the kinds of joints made in this way are shown in Fig. 14–35.

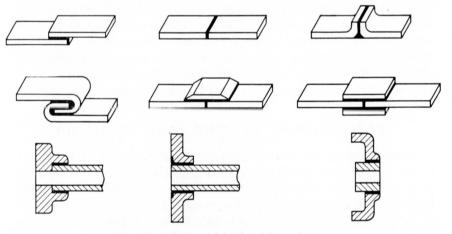

Fig. 14—35. Several kinds of brazed joints.

Filler metals may be divided into two classes: copper alloys and silver alloys. There are a number of different alloys in each class. Each serves a certain purpose best, such as joining certain kinds of metals, being suitable for a particular process, or giving certain properties to a joint. Some are considered general-purpose alloys and are satisfactory for most jobs, but the selection of the best alloy for any particular job entails a number of factors, and space does not allow their full treatment here.

Copper alone or alloyed with zinc, tin, nickel, phosphorous, or silver, separately or together, is brazed at 1300° to 2150°F. Some of these alloys withstand temperatures to 800°F in service, but most are not considered serviceable above 500°F.

Brazing done with silver alloys is called *silver brazing* or *silver soldering*. Silver alone or alloyed with copper, zinc, cadmium, tin, manganese, nickel, or phosphorous is brazed at 1175° to 1550°F. Some metals and parts must be joined at these lower temperatures to avoid overheating or warping. Service temperatures should usually not be over 500°F. Silver brazed joints are about as strong and sometimes stronger than copper brazed joints, but the silver alloys are relatively expensive.

The bond between a brazing metal and the clean metal of the parts joined is due to some diffusion of the brazing metal into the hot base metal and to some surface alloying of the metals. A good joint is at least as strong as the filler metal. If the base metal is weaker than the filler metal, failure occurs outside the joint. If the base metal is stronger, the joint fails but at a stress much higher than the tensile strength of the filler metal. A good joint can only be obtained with a minute clearance between the surfaces being joined and by the practice of proper brazing techniques that assure full penetration of the joint by the filler metal. Tests of stainless steel with a tensile strength of 160,000 psi joined in a butt joint by means of a silver alloy of 70,000 psi strength showed a maximum joint strength of 130,000 psi with a clearance of 0.0015 in. in the joint. The strength dropped off almost proportionately to about 40,000 psi as the clearance was increased to 0.024 in. Rules for selecting brazing materials and designing brazed joints properly are given in reference- and hand-books.

Surfaces must be thoroughly cleaned before brazing and then usually are covered with a flux to obviate oxidation. Borax is a widely used flux, but many proprietary brands are available. In general, the parts are heated and the brazing metal is applied to the joint. The actual heating may be done in a number of ways. Torch brazing is common because it is convenient. Furnace brazing, particularly in controlled atmospheres, is a favorite for production. Induction heating is useful to confine the heat to the joint if general heating must be avoided. Resistance brazing is done on some small parts in production. Parts may be dipped in molten filler metal or have it poured over them. They may be heated by being dipped in a bath of molten salt or flux. Immersion is particularly suitable for brazing multiple joints uniformly. For some special production jobs, fixtures are used to hold the parts and heat them by electrical resistance elements.

Brazing is commonly done to join steel, copper, brass, bronze, aluminum, and cast iron, together or to each other. The process is adaptable to mass production techniques. Joints are ductile and resistant to fatigue and corrosion. The strengths, operating temperatures, and costs of brazed joints are less than those from fusion welding but more than from soft soldering.

Soldering. *Soldering* or *soft soldering* is the process of joining metals by means of alloys that melt between 350° and 700°F. They are generally lead and tin alloys described in Chap. 7. The metals mostly joined by soldering are iron, copper, nickel, lead, tin, zinc, and many of their alloys. Aluminum can be soldered by special means.

The strength of a soldered joint depends on surface alloying and upon mechanical bonding, such as crimping, between the joined parts. The solder alone has a low unit strength, little resistance to fatigue, and is limited to operating temperatures below 300°F. Tests on various soldered copper sleeve joints showed shear strengths from about 3000 to 6000 psi at 85°F. Thin films are necessary for the strongest joints. Thicknesses of 0.003 in. on copper and 0.005 in. on steel are desirable.

For soldering, a flux is generally necessary to rid the surface of oxides to obtain intimate contact between the solder and base metal. Zinc chloride is most efficient but corrosive as a flux. Rosin does not clean as well but is non-corrosive, and must be used for dependable electrical connections. There are a number of soldering techniques, some for particular materials. In general the flux is applied first, the parts are heated at the joint to just above the melting point of the solder, and then the solder is touched to and flows into the joint. Any source of clean heat is satisfactory. A heated copper soldering iron or soldering copper is widely used for general-purpose work. An open flame from an alcohol, gasoline, or gas torch may be played directly on the joint. A heated neutral gas, like nitrogen, may be necessary for some extremely fussy work. Induction or resistance heating or immersion of the workpieces in a solder bath are fast methods and adapted to production.

Soldering produces liquid- and gas-tight joints quickly and at low cost. Temperatures are not high, equipment is simple, and the method is the most convenient and feasible means of making joints in the workshop, laboratory, or home where often the equipment for other processes is not available. Soldering provides positive and dependable electrical connections. If a soldered joint is strong and durable enough for a particular purpose, it is usually the most economical.

Questions

1. What is the principle of arc welding in its two basic forms?

2. What is the optimum amount of electric current to expend in metal-arc welding?

3. How do d-c and a-c compare for arc welding?

4. What are the functions of coatings on shielded electrodes?

5. What are welding positioners, and what are their advantages?

6. How is automatic-arc welding done, and what are its limitations?

7. What are the advantages of each of the several sources of current for arc welding?

8. How are arc welder sizes designated, and under what conditions?

9. What are the necessary current characteristics of a power source for manual-arc welding, and why?

10. What two kinds of power sources are used for automatic welding and what are their principles of operation?

11. Explain the Tig and Mig systems of arc welding.

12. What is atomic hydrogen arc welding, and what are its advantages and disadvantages?

13. What is submerged-arc welding, and where does it serve best?

14. How is stud welding done, and what does it accomplish?

15. How do the main automatic-arc welding methods compare with each other?

16. What are the principles of operation for resistance welding?

17. How are the electrodes protected in resistance welding?

18. What must be the relationship between current and time in resistance welding?

19. What effect does the electrical resistance of a metal have on the ease of welding it by resistance methods?

20. What are the common elements of resistance welding machines?

21. What is meant by a resistance welding machine rating of 1000 kva at 50% duty cycle?

22. What effect on the available a-c results from placing a workpiece between electrodes of a resistance welding machine?

23. What are the relative and optimum conditions of time, current, and tip force in a spot welding operation?

24. What is meant by heat balance, and how is it obtained?

25. What are the major features of spot welding machines?

26. On what principles does projection welding operate?

27. What is seam welding and what are its advantages and disadvantages?

28. Compare upset-butt welding, flash-butt welding, and percussion welding as to the ways they are done and their relative merits and limitations.

29. What is the principle of Thermit welding? What can it do better than other processes?

30. What properties make acetylene the favorite for gas welding?

31. Describe the features of a gas welding operation.

32. In what ways is gas welding of advantage?

33. What are the uses of oxy-hydrogen gas welding?

34. What are the elements of common arc- or gas-welded joints?

35. What are welding symbols, and what do they do?

36. How does welding affect grain size and structure of a metal?

37. To what extent does steel harden in welding? Why? What effect does it have on the weldment?

38. What causes weldments to crack, and what are the remedies? Explain the reasons for the events.

39. What causes inclusions and voids in a weld, and how can they be prevented?

40. Why is hydrogen detrimental to welds?

41. How does welding make metals susceptible to corrosion?

42. In what ways are weldments heat treated, and for what purposes?

43. How is a knowledge of welding principles and practices of value to a machine designer?

44. How may welds be inspected economically?

45. What are the elements of cost of welding, and how are they estimated?

46. How do weldments compare with castings?

47. How does welding compare with riveting?

48. How does an oxygen jet cut steel?

49. What is the difference between flame cutting and flame machining?

50. What is oxygen-lance cutting and for what is it used?

51. What can be done by flame cutting?

52. How are flame cutting costs estimated?

53. How does flame cutting compare with metal shearing? With friction sawing? With machining?

54. Why is it difficult to flame cut some materials, and what can be done for them?

55. How is electric-arc cutting done and what are its limitations? How does it excel?

56. What is oxygen-arc cutting?

57. How is cutting done under water?

58. How is metal sprayed, and what does it accomplish?

59. What are the major disadvantages of sprayed surfaces?

60. What is surfacing or hard facing, and why is it done?

61. What are the classes and properties of materials used for surfacing?

62. What is the difference between braze welding and brazing, and how are they alike?

63. What is the nature of a braze-welded bond?

64. What are the advantages of braze welding and brazing?

65. What metals are used for brazing, and how do they affect the properties of the joints?

66. What are the fundamental requirements for a good brazed joint?

67. What is soldering and how does it compare with brazing?

Problems

1. Show how the weld cost in $/ft is computed from the data given in Table 14–1 and accompanying text
   (a) for conventional metal-arc with coated electrode,
   (b) for metal-arc with powder metal electrode,
   (c) for manual submerged-arc process,
   (d) for manual CO_2 gas-shielded process.

2. Arc welding to lay down 12 lb per hr is to be done with automatic machines that are capable of welding at that rate while the arc is on. Labor costs $2.50 per hr. Overhead is not thought to be much different for either case and is neglected. For the submerged-arc welding process, flux costs $0.11 per lb and is used at the rate of 1.5 lb per lb of electrode wire consumed. The wire costs $0.12 per lb, and the deposition efficiency is 100%. The duty cycle is 60%. For the CO_2 gas-shielded welding process, gas costs 1.2 cents per cu ft and is used at the rate of 30 cu ft per hr of welding time. The wire costs $0.25 per lb, and the deposition efficiency is 90%. The duty cycle is 80%.
   (a) Which process appears more economical for this job?
   (b) Why are the deposition efficiency and the duty cycle different for the two processes?

3. Conventional welding equipment costs $500, and equipment for manual CO_2 gas-shielded welding costs $2000. For the conditions shown in Table

14–1, how much welding must be done to justify the more expensive equipment? Interest and taxes on the investment need not be considered.

4. (a) A resistance welding machine has a rating of x kva with a 50% duty cycle. The impedance of the secondary circuit of the transformer is R, ohms, and the voltage is v, volts. How much heat, H_1, is generated in the secondary circuit during any period of time T, in minutes?

(b) If the machine is operated to deliver y kva, and other conditions remain the same, except that the duty cycle is changed to a value C, how much heat, H_2, is generated in a time period T?

(c) Set up an expression for C in terms of x and y for operating the machine at maximum output without overheating.

(d) A resistance welder is rated at 50 kva at 50% duty cycle. Secondary voltage is 5 v and does not change. A job is put on the machine to draw 15,000 amps. What is the most the duty cycle may be for 15,000 amp?

5. A spot welding machine has a throat depth of 12 in. with 8 in. between horns. The secondary loop impedance is 165×10^{-6} ohms. If the throat depth is changed to 30 in., the impedance is increased to 340×10^{-6} ohms. The secondary voltage is 6 v. How much does the secondary current decrease with the change in throat depth?

6. A single-groove butt weld is to be made between two pieces of steel plate.

(a) What kind of steel is least likely to crack from the welding? Why?

(b) If a steel of 0.5% carbon content and medium hardenability is selected, which welding process is least likely to crack it? Why?

(c) If arc welding is used for the steel specified in part (b), what can be done to lessen the chances of cracking?

7. Estimate the cost of a plain-butt joint weld 18 in. long on ¼ in.-thick plate at 70% efficiency. Power costs $0.02 per kwhr, labor and overhead $5 per hr, and electrodes $0.15 per lb.

8. It is found in a certain shop that welding speed for a square butt joint in the vertical position is 80% of that for the flat position as given in Fig. 14–28. The welder is paid $2.25 per hr and overhead is $4 per hr. Welding efficiency is 50%. Electrodes cost $0.10 per lb, and electricity $0.02 per kwhr. What is the cost per foot of vertical square butt welds in each of the following sizes of plates?

(a) ¼ in.   (b) ⅜ in.   (c) ½ in.

9. A cast base for a machine tool weighs 4900 lb. The pattern costs $275, and cast iron $0.20 per lb. The cost to clean a casting is $12.

A welded design for the base weighs 2500 lb. Steel costs $0.08 per lb. Fabrication requires 100 hr at $8 per hr for labor and overhead. Set-up and preparation take 15 hr for a lot. Templates for cutting the steel cost $30.

(a) For how many pieces is the cost of a casting the same as the cost of a weldment?

(b) Which process would be cheaper for 25 pieces? How much? Why might this not be the deciding factor?

10. A welding shop that needs work is willing to cut its rate for labor and overhead to $7.50 per hr. If all other conditions stated in Prob. 9 are the same, what effect does the new rate have upon the choice of process?

11. A lot of 40 gear segments are to be rough-flame cut by machine and then finished by machining. The length of cut for each segment is 130 in. Four segments can be cut at one time from a template that costs $100. Oxygen costs $0.60 per 100 cu ft, and acetylene $2.75 per 100 cu ft. The labor and overhead rate in the shop is $5 per hr. An hour is required to set up and tear down the job. What is the cost per piece for flame cutting?

References

Morris, Joe L., *Welding Principles for Engineers,* Prentice-Hall, Inc., Englewood Cliffs, N. J., 1951.

Procedure Handbook of Arc Welding Design and Practice, The Lincoln Electric Co., Cleveland.

Welding Handbook, American Welding Society, New York.

CHAPTER 15

Measurement and Inspection

"When you can measure what you are
speaking about you know something
about it."

Lord Kelvin

The basic purpose of manufacturing is to produce engineering materials and products with specified shapes, sizes and finishes. These shape, size and finish specifications are generally found on the part drawing or the manufacturing drawing, and they are often referred to as *quality characteristics*.

INTERCHANGEABLE MANUFACTURE

Our modern manufacturing system, based on the concepts of interchangeable manufacture, requires that each part or assembly going into a final product be made to definite size, shape and finish specifications. Refrigerator compressor pistons, for example, must be machined within limits so that a piston selected at random will fit and function properly in the compressor model for which it was designed. This interchangeable manufacturing system is to a large degree responsible for the high standard of living enjoyed by the people of this country today. It makes possible the standardization of products and methods of manufacturing and provides for ease of assembly and repair of products.

368

INSPECTION

The mass production of interchangeable product is not altogether effective without some means of appraising and controlling product quality. Production operators are required, for example, to machine a given number of parts to the specifications shown on a drawing. There are often many factors that cause the parts to deviate from specifications during the various manufacturing operations. A few of these factors are variations in raw materials, deficiencies in machines and tools, poor methods, excessive production, and human errors.

Provisions must be made to detect errors so that the production of faulty parts can be stopped. The inspection department is usually charged with this responsibility, and its job is to interpret the specifications properly, inspect for conformance to those specifications, and then convey the information obtained to the production people who can make any necessary corrections to the process. Inspection operations are performed on raw materials and purchased parts at *receiving inspection*. *In-process inspection* is performed on products during the various phases of their manufacture, and finished products may be subjected to *final inspection*.

Quality control. The word "control" implies regulation, and of course, regulation implies observation and manipulation. Thus, a pilot flying an aircraft from one city to another must first set it on the proper course heading and then must continue to observe the progress of the craft and manipulate the controls so as to maintain its flight path in the proper direction. *Quality control* in manufacture is an analogous situation. It is simply a means by which management can be assured that the quality of product manufactured is consistent with the quality-economy standards that have been established. The word "quality" does not necessarily mean "the best" when applied to manufactured products. It should imply "the best for the money."

STATISTICAL QUALITY CONTROL

Increasing demands for higher quality of product often result in increased cost of inspection and surveillance of processes and product. The old philosophy of attempting to inspect quality into a product is time consuming and costly. It is, of course, more sensible to control the process and make the product correctly rather than rely on having to sort out defective product from good product. Certain statistical techniques have been developed which provide economical means of maintaining continual analysis and control of processes and products. These are known as *statistical quality control methods*, and many of them are formulated on the following basic statistical concepts:

1. A *population* or *universe* is the complete collection of objects or measurements of the type in which we are interested at a particular time. The population may be finite or infinite.
2. A *sample* is a finite group or set of objects taken from a population.
3. The *average* is a point or value about which a population or a sample set of measurements tends to cluster. It is a measure of the ordinary-ness or central tendency of a group of measurements.
4. *Variation* is the tendency for the measurements or observations in a population or a sample to scatter or disperse themselves about the average value.

In many cases the sizes observed from the inspection of a dimension of a group of pieces have been found to be distributed as shown in Fig. 15–1. If the pins represented in Fig. 15–1 include all the existing pins of a particular type, then this would be referred to as a *population distribution*. If those pins represent only a portion of a larger batch of the same type pins, then it would be called a *sample distribution*.

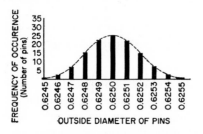

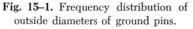

Fig. 15–1. Frequency distribution of outside diameters of ground pins.

The pattern of variation shown in Fig. 15–1 is typical of that obtained from data taken from many natural and artificial processes. It is referred to as a *normal distribution*, and the smooth curve formed by this distribution is called the *normal curve*. This, like many other distributions, can be described by its arithmetic average (measure of central tendency), called $\overline{X}$ and its standard deviation (measure of variation or dispersion) called σ. The formulas for these factors are:

$$\overline{X} = \frac{\overset{n}{\underset{1}{\Sigma}}X_i}{n} \tag{15-1}$$

$$\sigma = \sqrt{\frac{\overset{n}{\underset{1}{\Sigma}}(X_i - \overline{X})^2}{n}} \tag{15-2}$$

If $\overline{X}$ and σ are calculated from a population distribution they are called population *parameters*. If they are calculated from the data of a sample they are called sample *statistics*.

The range value, R, is often used as a measure of variation or dispersion for small samples. The range is the difference between the largest and smallest observed values in a sample set of values; $R = X_{\max} - X_{\min}$.

The greater portion of the area under the normal curve is included between the limits $\overline{X} + 3\sigma$. The curve actually continues out to plus and minus infinity, but the area under it beyond plus and minus three standard deviations from the mean is practically negligible.

The areas under intervals of the normal curve commonly used in statistical quality control practice are shown in Fig. 15–2. These mean that if a population of values is normally distributed, then 99.73% of the values from that population will probably appear within the limits of $\overline{X} \pm 3\sigma$. Only 0.27% are expected to fall beyond those limits. Similarly 95.46% of the values normally fall within the limits $\overline{X} \pm 2\sigma$, and 68.26% within $\overline{X} \pm 1\sigma$.

If the manufacturing specification on the pins shown in Fig. 15–1 was 0.6250 ± 0.0005 and if the limiting dimensions of that specification (0.6245 to 0.6255) corresponded to plus or minus three standard deviations from the mean, then 99.73% of the pins from that population would be expected to be within specifications.

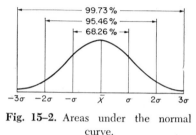

Fig. 15–2. Areas under the normal curve.

Only 0.27% would be expected not to conform to specifications. Most distributions encountered in industrial inspection activities are not exactly normal, but many approach normality. As a distribution approaches normality, its properties approximate those given. Tables of areas under the normal curve for various values of standard deviations from the mean are given in texts on statistical quality control.

Process control charts. One of the statistical tools that is commonly used in quality control work to evaluate the process is the control chart. A control chart is simply a frequency distribution with the observed values plotted as points joined by lines in the order of occurrence so that each value retains identity relative to time. The chart is provided with limit lines, called *control limits*, within which the points fall if influenced only by chance causes.

Two of the most common charts used in process control are the chart for averages, $\overline{X}$-chart, and the chart for ranges, R-chart. Figure 15–3 shows an example of such charts for a rough turning operation on the outside diameter of steel shafts. The first point on the $\overline{X}$-chart of Fig. 15–3

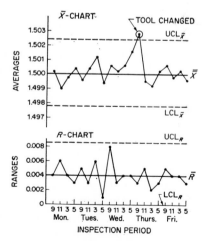

Fig. 15–3. Quality control chart showing averages and ranges of samples.

was determined by measuring the diameters of five shafts and then calculating the average of those measured values. Each succeeding point is also an average of the measured diameters of five shafts. Average values are plotted instead of individual values because sample averages tend to be more normally distributed than single values. The central line of the $\overline{X}$-chart represents the grand average of the subgroup averages and is

$$\overline{\overline{X}} = \frac{\overset{k}{\underset{1}{\Sigma}}\overline{X}}{k}$$

where k is the number of subgroups of 5 shafts each. The control limits are set at three standard deviations of the sample averages from the grand average, and are called *upper control limit* ($UCL = \overline{\overline{X}} + 3\sigma_{\overline{x}}$) and *lower control limit* ($LCL = \overline{\overline{X}} - 3\sigma_{\overline{x}}$). From Formula 15–2

$$\sigma_{\overline{x}} = \sqrt{\frac{\overset{k}{\underset{1}{\Sigma}}(\overline{X} - \overline{\overline{X}})^2}{k}}$$

Theoretically chances are that less than 3 out of 1000 points will fall outside the limits as long as no change is made in the system producing the values.

The range of values of the R-chart of Fig. 15–3 are obtained from the same subgroups of five samples each as were the $\overline{X}$ values. The central line, $\overline{R}$, represents the average of the subgroup ranges. Control limits on range charts are calculated by multiplying the average range by a factor which may be obtained from texts on statistical quality control.

The $\overline{X}$-chart of Fig. 15–3 indicates that the process average remained in a state of statistical control until the nine o'clock inspection period on Thursday, at which time a point exceeded the upper control limit. In this case, the out of control point was found to be caused by a worn cutting tool. Replacement of the tool caused the subsequent points to fall well within the control limits. This shows how a major change in the systems is reflected by the chart. Points that fall outside the limits of either chart signal difficulty with the process and call for corrective action.

Sampling inspection. Inspection operations are costly and do not contribute directly to the value of the product. Therefore, the amount of inspection should be kept to a minimum consistent with the quality requirements of the product. In order to be assured that each and every part produced conforms to specifications it is usually necessary to perform *100% inspection* on them. However, if a few defective items can be tolerated among a large number of good items, then an inspection procedure known as *sampling* can be applied. In this procedure a given number of parts are chosen at random from a group or lot of parts and are inspected for conformance to certain specifications. According to previously determined acceptance criteria, the lot of parts is judged acceptable or rejectable on the basis of the sample results.

There are quite a number of published sampling plans available based on *single sampling, double sampling* or some form of *sequential* or *group sequential* sampling. A typical single-sampling plan might require the inspection of 110 random samples from a lot of 1300 parts. If only 3 or less of the 110 were found to be defective, the lot would be accepted. The lot would be rejected if more than three defectives were detected in the sample of 110.

Sampling plans are selected on the basis of the amount of risk that can be tolerated in accepting defective material and rejecting acceptable material. Information about these risks is obtained from the *operating characteristic curve* of the sampling plan. Figure 15–4 shows an operating characteristic curve for the single-sampling plan described in the previous paragraph. From this curve it is observed that with the quality of the material coming in to inspection being 1% defective (point p_1 on the abscissa), the material would be accepted by the sampling plan about 97% of the time. If the material coming in were 6% defective

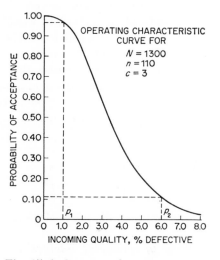

Fig. 15–4. Operating characteristic curve for a single sampling plan.

(point p_2 on the abscissa), it would be accepted only about 11% of the time. Thus, a sampling plan should be selected that will satisfy the demands of both the producer and consumer of the material being manufactured, so that each party will be aware of the risks inherent in sampling.

MANUFACTURING SPECIFICATIONS

Effective interchangeability relies upon complete specifications of the dimensions of a part or group of parts making up a product. Modern mass manufacturing systems are so complex that it is usually not economical for one skilled man to machine and fabricate all of the individual parts that go into an assembly. Rather, it is necessary that the various parts be worked upon by numerous individuals who are responsible for only one or perhaps a few operations on one of the component parts of a product. Thus, exacting specifications relative to the dimensions of these parts must be supplied to the workmen so that they may produce articles that can be assembled with a minimum of costly hand fitting and re-working.

Tolerances. Idealistically it would be desirable to manufacture parts to an exact size, but this is not physically practical nor economically feasible. To grind a cylindrical shaft to exactly one inch diameter would require a grinding machine of ultimate perfection—perfect spindle bear-ings, perfect way surfaces, perfect balance of the grinding wheel, etc. Even though such a machine could possibly be built and maintained in such a state of perfection, it would be beyond the realm of practical measurements to determine whether or not the shafts ground on the machine were exactly one inch in diameter. For this reason and others previously cited, it is necessary that some deviation be allowed from the exact theoretically desired size of a part. This deviation is usually referred to as a *manufacturing or working tolerance* and may be defined as the *permissible variation in a dimension.*

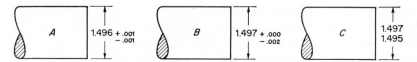

Fig. 15–5. Methods of assigning tolerances.

Ways of specifying tolerance. Manufacturing tolerances may be as-signed according to three different systems as shown in Fig. 15–5. Part A is assigned a *bilateral tolerance;* part B has a *unilateral tolerance;* and part C has the size specified in terms of *limiting dimensions* or *manufac-turing limits.* Notice that all three parts have the same total amount of tolerance and the same limiting dimensions.

There are certain advantages to specifying tolerances according to one or the other of these systems. A unilateral tolerance often implies that it is more critical for a certain dimension to deviate in one direction than in another. Unilateral tolerances are also more realistically applied to certain machining processes where it is common knowledge that dimen-sions will most likely deviate in one direction. For example, in drilling a hole with a standard size drill, the drill is more likely to produce an oversize rather than an undersize hole. Unilateral tolerances also facili-tate the specification and application of standard tools and gages. The application of unilateral tolerances also permits easy revision of tolerances without affecting the allowance or clearance conditions between mating

parts. Thus, this system of tolerancing usually finds the greatest acceptance in industrial application.

More recently the trend has been to utilize the bilateral tolerance
system as more desirable for manufacturing dimensions. This system
vividly points out the theoretically desired size and indicates the possible
and probable deviations that can be expected on each side of that theoretical size. Bilateral tolerances are easier to add together.

Clearance. One of the basic reasons for specifying precise limiting
dimensions for machined objects is to be assured that component parts
of an assembly will fit properly and function well under certain operating conditions. For example, a crankshaft must be free to rotate within
the confines of the main bearings. Yet it must not fit so sloppily that excessive vibrations cause possible damage to the shaft or engine block.
There must be a limited amount of free space between the shaft and the
bore. This free space is usually referred to as *clearance,* and it may be
defined as the *intentional difference in the sizes of mating parts.* In many
cases it is necessary that mating parts be assembled more or less permanently; one part being pressed firmly into another. Thus, a given
amount of what is termed *negative clearance* or *interference* must be
assigned to this condition to assure a tight fit. The minimum clearance
or maximum interference between mating parts is called *allowance.*
Other mating parts must fit together with no perceptible freeness and
yet require little or no pressure on assembly. This is usually termed a
metal-to-metal or *transitional* fit. These three general categories of fits
(clearance, transition, and interference) may be broken down further to
suit specific conditions.

DEVELOPMENT OF MANUFACTURING SPECIFICATIONS

The tolerance that should be assigned to a dimension is that which
gives an economic balance between quality and cost. For a given tolerance on a dimension some parts can be expected to be farther from the
most desirable size than others and be able to function less well or wear
not as long. If a larger tolerance is assigned, more parts can be expected
to be inferior, but still within limits, and the total value of the product
will be less. In general, the value of the product in a hypothetical case
is shown by the upper curve of Fig. 15–6 to decrease in some manner as
tolerance is increased.

A large tolerance for a given dimension can be held more easily and
is cheaper than a small tolerance. Each machine and process has a certain capability. Within that range more care and skill are required, the
closer the limits that must be held. If smaller tolerance are demanded,

resort must be made to other and usually more costly processes. Thus, in a typical case depicted by the lower curve of Fig. 15–6, cost increases as the tolerance decreases. The curve, of course, is different for every situation. Such a curve may represent grinding a diameter, or a similar composite curve may be true for turning, grinding, or even Superfinishing for the smallest tolerances.

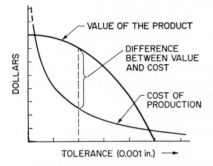

Fig. 15–6. Curves of value and cost showing location of ideal tolerance.

If for a particular situation, the value and cost curves are plotted on the same scale, the result is as shown in Fig. 15–6. The ideal tolerance is that which gives the largest difference between value and cost. It would be worthwhile to ascertain this ideal tolerance for large quantity production because of the savings involved. Otherwise it could be approximately set because tolerances within a range are close enough for practical purposes.

Certain dimensions of non-mating parts or products such as the length of a handle or diameter of a handwheel may not require very precise specifications because their functional effectiveness does not depend on whether or not their dimensions vary by as much as say ±¼ in. However, for the sake of uniformity of method, stock usage, packing, etc., a nominal amount of tolerance (±0.10, ±1/64, or ±1/32 in.) is usually specified.

Assembly methods. Basically there are two methods of assembly for mass-produced components, random assembly and selective assembly. In random assembly, the mating parts must be made to a tolerance that will permit any component selected at random to fit properly with any randomly selected mating component. Normally in selective assembly, the components are put into groups according to size and then assembled with mating components also segregated by sizes. For example, a shaft diameter may be produced to a tolerance of 0.001 in., with a nominal diameter of 1 in. and actual limits of 1.000–0.999 in. The bearing may likewise have a tolerance of 0.001 in. with actual limits of 1.001–1.000 in. The clearance between parts assembled at random may be anywhere from 0 to 0.002 in. In the event the clearance must not be over 0.001 in. without excessive losses in the product, two courses of action are open. One is to reduce the tolerance on each part, at greater cost. The other is to make and divide the shafts into two groups, one with limits from 0.9995 to 1.0000 in. and the other from 1.0000 to 1.0005 in., which still embraces a production tolerance of 0.001 in. The bearings, made to the same tolerance as before, are divided into two groups corresponding to 1.0000 to 1.0005 to 1.0010 in. Now by assembling from proper groups, clearances can be held to 0.001 in. or less. This is called selective assembly, and in some cases is more economical than manufacturing to small tolerances.

Tolerances on linear dimensions. The exact theoretically desired size of a part is usually referred to as the *basic size,* and it is the size from which variation is permitted. A *standard size* is a size corresponding to the commonly used subdivisions of a unit of length. The common fractions of an inch are examples of standard sizes. A *nominal size* is that size which is approximated by a standard size.

Tolerances are usually developed to conform to certain standardized design procedures. Two commonly used procedures are called *standard hole practice* and *standard shaft practice.* In standard hole practice the basic size of the hole is assigned a standard size, and a positive unilateral tolerance is applied. The basic size of the mating shaft is determined by subtracting the prescribed allowance from the standard size for a clearance fit, or adding the prescribed allowance to the standard size for an interference fit. A negative unilateral tolerance is assigned to the shaft. Notice that the holes and shafts of Fig 15–8 are dimensioned according to standard hole practice. This system permits the use of standard reamers for finishing holes and standard limit plug gages for checking.

Standard shaft practice designates the maximum limiting size of commercial shafting as the standard size and applies a negative unilateral tolerance to it. The basic size of the hole is determined by adding the prescribed allowance to the standard size for a clearance fit, or subtracting the prescribed allowance from the standard size for an interference fit. The hole is assigned a positive unilateral tolerance.

Standards for allowances and tolerances. One very common method for determining allowances and tolerances for mating parts is through the use of formulae or tables prepared by technical organizations. For example, the American Standards Association has developed tables of preferred limits and fits for cylindrical parts (ASA B4.1—1955), in which hole and shaft limits are provided for five basic types of fits.

Table 1 of the standard, a portion of which is shown in Fig. 15–7, gives limits for running and sliding fits applicable to nominal hole sizes ranging from 0.400 in. to 200 in. Nine sub-classes of this type fit are provided ranging from *Close Sliding Fits* (RC 1), intended for accurate location of parts which must assemble without perceptible play, to *Loose Running Fits* (RC 9) for use with commercial shafting and tubing. Limits for three types of locational fits (clearance, transitional, interference) are also tabulated. *Locational Clearance Fits* (LC 1–11) are for mating parts

Nominal Size Range Inches	Class RC 1	Standard Limits		Class RC 2	Standard Limits		Class RC 3	Standard Limits		Class RC 4	Standard Limits	
Over / To	Limits of Clearance	Hole H5	Shaft g4	Limits of Clearance	Hole H6	Shaft g5	Limits of Clearance	Hole H6	Shaft f6	Limits of Clearance	Hole H7	Shaft f7
0.04– 0.12	0.1 / 0.45	+0.2 / 0	− 0.1 / − 0.25	0.1 / 0.55	+ 0.25 / 0	− 0.1 / − 0.3	0.3 / 0.8	+ 0.25 / 0	− 0.3 / − 0.55	0.3 / 1.1	+ 0.4 / 0	− 0.3 / − 0.7
0.12– 0.24	0.15 / 0.5	+0.2 / 0	− 0.15 / − 0.3	0.15 / 0.65	+ 0.3 / 0	− 0.15 / − 0.35	0.4 / 1.0	+ 0.3 / 0	− 0.4 / − 0.7	0.4 / 1.4	+ 0.5 / 0	− 0.4 / − 0.9
0.24– 0.40	0.2 / 0.6	+0.25 / 0	− 0.2 / − 0.35	0.2 / 0.85	+ 0.4 / 0	− 0.2 / − 0.45	0.5 / 1.3	+ 0.4 / 0	− 0.5 / − 0.9	0.5 / 1.7	+ 0.6 / 0	− 0.5 / − 1.1
0.40– 0.71	0.25 / 0.75	+0.3 / 0	− 0.25 / − 0.45	0.25 / 0.95	+ 0.4 / 0	− 0.25 / − 0.55	0.6 / 1.4	+ 0.4 / 0	− 0.6 / − 1.0	0.6 / 2.0	+ 0.7 / 0	− 0.6 / − 1.3
0.71– 1.19	0.3 / 0.95	+0.4 / 0	− 0.3 / − 0.55	0.3 / 1.2	+ 0.5 / 0	− 0.3 / − 0.7	0.8 / 1.8	+ 0.5 / 0	− 0.8 / − 1.3	0.8 / 2.4	+ 0.8 / 0	− 0.8 / − 1.6
1.19– 1.97	0.4 / 1.1	+0.4 / 0	− 0.4 / − 0.7	0.4 / 1.4	+ 0.6 / 0	− 0.4 / − 0.8	1.0 / 2.2	+ 0.6 / 0	− 1.0 / − 1.6	1.0 / 3.0	+ 1.0 / 0	− 1.0 / − 2.0
1.97– 3.15	0.4 / 1.2	+0.5 / 0	− 0.4 / − 0.7	0.4 / 1.6	+ 0.7 / 0	− 0.4 / − 0.9	1.2 / 2.6	+ 0.7 / 0	− 1.2 / − 1.9	1.2 / 3.6	+ 1.2 / 0	− 1.2 / − 2.4
3.15– 4.73	0.5 / 1.5	+0.6 / 0	− 0.5 / − 0.9	0.5 / 2.0	+ 0.9 / 0	− 0.5 / − 1.1	1.4 / 3.2	+ 0.9 / 0	− 1.4 / − 2.3	1.4 / 4.2	+ 1.4 / 0	− 1.4 / − 2.8
4.73– 7.09	0.6 / 1.8	+0.7 / 0	− 0.6 / − 1.1	0.6 / 2.3	+ 1.0 / 0	− 0.6 / − 1.3	1.6 / 3.6	+ 1.0 / 0	− 1.6 / − 2.6	1.6 / 4.8	+ 1.6 / 0	− 1.6 / − 3.2
7.09– 9.85	0.6 / 2.0	+0.8 / 0	− 0.6 / − 1.2	0.6 / 2.6	+ 1.2 / 0	− 0.6 / − 1.4	2.0 / 4.4	+ 1.2 / 0	− 2.0 / − 3.2	2.0 / 5.6	+ 1.8 / 0	− 2.0 / − 3.8

Limits are in thousandths of an inch
Limits for hole and shaft are applied algebraically to
the basic size to obtain the limits of size for the parts

Fig. 15–7. Abbreviated table of running and sliding fits extracted from American Standard Preferred Limits and Fits for Cylindrical Parts (ASA B4.1—1955) with permission of the publisher, The American Society of Mechanical Engineers, 29 West 39th Street, New York 18, N. Y.

which are normally stationary, but which can be assembled or disassembled freely. As a compromise between clearance and interference fits, *Transition Location Fits* (LT 1–7) are used where accuracy of location is important, but small amounts of clearance or interference is acceptable. Limits for *Locational Interference Fits* (LN 2 or 3) may be applied where rigidity of alignment and accuracy of location is important. Five classes of force and shrink fit limits are also provided ranging from *Tight Drive Fits* (FN 1) for parts requiring light assembly pressure, to *Force Fits* (FN 5) which are intended for parts which can be highly stressed, or for shrink fits in members where heavy force fit pressures are impractical.

Fit classifications RC 1 and FN 1 are exemplified in Fig. 15–8. Basic hole size in each case is one inch. Standard hole practice and unilateral tolerances are also applied.

Tolerances for 100% interchangeability. If the amount of clearance or interference required between mating parts is known, the tolerances for

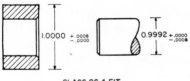

CLASS RC 4 FIT

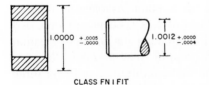

CLASS FN I FIT

Fig. 15–8. Dimensions on shaft and hole for Class RC 4 and Class FN 1 fits.

100% interchangeability can be determined quite easily by simple addition. The shaft and bearing assembly of Fig. 15–9 illustrates this procedure. For this assembly it is assumed that nominal assembly size is 2 in. with a minimum total clearance of 0.002 in. and a maximum total clearance of 0.008 in. Tolerance is shown bilateral from basic size but could be specified in any way. For purposes of analysis, Fig. 15–9 shows the shaft resting on the bottom of the bearing so that maximum and minimum total clearances can be observed. Tolerances and basic sizes may be obtained by simply summing dimensions from a reference surface of the part under consideration. The tolerance on the shaft may be determined as follows:

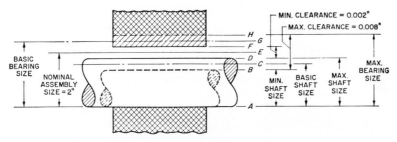

Fig. 15–9. A diagram illustrating extreme positions for a shaft and bearing.

Starting at B, $\overline{BD} + \overline{DE} - \overline{EB} = 0$

Where $\overline{BD}$ = tolerance on the shaft, $\overline{DE}$ = half of the minimum clearance = 0.002/2, and $\overline{EB}$ = half of the maximum clearance = 0.008/2.

Thus $\overline{BD} + 0.002/2 - 0.008/2 = 0$

Or $\overline{BD} = 0.004 - 0.001 = 0.003.$

Other dimensions may be determined by a similar process.

Determination of tolerances for statistical average interchangeability. Methods of statistical analysis may be applied to increase tolerances and effect manufacturing economies. The statistical concepts applicable to this problem are those of the normal distribution and its parameters $\overline{X}$ and σ defined by Eqs. (15–1) and (15–2). Theory and experience have shown that if the variations of the dimensions of the parts approximate a normal distribution, as they commonly do, and the parts are selected at random, the distribution of fits obtained is practically normal. Also, the mean value of the clearance is

$$\overline{X}_{\text{clearance}} = \overline{X}_{\text{bearings}} - \overline{X}_{\text{shafts,}} \qquad (15\text{–}3)$$

and the standard deviation of the variations in the clearance is

$$\sigma_{\text{clearance}} = \sqrt{\sigma^2_{\text{bearings}} + \sigma^2_{\text{shafts}}} \qquad (15\text{-}4)$$

where the σ's for bearings and shafts are the standard deviations of the variations in sizes from the means.

In the case of the bearing and shaft assembly of Fig. 15–9, $6 \times \sigma_{\text{clearance}} = 0.008 - 0.002 = 0.006$, and $\sigma_{\text{clearance}} = 0.001$. If not specified otherwise, $\sigma_{\text{bearing}} = \sigma_{\text{shaft}} = \sigma_{\text{p}}$, and $\sqrt{\sigma^2_{\text{p}} + \sigma^2_{\text{p}}} = 0.001$ from Eq. (15–4). Thus $\sigma_{\text{p}} = 0.0007$, and the tolerance for bearing or shaft is $6\sigma_{\text{p}}$ or 0.0042 in. This permits 40% more tolerance on the parts than is required for 100% interchangeability. Yet if the prescribed conditions are met, less than 3 assemblies out of 1000 can be expected to have clearances greater or less than specified.

Geometric dimensions and tolerances. The limit dimensions of the simple cylindrical piece on the left of Fig. 15–10 define the maximum and minimum limits of profile for the work. The form or shape of the part may vary as long as no portions of the part exceed the maximum profile limit or are inside the minimum profile limit. If a part is everywhere on its maximum material limit of size, it should be of perfect form. This is referred to as the *maximum material condition* and is at the low limit for a hole or slot but of the high limit for a shaft, bolt pin, etc.

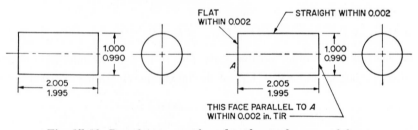

Fig. 15–10. Part drawings with and without tolerances of form.

If it is desired to provide greater control on the form than is imposed by the limit dimensions, then certain tolerances of form must be applied. In most cases these tolerances appear in the form of notations on the drawing as is illustrated on the right in Fig. 15–10.

STANDARDS FOR MEASURING AND GAGING

The effectiveness of an interchangeable manufacturing system is dependent upon the existence of an acceptable set of standards upon which all measurements are based. When each of several component parts of an assembly are made in different places in the nation or the world, it is necessary that each supplier use comparable measurement standards if the components are to fit properly upon assembly.

Length standards. The fundamental unit of length in the United States is the inch. The standard inch is derived from the fundamental unit of length, the meter, which, according to the 11th General Conference on Weights and Measures in Paris, France on October 14, 1960, is 1,650,763.73 wavelengths of the orange-red light emitted from krypton-86 in a liquid nitrogen bath at 63°K. By act of Congress in 1866 the legal yard in the United States was defined as 3600/3937 of the length of the meter at 68°F, thus making one meter equal to 39.37 in. From this, 1 inch is equal to 25.4000508 mm. For commercial convenience, the Director of the National Bureau of Standards has declared the inch equivalent to 25.400000 mm, which is adequate for practical purposes.

End standards. The use of the primary length standard by most individual industries would be prohibitive. Sets of end standards, called *gage blocks,* have been developed to provide industry with relatively low cost length standards. Gage blocks are usually small rectangular or square blocks of steel or cemented carbide with two parallel faces precision lapped to within a few millionths of an inch of a specified size.

Three classes of gage blocks are available; *Class AA master gage blocks* are guaranteed accurate to within ±0.000002 in. per in. of length and are primarily used as master gages for checking other gage blocks or for highly precise laboratory applications. *Class A reference or inspection gage blocks* are accurate to ±0.000004 in. per in. of length, and are used in calibrating measuring instruments, setting gages and in close layout work. *Class B working gage blocks* are accurate to ±0.000008 in. per in., and are used in shop operations for layout, inspection, and machine setting. All blocks usually have end surfaces that are flat, true planes within 0.000002 in. level, and the two end planes are usually parallel within 0.000002 in.

Gage blocks may be purchased individually or in sets containing as few as five or as many as 116 individual blocks. One gage block manufacturer makes blocks in all decimal sizes from 0.050000 in. to 4.000000 in., and in fractional sizes from $\frac{1}{16}$ to $\frac{7}{64}$ in. Various combinations of the blocks in a set may be wrung together to obtain many different total lengths. For example, one manufacturer provides an 81-block set of gage blocks that can be assembled into 120,000 combinations to provide length standards from 0.1001 in. to over 25 in. in increments of 0.0001 in. The cost of such a set of Class AA blocks is about $1000. Figure 15–11 shows a gage-block set containing special accessories for gaging external and internal dimensions, scribing lines, and marking centers.

Perhaps the most important property of a material used for a dimensional standard is its coefficient of thermal expansion. When a gage is said to have a certain length it is understood that this is its length at the standard temperature of 68°F or 20°C.

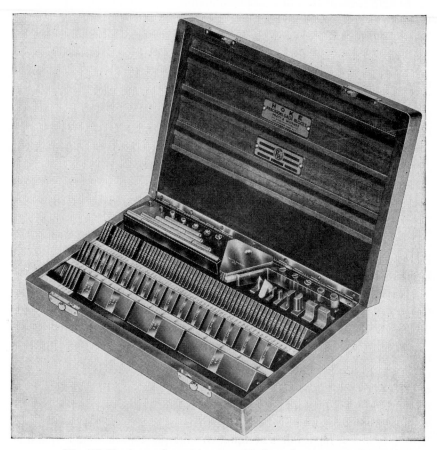

Fig. 15–11. A set of precision gage blocks and accessories. (Pratt and Whitney Photo from Pratt and Whitney Division, Niles-Bement-Pond Co., W. Hartford, Conn.)

MEASURING AND GAGING INSTRUMENTS

During the various stages of processing and at the end of a process it is often necessary to check the articles of manufacture for conformance to specifications. If adequate information is to be obtained as to how far the product is from specifications, a measurement process is implied. Such information is particularly useful for adjusting tools and machines or for renewing worn tools. If it is desired to know only that a part does or does not conform to specifications with no concern as to how much it does not conform, then a gaging process may suffice. Gaging is often employed in mass production processes because it requires the least time to sort bad from good parts. Inspection personnel are needed with less skill than for many measuring processes. Thus, *measuring* is used to find the actual size of a dimension, while *gaging* merely compares the dimensions to a standard.

The component parts making up the modern world automotive, aircraft, and missile assemblies often require near perfection in accuracy, thus requiring the ultimate in precision of measurement. *Precision of measurement* of an instrument is the smallest increment of size that it is capable of indicating. Instruments capable of measuring to 0.001 in. are often referred to as *precision measuring instruments,* but instruments measuring to 0.0001 or even 0.000001 in. are not uncommon today.

Measuring instruments may be *direct reading* or of the *transfer type.* An ordinary steel rule such as is shown in Fig. 15–12(31) contains a graduated scale from which the size of a dimension being measured can be determined directly, while the spring caliper of Fig. 15–12(1) contains no scale graduations. It is adjusted to fit the size of a dimension being measured and then is compared to a direct reading scale so as to obtain the size of the dimension.

Most of the available measuring instruments may be grouped according to certain basic principles of operation. Many simple instruments use only a graduated scale as a measurement basis, while others may have two related scales and use the vernier principle of measurement. In a number of instruments the movement of a precision screw is related to two or three graduated scales to form a basis for measurement. Many other instruments utilize some sort of mechanical, electrical or optical linkage between the measuring element and the graduated scale so that a small movement of the measuring element produces an enlarged indication on the scale. Air pressure or metered air flow is used in a few instruments as a means of measurement. These operating principles will be more fully explained in the descriptions of a few of the instruments in which they are applied.

Basic measuring instruments and gages. People in nearly every craft, whether they be television repairmen, automotive mechanics, or telephone installers, have a set of tools applicable to their work. Similarly, machinists, machine operators, tool makers, etc. have a variety of basic measuring and gaging equipment which they use in their daily work and which may be considered tools of their trade. Many of these are often referred to as *standard* or *general-purpose* tools, and for the most part they are relatively simple in construction. The results obtained from the use of these tools are considerably dependent upon the skill and dexterity of the person using them. For instance, the accuracy obtained in many cases depends upon the amount of pressure applied to the measuring elements. Thus the craftsman through training and experience acquires the sense of touch necessary to apply the tools properly. A group of basic instruments is shown in Fig. 15–12. The group includes direct reading and transfer-type linear measuring instruments, angular measuring de-

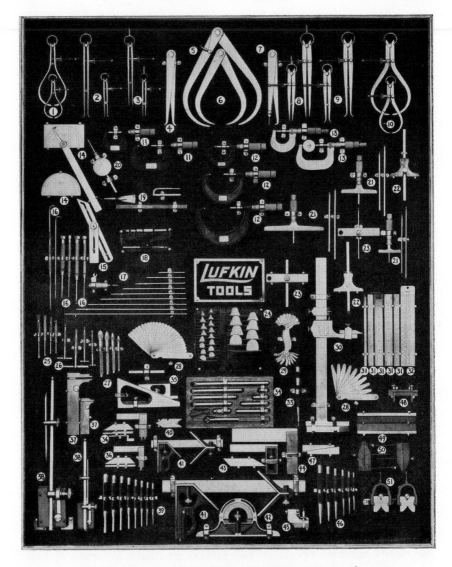

Fig. 15–12. Standard measuring instruments. (1) Outside spring calipers, round leg. (2) Inside spring calipers. (3) Spring dividers. (4) Inside firm joint caliper. (5) Outside firm joint caliper with adjusting screw. (6) Outside firm joint caliper. (7) Firm joint hermaphrodite caliper. (8) Spring divider. (9) Inside spring caliper. (10) Outside spring caliper. (11) Outside micrometer calipers, medium weight. (12) Outside micrometer calipers, heavy duty. (13) Outside micrometer calipers, with lock nut and ratchet stop. (14) Steel protractors. (15) Universal bevel. (16) Scribers. (17) Inside micrometer set, solid rods. (18) Steel rule set and holder. (19) Universal indicator. (20) Dial test indicator. (21) Micrometer depth gages. (22) Depth rules. (23) Depth gage. (24) Radius gage set. (25) Small hole

vices, fixed and adjustable gaging devices, layout tools, and other miscellaneous metal-working accessories.

Basic direct reading measuring instruments. Most of the basic or general-purpose linear measuring instruments are typified by the steel rule, the vernier caliper, or the micrometer caliper.

Steel rules are used effectively as *line measuring devices,* which means the ends of a dimension being measured are aligned with the graduations of the scale from which the length is read directly. Steel rules are found in depth rules, Fig. 15–12(22 and 23), for measuring the depth of slots, holes, etc. They are also incorporated in slide calipers, Fig. 15–12(37), where they are adapted to *end measuring, operations,* which are ofttimes more accurate and easier to apply than in line measuring.

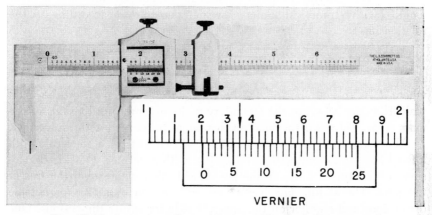

VERNIER

Fig. 15–13. A vernier caliper. (Courtesy The L. S. Starrett Co.)

Verniers. The *vernier caliper* shown in Fig. 15–13 typifies the type of instrument using the vernier principle of measurement. The usual vernier consists of a main scale and vernier scale. The main scale is divided into inches with each inch subdivided into tenths, and each tenth into four divisions such that the smallest increment on the scale is equivalent to $\frac{1}{40}$ or 0.025 in. The vernier scale slides along the edge of the main scale

gages. (26) Telescoping gages. (27) Pin vises. (28) Thickness gages. (29) Screw pitch gage. (30) Vernier height gage. (31) Steel rules. (32) Mechanics' reference table. (33) Automatic center punch. (34) Inside micrometer set, tubular. (35) Planer and shaper gage. (36) Die makers squares. (37) Slide calipers. (38) Universal surface gages. (39) Drive pin punches. (40) Center gage. (41) Combination square. (42) Bevel protractor. (43) Double squares. (44) Steel square. (45) Right angle rule clamps. (46) Center punches. (47) Tapered parallels. (48) Rule clamps. (49) Hold down parallels. (50) Tool makers parallel clamps. (51) V-blocks and clamps.

and is divided into 25 equal divisions so that these 25 divisions are the same in total length as 24 divisions on the main scale. Each division on the vernier scale is then equal to $\frac{1}{25}$ of (24×0.025) or 0.024 in., which is 0.001 in. less than each division of the main scale. Aligning the zero lines of both scales would cause the first lines on each scale to be 0.001 in. apart, the second lines 0.002 in. apart, etc. A measurement on a vernier is designated by the positions of the zero line of the vernier and the line on the vernier that coincides with a line on the main scale. For example, the lower right-hand illustration of Fig. 15–13 shows a reading of 1.206. The zero index of the vernier is located just beyond the 1.200 line on the main scale and the sixth line on the vernier coincides with a line on the main scale indicating the zero index is 0.006 in. beyond the 1.200 line. Thus, $1.200 + 0.006 = 1.206$ in.

A vernier may be designed to indicate practically any increment of length (within practical limits of visual perception) according to the relationship

$$\frac{d_m(d_s + 1)}{I} = 1 \tag{15-5}$$

where d_m is the number of divisions in one unit of length on the main scale, d_s is the length of the secondary scale measured in divisions of the main scale, and $1/I$ is the smallest increment to be read with the vernier.

The vernier caliper shown in Fig. 15–13 consists of a steel rule with a fixed jaw at one end and a sliding jaw with a vernier. Outside dimensions are measured between the jaws; inside dimensions over the tips of the jaws. The sliding jaw has a vernier scale on one side for outside dimensions and another on the opposite side for inside dimensions. One of the main advantages of a vernier caliper is the length it covers.

The vernier height gage of Fig. 15–12(30) is similar to a vernier caliper except that the fixed jaw has been replaced by a fixed base, and the sliding jaw may have a scriber attached to it for layout work or a dial indicator for measuring or comparing operations.

Micrometer. The *micrometer caliper* illustrated in Fig. 15–14 is representative of the type of instrument using a precision screw as a basis for measuring. The measuring elements consist of a fixed anvil and a spindle that moves lengthwise as it is turned.

The screws of standard micrometers have a lead of $\frac{1}{40}$ or 0.025 in. so that one complete revolution of the thimble produces a spindle movement of this amount. The graduated scale on the barrel of the instrument is divided into tenths of an inch and each tenth is further subdivided into four equal parts such that the smallest linear division is $\frac{1}{40}$ or 0.025 in. Thus, one revolution of the spindle causes the bevelled edge of the thimble to move through one small division on the barrel scale. The periphery of

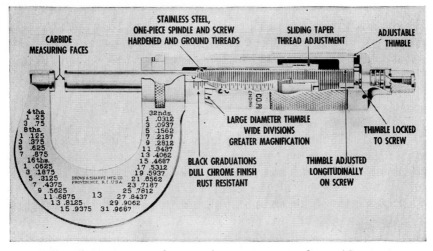

Fig. 15–14. A sectional view of a micrometer caliper. (Courtesy Brown and Sharpe Mfg. Co.)

the bevelled edge of the thimble is graduated into 25 equal divisions, each space representing $\frac{1}{25}$ of a complete rotation of the thimble or a movement of the spindle of 0.001 in.

A reading on a micrometer is made by adding the thimble division which is aligned with the longitudinal barrel line to the largest reading exposed on the barrel scale. For example, in Fig. 15–15 the thimble has exposed the number 2, representing 0.200 in., and one small division worth 0.025 in. The thimble division 16 is aligned with the longitudinal barrel line indicating that the thimble has moved 0.016 in. beyond the last small division on the barrel. Thus, the final reading is obtained by summing the three components, $0.200 + 0.025 + 0.016 = 0.241$ in.

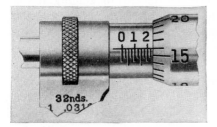

Fig. 15–15. A micrometer reading of 0.241 inch. (Courtesy Brown and Sharpe Mfg. Co.)

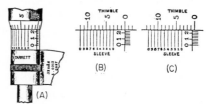

Fig. 15–16. The scales on a vernier micrometer caliper. (Courtesy The L. S. Starrett Co.)

A vernier micrometer caliper such as is shown in Fig. 15–16(A) has a vernier scale on the barrel permitting measurements to 0.0001 in. The vernier scale has ten divisions over a length equivalent to nine divisions around the thimble. Thus, the difference in length of a division on the barrel and one on the thimble is $0.001 - \frac{1}{10}(9 \times 0.001) = 0.0001$. A vernier micrometer is first read to the nearest 0.001 by use of the basic scales and then the vernier reading is added. The reading in Fig. 15–16(B) is 0.2500 in., while that in Fig. 15–16(C) is 0.2507 in.

Micrometer caliper. The micrometer caliper, or *mike* as it is often called, is an end measuring instrument for use in measuring outside dimensions. Although the mike is fairly easy to apply, the accuracy it gives depends upon the application of the proper amount of torque to the thimble. Too much torque is likely to spring the frame and cause error in the measurement. The micrometer of Fig. 15–14 is provided with a ratchet device on the end of the thimble to permit the application of a uniform pressure to parts being measured. The indicating micrometer of Fig. 15–17 has a built-in dial indicator to provide a positive indication of measuring pressure applied. The instrument can also be used like an indicating snap gage.

A standard micrometer is limited to one inch range. Thus, different micrometers are needed to measure a wide range of dimensions.

The precision screw principle is also applied directly in other measuring instruments such as the type of inside micrometer shown in Fig. 15–12(17 and 34), the micrometer depth gage, Fig. 15–12(21), and the internal micrometer plug. It is also used as a device to provide precise calibrated linear movement to staging devices and other moving components of toolmakers' microscopes and optical projecting comparators.

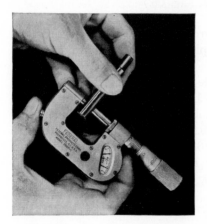

Fig. 15–17. An indicating micrometer. (Courtesy Federal Products Corp.)

Basic transfer-type linear measuring devices. Transfer-type linear measuring devices are typified by the spring caliper, spring divider, firm joint caliper, telescoping gage, and small hole gage. Examples of each of these are shown in Fig. 15–12.

The outside caliper is used as an end measure to measure or compare outside dimensions, while the inside caliper is used for inside diameters, slot and groove widths and other internal dimensions. They are quite versatile, but due to the construction and method of application their accuracy is somewhat limited.

ANGULAR MEASURING DEVICES

The unit standard of angular measurement is the degree. The measurement and inspection of angular dimensions is somewhat more difficult than linear measurement and may require instruments of some complexity if a great deal of angular precision is required.

Simple angle measuring tools. The *combination set* consists of a center head, protractor and square with a 45° surface, all of which are used individually in conjunction with a steel rule. The heads are mounted on the rule and clamped in any position along its length by means of a lock screw. The parts of such a set are shown in Fig. 15–12(41 and 42). The center head is used to scribe bisecting diameters on the end of a cylindrical piece to locate the center of the piece. The protractor reads directly in degrees. Both the square head and the protractor may contain a small spirit level. A *bevel protractor* utilizes a vernier scale to show angles as small as five minutes.

Sine bar. The sine bar is a relatively simple device for precision measuring and checking of angles. It consists of an accurately ground flat steel straight edge with precisely affixed round buttons, a definite distance apart, and of identical diameters.

Figure 15–18 illustrates one method of applying a sine bar in the determination of the angle α on the conical surface of the part located on the surface plate. For precise results, a sine bar must be used on true surfaces. In Fig. 15–18 the center to center distance of the sine bar buttons is 5 in., and the distances A and B are determined by means of gage blocks or a vernier height gage to be 1 and 3.5352

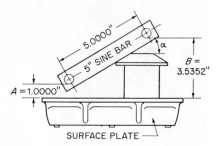

Fig. 15–18. An application of a sine bar.

in. respectively. Thus, the sine α equals $(3.5352 - 1)/5 = 0.50704$ in., and from trigonometric tables the angle α is 30°28′.

Dividing heads. Mechanical and optical dividing heads are often employed in the circular measurement of angular spacing. The mechanical dividing head is described in Chap. 24. The optical dividing head performs the same function but more precisely. One make has a disk around its main spindle with graduations in fine increments inscribed around its circumference. These are viewed through a microscope.

LAYOUT INSTRUMENTS AND LOCATING DEVICES

Considerable metal and wood working, particularly in jobshop work, pattern building, model building, and tool and die work, is done to layout lines, circles, center locations, etc. scribed on the workpiece itself. Chalk or dye is often applied to the work surface before scribing so that the lines can be readily seen.

A *surface plate* provides a true reference plane from which measurements can be made. A cast iron surface plate is a heavy ribbed boxlike casting that stands on three points (that establishes a plane) and has a thick and well supported flat top plate. The method by which a true surface is obtained is described in Chap. 21. New plates generally have an average of 18 bearing spots per sq in. that do not vary from a true plane by more than 0.0002 in. The use of ceramic materials for surface plates is becoming increasingly popular because of their hardness, resistance to corrosion, minimum response to temperature change, and nonmagnetic qualities. Fig. 15–19 shows a black granite surface plate used in layout work. Reference surfaces may also be obtained by the use of bar parallels, angle irons, v-blocks, and toolmakers flats.

Fig. 15–19. A granite surface plate being used in layout work.

A variety of hand marking tools such as the scriber, spring divider and center punch are employed by the layout man. These tools are shown in Fig. 15–12. The *surface gage*, Fig. 15–12(38), consists of a base, an adjustable spindle and a scriber, and may be used as a layout instrument. The scriber is first adjusted to the desired height by reference to a steel rule or gage blocks and then the gage is moved to the workpiece and a line is scratched on it at the desired location. The vernier height gage may be employed in a similar manner.

GAGES

Classes of gages. In mass manufacturing operations it is often uneconomical to attempt to obtain absolute sizes during each inspection operation. In many cases it is only necessary to determine whether one or more dimensions of a mass produced part are within specified limits. For this purpose a variety of inspection instruments referred to as *gages* are employed. However, the distinction between gaging and measuring devices is not always clear as there are some instruments referred to as gages that do give definite measurements.

To promote consistency in manufacturing and inspection, gages may be classified as working, inspection, and reference or master gages. *Working gages* are used by the machine operator or shop inspector to check the dimensions of parts as they are being produced. Working gages usually have limits within those of the piece being inspected. *Inspection gages* are used by the inspection personnel to inspect purchased parts when received or manufactured parts when finished. These gages are designed and made so as not to reject any product previously accepted by a properly designed and functioning working gage. *Reference* or *master gages* are used only for checking the size or condition of other gages, and represent as exactly as possible the physical dimensions of the product.

A gage may have a single size and be referred to as a *nonlimit gage,* or it may have two sizes and be referred to as a *limit gage.* A limit gage, often called a "go" and "not go" gage, establishes the high and low limits provided by the tolerance on a dimension. A limit gage may be either *double end* or *progressive.* A double end gage has the "go" member at one end and the "not go" member at the other end. Each end of the gage is applied to the workpiece so as to determine its acceptability. The "go" member must pass into or over an acceptable piece, but the "not go" member should not. A progressive gage has both the "go" and "not go" members at the same end so that a part may be gaged with one movement. A progressive gage is applied more quickly, but there are some limitations to its use. For instance, a progressive plug gage cannot be used to check the entire length of a hole if the hole is deeper than the length of the "go" section of the gage.

Some gages are *fixed* in size while others are *adjustable* over certain size ranges. Fixed gages are usually less expensive initially, but they have the disadvantage of not permitting adjustment to compensate for wear.

Most gages are subjected to considerable abrasion during their application and must therefore be made of materials which are resistant to wear. High-carbon and alloy steels have been used as gage materials for many years because of their relatively high hardenability and abrasion resistance. Further increased surface hardness and abrasion resistance may be obtained from chrome plating or cemented carbides as surface material on gages. Some gages are made entirely of cemented carbides or they have cemented carbide inserts at certain wear points. Chrome plating is also used as a means of rebuilding and salvaging worn gages.

Common gages. *Plug gages* are used to check holes of many different sizes and shapes. There are plug gages for straight cylindrical holes, tapered, threaded, square, and splined holes. A *straight cylindrical double end plug gage* is shown in Fig. 15–20(L). Fig. 15–20(U) is of a *progressive plug gage* where both the "go" and "not go" sections of the gage are on the same end of the handle. A *double end thread plug gage* is in Fig. 15–20(O). A *tapered plug gage* Fig. 15–20(F), has only one gaging member and it is marked to show how far it should enter a tapered hole.

Larger holes are gaged with *annular plug gages,* which are shell-constructed for light weight, and *flat plug gages,* made in the form of diametral sections of cylinders.

A common type of *plain ring gage* shown in Fig. 15–20(A) has a flanged section to reduce weight and facilitate handling. *Thread ring gages,* as illustrated in Fig. 15–20(C), are usually of the adjustable type. The adjustable feature permits the gage to be set to correct size by means of a master thread roll of the exact desired size. They are often used in "go" and "not go" sets.

Snap gages are used somewhat like a caliper for checking external dimensions. They may be double end or progressive and solid or adjustable. The C-shaped *limit snap gage* shown in Fig. 15–20(S) has two adjustable anvils set to desired limits with gage blocks. Snap gages may also be fitted with special anvils, buttons or rolls for checking external threads and other forms.

Form gages may be used to check the contour or profile of a workpiece for conformance to certain shape or form specifications. Form gages made from sheet metal and called profile or template gages are shown in Fig. 15–20(E,G and T). A set of standard *radius gages* is shown in Fig. 15–12(24).

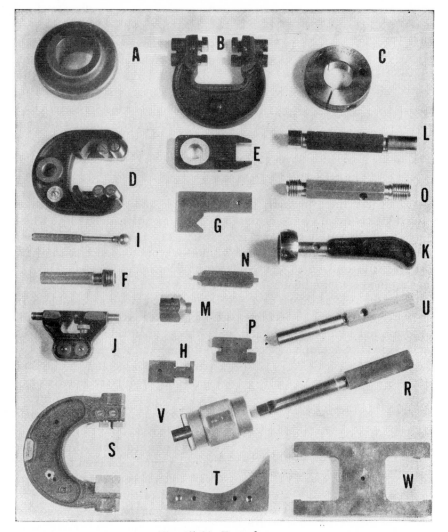

Fig. 15–20. Typical gages.

Flush pin gages are used to check conformance to tolerance limits on surfaces of different heights. Figure 15–21 illustrates the principle of operation of this type gage when used to gage the depth of a hole. The height of the step on pin *B* represents the tolerance on the depth of the hole. For a hole depth to be acceptable, the top surface plane of collar *A* must be somewhere between the steps of pin *B*. An inspector normally uses his finger or fingernail to feel and compare these surfaces.

Gage sizes. In gage making, as in any other manufacturing process, it is economically impractical to attempt to make gages to an exact size.

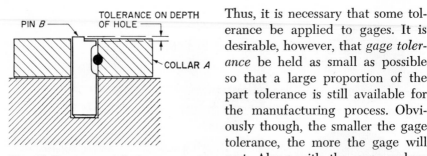

Fig. 15–21. A typical flush pin gage for gaging the depth of a hole.

Thus, it is necessary that some tolerance be applied to gages. It is desirable, however, that *gage tolerance* be held as small as possible so that a large proportion of the part tolerance is still available for the manufacturing process. Obviously though, the smaller the gage tolerance, the more the gage will cost. Along with the gage makers tolerance it is usually necessary to provide a *wear allowance*.

There are three methods of applying tolerances to gages, each of which affects the outcome of the inspection operation differently. These three methods are illustrated in Fig. 15–22. The first is to use unilateral gage tolerance and make the gage within the work tolerance as shown at A. This will result in some acceptable product being rejected. The second method is to use bilateral gage tolerance about the limiting specifications on the part as shown at B. This might allow some acceptable parts to be rejected or some rejectable parts to be accepted. The third method is to use unilateral tolerance and make the gage outside the work tolerance as in C. Gages made according to this method will permit defective parts to be accepted at the start and continue to be accepted as long as the gage is in use but provides the most manufacturing tolerance.

There is no universally accepted policy for the amount of gage tolerance. A number of industries where part tolerances are relatively large use 20% of the part tolerance for working gages and 10% for inspection gages. For each of these gages, one half of the amount is used for wear on the "go" member and one half for gagemakers tolerance on both the "go" and "not go" members. This method has been used to determine the tolerances for the plug gages shown in Fig. 15–23 for checking a hole with a diameter of

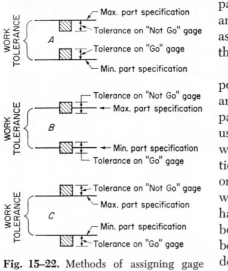

Fig. 15–22. Methods of assigning gage tolerances.

$0.500 \begin{smallmatrix} +0.002 \\ -0.000 \end{smallmatrix}$ in. The total part tolerance is 0.002 in. Thus 20% of 0.002 gives 0.0004 in. for the work gage, and 10% of 0.002 gives 0.0002 in. for the inspection gage, applied unilaterally.

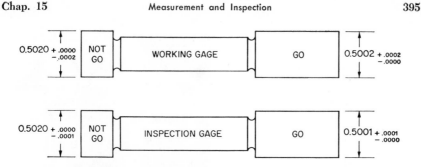

Fig. 15–23. Specifications on working and inspection limit plug gages.

The American Standards Association issues tables of recommended wear allowances and gagemakers' tolerances for both straight and tapered cylindrical gages. These tables provide a more liberal gage tolerance as the size of the work, and thus the gage, becomes larger. Straight cylindrical gages have been standardized in four classes, each of a different degree of precision.

INDICATING GAGES AND COMPARATORS

Indicating gages or comparators employ a means to magnify how much a dimension deviates, plus or minus, from a given standard to which the gage has been set. Most instruments of this type indicate actual units of measurement, but some only indicate whether a dimension deviates within a given tolerance range. They are true precision instruments and frequently are sensitive to as little as 0.000010 in.

Indicating gages and comparators may be basically grouped into four classes—mechanical, electrical, optical, and pneumatic. A few instruments combine several of these methods.

Mechanical indicating gages and comparators. Mechanical indicating gages and comparators employ a variety of mechanical elements. One type of mechanical indicating gage is typified by the dial indicator. Figure 15–24 illustrates the basic operating elements of such an instrument. Movement of stem *A* is transmitted by means of an involute rack through a compound gear train *B* and *C* to a pointer *D*, which moves around a dial face. Small springs are usually incorporated in the mechanism to maintain a uniform force on the stem and return the pointer to its original position after the gage is removed from the object being checked.

Dial indicators may be applied to nearly all kinds of measuring and gaging operations including checking for geometric accuracy. Figure 15–25 shows a dial indicator being used to check the runout of the bore of a cylindrical workpiece held in a chuck. They may also be used in checking machines and tools, for alignment of centers and runout of cutters.

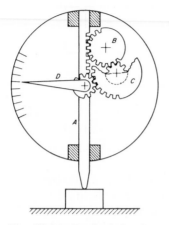

Fig. 15–24. Simple dial indicator mechanism.

Fig. 15–25. A dial indicator with an attachment for checking the runout of the bore of a piece held in a chuck. (Courtesy Brown and Sharpe Mfg. Co.)

Dial indicators are often incorporated in measuring instruments and gages to promote greater accuracy and ease of operation. This is exemplified in the indicating micrometer of Fig. 15–17.

Electrical indicating gages and comparators. Electrical devices are used as a means of detecting and amplifying small movements of a work contacting element. The typical electric comparator has a base and frame supporting a pick-up head or transducer. Movement of a stem attached to the head causes a change in some electrical characteristics of the circuit. This changes the flow of current which is amplified and moves the hand of a meter. Gages employed principally in the checking of precision metal products can be classified according to the electrical principle used in the pick-up head. Most of those indicating dimensional units use either a differential transformer, an inductance bridge, a strain gage, or a capacitor as a means of detecting movement of the gaging element. Figure 15–26 illustrates the principle of operation of one type of differential transformer pick-up. The armature, to which the gage pick-up element is attached, is centered mechanically between the two secondary windings. Movement of the armature in either direction from the central position produces an unequal distribution of flux between the two secondary windings and the primary. The voltage induced into the secondaries and the current change in proportion to the armature movement.

An electric comparator, called an *Electrolimit Gage,* is shown in Fig. 15–27 being used to check or measure the outside diameter of a roll. The instrument is first set to a dimension by means of gage blocks. Then the workpiece is positioned between the anvil and the stem, and its deviation from the dimension is shown on the dial. A comparator of the type shown in Fig. 15–27 costs about $500.

Another class of electrical gages, commonly referred to as *electric limit gages*, are used in automatic and semi-automatic gaging and for gaging multiple dimensions. These gages employ extremely sensitive limit switches that are usually set with master gages and open or close an electric circuit when parts outside the limits are placed in the gage. These gages commonly activate signal lights, buzzers, or mechanical sorting devices for good and bad pieces.

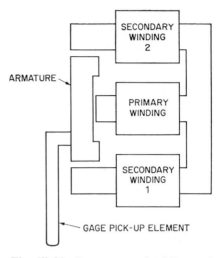

Fig. 15–26. One type of differential transformer used in electrical gages.

Pneumatic gages and comparators. *Pneumatic* or *air gaging* is essentially a means of measuring or checking dimensions by sensing the changes in flow or pressure in a pneumatic circuit caused by the restriction of air flowing from an orifice. The two basic types of air gages are the air-flow type and the back-pressure type. Figure 15–28 illustrates the principle of operation of the flow-type gage. Compressed air cleaned and dried through a filter and at regulated constant pressure passes through a vertical tapered glass tube containing an indicator float and then out through a supply line into a gaging head where it escapes through one or more orifices. The indicator floats on a cone of air passing through the glass tube, and different rates of flow of the air through the glass tube cause the indicator to assume different vertical positions. As the clearance between the gage head orifice and workpiece

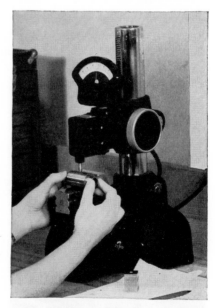

Fig. 15–27. An electric comparator. (Pratt and Whitney Photo from Pratt and Whitney Div. Niles-Bement-Pond Co., W. Hartford, Conn.)

surface increases, the rate of flow of air escaping from the orifice increases and causes the float to be raised to a higher position in the tube. The principle here is that the rate of mass flow is the same throughout the system, thus causing the velocity throughout to be proportional to the effective cross-sectional area between the gage head and workpiece.

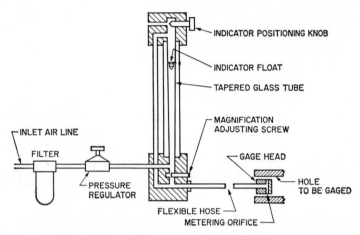

Fig. 15–28. A diagram of a flow type air gage.

Back-pressure type pneumatic gages use a variety of pressure sensitive devices to detect and amplify variations in air pressure in the gage system. Bourdon tubes, water columns, and bellows are common among these.

Fig. 15–29. An air gage. (Courtesy The Sheffield Corp.)

A flow-type air gage equipped with an air plug for gaging cylindrical holes is shown in Fig. 15–29. The gage is set by master ring gages corresponding to the limiting dimensions of the hole to be gaged. Pointers are positioned along a vertical scale to indicate these limiting dimensions. As long as the indicator float rises to a position between the pointers, the hole being gaged may be considered as being of acceptable size. A single-column air gage of the type shown in Fig. 15–29, complete with air plug and master setting gages, costs around $550.

Air gaging methods may be applied to the measurement of linear and geometric dimensions of both inside and outside surfaces. An air plug is always smaller than the hole, and wear is slight, and insertion quick and easy. Also, the flowing air helps keep surfaces clean.

Optical comparators. Many industrial products and component parts are so small and of such complex configuration as to require magnification for accurate discernment. For this purpose a number of measuring and gaging instruments using various optical systems, such as the tool-makers' microscope, the binocular microscope, and the optical projecting comparator, find wide application in the inspection of small parts and tools.

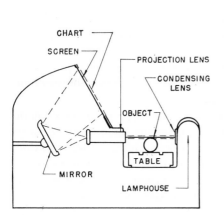

Fig. 15–30. A diagram of an optical comparator system.

Fig. 15–31. An optical projecting comparator. (Courtesy Eastman Kodak Co.)

The optical projecting comparator projects a magnified image of the object being measured onto a screen where it is compared to a master chart or drawing. Projecting comparators may have optical systems for contour (diascopic) or front surface (episcopic) projection or both. For *diascopic projection* the light rays pass over and around the object being checked and through the projection lens as illustrated in Fig. 15–30. In *episcopic projection* the light rays are directed against the side of the object being measured and are then reflected back through the projection lens. This method enables the checking of surface conditions and the dimensions of surface openings which do not extend clear through the workpiece.

Figure 15–31 shows the projecting comparator being used to inspect surface details and holes of a Geneva cam by means of the front surface illumination method. In many machines it is possible to use diascopic and episcopic illumination simultaneously so that both contour and surface characteristics may be observed at the same time.

Tolerances of 0.001 in. and smaller may be checked quite rapidly on optical projecting comparators as the lens magnification enlarges small dimensions to readily visible sizes. For example, 0.0002 in. on a workpiece becomes 0.010 in. on the screen after 50 magnifications. Projectors are commonly available with projection magnifications of 10X, 20X, 31.25X, 50X, 62.5X, and 100X. One model having these magnifications, a 20 in. by 7¼ in. work stage, and a 14½ in.-diameter frosted screen costs about $3000.

Automatic gaging systems. Many modern industrial processes have been automated to a high degree and the inspection process must be automated, too, to keep pace.

Automated control and gaging systems usually fall into two broad categories; in-process or on-the-machine gaging control, and post-process or after-the-machine gaging control. For in-process gaging control a gaging device is applied to the workpiece while it is being processed. Information from the gaging device is fed back to control the machine as described in Chap. 35 on Automation.

Post-process or after-the-machine gaging control exists when automatic gaging equipment located adjacent to the processing facilities are used to check the product after it leaves the process or machine, rather than during the processing itself. This method may provide feedback information to the machine as well as information to a sorting device which automatically segregates the product into certain size categories.

INTERFEROMETRY

Interferometry, the science of measuring with light waves, may be used for precision measurements to a few millionths of an inch. Such measurements are based on the phenomenon of light wave interference and can be easily made with an optical flat and monochromatic light source of known wave length.

The optical flat is a plane lens usually a clear fused quartz disk from 2 to 10 in. in diameter and ½ to 1 in. thick. The faces of a flat are accurately polished to nearly true planes; some have surfaces within 0.000001 (one microinch) of true flatness.

Helium is most commonly used in industry as a source of monochromatic or single wave length light because of its convenience. Although helium radiates a number of wave lengths of light, that portion which is emitted with a wave length of 23.13 millonths of an inch is so much stronger than the rest that the other wave lengths are practically unnoticeable.

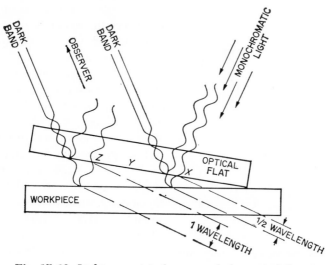

Fig. 15–32. Light wave interference and the optical flat.

The principle of light wave interference and the operation of the optical flat are illustrated in Fig. 15–32, wherein an optical flat is shown resting at a slight angle on a workpiece surface. Energy in the form of light waves is transmitted from a monochromatic light source to the optical flat. When a ray of light reaches the bottom surface of the flat it is divided into two rays. One ray is reflected from the bottom of the flat toward the eye of the observer, while the other continues on downward and is reflected and loses ½ wave length on striking the top of the workpiece. If the rays are in phase when they reform, their energies reinforce each other, and they appear bright. If they are out of phase, their energies cancel and they are dark. This phenomenon produces a series of light and dark fringes or bands along the workpiece surface and the bottom of the flat as is illustrated in Fig. 15–33. The distance between the workpiece and the bottom surface of the optical flat at any point determines which effect takes place. If the distance is equivalent to some whole number of half wave lengths of the monochromatic light then the reflected rays will be out of phase, thus producing dark bands. This condition exists at positions X and Z of Fig. 15–32. If the distance is equivalent to some odd number of quarter wave lengths of the light then the reflected rays will be in phase with each other and produce light bands. The light bands would be centered between the dark bands. Thus, a light band would appear at position Y in Fig. 15–32.

Since each dark band indicates a change of ½ wave length in distance separating the work surface and flat, measurements are made very simply by counting the number of these bands and multiplying that number by ½ the wave length of the light source. This procedure may

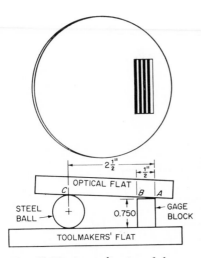

be illustrated by the use of Fig. 15–33. There the diameter of a steel ball is compared with a gage block of known height. Assume a monochromatic light source with a wave length of 23.13 microinches. From the four interference bands on the surface of the gage block, it is obvious that the difference in elevations of positions A and B on the flat is equal to $4 \times 23.13/2$ or 46.26 microinches. By simple proportion the difference in elevations between points A and C is equal to $(46.26 \times 2.5)/0.5$ or 231.3 microinches. Thus the diameter of the ball is $0.750 + 0.0002313$ in. or 0.7502313 in.

Fig. 15–33. An application of the optical flat.

Optical flats are often used to test the flatness of surfaces. The presence of interference bands between the flat and the surface being tested is an indication that the surface is not parallel with the surface of the flat.

SURFACE QUALITY

For high-quality products surface quality is commonly specified along with linear and geometric dimensions. A precise dimension means nothing unless referred to a good surface. The quality of its surface often determines how well a part performs. An automotive brake drum, for example, may function quite effectively if the contact surface of the drum has a certain degree of surface roughness, but may not work at all if the surface is too smooth. On the other hand, too much roughness on bearing surfaces of high-speed engine parts may result in excessive heat and ultimate failure.

Surface characteristics. The American Standards Association has provided a set of standard terms and symbols to define such basic surface characteristics as profile, roughness, waviness, flaws and lay. *Profile* is defined as the contour of any section through a surface. *Roughness* refers to relatively finely spaced surface irregularities such as might be produced by the action of a cutting tool or grinding wheel during a machining operation. *Waviness* consists of those surface irregularities which are of greater spacing than roughness. Waviness may be caused by vibrations, machine or work deflections, warping, etc. *Flaws* are surface irregularities or imperfections which occur at infrequent intervals and at random locations. Such imperfections as scratches, ridges, holes, cracks, pits, checks, etc. are included in this category. *Lay* is defined as the direction of the predominant surface pattern. These characteristics are illustrated in Fig. 15–34.

Surface quality specifications. Standard symbols to specify surface quality are illustrated in Fig. 15–35. Roughness is the most commonly specified characteristic and is usually expressed in units of microinches. Roughness provides a measure of the deviation of the surface irregularities from an average plane through the surface. In most cases, the root mean square (rms)

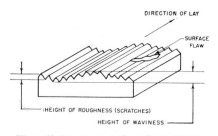

Fig. 15–34. A typical surface highly magnified.

deviation is used. Thus, in Fig. 15–36, the root mean square deviation of the ordinates of y_1, y_2, ..., y_n would be given by the formula, rms deviation $= [(\Sigma y_i^2)/n]^{1/2}$, where y_i is the deviation of a point on the surface above or below the average plane, and n is the number of points included in the sum.

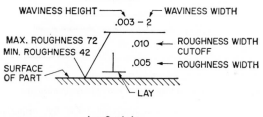

Lay Symbols

=	Parallel to the boundary line of the nominal surface
⊥	Perpendicular to the boundary line of the nominal surface
X	Angular in both directions to the boundary line of the nominal surface
M	Multidirectional
C	Approximately circular relative to the center
R	Approximately radial relative to the center of the nominal surface

Fig. 15–35. Specifications of surface quality.

Waviness height alone may be specified, or it may be accompanied by a width specification. Thus, in Fig. 15–35, the specification 0.003–2 means that no waves over 0.003 in. high are allowed in any 2 in. of length. If no width specification is given, it is usually implied that the waviness height specified must be held over the full length of the work. Other specifications in Fig. 15–35 are less common.

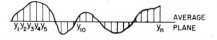

Fig. 15–36. A profile of surface roughness.

Surface finishes produced by metal machining. Each machining process generally produces a characteristic surface. Thus, operations like turning and shaping produce parallel lines of roughness on the surface as a result of the continuous cutting action and feed movement of the single edge cutting tools. Grinding operations, due to the large number of small cutting edges coming into contact with the surface, produce a directional pattern consisting of many small scratches that vary in length and often overlap. Operations like honing and lapping produce multidirectional or crisscross patterns. A Superfinished surface is supposed to have no perceptible surface scratch pattern.

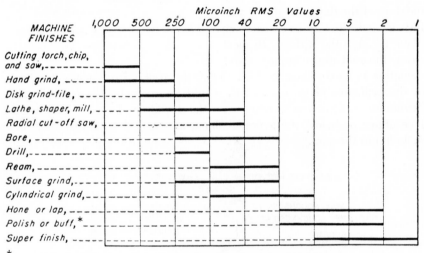

*Dependent on previous surface finish and grit and grade of abrasive.

Fig. 15–37. Range of surface roughness produced by various machining operations.

Some machining processes are capable of producing smoother surfaces than others. In commercial machining operations the surface roughness that might be expected usually lies within a certain range, and the actual roughness obtained depends upon factors such as the condition of the machine and tools and the care and skill exercised by the operator. A comparison of the ranges of surface roughness expected from common operations is shown in Fig. 15–37.

Cost versus surface quality. The specification of a smoother surface than is needed to satisfy functional requirements may result in excessive manufacturing cost. For example, a roughness specification of 100 microinches may be obtainable by one finish turning operation on a lathe, while a finish of 20 microinches may require additional operations such as grinding or honing, thus adding to the manufacturing costs. In many cases a high degree of surface roughness is specified in order to call attention to the fact that a smooth surface is not necessary and that unnecessary time and effort should not be expended. Figure 15–38 shows a typical surface finish-versus-cost curve which illustrates how the specification of finer surface finishes tends to affect the cost of producing that finish.

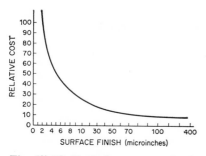

Measurement of surface finish. Surface finish may be measured quite accurately by complex electrical instruments or may be roughly estimated by comparing the surface with a standard specimen. Waviness is normally measured by sensitive dial indicators. Roughness may be determined by a number of methods.

Fig. 15–38. Typical cost versus finish curve.

Precise surface roughness measurements may be made quantitatively with the *Profilometer* or the *Brush Surface Analyzer*. Figure 15–39 illustrates the principle of operation. A diamond-pointed stylus or follower in a head is moved at a constant rate across the surface being measured. As the stylus passes over the surface, it rises and falls at a rate depending upon the surface roughness. These movements excite electrical impulses that are amplified and actuate a meter reading in units of microinches, rms. Such means may also operate a recording device that draws a trace of the surface profile magnified on a moving tape.

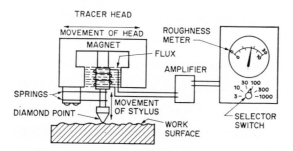

Fig. 15–39. A diagram to show how the Profilometer indicates surface roughness.

Questions

1. What is meant by interchangeable manufacture and how does it contribute to our standard of living?

2. Why is it sometimes necessary to inspect articles of manufacture?

3. What is the primary responsibility of the inspection department?

4. Where may inspection operations be performed in manufacturing?

5. Explain the difference between inspection, quality control, and statistical quality control.

6. What is the basic philosophy of statistical quality control?

7. Explain the difference between a sample and a population.

8. What is a statistic?

9. At what stage of manufacturing are control charts most effectively applied?

10. Why are average values $(\bar{X})$ plotted instead of individual values (X) on a control chart?

11. In process control why is it necessary to use both a chart for averages and a control chart for ranges?

12. What are some of the advantages of sampling?

13. Name five industrial products and characteristics of each which would make sampling mandatory.

14. How can one determine what risks are involved in using a particular sampling plan?

15. Define the term "tolerance."

16. Give three different ways of specifying tolerance.

17. Define the term "clearance."

18. Define the term "allowance."

19. What are the three general categories of mating part fit conditions?

20. Define the terms "basic size," "standard size," and "nominal size."

21. Why are tolerances sometimes required on geometric dimensions?

22. What is the fundamental unit of length in the United States?

23. What are gage blocks and what are they used for?

24. What is the difference between a measuring process and a gaging process?

25. In referring to an inspection instrument, what is meant by the term "precision of measurement?"

26. Explain the difference between a line measuring device and an end measuring device.

27. What effect does the application of excessive torque on the spindle of a micrometer have on the accuracy obtained of a dimension being measured?

28. Explain the theory of a vernier scale.

29. Explain the necessity for working, inspection, and master gages in manufacturing.

30. Indicate which of the three methods of applying tolerances to gages should be used if adequate customer satisfaction is the primary criterion.

31. Explain how a dial indicator might be used to check for misalignment of the headstock and tailstock centers of an engine lathe.

32. Describe the basic features of a flow-type air gage and explain the operating principles of such an instrument.

33. Give two examples of manufactured articles where the optical comparator equipped with episcopic illumination would be a valuable inspection tool.

34. What sort of surface pattern or lay would be generated by an internal honing operation?

Problems

1. If the distribution of a particular dimension of a population of manufactured parts can be represented by the normal curve, what proportion of those parts would occur between the mean dimension and plus and minus one standard deviation?

2. A hole and mating shaft is to have a nominal assembly size of 1½ in. The assembly is to have a maximum total clearance of 0.006 in. and a minimum total clearance of 0.002 in. (a) Determine the specifications of the parts for 100% interchangeability, (b) for statistical average interchangeability.

3. A hole and mating shaft are to be machined to a Class RC 2 fit. The basic hole size is 2 in. Using standard hole practice and unilateral tolerance, determine the manufacturing specifications for the hole and shaft according to the standards given in Fig. 15–7.

4. Make a sketch of the graduated scales of a vernier micrometer caliper with a reading of 0.6865.

5. Determine the specification for the "go" and "not go" ends of a set of manufacturing and inspection plug gages to be used in checking a hole with diameter specification of $1.000 \begin{array}{c} + 0.003 \\ - 0.000 \end{array}$.

6. An optical flat is used to check a workpiece under a monochromatic light having a wave length of 23.2 microinches in the manner illustrated by Fig. 15–32. The distance from the center of one band to the center of the next is 0.25 in. What is the angle between the surfaces of the optical flat and workpiece expressed in microinches per in.?

7. Two gage blocks are set up for calibration under a monochromatic light having a wave length of 23.2 microinches in the manner shown in Fig. 15–40. The distance from the center of one band to the center of the next is 0.1 in. Distance x is ¾ in. and y is 1 in. The height of block B is 0.999973 in. What is the height of block A?

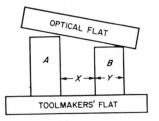

Fig. 15–40. Comparison of gage block heights.

References

Michelon, Leno C., *Industrial Inspection Methods*, Harper and Bros., New York, 1950.

Cowden, Dudley J., *Statistical Methods in Quality Control*, Prentice-Hall, Inc., Englewood Cliffs, N. J., 1957.

16

How Metals Are Cut

Most materials can be and are cut to desired sizes and shapes, but in engineering practice the chief concern is with metal cutting.

Why metal is cut. It has been said that the loss of a few ounces of metal on the working surfaces of an automobile engine weighing hundreds of pounds is enough to make the engine useless. In a good engine the functional surfaces of the parts must have definite shapes and sizes so they fit and work together perfectly. The purpose of metal cutting for all products is to finish surfaces more closely to specified dimensions than can be done by other methods. Parts formed roughly by other processes, like founding and forging, normally have some or all of their surfaces refined by cutting. For instance, most engine blocks are cast and then their cylinders, faces, and bearing surfaces are cut to size. By various cutting processes, metal surfaces can be refined to any discernible degree of accuracy, truth, or smoothness desired. The greater the degree of refinement, the more the cost.

Metal cutting is a convenient way of making one or a few pieces of almost any shape from an available chunk of raw material. Large amounts of material can be cut away when necessary. But metal cutting is not limited to making parts in small quantities. It can readily be adapted to fast, automatic and accurate production. Certain metal removable processes, such as grinding, are capable of finishing very hard substances.

How cutting is done. In all metal-cutting operations an edged tool is driven through material to remove chips from the parent body and leave geometrically true surfaces. All else that occurs merely contributes to that action. The kind of surface produced by the operation depends on the shape of the tool and the path it traverses through the material. If a workpiece is rotated about an axis and a tool is traversed in a definite path relative to the axis, a surface of revolution is generated. If the tool path is parallel to the axis, the surface is a cylinder as indicated by Fig. 16–1(A). This is called *straight turning* or just *turning*. An inside cylindrical surface is generated in the same way by *boring*, as depicted in Fig. 16–1(B). If the tool path is straight but not parallel to the workpiece axis, a conical surface is generated. This is called *taper turning*, as in Fig. 16–1(C). Both outside and inside tapers can be generated. If the tool is directed in a curved path as shown in Fig. 16–1(D), a profile of varying diameter is generated by *contour turning*. In the foregoing examples, the shape of the surface generated depends more upon the path than the form of the tool. A surface of revolution may also be machined by plunging a tool into a revolving workpiece. The profile cut in that way corresponds to the form of the cutting edge of the tool. *Contour forming* done in that way is illustrated in Fig. 16–1(E). Straight and tapered surfaces may be formed in a similar manner.

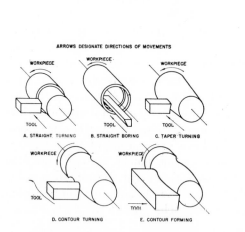

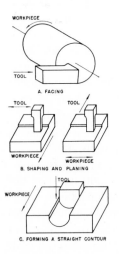

Fig. 16–1. Diagrams to show how surfaces of revolution are generated and formed.

Fig. 16–2. Diagram to show how plane surfaces are generated and formed.

A plane surface on the end or shoulder of a workpiece may be generated by revolving the piece and feeding a tool at a right angle to the axis as shown in Fig. 16–2(A). This is called *facing*. Planes may also be generated by a series of straight cuts, without revolution of the work-pieces, as illustrated in Fig. 16–2(B). If the tool is reciprocated and the workpiece is moved a crosswise increment at each stroke, the operation is called *shaping*. *Planing* is done by reciprocating the workpiece and mov-ing the tool a little for each stroke. Formed contours can be cut by these methods by varying the depth of cut or by using a formed tool as indi-cated in Fig. 16–2(C).

Surfaces may be machined by tools having a number of edges that can cut successively through the material. Drills for opening holes are of this type. A drill may turn and be fed into the workpiece, or the piece may revolve while the drill is fed into it. Boring also is often done with tools having several edges. Plane and contour surfaces are machined by milling cutters. A milling cutter has a number of teeth on its periphery. The teeth remove chips as the cutter revolves and moves over the work-piece as typified in Fig. 16–3.

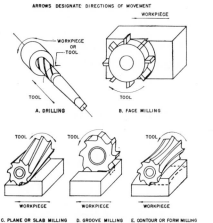

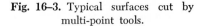

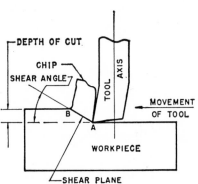

Fig. 16–3. Typical surfaces cut by multi-point tools.

Fig. 16–4. A diagram of the action of a cutting tool.

The act of metal cutting is in some ways like cutting a slice of bread. There the knife is moved rapidly back and forth and at each stroke pene-trates the bread a certain amount. When metal is cut, the workpiece surface is driven with respect to the tool, or the tool with respect to the surface, at a relatively high rate of speed. This is called the *cutting speed* or *speed* and is expressed in feet per minute (fpm) or surface feet per minute (sfpm). Its magnitude is commonly in the range of 100 to 1000 ft per min. At the same time the tool is advanced comparatively slowly in a direction generally perpendicular to the speed. This motion is called the *feed* and is defined as *the distance the tool advances into or along the workpiece each time the tool point passes a certain position in its travel over the surface.* Feed is expressed in a fraction or thousandths of an inch per revolution for turning; per stroke for shaping; or per tooth for milling.

The depth of cut is the normal distance from the surface being removed to the surface exposed by a cutting tool. It is measured in inches.

In turning, the rate of travel of the surface of the workpiece is the speed; the distance the tool advances per revolution at a right angle to the speed is the feed, and half the amount the diameter is changed by the action is the depth of cut. In milling, the peripheral rate of travel of the cutter is the speed; the distance the workpiece advances between the time one tooth makes contact and the next is the basic feed; and the normal distance from the original surface to the surface left by the cutter is the depth of cut.

A workpiece or cutter must be revolved at the number of revolutions per minute (rpm), designated by N, that will give the required surface speed of V in fpm. If the diameter is d inches, in one revolution a point on the periphery travels a distance of $\pi d/12$ ft. The necessary rate of rotation is then

$$N = \frac{V}{\pi d/12} = \frac{12V}{\pi d} \tag{16-1}$$

For practical purposes, π can be considered to be 3, and

$$N = 4V/d. \tag{16-2}$$

The rate of metal removal in cubic inches per minute is

$$Q = 12 \times V \times f \times d \tag{16-3}$$

where f = the width of uncut chip in inches, equivalent to the feed in ipr, and d = the depth of cut in inches.

Machine tools. Metal may be cut by simple hand tools such as hammer and chisel, file, saw, or stone. These are used today to remove metal in small amounts or as makeshifts. At one time such tools were about the only means available for cutting metals. Obviously the articles cut from metal solely by hand tools were few and quite expensive.

With the advent of the industrial revolution, the invention and development of devices like the steam engine and textile machinery called for faster and more accurate methods of cutting metals. Machines were devised to apply power to metal cutting and cut with consistent precision. These superior tools were given the name of *machine tools,* in contrast to hand tools, and the work done by them is called *machining.*

Machines for turning, drilling, boring, and planing came into being early. At first it was considered quite an accomplishment just to make a few articles of metal precisely; later the demand arose for varieties of products and in quantities. Machining methods were applied to making firearms and clocks, the reaper and sewing machines, and a multitude of new inventions still coming along. Other machine tools like the milling machine, turret lathe, and grinding machine were developed to cut metal faster, reduce labor, and increase precision. To meet the demands of the present century for production in large quantities, highly specialized and automatic machine tools have been developed. The basic types of machine tools and the principles of their operation will be described in connection with the processes for which they are used.

THE MECHANICS OF METAL CUTTING

How a tool penetrates metal. The most important part of a metal machining operation is the spot where the cutting tool meets the workpiece and pries away chips. An understanding of what happens in the cutting zone is necessary to appreciate what makes a good cutting tool and how it should be operated. The basic action is the same whether a single edge is cutting or several edges in a multiple tooth tool are cutting at the same time or in succession.

When a tool cuts metal, it is driven by a force necessary to overcome friction and the forces that hold the metal together. The metal that the tool first meets is compressed and caused to

Fig. 16–5. A photomicrograph showing how a chip is formed and ruptured from a brittle material. Successive positions of the advancing tool are depicted from top to bottom. (Courtesy The Cincinnati Milling Machine Co.)

flow up the face of the tool. The pressure against the face of the tool and the friction force opposing the metal flow build up to large amounts. Figure 16–4 is a diagram of the action in a single plane of a cutting tool forming a chip. At point A the material may be sheared by the advancing tool or torn by the bending of the chip to start a crack. The stress in the material ahead of the advancing tool reaches a maximum value in a plane approximately perpendicular to the tool face. That plane is known as the *shear plane,* and one edge is depicted by the line AB of Fig. 16–4. When the strength of the metal is exceeded, rupture or slippage occurs along the shear plane. With further movement, new material is compressed by the tool, and the cycle is repeated again and again. As it travels along, the cutting edge scrapes and helps clean up the surface.

Types of chips. When a brittle material like cast iron or bronze is cut, it is broken along the shear plane. The same may happen if the material is ductile and the friction between chip and tool is very high. The chips come off in small pieces or segments and are pushed away by the tool as illustrated in the highly magnified view of Fig. 16–5. A chip formed in this way is called a *Type I* or *segmental chip.*

A ductile material, like aluminum, is not broken up but comes off like a ribbon as shown by the highly magnified section of Fig. 16–6. This is

Fig. 16–6. A photomicrograph of a continuous chip. (Courtesy The Cincinnati Milling Machine Co.)

known as a *Type II* or *continuous chip.* An evident line of demarcation separates the highly distorted crystals in the chip from the undistorted parent material. That line is the edge of the shear plane at one instant and corresponds to the line of AB of Fig. 16–4. As the material slips along one plane, it is work-hardened and resists further distortion. The stresses build up on the next plane to bring about slippage in new material, and so on.

When steel is cut, a continuous chip is formed, but the pressure against the tool is high, and the severe action of the chip quickly rubs the natural film from the tool face. The freshly cut chip and the newly exposed material on the face of the tool have an affinity for each other, and a layer of highly compressed material adheres to the face of the tool. Such a formation is illustrated in Fig. 16–7 and is called a *built-up edge.* The chip is a *Type III* or *continuous chip with built-up edge.* As the cut progresses, the pile on the face of the tool becomes large and unstable. At frequent intervals pieces topple from the pile and adhere to the work

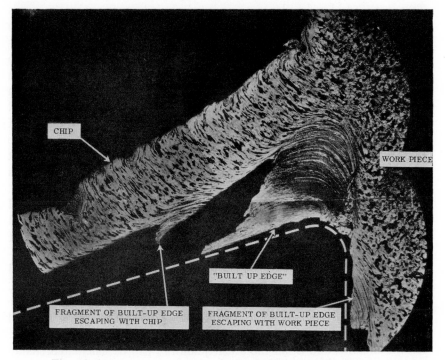

Fig. 16–7. A composite photograph of a highly magnified chip and a built up edge. (Courtesy The Cincinnati Milling Machine Co.)

surface or pass off with the chip. The fragments of built-up edge are the main causes of roughness of a cut surface. The built-up edge pushes on ahead of the tool and to some extent protects the edge.

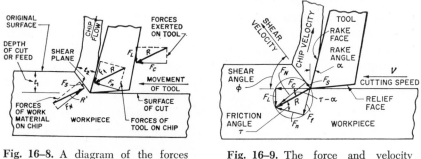

Fig. 16–8. A diagram of the forces exerted by a cutting tool.

Fig. 16–9. The force and velocity system of a cut.

Cutting forces and temperature. Figure 16–8 depicts the formation of a Type II chip with the single cutting edge of the tool at right angles to the direction of movement, and the surface cut parallel to the original.

This case is idealized and easy to understand, and the principles it reveals are true for all forms of metal cutting. The tool exerts a force R on the chip with a normal component F_n and a friction component F_f that opposes the flow of the chip up the tool face. For equilibrium, the chip must be subjected to a substantially equal and opposite reaction R' from the workpiece at the shear plane with a normal component F_N and a shearing force F_S along the shear plane. For convenience, the force R applied to the tool is resolved into a component F_C in the direction of movement of the tool and a normal component F_L. To illustrate the relationship, all the forces may be represented by the force R acting at the edge of the tool with the components in their respective positions as in Fig. 16–9.

Since the chip is formed off the shear plane, its thickness is related to the length of the shear plane. This thickness t_2 can be measured; and from it and the precut chip thickness t_1 and the known rake angle (α) of the tool, the shear plane angle (ϕ) can easily be calculated. A close approximation is that $t_1/t_2 = \sin \phi$. All the components of force as arranged in Fig. 16–9 are sides of right triangles with a common hypotenuse R, the diameter of the force circle, and can readily be related by simple trigonometry. The components of force, F_C and F_L applied to the tool can be measured by means of a dynamometer. From these forces and the known angles α and ϕ, all the other quantities can be calculated. As an additional technique, use is made of the fact that the dissimilar tool and workpiece material form a thermocouple, and from them the cutting temperatures can be measured. All of these things have been done by research investigators, and the detailed descriptions of their work and calculations can be found in treatises on metal cutting.

The tool exerts a tremendous pressure upon the chip, normally of the order of several hundred thousand pounds per square inch. The intimate contact between chip and tool face induced by such pressures and the high-temperature conditions conducive to welding the materials together cause a large frictional resistance to the flow of the chip up the tool face. The coefficient of friction is usually over 0.5 and often over 1, as compared with a coefficient of less than 0.2 normally experienced in mechanical devices. Rubbing of the chip under these conditions wears the rake face of the tool severely. The application of a cutting fluid or substance to provide lubrication, a sharp and smooth tool, or the choice of work and tool materials with a low natural coefficient of friction help to decrease the cutting forces and increase the endurance of the tool.

Work is done in sliding the chip along the tool face and in shearing the material along the shear plane. Almost all this work is converted into heat at those places. About 80% or more of the heat passes off in the chips; most of the remainder goes into and contributes largely to the deterioration of the tool. A cutting fluid applied to the cutting zone as a coolant helps to take away some of the heat and to keep down the temperature of the tool.

THE VARIABLES OF METAL CUTTING

The effects of cutting speed. When a typical steel is cut, the temperature of the tool face may be around 1000°F at a speed below 100 fpm. As the cut speed is increased, the chip slides faster along the tool face, more work is done, and more heat is produced. A smaller proportion of this heat goes into the tool, but, the actual quantity of heat entering the tool in a given time remains about the same. At the same time, the chip curls more away from the tool, and the area of contact between chip and tool face decreases. With the same amount of heat passing through, the temperature of the spot increases. The rise in temperature is less than proportional to the increase in speed. For a typical steel the temperature may reach 1400°F at a cutting speed of 300 to 400 fpm.

As speed increases and temperature rises, the chip material next to the tool face becomes weaker and shears more easily in friction. Both the coefficient of friction and the friction force decrease. Whereas the friction conditions for cutting steel at speeds below 100 fpm may be such as to cause the formation of a built-up edge, their change with increased speed leads to the dimunition and eventual disappearance of the built-up edge. The surface finish produced is correspondingly improved.

The angle ϕ of the shear plane increases with speed. It should be recognized that the force R of the tool on the chip sets up stresses throughout the base of the chip and adjacent workpiece material. In a quasi-plastic material such as metal these stresses occur in all directions with a definite intensity in each direction. The shear plane represents that direction along which the stresses have a magnitude sufficient to cause plastic deformations in the material. As the force applied to the material changes in size and direction, the pattern of the stresses changes likewise. When the speed is increased, the friction force and the friction angle (τ) both decrease. This means the resultant, R, of Fig. 16–9, must rotate clockwise. The pattern of stresses rotates correspondingly and the angle ϕ of the shear plane becomes larger.

As the shear angle ϕ increases, the distance along the shear plane from the tool point to the original surface decreases. That means the area of the shear plane is reduced. For a substantially constant shearing strength of the material, the shearing force, F_S, required to cause deformation of the material is smaller. As a result, the force R needed to cause formation of the chip can and does decrease, as do its components F_C and F_L. This phenomenon usually does not appear until the cut speed rises to around 100 fpm. Then the cutting force falls off rapidly at first but at a less rapid rate as the speed is increased further. Although decreases in cutting forces of as much as 50% have been found in some cases, the reduction is generally less than 15%.

The effect of feed. The depth of cut designated by t_1 in Fig. 16–8 is equivalent to the feed in turning and most other operations and will be referred to as feed in this discussion. As the feed is increased, the tool presses against more material, more work is done, and the temperature at the interface increases. However, an increase in feed causes a smaller rise in temperature than does a corresponding increase in speed. In turning steel under a typical set of conditions, the temperature rose from 1100°F to only 1250°F when the feed was increased from 0.003 to 0.010 in. per rev. Thus the rate of metal removal may be increased by increasing the feed with less temperature rise and consequently less wear on the tool than by increasing the speed.

As the feed is increased, the shear angle ϕ increases for essentially the same reasons as explained for speed. An increase in feed with speed constant removes more material and the cutting forces increase, as would be expected, but not in proportion. In a typical case the cutting force was found to increase from 150 to 400 lb when the feed was increased from 0.003 to 0.010 in. per rev.

Effect of rake angle. The rake angle (α) shown in Fig. 16–9 is considered positive to the right of the vertical and negative to the left. Any change in the angle changes the direction of the resultant force applied by the tool to the chip and changes the stress pattern. An increase in the rake angle increases the shear angle and decreases the forces required to deform the work material but at the same time decreases the mass of the tool point.

Energy and power. The cutting force F_c of Figs. 16–8 and 16–9 has the same direction as the cutting speed, V, in fpm. The power, in hp, required for a cut is

$$P = F_c V / 33{,}000. \qquad (16\text{–}4)$$

In most cutting operations feed in the direction of the force F_L is insignificant.

As the speed, feed, or depth of cut in an operation are increased, more metal is removed and the power required is increased. The increase is not proportional because F_c varies less than proportionally with speed, feed, or depth of cut as has been shown. A measure of the work efficiency of an operation is the amount of power required to remove each cubic inch of metal. This is the unit power

$$P_u = P/Q; \qquad (16\text{–}5)$$

where Q is the rate of metal removal in cubic inches per minute. Values of P_u have been found for various conditions, and some of the important ones are given later in this text when cutting performance is discussed.

If the unit power for a particular type of operation is known, then the total power to cut at a desired rate of metal removal can be calculated from

$$P = QP_u. \qquad (16\text{-}6)$$

After the power has been found, the cutting force can be ascertained from

$$F_c = \frac{33,000\, P}{V}. \qquad (16\text{-}7)$$

As an example, assume that cast iron is to be turned at a speed of 200 fpm and with a feed of 0.010 in. per rev and depth of cut of 0.25 in. The rate of metal removal $Q = 0.010 \times 0.25 \times 12 \times 200 = 6$ cu in./min. The unit power consumption for this type of operation has been found to be 0.4 hp/cu in./min. The power required for the cut is $P = 6 \times 0.4 = 2.4$ hp at the tool point. The cutting force $F_c = \dfrac{33,000 \times 2.4}{200} = 396$ lb.

Tool wear. After a tool has been cutting for some time, depending upon conditions, its cutting edge breaks down. The chip rubbing over the rake face may wear a crater that grows until it undermines the edge. The relief face of Fig. 16–9 rubbing over the cut surface and abraded by the chip particles may wear away just behind the edge. Too high a temperature may soften the tool, and the edge may be wiped away. Hard work material may chip or crumble the cutting edge. Often a combination of these factors causes tool failure. When the edge breaks down, the tool ceases to cut cleanly, and cutting forces and power consumption rise rapidly.

The length of time a tool cuts before it has to be resharpened is called the *tool life.* The amount of metal removed in this time is sometimes made the measure of tool life. A tool should be removed and reground before it wears to where an excessive and uneconomical amount of material must be ground from its faces to recondition it. A practical criterion for judging when a tool should be resharpened is the amount of wear on the relief face. A common standard for cemented carbide tools is that a tool should be removed from cutting when the worn band on the relief face has grown to $\frac{1}{32}$ in. from the cutting edge. After a tool has been reground a number of times, it must be reworked or replaced. Tool material and the labor for sharpening, resetting, readjusting and reworking tools make up a definite part of the cost of any machining operation. Throw-away tools that are not reground may be run to imminent destruction.

Vibration and chatter. Metal cutting is inherently cyclic. Cutting forces build up as the tool penetrates the material and deflect the tool, even if slightly. When rupture or shear occurs to form the chip and the forces momentarily drop, the tool springs back. Even in a seemingly continuous cut fluctuations can occur because of the change in the cutting force with the relative velocity of the tool and the workpiece. The body of the tool is being driven through the material at a constant velocity. As it penetrates, the tip of the tool is sprung backwards by the increasing resistance it meets, and the relative velocity between the cutting edge and workpiece decreases accordingly. At the lower velocity the forces rise, and the tool is stressed still more. When the bending moment in the tool becomes large enough, it begins to move the tool back to its original shape. That increases the relative speed between the cutting edge and workpiece, and the cutting forces drop. The tool springs back until equilibrium is reached, the relative velocity decreases, the cutting forces start to rise, and another cycle begins.

Vibrations in cutting occur at high frequencies and often induce sympathetic vibrations in machine tool members, and workpieces. Noticeable vibration in metal-cutting operations is called *chatter*. It may be quite noisy and obnoxious, can cause damage to machines, and defaces work surfaces with patterns called *chatter marks*. Common remedies to decrease chatter are to use a heavier tool, reduce speed, feed, or depth of cut, and alter the form of the tool to decrease the length of cutting edge in contact with the material.

METAL CUTTING TOOLS

Metal cutting tools may be classified as single-point and multiple-point tools. The latter are in effect, and act like, combinations of single-point tools. Thus the factors that give single-point tools their characteristics also are basic to multiple-point tools. In this chapter the elements of cutting tools will be discussed in detail in connection with single-point tools. Later the features of multiple-point tools, such as drills and milling cutters, will be described along with the processes for which they are used.

The factors that determine how a cutting tool performs are: (1) the tool material, (2) the shape of the tool point, and (3) the form of the tool.

Cutting tool material. Hardness is the first requisite of a cutting tool material because it must be able to penetrate other materials. Toughness is also desirable to withstand shock. Cutting tools must work upon many kinds of metals and under a variety of conditions. No one cutting material is best for all purposes. The principal cutting tool materials are:

(1) carbon tool steel, (2) high speed steel, (3) cast nonferrous alloys, (4) cemented carbides, (5) sintered oxides, (6) diamonds, and (7) artificial abrasives. The last will be described in connection with the grinding processes in Chap. 28.

Carbon tool steel. Carbon tool steel is the oldest kind of cutting material but is little used today. It contains from 0.90 to 1.2% carbon and few alloying elements. Its chief disadvantage is that it softens at temperatures above 400°F and therefore is limited to very slow cutting speeds and light duty. At low temperatures carbon tool steel is hard, wear-resistant, and as serviceable as more expensive materials for some applications. It is comparatively inexpensive and suitable for special tools, like odd sizes of drills, that are infrequently and lightly used and do not warrant much investment. It is easy to fabricate and simple to harden.

High-speed steel. High-speed steel is so named because it cuts at higher speeds than other steels. Even so, it is limited to speeds and conditions that do not give rise to temperatures above about 1100°F. At red heat high-speed steel loses its hardness and breaks down quickly. It is moderate in cost and tough, which makes it preferable in many cases to harder but more brittle and expensive materials. For instance, high-speed steel is able to withstand interrupted cuts better than harder materials. High-speed steel can be made into various forms of tools with reasonable facility but requires care in its heat treatment.

One of the oldest and most common types of high-speed steel is known as 18–4–1. It contains about 0.55 to 0.75% carbon, 18% tungsten, 4% chromium, and 1% vanadium. Molybdenum is used in some types to eliminate partially or wholly the need for tungsten. A general purpose and widely used "moly" high-speed steel contains 8% molybdenum, 4% chromium, 1½% tungsten, and 1% vanadium. Its performance is comparable to tungsten high-speed steel. Cobalt is sometimes added to high-speed steel to improve red hardness, and vanadium to increase hardness.

Cast nonferrous alloys. Cast nonferrous alloys contain no iron and cannot be softened by heat treatment so as to be machined easily. They must be cast to shape and ground to size. A typical cast nonferrous alloy has the trade name of *Stellite* and contains 43 to 48% cobalt, 17 to 19% tungsten, 30 to 35% chromium, and about 2% carbon, depending upon the grade and purpose. Stellite retains its hardness and becomes tougher at red heat. It has a particularly hard skin that stands the abrasive action of such materials as cast iron, malleable iron, and bronze.

Cemented carbides. Cemented carbides, *sintered carbides*, or just *carbides* are composed of very hard particles held together by a metallic bond. The primary ingredient is tungsten carbide in most commercial tools, but it is often mixed with various amounts of tantalum, titanium, and columbium carbides to improve resistance to abrasion and lower the coefficient of friction, which is particularly beneficial in cutting steel. A binder of cobalt, or occasionally nickel, is added to the carbide particles. Of recent origin, titanium carbide with a binder of nickel and molybdenum has shown superior results in some cases. The manufacture of cemented carbides from powder metals is described in Chap. 10.

Cemented carbides have a high first cost but are economical for machining parts in large quantities and are used for that purpose more than any other material. For cutting steel and iron, cemented carbides are commonly run at speeds from several hundred to 1000 fpm. Carbides are made in a number of grades by varying the sizes and proportions of the carbide particles and the amount of binder. At one extreme are the hardest but most brittle carbides with high resistance to abrasion and wear. In the other grades hardness is sacrificed in various degrees for strength and shock-resistance. Cemented carbides are made and sold under a number of trade names such as *Kennametal* and *Carboloy*.

Sintered oxides. *Sintered oxides, cemented oxides,* or *ceramics* are basically compressed and sintered aluminum oxide powder, with sometimes the addition of small amounts of other metallic oxides and binder. This type of material is harder than the others described so far, retains its hardness and strength up to 2000°F, and has a low coefficient of heat conductivity and a low coefficient of friction cutting the common metals. It performs best at speeds of 400 to 1400 fpm, in some cases up to 3000 fpm. This material is brittle and has low rupture strength and resistance to mechanical shock. As a result it has been found competitive mostly for relatively light cuts particularly with non-ferrous and non-metallic materials. It must be used on machine tools that have ample speeds and are rigid enough to resist vibration. It has not been found satisfactory for interrupted cuts.

Tests have shown practically no difference between the surface finishes obtainable with ceramic and cemented carbide tools. Tools of both materials are normally operated at finish cutting speeds in the range where a built up edge is not formed. On comparable operations, the cutting forces and power of ceramic tools have been found to be about 80% of those for carbides, apparently because of a low coefficient of friction.

Diamonds. The diamond is the hardest known material and can be run at cutting speeds up to 5000 fpm. Diamonds are suitable for cutting very hard material and producing fine finishes. They are brittle, do not conduct heat well, and are limited to light cuts of only a few thousandths of an inch in size. A typical application is the precision boring of holes.

Comparison of cutting tool materials. A comparison is made in Table 16–1 of the costs and performances of the common cutting tool materials. In general the higher priced materials save on operating cost, on jobs where they can be used. This comparison is of course made on the basis of conditions suitable to the use of all these materials. Each material is subject to limitations, as has been pointed out, and so provides areas for other materials.

TABLE 16–1. COMPARISON OF CUTTING TOOL MATERIALS

Material	Relative tool cost (1)	Typical cut speeds	Cutting cost ($ per cu in.) (2)
Carbon tool steel	0.10	40	0.25
High-speed steel	0.50	90	0.13
Nonferrous alloy	2.00	150	0.06
Cemented carbide	5.25	500	0.04
Sintered oxide	12.00	800	0.02

1. Prices are typical for a ⅜ in. square tool bit but vary with quantity, grade, and market conditions.
2. Estimates based on performance under ideal conditions, cutting cold-drawn SAE 4140 steel, with labor and overhead rate of $6 per hr.

Table 16–2 shows the detailed calculations for comparing three of the cutting tool materials. The conditions given are those reported for actual jobs on which the tools were used successfully. The amount of stock removal during the life of a tool is calculated by multiplying the speed by 12 by the feed by the depth of cut and by the tool life. The total time charged to each tool includes the cutting time plus the time to resharpen the tool. The tool cost per cubic inch of metal removed was calculated by dividing the cost of the tool by the number of times the tool could be resharpened and then by the amount of stock removed.

Table 16–2 shows that with an operating cost, including labor and overhead, of $6 per hr the sintered oxide tool is the most economical although it costs more than the others. If an unrealistic figure of $0.60 per hr is assumed for the operating cost, the cemented carbide tool has a slight advantage. Under other conditions than those shown, a similar analysis might reveal either the high-speed steel or the cemented carbide tool at an advantage. A simple example is that of a cut so heavy as to break the brittle sintered oxide tool frequently.

TABLE 16–2. A DETAILED COMPARISON OF THE COST OF TURNING SAE
4140 COLD-DRAWN STEEL WITH SEVERAL CUTTING TOOL MATERIALS

Tool material	High-speed steel	Cemented carbide	Sintered oxide
Speed (fpm)	91	508	818
Feed (ipr)	0.013	0.010	0.017
Depth of cut (in.)	0.058	0.058	0.058
Tool life (min)	60	52	20
Stock removal during tool life (cu in.)	49.4	184	194
Time to resharpen tool (min)	5	15	15
Total time (min)	65	67	35
Unit time (min/cu in.)	1.32	0.36	0.18
Operating cost at $6/hr ($/cu in.)	0.132	0.036	0.018
Tool cost ($/cu in.)	0.0002	0.002	0.004
Total cost ($/cu in.)	0.132	0.038	0.022
Operating cost at $0.60/hr ($/cu in.)	0.0132	0.0036	0.0018
Tool cost ($/cu in.)	0.0002	0.0020	0.0040
Total cost ($/cu in.)	0.0134	0.0056	0.0058

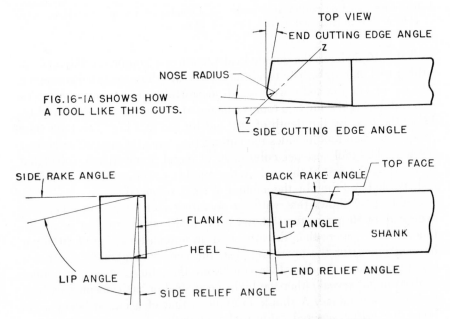

Fig. 16–10. Conventional cutting tool angles.

CUTTING TOOL SHAPES AND FORMS

Tool angles. The *point* is that part of a cutting tool where cutting edges are found. It is on the end of the *shank* or *body*. The surfaces on the point bear definite relationships to each other and are defined by angles. The angles of a single-point cutting tool of a type used on a lathe, shaper, or planer are sketched in Fig. 16–10. The main elements that define the shape of a tool point are the back rake, side rake, end relief, side relief, end-cutting edge, and side-cutting edge angles and nose radius. The angles are measured in degrees and the radius in inches. The shape of the tool often is designated by a series of numbers specifying the values of the angles and radius in the order just listed. Thus a tool with a shape specified as 8-14-6-6-6-15-³⁄₆₄ has 8° back rake, 14° side rake, 6° end relief, 6° side relief, 6° end-cutting edge, 15° side-cutting edge angle and a ³⁄₆₄ in. nose radius.

The positions of the angles on a tool are determined by the way the tool acts. A lathe tool as depicted by Fig. 16–10 is designed to enter the material top first and the rake angles are on the top face. The sizes of the angles largely affect tool performance.

Relief angles. The purpose of a relief angle, as the name implies, is to enable a surface of the tool to clear the work and not rub. The amount of relief needed depends on the kind of cut. A turning tool is fed sideways into the work, and the side relief must be greater than the helix angle of the cut. Relief angles normally assigned are those that are effective when the tool is at the same height as the center of the workpiece. The amount of relief should not be more than necessary for free cutting because too much relief removes support from the cutting edge and weakens the tool. Relief angles between 5° and 12° are usually ground on lathe tools. Carbide and ceramic tools commonly have small relief angles, from 6° to 8°, for maximum support of their brittle cutting edges. Often a secondary relief angle, called a *clearance angle,* is ground on the shank below the insert of a carbide or ceramic tool. A shaper or planer tool is subject to repeated shocks as it enters the material at the start of its strokes and is given relief angles as small as 4°. In general, relief angles should be small to cut hard materials but may be larger for soft materials. As long as a relief angle is large enough to avoid rubbing, it has no effect upon forces, power, or surface finish.

Rake angles. The rake angle of a tool affects the angle of shear during the formation of a chip. The larger the rake angle, the larger the shear angle and the lower the cutting force and power. A large rake angle is conducive to good surface finish. However, increasing the rake angle decreases the cutting angle and leaves less metal at the point of the tool to support the cutting edge and conduct away the heat. Harder tool materials are generally given smaller rake angles. A practical rake angle represents a compromise between a large angle for easier cutting and a small angle for tool strength. In general, the rake angle is small for cutting hard materials and large for soft ductile materials. An exception is brass which is cut with a small or negative rake angle to keep the tool from digging into the work.

The two conventional components of rake are back rake and side rake, designated by the rake angles of Fig. 16–10. The tool shown is designed to cut on the side-cutting edge, the nose radius, and to some extent on the front-cutting edge. The chip separated by the cutting edges flows along a line Z–Z. The true rake angle is the compound angle in the plane through Z–Z normal to the base of the tool and is determined by both the side and the back rake angles. Side rake is more important than back rate on side cutting tools for turning and similar operations. A steep side rake angle tends to direct the chip to the side away from the tool holder, reduces side deflection of the tool, cuts down the force in the direction of feed, and weakens the tool less than a steep back rake angle. Accordingly, most or all of the rake generally is applied to the side rake of a turning tool. Typical ranges for rake angles are given in Table 16–3.

TABLE 16–3. TYPICAL RAKE ANGLES—DEGREES

Work material	High-speed steel	Nonferrous cast alloys	Cemented carbides
Hard cast iron	5 to 10	0 to 4	−10 to 4
Soft cast iron	8 to 15	0 to 8	−2 to 8
Hard steel	5 to 10	0 to 20	−10 to 3
Soft steel	8 to 20		0 to 4
Aluminum	15 to 40		10 to 20
Brass	−4 to 0		0 to 4

The rake angles shown in Fig. 16–10 are positive. Rake angles measured counterclockwise from zero are called *negative rake angles*. They have been found to give good results on carbide and ceramic tools under certain conditions such as where the tool is subjected to severe shocks from interrupted cuts. A tool with negative rake receives initial impact behind the cutting edge when it starts to cut, and its edge has added material for support. A negative rake angle does increase the cutting forces at lower speeds and gives a poor finish, but carbide tools with negative rake can be run at high speeds where cutting forces drop off. Tests have shown that at such operating speeds, a 7° negative rake angle on carbide tools results in cutting forces and power requirements only 8.4% higher than with zero rake angle.

Cutting edge angles. An end-cutting edge angle gives clearance to the trailing end of the cutting edge and reduces drag that tends to cause chatter. Too large an end-cutting edge angle takes away material that supports the point and conducts away heat. An angle of 8° to 15° has been found satisfactory in most cases for side-cutting tools, like turning and boring tools. Sometimes a flat $\frac{1}{16}$ to $\frac{5}{16}$ in. long is ground on the front edge as shown in Fig. 16–11 so that the edge can get in a wiping action to help produce a good finish. End-cutting tools, like cut off and necking tools, often have no end-cutting edge angle.

A *side-cutting edge* or *lead angle* affects tool life and surface finish. It enables a tool that is fed sideways into a cut to contact the work first behind the tip. A side-cutting edge at an angle has more of its length in action for a definite depth of cut than it would without the angle, and the edge last longer. On the other hand, the larger the angle, the greater the component of force tending to separate the work

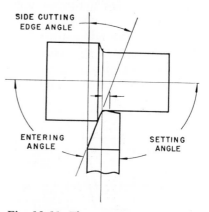

Fig. 16–11. The positioning angles of a tool.

and tool. This promotes chatter. The most satisfactory side-cutting edge angle is generally 15°, although advantage is found in angles as large as 30° to 45° for heavy cuts. No side-cutting edge angle is desirable when cutting castings or forgings with hard and scaly skins because then the least amount of tool edge should be exposed to the destructive action of the skin.

A *nose radius* is favorable to long tool life and good surface finish. A sharp point on the end of a tool is highly stressed, short lived, and leaves a groove in the path of cut. As the nose radius is increased from zero, the improvements in surface finish and permissible cutting speed in represent- ative tests are indicated by Fig. 16–12.

The amount of nose radius than can be put on a tool is limited be- cause too large a radius is conducive

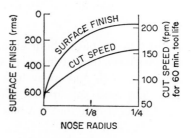

Fig. 16–12. Variations of surface finish and tool life with nose radius of a turning tool.

to chatter. Radii $\frac{1}{64}$ to $\frac{1}{4}$ in. are common but $\frac{1}{32}$ to $\frac{1}{8}$ in. are most often used. The size of a nose radius may be prescribed by the fillet that must be left in the corner at the end of a cut.

The actual effect of the cutting edge angles in practice depends upon the angle to which the shank of the tool is set with respect to the work-piece, as indicated by Fig. 16–11. The entering angle is 180° minus the sum of the side-cutting edge and setting angles.

The physical condition of the cutting edge and face of a tool has a considerable effect upon performance. A tool that is ground so that the cutting edge is jagged will break down quickly. Also, a keen cutting edge and a good finish on the tool face are helpful in minimizing the formation of a built-up edge and promote good surface finish on the workpiece. A good practice is to stone a high-speed steel tool after it is ground to whet the cutting edge and improve the finish of the face. Carbide and ceramic tools are usually finish ground with fine grit diamond wheels. A carbide or ceramic tool for cutting steel may have its edge chamfered or "dubbed" 0.002 to 0.005 in. at 45° by means of a hand hone to remove weak irregu-larities along the edge.

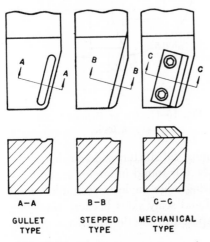

A–A
GULLET TYPE

B–B
STEPPED TYPE

C–C
MECHANICAL TYPE

Fig. 16–13. Three common types of chip breakers.

Chip breakers. A continuous type chip from a long cut can be quite troublesome. Such chips become tangled around the work-piece, tool, and machine members and are dangerous to the operator because they are hot and sharp. At high speeds chips come off fast, often out of control and do not tend to curl. Chip breakers are adjuncts to cutting tools for breaking con-tinuous chips into small pieces for easy disposal as they are formed.

Three common types of chip breakers are shown in Fig. 16–13. The gullet type is a groove and the stepped type an offset, both ground into the rake face of the tool. The former weakens the cutting edge somewhat and is suitable only for mod-erate feeds. Both take away tool material, must be reground when the tool is sharpened, and are not adjustable. Free of these disadvantages is the mechanical type that is a block of hard tool material clamped on the face of the tool.

Tool shapes. Although the elements that have been described are found in all single point cutting tools, they are put together in many ways to satisfy various requirements. Common shapes of tools used for turn-ing, facing, shaping, planing, and boring are illustrated in Fig. 16–14. These are only a few of many varieties.

Some side-cutting tools are designed to cut in one direction, others

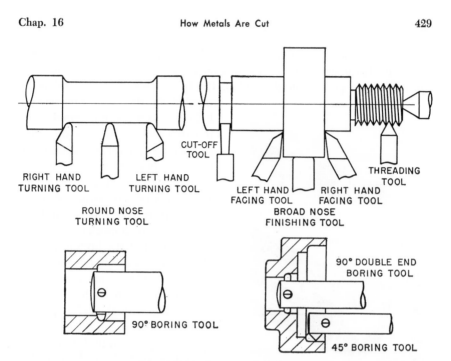

RIGHT HAND
TURNING TOOL

LEFT HAND
TURNING TOOL

CUT-OFF
TOOL

ROUND NOSE
TURNING TOOL

LEFT HAND
FACING TOOL

RIGHT HAND
FACING TOOL

BROAD NOSE
FINISHING TOOL

THREADING
TOOL

90° BORING TOOL

90° DOUBLE END
BORING TOOL

45° BORING TOOL

Fig. 16–14. Common tool shapes.

in another. They are called right-hand or left-hand tools. The hand is revealed when the tool is placed with its nose pointing at an observer. If the cutting edge is on his right side, the tool is a right-hand tool, and vice versa.

Single-point tools. Single-point tools are formed in a number of ways to suit the various kinds of cutting materials. Small pieces of tool material, called bits, are ground on their ends and fastened in toolholders like those in Fig. 16–15. To make a large solid tool, a piece of high-speed steel may be welded on the end of an inexpensive soft steel shank.

Small pieces of expensive cutting materials are commonly brazed, cemented, strapped or clamped onto heavy shanks of soft

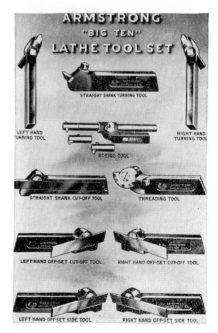

Fig. 16–15. Forged toolholders and bits. (Courtesy Armstrong Bros. Tool Co.)

steel. Tools made in this way are said to be *tipped*. Cemented carbides made in this manner are shown in Fig. 16–16. View A depicts an insert brazed into a pocket on the end of the tool shank. Tips brazed or ce-

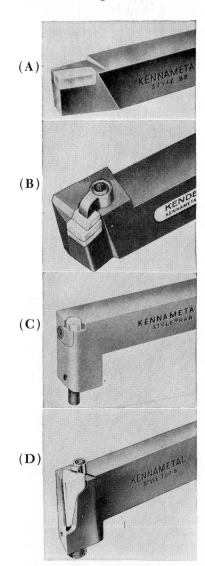

mented in this way are securely held, but as a result of brazing and the different coefficients of expansion of the adjacent materials, inherent stresses may be set up that weaken or crack the tip. In view B a sandwich consisting of a carbide chip breaker, tool bit, and support is held by a mechanical clamp. The support at the bottom is made of cemented carbide because it has a high modulus of elasticity, about 7×10^7, and deflects less than half as much as steel under a load. Eight corners of the bit can be rotated into position and used before the bit needs to be resharpened or discarded. In many cases it is more economical to throw away such bits than to resharpen them. Views C and D show ways of mounting longer inserts in clamp type holders.

A comparison of tool forms. Table 16–4 shows the results of a study made in one plant of the relative costs of three popular types of carbide tools. Type A was a brazed tipped tool with a $\frac{1}{4} \times \frac{9}{16} \times 1$ in. insert and no chip breaker, like the one in Fig. 16–16(A). Type B was a $\frac{1}{4}$ in. thick triangular throwaway bit similar to Fig. 16–16(B). Type C was a $1\frac{1}{2}$ in. long triangular insert clamped as in Fig. 16–16(D). The size of both triangular bits was

Fig. 16–16. Typical cemented carbide tipped tools. (Courtesy Kennametal, Inc.)

designated by a $\frac{3}{8}$ in.-diameter inscribed circle.

Because of their construction, the type A tools are normally ground one at a time. Under these conditions, the throwaway type B bits are more economical. In this plant fixtures were used to sharpen 54 of the long type C clamped inserts at one time by lapping. The results of this study are given to show the nature of the costs involved and the way of making such a study. The results might very well be quite different in another situation, such as one where the need for tools would be much less and would not justify the sharpening of the bits in quantities.

TABLE 16–4. Costs for Three Types of Carbide Cutting Tools

Cost item	Type of tool		
	A	B	C
1. Number of cutting edges per tool	1	6	6
2. Average stock removed per sharpening (in.)	0.030 (one end)	not sharpened	0.060 (two ends)
3. Number of times tool is resharpened	21	0	23
4. Number of tools resharpened at once	1	1 (replaced)	54
5. Number of edges restored at each sharpening (item 1 × item 4)	1	6 (replaced)	324
6. Total number of edges during life of tool [(1 + item 3) × item 5]	22	6	7776
7. Cost of each sharpening operation	$0.75		$6.00
8. Total cost of sharpening (item 3 × item 7)	$15.75		$138.00
9. Average cost of new tools (cost per tool × item 4)	$3.65	$0.90	$270.00
10. Total cost (item 8 + item 9)	$19.40	$0.90	$408.00
11. Cost of each cutting edge (item 10 ÷ item 6)	$0.88	$0.15	$0.053

From "Carbide Inserts + Automatic Lapping = Minimum Tool Cost" by W. C. Thuerwachter in *American Machinist*, May 20, 1957.

Form tools. A form tool has a cutting edge with a definite profile or contour that produces a desired form on the workpiece in the manner indicated in Fig. 16–1(E). A form tool may be made by grinding a profile on the end of an ordinary single-point tool or bit. That is done for small and simple profiles like circular arcs. Two common types for production work are flat and circular form tools (Fig. 16–17).

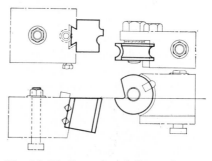

Fig. 16–17. Examples of flat and circular form tools and holders.

A *flat form tool* has a cross section approximating a square or rectangle. The form is along one side and exposed on top. The tool is located and held to the holder by a dovetail, tongue, groove or slot. A *circular form tool* is round and has a cut out segment that exposes the formed cutting edges. It has an axial hole, some plain and some threaded, for mounting on a screw or stud on the holder. Serrations on one side of the hub, locking pins, or keys are added to keep the tool from rotating. Circular form tools are more expensive than flat form tools but last longer.

A *skiving tool* is a type of flat form tool that is fed tangentially past the workpiece to produce a shaving action for finishing cuts.

Form tools are sharpened by grinding the rake face behind the cutting edge. Because of the angles at which a form tool must be ground and positioned, it usually must be designed with a form somewhat different from that desired on the workpiece.

CUTTING FLUIDS

Purpose. Fluids are commonly applied to metal-cutting operations, chiefly to cool the tool and workpiece and to provide lubrication. In some cases little benefit is derived from a cutting fluid, but in most cases increases of 20 to 50%, and sometimes more, in cutting speed is possible with the same tool life when a cutting fluid is used as compared with dry cutting.

A cutting fluid is often called a *coolant,* and cooling is an important function at all cutting speeds but is most important at speeds over 200 fpm. High temperatures are the chief cause of tool wear. An overheated workpiece may warp. Coolants help correct these situations.

Cutting fluids serve to lubricate the chip sliding over the tool face. The evidence is that capillary action tends to draw the fluid in through the natural grinding scratches on the face of the tool, but this is only effective at low speeds. Lubrication reduces friction forces acting on the tool, improving tool life and decreasing power consumption. The tendency to form a built-up edge is decreased by lubrication, and surface finish is improved, but speed is much more effective than cutting fluid in improving finish.

A cutting fluid is useful in cooling and washing away the chips formed in an operation. A fluid also should be capable of lubricating exposed machine elements, prevent corrosion, and not be harmful to the operator.

A cutting fluid is usually flowed in a copious stream on top of the chip and tool. This generally is sufficient at low speeds. A more effective method is to direct the fluid upward between the relief face of the tool and the work surface. This is messy at high speeds if the fluid is squirted in a stream. A better system is to spray a mist of fluid droplets and compressed air into the space between tool and work.

Kinds of cutting fluids. Cutting fluids may be classified as: (1) gases, (2) water solutions, (3) oils, and (4) waxes.

Gases are relatively unimportant cutting fluids. Compressed air is sometimes blown on cast iron being cut. Carbon dioxide released from high pressure and expanded to create low temperatures as it is blown on an operation has limited usage.

Water is the best medium and the most effective fluid for high-speed cutting but has little lubricating value and causes rust and corrosion. Chemical compounds are sometimes added to water to help prevent rust. These may add detergency to the solution but little lubricity and may form harmful deposits on machine slides and bearings.

The most popular cutting fluids are those known as *soluble oils*. These are emulsions of mineral oil with an emulsifier such as soap in water. Mixtures vary from 5 to over 100 parts of water to one of oil. Other compounds are added to give various properties, such as extreme pressure resistance when needed. The mixtures vary in character from heavy solutions with high lubricity and cushioning suitable for heavy turning, milling, broaching, and similar operations to light solutions with little lubricity but high detergency suitable for fine grit grinding and other high-speed operations. The cost of the soluble oil solutions is low.

Three classes of cutting oils not used as emulsions are: (1) straight mineral oils, (2) fixed or fatty oils, and (3) oils that are mixed with other compounds.

Straight mineral oils, have some disadvantages and are not widely used. They have a specific heat about half that of water and a low degree of adhesion or oiliness but are very stable and do not develop disagreeable odors. They range in viscosity from kerosene used on magnesium and aluminum to the light paraffins for free cutting brass.

Fatty oils are oils from which soap can be made. At one time they were almost the only oils used in cutting. One of them, lard oil, is highly regarded for difficult work like threading and tapping. The fatty oils have a high degree of oiliness, adhesion, and penetration and a relatively high specific heat. Their fluidity changes slowly with temperature. However, the fatty oils are expensive, become rancid and odorous, and have a tendency to become gummy or dry when heated. They are used mostly at the present time for compounding cutting oils in which their good qualities are combined with those of mineral oils.

Sulfur and, to a lesser degree, chlorine are mixed with both mineral or fatty and some soluble oils to make *cutting oil compounds* that have high antiweld properties and promote free machining. These compounds play an important part in modern metal-cutting practice, being used extensively on automatic screw machines, gear cutting, broaching, and other high-production operations. They are particularly advantageous for tough, stringy, and unusually soft materials and help in producing good finishes and close tolerances on metals difficult to machine.

Certain *waxes* are adsorbed strongly to metallic surfaces and augment the actions of other ingredients to form cutting fluids having high-pressure and -temperature lubrication properties. It is not easy to incorporate wax successfully in a cutting fluid, and indiscriminate attempts to apply it have failed and given wax a bad reputation as a cutting fluid ingredient in some quarters. Where successful, the results with wax have been rather spectacular, but the applications are limited.

Questions

1. Why is metal cut?

2. How is a surface generated? How is a surface formed?

3. Describe the actions of drilling and milling.

4. What is meant by the cutting speed of an operation? The feed? The depth of cut?

5. Describe what takes place when metal is cut.

6. Name and describe three kinds of chips.

7. Draw a diagram of the forces acting on a chip during its formation.

8. What conditions promote a low coefficient of friction between chip and tool? Why is this desirable?

9. What effect does an increase in cutting speed have upon the heat entering and temperature of a cutting tool?

10. As cutting speed is increased, what happens to the frictional force on the face of the tool, the angle of the shear plane, and the shearing force?

11. What effect does an increase in feed have upon the temperature on a cutting tool face?

12. As feed is increased, what happens to the frictional force on the face of the tool, the angle of the shear plane, and the shearing force?

13. How do the shear plane angle and the shearing force vary with the rake angle of a tool?

14. How is the power required for an operation affected by changes in speed, feed, or depth of cut?

15. In what ways may a tool wear?

16. What is chatter? Why is it harmful?

17. Name and describe the principal cutting tool materials.

18. What determines which cutting tool material is best for an operation?

19. Name in conventional order and describe the angles of a cutting tool.

20. What is the purpose of relief angles?

21. Why are rake angles important? Which is more important, back or side rake?

22. What is the purpose of the front-cutting edge angle? The side-cutting edge angle?

23. Specify the effect upon forces, power consumption, and tool life of each angle and the nose radius of a cutting tool.

24. What is a chip breaker and what purpose does it serve?

25. Describe three types of chip breakers.

26. What are the common shapes of single point tools?

27. What is a form tool? Describe two kinds.

28. What are the purposes of cutting fluids?

29. What are the principal kinds of cutting fluids?

30. How are cutting fluids applied to metal-cutting operations?

Problems

1. Calculate the number of revolutions per minute for each of the following diameters to get the specified cutting speeds.

	a	b	c	d	e	f
Diameter, in.	4	12	7	18	1	9
Cut speed, fpm	60	75	90	100	200	300

2. If each of the following diameters is rotated at the number of revolutions per minute specified for it, what is its surface speed in fpm?

	a	b	c	d	e	f
Diameter, in.	3	18	10	5	7	12
Revolutions per min	230	70	20	160	200	160

3. What is the rate of metal removal for each of the following situations?

	a	b	c
Cut speed, fpm	200	50	350
Feed, ipr	0.010	0.030	0.008
Depth of cut, in.	¼	⅜	0.06

4. In a cutting operation like that depicted in Figs. 16–8 and 16–9, the feed t_1 is 0.004 in. and the chip is found to have a thickness t_2 of 0.010 in. The cutting force F_c is 300 lb and the normal force F_L is 170 lb. The rake angle of the tool is $+10°$. Find:
(a) An approximate value for the shear angle ϕ.
(b) The size of the force R exerted by the tool on the chip.
(c) The coefficient of friction on the face of the tool.
(d) The size of the friction force F_f and the normal force F_n.
(e) The sizes of the shearing force F_s and the normal force F_N.

5. In a cutting operation like that depicted in Figs. 16–8 and 16–9, the feed t_1 is 0.005 in. and the depth of cut normal to the plane of the paper is 0.100 in. The cutting speed is 800 fpm. The cutting force F_c is found to be 400 lb and the normal force F_L 200 lb. The rake angle of the tool is +8°. Find:

   (a) The power required for the cut in hp.

   (b) The rate of metal removal in cu in. per min.

   (c) The unit power in hp per cu in. per min.

6. A workpiece is being cut at 250 fpm, and the power is found to be 2.8 hp. The feed is 0.010 in. per rev and the depth of cut is 0.200 in.

   (a) What is the cutting force in lb?

   (b) What is the unit power consumption in hp per cu in. per min?

7. A shaft 64 in. long and 4 in. in diameter is turned from tough steel having a hardness of 22 to 26 Rc. With a high-speed steel tool the speed is 78 fpm, the feed 0.020 ipr, and the depth of cut 0.050 in. The tool must be ground four times before it finishes one shaft and can be ground forty times before being discarded. The cost of a tool bit is $0.65. It takes ten minutes to grind and replace the tool bit.

   A sintered oxide tool bit with 6 edges and costing $2.90 is put on the job. After all six edges are dull, this bit is not sharpened but is thrown away. It cuts with a speed of 295 fpm, a feed of 0.020 ipr, and a depth of cut of 0.050 in. Two edges must be used to cut one shaft.

   The cost for labor and overhead in the shop is $8 per hr. Which tool is the more economical?

8. A workpiece of SAE 4340 steel (300 Bhn) is rough turned for a distance of 18 in. with a stock removal of 0.435 in. on a side of a 5½ in.-diameter.

   With high-speed steel tools, the speed is 80 fpm and feed 0.012 ipr. The tool must be resharpened for each piece. The tool costs $0.80 and can be reground 40 times. Time for sharpening the tool is 30 min for each piece.

   A cemented carbide tool costs $2.74 and can be ground 10 times. It is operated at 330 fpm with a feed of 0.024 in. per rev. It can turn 10 pieces before having to be sharpened, but the time to sharpen and reset it is 100 min. The labor and overhead rate is $6 per hr. Which tool is the more economical for the job?

9. A workpiece has a hardness of 34 to 36 Rockwell C and is turned on the end to a diameter of 1.810 in. from a 2½ in.-diameter for a length of 5.530 in.

   A brazed carbide insert tool has been making the cut on production at 215 fpm with a feed of 0.011 in. per rev. Fifty pieces are obtained between tool grinds. The tool can be reground four times and costs $6.26 new. Each grind costs $1.

   A throwaway replaceable insert tool is tried on the job. Because the tip is free from brazing strains, this tool can be operated at 300 fpm with a 0.015 in. feed and completes 60 pieces per cutting edge. Three edges are available. Each insert costs $2.30, and the holder which lasts for 10 inserts costs $17.50.

Can the use of throwaway replaceable inserts be justified on this operation where the labor and overhead rate is $5 per hr?

References

American Society of Tool Engineers, *The Tool Engineers Handbook,* McGraw-Hill Book Co., Inc., New York.

Boston, O. W., *Metal Processing,* John Wiley and Sons, Inc., New York, 1951.

17

Economics of Metal Cutting

The efficiency of a metal-cutting operation can be judged from three main standpoints of: (1) the life of the cutting tool, (2) forces and power, and (3) surface finish and dimensional accuracy. The first two criteria determine costs. The third is concerned with the results obtained. Economy is achieved in an operation when the necessary results are obtained at the lowest possible cost within the period of time desired.

The factors within an operation that may be varied to change the costs and results are: (1) speed, (2) feed and depth of cut, (3) work material, (4) tool material, (5) tool form and shape, and (6) cutting fluid. The nature and effects of the last three of these have been discussed in Chap. 16. The first three will be dealt with in the following pages.

CUTTING SPEED

Speed and tool life. Tests with many materials under many conditions have shown that tool life is shorter, the higher the cutting speed. In most cases this follows the relationship that

$$VT^n = C. \tag{17-1}$$

In this expression, V stands for the cutting speed in feet per minute and T for the tool life in minutes. C is a constant that is different for each change in work material, tool material, tool form and shape, size and shape of cut, and cutting fluid. The exponent n also varies with the same changes, but for any tool and work material combination n has a value that does not vary much with changes in the other factors.

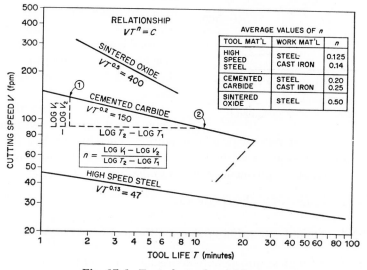

Fig. 17–1. Typical speed-tool life curves.

Expression (17–1) is a straight line when plotted on log–log coordinates, as shown for several typical cases in Fig. 17–1. The exponent n is the slope of the line. Approximate values of n for several average conditions are tabulated. The constant C has the same value as the cutting speed for a one minute tool life in each case. Each line in Fig. 17–1 represents a specific set of conditions. If any of the conditions changes, the situation would be represented by a new line. These are empirical curves that have been found to apply within the usual range of cutting speeds, but at times the trend is in a different direction at low or high speeds for a tool material, as indicated by the broken line at one end of the curve for cemented carbide. Values for C and n have been determined for many specific conditions and are given in reference- and handbooks. If such information is not available for a specific operation, tool life can be measured at several cutting speeds and the points plotted and connected by a line to obtain the necessary data.

Economical tool life. The tool life vs speed relationship does not alone tell what the speed should be for an operation. What must also be taken into account is the cost of operating at various speeds. As depicted in Fig. 17–2, when the cutting speed is low, tools last a long time and

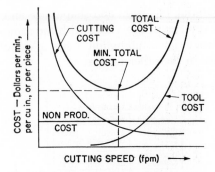

Fig. 17–2. The elements of cost in a metal cutting operation.

tool cost is low. At the same time metal removal is slow, and the cutting cost and total cost are high. On the other hand, at high speed cutting cost is low, but tool cost is high and makes the total cost high. At some intermediate cutting speed, the total cost is at a minimum. The tool life corresponding to this cutting speed is the economical tool life.

An easy way to find the economical tool life is to consider the costs in terms of minutes expended in cutting. Each minute has a certain cost, so the results are consistent. On this basis, the tool cost can be expressed in minutes equivalent to cutting minutes, as follows:

(a) t_1 = minutes to change the tool

(b) t_2 = minutes to grind or sharpen the tool = $\dfrac{t_s \times R_s}{N_2 \times R_c}$

(c) t_3 = minutes equivalent to depreciation cost of tool

$$= \frac{C_T}{N_1 \times N_2 \times R_c}.$$

In the preceding equations, t_s = tool grinding time in minutes; R_s = labor and overhead rate in the tool grinding department in dollars per minute; R_c = labor and overhead rate applied to the metal-cutting operation in dollars per minute; C_T = original cost of the cutting tool in dollars; N_1 = the number of times the tool can be ground (including once when the tool is made); and N_2 = number of cutting edges obtained per grind.

The total equivalent minutes required to replace the tool when it becomes dull are $t = t_1 + t_2 + t_3$.

The amount of metal in cubic inches cut during the life of a tool is

$$Q_T = 12VTfd \tag{17-2}$$

where f = feed which is equivalent to the width of cut in inches, and d = depth of cut in inches.

The total time chargeable to the operation during the life of one tool is $T + t$. Thus the rate of metal removal in cubic inches per chargeable minute is

$$R = \frac{Q_T}{T+t} = \frac{12VTfd}{T+t} = \frac{12CT^{1-n}fd}{T+t} \tag{17-3}$$

The total cost for the operation is at a minimum when the maximum cubic inches of material are removed per chargeable minute. This condition can be found from an operation of the calculus expressed as $\frac{dR}{dT} = 0$ in which all factors except T and R are considered constant. A calculation made in this way results in the expression for economical tool life in minutes

$$T_m = \left(\frac{1}{n} - 1\right)t \tag{17-4}$$

The cutting speed that corresponds to the economical tool life can be found from Formula (17-1). That is the speed at which the operation should be run for lowest total cost.

If the tools are ground away from the machine and cutting is stopped only to replace tools, the tool life that gives the maximum rate of production (a certain amount of production in the shortest time without regard to cost) is

$$T_b = \left(\frac{1}{n} - 1\right)t_1 \tag{17-5}$$

As an example, the labor and overhead rate for an operation is $0.121 per min. Tool changing time is ½ min; labor and overhead rate for tool grinding is $0.133 per min; time to grind a tool is 15 min; a tool costs $5.23 and can be ground 8 times; and 8 cutting edges are obtained from each grind. The tool is 78B cemented carbide; the work material SAE 4340 steel; and $VT^{0.2} = 544$ applies. At what speed should the operation be run to obtain the economical tool life? What tool life and speed will give the maximum rate of production?

The equivalent minutes of tool cost

$$t = 0.5 + \frac{15 \times 0.133}{8 \times 0.121} + \frac{5.23}{8 \times 8 \times 0.121}$$

$$= 0.5 + 2.066 + 0.675 = 3.241 \text{ min.}$$

$$T_m = \left(\frac{1}{0.2} - 1\right) 3.241 = 13 \text{ min.}$$

$$V_m = \frac{544}{13^{0.2}} = 325 \text{ fpm.}$$

and

$$T_b = \left(\frac{1}{0.2} - 1\right) 0.5 = 2 \text{ min.}$$

$$V_b = \frac{544}{2^{0.2}} = 472 \text{ fpm.}$$

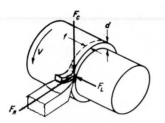

Fig. 17–3. The forces acting on
a turning tool.

Speed vs forces, powers and surface finish. The three components of force acting on a turning tool are shown in Fig. 17–3. The cutting force F_c acts in the direction of the speed, V, at the tool point and the resulting power accounts for over 95% of that normally consumed in the cut. The feed movement in the direction of F_L is small and there is no motion in the direction of F_R in this case.

The cutting force F_C generally decreases as speed is raised above 100 fpm and power declines accordingly, but the decrease is usually less than 15% within ordinary operating speed ranges. Any saving in power that might be realized by changing speed is normally insignificant as compared to the main labor and overhead operating costs.

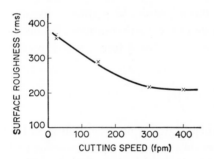

Fig. 17–4. Average values of surface finish obtained on 5 materials at various cutting speeds.

As speed is increased, the built-up edge on the face of a cutting tool gets smaller and at a sufficiently high speed disappears, improving surface finish. The actual improvement in any case depends upon the material and other conditions of the cut. An indication of the trend in the case of several tests is given in Fig. 17–4. Because good surface finish is one of the aims of finishing cuts, such cuts generally are taken at higher speeds than heavier roughing cuts. In the case of a finishing cut, the surface finish obtained may be a more important consideration than the very lowest cost.

Practical operating speeds. For ordinary turning operations the economical tool life generally is ½ to 1½ hr. The economical cutting speed for any operation depends upon a number of factors, as has been shown, and is not likely to be identical for any two operations. Only when production is high is it worthwhile to make a study to ascertain the economical cutting speed for an operation. If only a few pieces of a kind are to be produced, a study might well cost more than could be saved on the job. As a rule, speeds within a reasonable range will give results close to those of the most economical cutting speed. For general practice, tables in reference- and hand-books are used. They specify cutting speeds that have been found economical under various conditions and can be used as a starting point in setting up an operation. The operator then may try higher or lower speeds as the job progresses to see if he gets better results. An example of a few such typical recommendations is given by Table 17–1.

TABLE 17–1. TYPICAL RECOMMENDATIONS FOR CUTTING SPEEDS

Surface Speed for Turning (ft per min)

Workpiece material	H.S.S.	Tool material Cemented carbide	Sintered oxide
Aluminum	280–920	420–1380	1000–4000
Yellow brass	80–310	175– 625	2000–3000
Cast iron:			
(160–180 Bhn)	40–130	120– 390	750–1000
Steel:			
1020	60– 90	140– 350	600–1000
x1112	75–160	250– 630	1000–1500
1040	45– 85	135– 350	600– 900
A2340	25– 70	110– 275	475– 550

FEED AND DEPTH OF CUT

Effect on tool life. Experiments have shown that the constant C of Formula (17–1) varies with feed and depth of cut in the empirical manner of

$$C = C_1/d^x f^y \qquad (17\text{–}6)$$

for many materials. C_1 is a constant that depends mainly upon work material and the tool. Exponents x and y vary somewhat with work material and tool, but O. W. Boston has found that for average conditions $x = 0.37$ and $y = 0.77$. Kronenberg has reported an average value of the exponent n in Formula (17–1) to be $\frac{1}{6}$. If these values are applied and Eqs. (17–1) and (17–6) are combined, the resulting expression is

$$VT^{1/6} = C_1/d^{0.37}\, f^{0.77}. \qquad (17\text{–}7)$$

As has been shown, the economical tool life depends upon the constant n and the tool costs and does not change appreciably as f and d are changed. Thus the factor T in Eq. (17–7) is considered a constant for practical illustration. Therefore, Eq. (17–7) shows that when f or d, or both, are increased or decreased in an operation, V must be decreased or increased accordingly to maintain an economical tool life. This is illustrated here by average figures for an average condition. The figures would be a little different in any specific case, but the relationships would be the same. This should be kept in mind throughout this discussion.

TABLE 17-2. VALUES OF C_1 FOR EQ. (17-7)

Work material	Conditions of cut	
	Dry	Cutting fluid
Aluminum	50.0	. . .
Brass	13.4	. . .
Cast iron:		
100 Bhn	4.4	6.0
200 Bhn	1.6	2.2
Cast steel	3.0	4.2
Steel:		
1015	6.0	8.4
1025	4.8	6.6
1035	3.8	5.4
1045	3.0	4.2
1060	2.0	2.8
Chrome-nickel alloy	3.2	4.6

The values given are for 18-4-1 H.S.S. For cemented carbide multiply by 4 for an average of C_1. These data are adapted from those given by N. E. Woldman and R. C. Gibbons, *Machinability and Machining of Metals*, McGraw-Hill Book Co., Inc., New York, 1951.

The effect that changes in the feed and depth of cut have upon the efficiency of metal removal of an operation can be appraised from Formula (17-2). If the V of Expression (17-7) is substituted in that equation,

$$Q_T = 12 \ C_1 \ Tfd/T^{1/6} \ d^{0.37} \ f^{0.77} = 12 \ C_1 \ T^{5/6} \ f^{0.23} \ d^{0.63}. \quad (17\text{-}8)$$

This relationship reveals a basic law of metal machining, that *as feed or depth of cut* (f or d), *or both, are increased and the cutting speed is decreased to keep the tool life substantially constant, the amount of material removed during the life of the tool and consequently the amount of material cut during each productive minute goes up.* Furthermore, since the exponent for d is larger, an increase in the depth of cut will produce a larger increase of material removal than the same proportionate increase in feed. Thus deep cuts with light feeds are more efficient than shallow cuts with heavy feeds, from the standpoint of tool life.

Practical considerations limit the actual amount of feed or depth of cut in an operation. The depth of cut cannot exceed the stock to be removed. Heavy cuts set up large tool forces, and these are limited by what the workpiece, tool, and material can stand. Heavier cuts call for more power, which can only be supplied up to the capacity of the machine. Heavy cuts cause poor surface finish, and cannot be tolerated if the surface finish must be good, as usually it must be in a final cut,

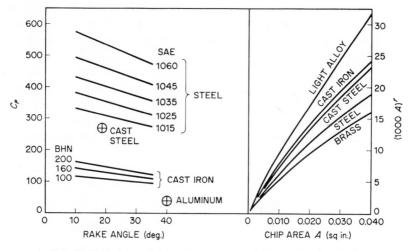

Fig. 17–5. Values of constants in equation $F_c = C_p (1000A)^r$ (Kronenberg).

Forces and power. The chip cross-sectional area, A, which is the product of feed times depth of cut, chiefly determines the size of the cutting force for a given material. The shape of the chip, defined by the ratio of feed to depth of cut, is relatively unimportant. Kronenberg has given the expression for pounds for cutting force

$$F_c = C_p(1000A)^r. \qquad (17\text{–}9)$$

Values for C_p and $(1000A)^r$ for a number of conditions are given in Fig. 17–5. This formula is convenient for estimating cutting force and power, but the influence of feed and depth of cut is revealed more by the relationship of average conditions found by Boston that

$$F_c = C_f\ d^{0.9}\ f^{0.8}. \qquad (17\text{–}10)$$

If this and Eq. (17–7) are substituted in the basic equation for horse-power,

$$P = F_c\ V/33{,}000 = (C_f\ d^{0.9}\ f^{0.8}/33{,}000)(C_1/T^{1/6}\ d^{0.37}\ f^{0.77})$$
$$= C_2\ d^{0.53}\ f^{0.03}. \qquad (17\text{–}11)$$

The constant C_2 is a collection of all the constants, including the tool life, which is held constant at its most economical value.

Unit power, in hp per cu in. per min, is

$$P_u = P/12Vdf = C_3/d^{0.1}\ f^{0.2}. \qquad (17\text{–}12)$$

The relationships (17–10), (17–11), and (17–12) show that the cutting force increases with feed or depth of cut, more with depth of cut than with feed, but less than proportionately in either case. For a constant tool life, power increases moderately with increases in depth of cut but almost not at all with increase in feed. The unit horsepower decreases moderately as either feed or depth of cut, or both, are increased. It must be remembered that these stipulations are based upon the premise that cutting speed is adjusted always to maintain economical tool life when other factors are varied. As was pointed out in Chap. 16, changes in cutting speed usually cause only small changes in cutting forces. Thus, the general rule is that heavy cuts are more efficient than light cuts from a power as well as a tool life standpoint but require adequate strength in workpiece and tools, and rigidity and power in the machine.

As an example of an estimate of requirements for an operation, it is assumed that a piece of 1035 steel is to be turned at 330 fpm. The machine has a 10 hp motor and efficiency of 75%. Then 7½ hp can be expected at the tool point, and $F_c = \dfrac{7.5 \times 33,000}{330} = 750$ lb. The question then might be, what feed can be used with a depth of cut of ¼ in.? From Fig. 17–5 and Formula (17–9), A is found to be 0.0025 in.² $= f \times ¼$, and $f = 0.010$ in. per rev.

As another example, a cut in 160 Bhn cast iron is to be taken at 220 fpm with a ⅜ in. depth of cut and a feed of 0.025 ipr. What should be the power of the machine? A rake angle of 10° is assumed. From Fig. 17–5, $F_c = 145 \times 6.9 = 1000$ lb, $P = \dfrac{1000 \times 220}{33,000} = 6.67$ hp at the tool point. For 75% machine efficiency, the machine should have a motor rated at least 9 hp.

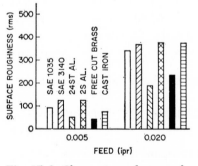
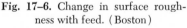

Fig. 17–6. Change in surface roughness with feed. (Boston)

Surface finish. A heavy feed is conducive to formation of a built-up edge and a rough surface finish. Figure 17–6 shows the surface roughness reported for several materials cut at a light and heavy feed. In the same tests, each feed was taken at three depths of cut; 0.010, $\frac{1}{16}$, and ⅛ in. At the light feed there was little difference in surface roughness at the three depths, but at the heavier feed, the surface roughness measured about 25% more at the ⅛ in. than at the 0.010 in. depth of cut. Feed seems to affect surface quality much more than depth of cut. Fine feeds and light cuts are necessary for the best surface finishes.

Practical feeds and depths of cut. As has been shown, the proper feed and depth of cut for an operation depends upon a number of factors and no recommendation can be made to cover all cases, but some indication of starting points can be given for turning, boring, and related operations. The depth of cut for finishing is generally 0.010 to 0.030 in., but for roughing may be as much as ½ in. and even more up to the limit of the tool and stock available. Feeds from 0.005 to 0.015 ipr are generally used for finishing, but they may be larger with broad nose tools. Feeds for roughing are usually as coarse as the workpiece, tool, and machine will stand. When the depth of cut does not exceed ¼ in., a feed of 0.015 to 0.040 ipr may be selected. For greater depths, a feed of 0.010 to 0.020 ipr may be used.

WORK MATERIAL

The word *machinability* has been used in many ways to describe properties of materials when they are cut. Probably its most common meaning is that it signifies how much force and power are required to remove stock from a material. In another sense, machinability has been used to signify how long a cutting tool lasts with one material as compared with others under standardized conditions. This is probably better termed *abrasiveness*. A third meaning implies how well a material takes on a good finish, and for that the term of *finishability* has been suggested.

One way of designating how easy or hard materials are to machine is to rate them on the basis of tests with respect to a standard. A rating of that kind for a few materials is given in Table 17–3.

TABLE 17–3. Machinability Ratings of a Number of Metals

Class I, Ferrous, rating over 70%

Material specs.	C1110	C1117	C1120	C1137	C1016	B1112	A4023	A4119
Hardness (Bhn)	137–166	143–179	143–179	187–229	137–174	179–229	156–207	170–217
Rating	85	85	80	70	70	100	70	70

Class II, Ferrous, rating 50 to 65%

Material specs.	C1141	C1020	C1040	A3120	A4032	A5120	NE8024
Hardness (Bhn)	183–241	137–174	179–229	163–207	170–229	170–212	174–217
Rating	65	65	60	60	65	65	60

Class III, Ferrous, rating 40 to 50%; Class IV, Ferrous, rating under 40%

Material specs.	A1320	A2330	A6120	A2515	Stainless 18-8	H.S.S.
Hardness (Bhn)	170–229	179–229	179–217	179–229		
Rating	50	50	50	30	25	30

Class V, Nonferrous, rating over 100%; Class VI, Nonferrous, rating under 100%

Material specs.	Mg. Alloys	2S Al.	Yellow brass	Mng. bronze	Monel cast metal	Inconel
Rating	500–2000	300–1500	200	40	35	45

This table condensed from the complete *Machinability Rating Tables* of the Independent Research Committee on Cutting Fluids. Machinability to the nearest 5% rating is based on 100% rating for AISI steel B1112, cold-rolled or cold-drawn Bessemer screw stock, machined with suitable cutting fluid at 180 fpm under normal conditions as to tool life and surface finish. Hardness values indicate a desirable range.

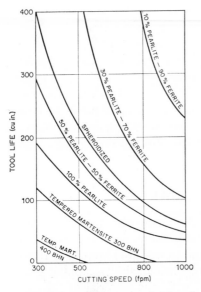

Fig. 17-7. Effect on tool life of various structures in a hypothetical steel as the result of various kinds of heat treatment. The basic forms of heat treatment and their effects are described in Chapter 5. (This chart indicates results from a study of machinability prepared by Curtiss-Wright Corp. for the U. S. Air Force.)

A wide range of machinability may be found among varieties of any one class of material. For instance, steels with different amounts of alloying elements have different properties, but even a steel with a specific chemical composition may vary greatly in machinability as it is heat treated in one way or another. In general, machining is more difficult the harder and tougher the material, but this does not alone determine how easily steel may be machined. The sizes of the metallic grains, the structure, and the proportions of the constituents are also important factors. An illustration is given in Fig 17-7 of the effect of various structures upon machinability as reflected by tool life vs cutting speed with all other variables held constant. Similar conditions apply also to other materials.

The properties of a metal desirable for long tool life and low power consumption are not always best for good surface finish. When most steels are raised to a red heat and cooled slowly, they are annealed. That makes them soft with a grain structure easy to cut, but a better finish is usually obtained if the metal is treated to make it harder.

The properties wanted in the material of a finished article often are not those desirable for good machinability. A finished part may be expected to have higher strength or be quite hard. Common practice is to anneal or normalize alloy steel parts in the rough, remove most of the stock by machining, heat treat again to get the desired properties for the finished product, and finish the surfaces by grinding when required.

Various elements are added to metals specifically to make them easy to machine. Such compositions are said to be *free machining* or *free cutting*. They permit high cutting speeds with long tool life, well broken up chips, and smooth and accurate finishes. Moderate amounts of sulfur or lead are added to steel to make it free cutting. These additions form inclusions that weaken the structure of the metal to some extent and necessitate some sacrifice of strength in the finished part. Nickel and molybdenum are added to cast iron, small amounts of selenium to stainless steel, lead to brass and bronze, and copper-lead and bismuth to aluminum to improve machinability.

COMPUTING AIDS

The relationships among the variables that determine the economy of metal cutting are charted in the monograph of Fig. 17–9. The example worked out on the chart explains its use. The chart is based upon an assumed power increase of 35% for dull tools, as compared with newly ground tools. Power consumption is charted only for plain-carbon steel. Heavy feeds generally are called for by solutions given by the chart and may have to be compromised in some cases to conform to the strengths of the workpieces, tools, and machines.

Fig. 17–8. Carboloy Machinability Computer. (Courtesy Carboloy Department of General Electric Co.)

A commercial electric calculator depicted in Fig. 17–8 is available for quick and easy computation of the relationships of the types just explained. This computer has electrical circuits comparable to the scales of the chart of Fig. 17–9. The values of the variables are set on dials which determine the characteristics of the circuits. When proper conditions are reached, the balancing of the circuits is shown on the meter at the top center of the computer panel.

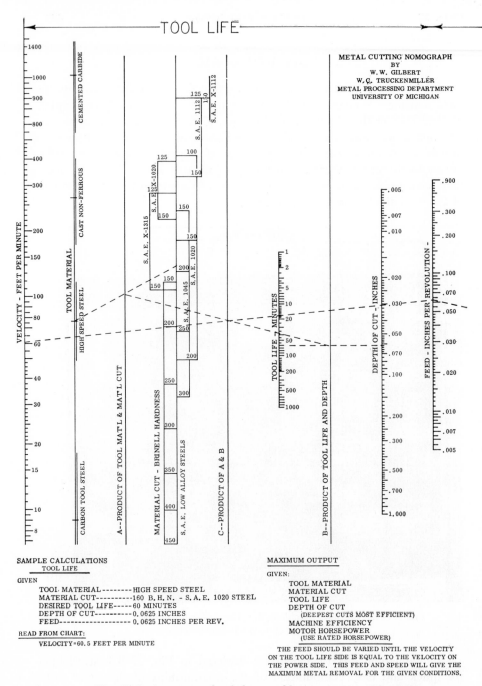

SAMPLE CALCULATIONS
TOOL LIFE

GIVEN

TOOL MATERIAL --------HIGH SPEED STEEL
MATERIAL CUT----------160 B. H. N. - S. A. E. 1020 STEEL
DESIRED TOOL LIFE-----60 MINUTES
DEPTH OF CUT----------0.0625 INCHES
FEED------------------0.0625 INCHES PER REV.

READ FROM CHART:

VELOCITY=60.5 FEET PER MINUTE

MAXIMUM OUTPUT

GIVEN:

TOOL MATERIAL
MATERIAL CUT
TOOL LIFE
DEPTH OF CUT
(DEEPEST CUTS MOST EFFICIENT)
MACHINE EFFICIENCY
MOTOR HORSEPOWER
(USE RATED HORSEPOWER)

THE FEED SHOULD BE VARIED UNTIL THE VELOCITY
ON THE TOOL LIFE SIDE IS EQUAL TO THE VELOCITY ON
THE POWER SIDE. THIS FEED AND SPEED WILL GIVE THE
MAXIMUM METAL REMOVAL FOR THE GIVEN CONDITIONS.

Fig. 17–9. A monograph of the variables in turning with single
point tools. This chart is based upon the assumption of cutting steel
dry. Cutting speeds may be increased 15 to 30% by means of soluble cutting oils and 10 to 25% by straight cutting oils.

450

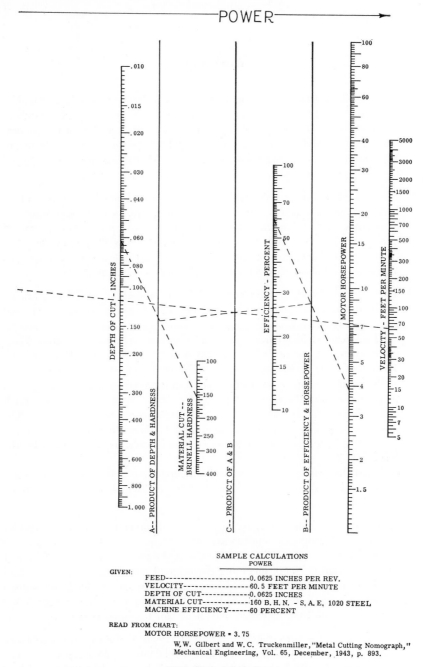

POWER →

DEPTH OF CUT - INCHES

A -- PRODUCT OF DEPTH & HARDNESS

MATERIAL CUT --
BRINELL HARDNESS

C -- PRODUCT OF A & B

EFFICIENCY - PERCENT

B -- PRODUCT OF EFFICIENCY & HORSEPOWER

MOTOR HORSEPOWER

VELOCITY - FEET PER MINUTE

SAMPLE CALCULATIONS
POWER

GIVEN:

FEED----------------------0.0625 INCHES PER REV.
VELOCITY----------------60.5 FEET PER MINUTE
DEPTH OF CUT------------0.0625 INCHES
MATERIAL CUT------------160 B.H.N. - S.A.E, 1020 STEEL
MACHINE EFFICIENCY------60 PERCENT

READ FROM CHART:

MOTOR HORSEPOWER = 3.75

W.W. Gilbert and W.C. Truckenmiller, "Metal Cutting Nomograph,"
Mechanical Engineering, Vol. 65, December, 1943, p. 893.

Fig. 17–9 (Cont.)

The chart is drawn for a single point tool of shape 8–14–6–6–6–15–3/64. If the best tool is used for each type of material, performance can be expected to be better than that calculated from the chart.

Problems

1. A bar of SAE 1035 steel is being turned on a lathe with a H.S.S. tool of the shape of 8-14-6-6-6-6-$\frac{1}{32}$ at a feed of 0.0127 in. per rev and a depth of cut of 0.050 in. It was found experimentally that a tool life of 60 minutes could be obtained at a cutting speed of 82.8 ft per min and a tool life of 120 minutes at a cutting speed of 76.6 fpm. What cutting speeds should be used to obtain tool lives of 30, 90, and 150 min?

2. When the tool taking the cut described in Prob. 1 reaches the end of its life, the operator takes it from the machine, sharpens it, and resets it. This takes him five minutes. The tool costs $0.80 new and can be ground altogether 20 times. The labor and overhead rate is $8 per hr. What is the economical tool life for the tool, and at what speed should it be run? What speed will give the fastest overall rate of metal removal?

3. Two cemented carbide tools are tried for an operation. One has a brazed insert and is designated as tool A. The other has a replaceable clamped insert and is called tool B.

   Tool A costs $2.65 new and can be ground a total of 6 times. Each grind gives one cutting edge and takes 5½ minutes at $0.133 per min. To change tools on the machine takes 2 minutes at $0.121 per min.

   The clamped insert of tool B has 8 cutting edges and can be put in place and rotated to a new edge in ½ minute at $0.121 per min. Each grind restores the 8 edges and takes 15 minutes at $0.133 per min. The insert costs $5.23 new and can be ground 8 times altogether.

   The tool life-speed characteristics of both tools are represented by the formula $V\ T^{0.2} = 550$.

   Find the economic tool life and corresponding cutting speed for each. When each tool is run at its economic speed, which does the job more cheaply?

4. A cemented carbide tool is turning a 2 in.-diameter by 6 in.-long cylinder of alloy steel under the conditions that depth of cut is ⅛ in., feed is 0.015 ipr, and $V\ T^{0.2} = 500$. The time to change the tool is one minute. The cost to grind a tool is $0.60, including the original cost of the tool. Labor and overhead is $3.60 per hr or $0.06 per min. The time to load and unload the workpiece is one minute. What is the minium cost per piece? What is the minimum time in which one piece can be done, regardless of cost?

5. It is decided to remove metal at a rate of 1.5 cu in./min from a workpiece with a depth of cut of 0.100 in. and a feed of 0.0125 in. per rev. The material is SAE 1025 steel and is cut dry. What should be the tool life? To what extent would the tool life be increased if the depth of cut were changed to 0.200 in. and the metal removal rate and feed were kept the same?

6. A 4¼ in.-diameter bar of SAE 1020 steel is being turned on an engine lathe with a high-speed steel tool at a speed of 100 fpm. At a feed of ⅟₃₀ in. per rev and a depth of cut of ⅛ in., the cutting force was found to be 730 lb. What horsepower is needed for this cut?

7. When the feed rate for the cut described in Prob. 6 was changed to ⅟₁₂₀ in. per rev and all other conditions remained the same, the cutting force was found to be 360 lb. What horsepower should be needed for a feed of 0.010 ipr?

8. To make a cut, feeds of 0.010, 0.015, 0.020, 0.030, and 0.040 in. per rev are available. The material is SAE 1035 steel, cut with a rake angle of 20°. The diameter of the 4 in.-diameter workpiece is to be reduced to 3 in., but not necessarily in one cut. Cutting speed will be 90 fpm. The machine has a 20 hp motor and a 75% efficiency. What should be the depth of cut, and how many cuts are required?

9. Given the following conditions for an operation:
   (a) Cemented carbide tool
   (b) Work material, SAE low-alloy steel with Bhn 300
   (c) Desired tool life 30 min
   (d) Depth of cut ⅜ in.
   (e) Machine efficiency 75%
   (f) Motor horsepower 15 hp.
   Find the proper speed and feed at which to operate from the nomograph of Fig. 17–9.

10. If in the operation described in Prob. 9 it is desired to raise the feed to 0.025 ipr and keep all other conditions except the power and speed constant, what motor horsepower would then be required? At what work surface speed?

References

Conn, Harry, "Optimation," *Automatic Machining*, May, 1957.

Woldman, N. E., and R. C. Gibbons, *Machinability and Machining of Metals*, McGraw-Hill Book Co., Inc., New York, 1951.

Turning

TURNING OPERATIONS

Small and medium size workpieces usually are turned around a horizontal axis. Turning operations may be divided into two classes; those done with the workpiece between centers and those done with the workpiece chucked or gripped at one end with or without support at the outer end.

Plain or straight turning. The principal kinds of operations done on work between centers are indicated in Fig. 18–1. The workpiece is driven by a dog clamped on one end. If work is to be done on both ends, the dog is clamped on each in turn, and the workpiece is reversed in position.

A workpiece held between centers deflects less under a given force than if held at only one end. Also, a workpiece runs true on good centers, and several diameters cut at the same or at different times are the most likely to be concentric if turned on centers.

To be turned on centers, a workpiece must have a center hole at each end. These holes have 60° conical bearing surfaces and are cut with a combination center drill and countersink, as in Fig. 18–2. This may be done with the workpiece chucked on a lathe or on a center drilling machine like a horizontal drill press.

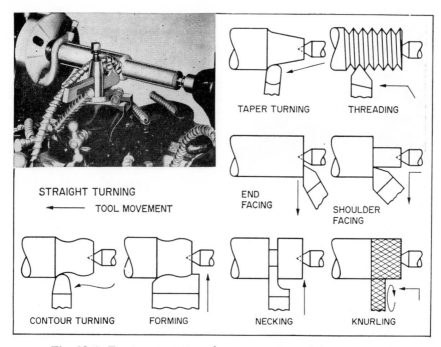

Fig. 18–1. Turning operations between centers. (Photo Courtesy
South Bend Lathe Works.)

Chuck work. When a workpiece is chucked,
the same operation can be done on it as between
centers. In addition, parting or cut off and internal operations can be done, like those illustrated in Fig. 18–3. The types of tools described
in Chap. 22 for drilling and related operations
are used to machine holes in chuck work.

Taper turning and boring. As illustrated in
Figs. 16–1 and 16–2, turning produces not only
straight, but also tapered outside and inside surfaces. A taper may be designated by the angle
between opposite sides or by the increase in diameter along the length, in inches per foot. Certain tapers are standard. The *Morse taper* found
on drilling machines and some lathes is approximately ⅝ in. per ft. Sizes are designated by
whole numbers from 0 through 7. No. 0 is the
smallest with a diameter of 0.356 in. at the large

Fig. 18–2. A combi-
nation center drill and
countersink. (Courtesy
Chicago-Latrobe Twist
Drill Works.)

end and a nominal length of 2 in. No. 7 has a large diameter of 3.270
in. and a length of 10 in. Other tapers used on lathes are the *Reed* and
Jarno tapers, each of 0.600 in. per ft.

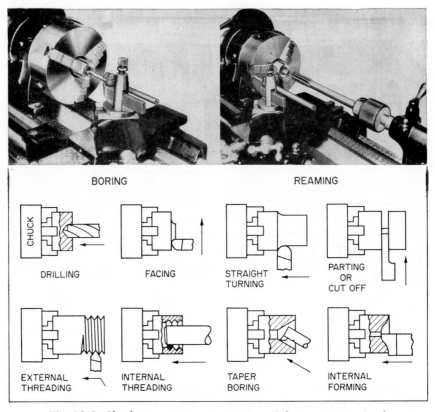

BORING   REAMING

CHUCK

DRILLING   FACING   STRAIGHT TURNING   PARTING OR CUT OFF

EXTERNAL THREADING   INTERNAL THREADING   TAPER BORING   INTERNAL FORMING

Fig. 18–3. Chucking operation in turning. (Photo courtesy South Bend Lathe Works.)

Three methods of generating tapers by off-setting the tailstock, swivelling the compound rest, and use of a taper attachment will be described when the equipment is discussed. Tapers may also be form cut, but the length of cut must be kept small so the force between tool and work does not become excessive.

THE LATHE

The basic machine tool on which turning operations are done is the lathe. A typical modern lathe of medium size is illustrated in Fig. 18–4. The diagram of Fig. 18–5 delineates the principal parts and movements of the lathe.

Principal parts of lathes. A lathe is built around a *bed,* made massive and rigid to resist deflection and vibration. On top of the bed at the left is the *headstock* that carries a revolving *spindle.* A lathe spindle is

Fig. 18–4. A modern 20 in. completely geared engine lathe. (Courtesy The Monarch Machine Tool Co.)

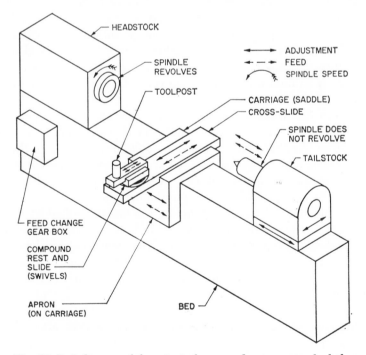

Fig. 18–5. A diagram of the principal parts and movements of a lathe.

hollow to take long barstock, and the diameter of the hole determines the largest size barstock that can be passed through the spindle for chucking. The spindle hole has a definite taper at the front end to receive tapered center and tool shanks. The *nose* or end of the spindle has true locating surfaces for positioning a chuck, as shown in Fig. 18–3, a faceplate, or a dog plate as in Fig. 18–1. The chuck or plate is held on by bolts or some similar means.

The workpiece is driven by the headstock spindle. Present day lathes have individual motor drives, usually of constant speed. Most of them have geared headstocks like the one in Fig. 18–4. The drive from the motor to the spindle goes through several gear combinations that are shifted by means of levers or dials on the outside of the headstock to change spindle speeds. On some small lathes, the drive from the motor to the spindle is through a belt and step pulleys to get several spindle speeds. In addition, a set of reduction gears may be engaged to get a lower series of speeds.

The *tailstock* is on the other end of the bed from the headstock. Its spindle does not revolve but can be moved a few inches lengthwise and clamped as desired. Drills, reamers, taps and other end-cutting tools are held and fed to the workpiece by the tailstock spindle, which is hollow with a taper to take the shanks of centers, drill chucks, drills, reamers, etc. The whole tailstock can be removed to and clamped in any position along the bed where it can best serve its purpose.

The body or top of the tailstock can be adjusted crosswise on its base. This may serve to align the tailstock with the headstock so work can be turned straight. On the other hand, the tailstock may be offset intentionally to hold a piece between centers at an angle for turning it tapered.

Between the headstock and tailstock is the *carriage* that has several parts that serve to support, move, and control the cutting tool. Of these parts, the *saddle* slides on ways on top of the bed. On top of the saddle is a *cross-slide* that is adjusted and fed at right angles to the length of the bed by a crank and graduated dial on the front of the saddle. Adjustments can be made to 0.001 in. in positioning a tool.

The commonest device for clamping the tool or toolholder to a lathe is a simple toolpost, shown in Fig. 18–1. It is normally mounted on a *compound rest* on top of the cross-slide. The compound rest has a graduated base and can be swivelled around a vertical axis. In this way, its slide can be set at any angle with the axis of a workpiece. The slide can be adjusted or fed by hand through a screw and nut controlled by a crank and graduated dial. The slide can travel only a few inches but is useful for feeding tools at an angle, such as for generating short and steep tapers.

The bracket that hangs from the front of the saddle is the *apron*. It contains the mechanism for moving the carriage along the bed. Turning the handwheel on the front of the apron turns a small pinion extending from the other side of the apron. The pinion is engaged with a rack attached to the bed and pulls the carriage along.

Power feed. Power comes to the apron for feeding the carriage through the leadscrew and feed rod along the front of the bed in Fig. 18–4. The leadscrew is used to move the carriage along at a precise rate for cutting a thread. The leadscrew passes through a split or half nut attached to the apron. This nut is normally spread apart but can be closed and engaged with the leadscrew by throwing a lever on the front of the apron.

The feed rod is used to save the leadscrew when other than threading operations are done. It drives a train of gears in the apron. Clutches in this gear train are engaged to apply the power either to moving the carriage along the bed or the cross-slide across the bed.

The power feed drive on a lathe is always taken off the headstock spindle. In that way the feed, whether for turning or thread cutting, is always related to the speed of the spindle. The drive goes through a set of reversible gears for setting the direction of feed and through a set of change gears for setting the amount of feed. With a definite setting of the feed change gears, the carriage travels a definite distance in inches for each revolution of the headstock spindle no matter how fast the spindle turns.

The feed change gears are in a sliding transmission gear box on the left of the bed below the headstock, as shown in Fig. 18–4 and indicated in Fig. 18–5. A chart on the box tells the operator how to shift the levers to select the available feeds, and changes can be made quickly. On some lathes the changes are made by means of pick-off gears. Most lathes have a large range of feeds. For example, a typical 14 in. general-purpose lathe cuts 66 different threads from 2 to 120 threads per in. and has 66 feeds from 0.0014 to 0.084 in. per rev. In general, larger lathes have fewer feed changes, and smaller lathes more.

Sizes and types of lathes. The rated size of a lathe indicates the largest diameter and length of workpiece it will handle. Thus a 14 in. lathe will swing a piece 14 in. in diameter over the bed ways. Some manufacturers designate the swing by four digits, like 1610. The first two designate the largest diameter that can be swung over the bed ways, the last two the diameter over the cross-slide; 16 in. and 10 in. respectively in the example. For length, some lathe makers specify the maximum distance between centers, in inches; others the overall bed length in feet. Thus one lathe designated to take 30 in. between centers may be the equivalent of another specified as 6 ft long.

More than the size needs to be considered in selecting a lathe. Complete specifications on lathes are given in manufacturers catalogs. As an example, two lathes have a swing capacity of 16 in. over the ways and 30 in. between centers. One weighs 2600 lb, has a 2 hp motor, and costs around $3000; the other weighs 7700 lb, takes a 20 hp motor, and has a price of around $13,000. Other things being equal, the more expensive lathe should be able to remove metal up to 10 times as fast as the cheaper one but costs only about 4⅓ times as much. Yet the extra power and rigidity may not be of any value if the lathe is not going to be used most of the time or is needed only for light work the smaller lathe can handle as well as the larger.

At the upper end of the size range, a lathe is rated to swing 50 in.-diameter and take 132 in. between centers. This is huge but not the largest. It weighs 47,200 lb, has a 50 hp motor, and costs around $55,000.

General types of lathes will be described in the paragraphs that follow to give a composite picture. Automatic lathes will be described in the next chapter.

Engine lathe. The engine lathe is one name for the common general purpose lathe. It has the principal parts already described and is depicted in Fig. 18–4. Bed sizes generally range from 4 to 16 ft, and swing capacities from 9 to 50 in. A typical 14 in.-engine lathe has 18 spindle speeds from 25 to 1500 rpm. One with 50 in. swing has a speed range of 1.8 to 157 rpm.

Bench lathe. Small lathes with beds up to 6 ft long and able to swing diameters up to 12 in. are commonly set on benches. In most cases they are as complete as larger lathes, only smaller and lighter. Typical speed ranges are from 125 to 4000 rpm.

Toolroom lathe. A toolroom lathe or toolmakers lathe looks like a regular engine lathe but is built more accurately, has more speeds and feeds available, has more accessories, and usually costs $500 to $1000 more than an engine lathe of the same size.

Speed lathe. A speed lathe has only a few units; a headstock, tailstock, and toolpost on a light bed, without power feed and only two or three high spindle speeds. Speed lathes are used for polishing, light metal spinning, and wood turning.

Duplicating lathe. A duplicating or tracer lathe is one with an attachment that enables the machine to turn, bore, and face all kinds of contours from templates. As the carriage moves along, the tool is made to follow a path that duplicates the path of a tracer finger moving along the template. Mechanical, air, and hydraulic devices are all used on various makes of tracer attachments to coordinate the movements of the tracer finger and tool. The only special equipment needed for each different job is the template, which is usually not costly. Set-up is quick because it requires only putting the template in position, mounting the workpiece, and adjusting a single tool. The machine will then reproduce as many multiple-diameter parts of one kind as desired. This arrangement is generally economical for moderate quantities of pieces, too many for individual treatment on the engine lathe and not enough to justify the multiple tooling and long set-up time of an automatic or turret lathe.

Fig. 18–6. A duplicating lathe equipped with an air-gage tracer. (Courtesy The Monarch Machine Tool Co.)

A typical job done on a duplicating lathe is shown in Fig. 18–6. A workpiece is turned between centers. As the tool is traversed, it is fed in or out by a hydraulic cylinder and piston attached to the tool slide. The tracer finger is on an arm attached to the tool slide and makes contact with the template on a rail bolted to the rear of the bed. The tracer activates a pneumatic circuit that governs the hydraulic infeed to the tool.

Production lathe. A production lathe is a stripped down lathe intended for moderate quantity production runs, generally for straight turning of single diameters and facing.

Special purpose lathes. Some lathes have features that enable them to do certain work. The *gap lathe* has a bed with a removable section under the spindle nose so that large work can be swung. *Wheel lathes* are made for finishing the journals and turning the treads of railroad car and locomotive wheels mounted in sets. *Oil country lathes* are used to make and maintain oil well drilling equipment and have holes from 7 to 16 in. through their spindles to accommodate large pieces.

ACCESSORIES AND ATTACHMENTS

Lathe accessories are common work- and tool-holders and supports such as chucks, collets, centers, drivers, rests, fixtures, and mandrels. Attachments are devices to facilitate specific operations. They include stops, thread chasing dials, taper attachments, and devices that enable milling, grinding, gear cutting, and cutter relieving to be done on the lathe.

Fig. 18–7. A cutaway view of the mechanism of a three jaw universal self-centering chuck. (Courtesy The Cushman Chuck Co.)

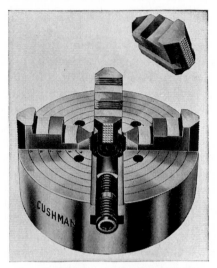

Fig. 18–8. A four jaw independent chuck. One jaw has been removed to show an operating screw. (Courtesy The Cushman Chuck Co.)

Chucks. A *universal* or *scroll chuck* has three jaws engaged and moved in unison by a scroll plate as shown in Fig. 18–7. A wrench inserted in any one of three pinions around the chuck body rotates the scroll plate, and the chuck is fast to operate. The jaws can grip outside or inside surfaces. Hardened serrated jaws are used on rough workpieces, and soft jaws that may be trued in place are applied to finished surfaces.

An *adjustable chuck* is a universal chuck mounted on an adapter that attaches to the spindle nose of a lathe. A good universal chuck can be expected to run out 0.002 in. when new, and the error increases with age. An adjustable chuck can be adjusted on the adapter to run as true as 0.0005 in.

As shown in Fig. 18–8, a *four jaw independent chuck* has jaws that are moved separately, each by a screw. The jaws will grip almost any shape of piece and can be adjusted to run as true as desired, but the chuck is slow to operate.

A *combination chuck* has jaws that can be moved together through a scroll plate or adjusted separately.

Two jaw chucks are adapted to hold workpieces of irregular shapes by means of slip jaws added to the permanent jaws. Each piece can be chucked in less time than with a four jaw chuck, but sufficient production is necessary to justify the special jaws.

Air- and *hydraulic-operated chucks* are quick, grip the work strongly, and are economical for production. A cylinder is carried on the rear of and revolves with the spindle of the machine. The piston actuates a rod lengthwise through the spindle and through levers opens and closes the jaws of the chuck. An air cylinder and chuck are mounted on the turret lathe of Fig. 19–4.

A *wrenchless chuck* is operated by a lever on a ring on the rear of the chuck body. The lever does not revolve with the chuck and can be actuated before the chuck body comes to rest. The action is fast, and wrenchless chucks often are used on production.

A *drill chuck* may be used on either the headstock or tailstock spindle of a lathe to hold straight shank drills, reamers, taps, or small diameter workpieces. The jaws of the drill chuck of Fig. 18–9 are wedged by the inside taper of the shell to grip a piece. The shell is fastened to the body that is screwed up or down on the shank to close or open the chuck.

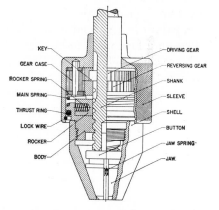

Fig. 18–9. A sectional view of a drill chuck. (Courtesy Wahlstrom Tool Division, American Machine and Foundry Co.)

Collets. A collet is a thin steel or brass bushing with lengthwise slots and an outside taper. When it is forced into the tapered sleeve of a collet chuck, the collet is sprung together slightly to grip a workpiece securely and accurately. The simple *collet chuck* of Fig. 18–10 is operated by turning the hand wheel on the left end of the spindle. Air and hydraulic cylinders are used to operate collet chucks for rapid production.

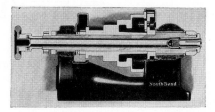

Fig. 18–10. A cross-section of a lathe headstock showing a draw-in collet chuck. (Courtesy South Bend Lathe Works.)

Centers and drivers. A lathe center has a 60° included angle taper at one end and a sticking taper at the other end to fit a machine spindle. Typical centers are shown in Fig. 18–11. A live center mounted on the tailstock wears less but is more expensive and not as accurate as a solid center.

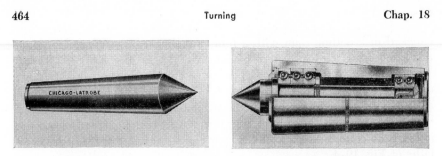

Fig. 18–11. A solid center, left. (Courtesy Chicago Latrobe Twist Drill Works). A ball bearing live center, right. (Courtesy Ready Tool Co.)

A *dog plate* on the spindle nose is shown in Fig. 18–1. A *face plate* is larger than a dog plate and has a number of radial slots for bolts. Workpieces are bolted on the front of the face plate.

A *fixture* is a special device fastened directly to the spindle nose or bolted on a face plate to hold and locate a specific piece or pieces. Fixtures are commonly used for quantity production of pieces on production, turret, and automatic lathes rather than engine lathes.

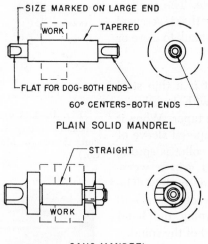

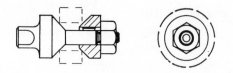

Fig. 18–12. Common mandrels.

A *mandrel* locates a workpiece from a hole. Common types are depicted in Fig. 18–12. A tapered mandrel is pressed into the workpiece hole.

Rests. A *center* or *steady rest* has three shoes that are brought up to contact and support a slender workpiece that would otherwise deflect too much under its weight or from the cutting forces. The shoes are carried in a bracket clamped on top of the bed. A *follower rest* is fastened to and moves along with the carriage with shoes that support the workpiece at the cutting tool position.

Fig. 18–13. Taper turning with a taper attachment. (Courtesy South Bend Lathe Works.)

Attachments. A *taper attachment* shown fastened to the rear of the lathe in Fig. 18–13 has a slide on top that is swivelled to the angle of the taper desired. A block riding on the slide is clamped to the rear extension of the cross-slide and causes the tool to cut along the angular path as the carriage is traversed along the bed.

As has been pointed out, outside tapers can be turned without an attachment by offsetting the tailstock but the adjustments required make that method slow. Inside or outside steep tapers can be generated by swivelling the compound rest but the length of taper must be short. Short or long and inside or outside tapers may be generated with the taper attachment, but steepness is limited. The attachment is easy to adjust, and the lathe may be reset easily for straight work.

A *relieving attachment* is a device for moving the cutting tool in and out in relation to the revolving workpiece to back off the teeth of multiple point tools such as milling cutters and reamers.

Stops of various kinds can be attached to the bed to position the carriage accurately and quickly for spacing grooves, facing shoulders, etc.

A variety of attachments are available for adapting the lathe to do milling, gear cutting, grinding, shaping and fluting. Such work can be done more efficiently on machines especially designed for it, and the lathe is justified only as an expedient where more suitable equipment is not available.

Lathe manufacturers have developed and are able to furnish many other ingenious attachments to enable lathes to perform special operations economically at moderate and large scale production rates. Examples of these are attachments for turning crankshafts and pieces with unusual shapes.

LATHE OPERATIONS

Practical limits. Lengthwise dimensions on a piece faced in a lathe are normally given a tolerance of $\pm \frac{1}{64}$ in. To hold closer tolerances requires time consuming cut-and-try adjustments unless carriage stops are used, and they do not save much unless several pieces are to be made.

Under average conditions, reasonable tolerances for rough turning and boring range from 0.005 in. for diameters under ½ in. to 0.015 in. for diameters over 2 in. For finished surfaces, tolerances from 0.002 in. for diameters below ½ in. to 0.007 in. for diameters above 2 in. are usual. A fluted reamer properly used will produce holes within 0.001 in. of nominal size. Smaller tolerances than these can be and are held on lathes, but the cost rises rapidly as the tolerance is reduced.

From single point turning and boring, surface roughness can be expected, ranging from 500 microinches rms to as fine as 40 microinches rms. Holes may be finished by reaming to as smooth as 20 microinches rms.

Because the simple lathe is versatile and flexible, it is not generally a fast producer. The tools can be arranged in many ways, but for the most part the tools can be used only one at a time; and for each piece and every different cut tools must be changed, set, and adjusted. This takes up an appreciable part of the time to make a part. If a quantity of pieces must be made, the time soon adds up to a large amount. A skilled machinist is required to operate a lathe properly, his time is expensive, and a sizeable part of his time is spent just waiting while the machine is cutting. It is not feasible for one man to operate more than one engine lathe at a time as a rule.

Where only a single cut is needed on a part, many pieces of that kind might well be produced on an engine lathe as economically as on any other machine tool. However, most parts require more treatment, and for them a lathe is suitable for making only a few pieces, except in cases where special equipment may be added. To do most work in larger quantities, more automatic machine tools of the lathe family are better.

Calculating cutting time. The time in an operation during which a machine is making a cut can be calculated. The cutting time in minutes is

$$T = \frac{L}{fN},\qquad\qquad (18\text{--}1)$$

where f is the feed in in. per rev and N is the number of rev per min. The length of cut L includes the length of surface cut plus the distance the tool is fed to enter and clear the cut, usually $\frac{1}{16}$ to $\frac{1}{4}$ in. for turning.

As an example, a 1 in.-diameter by 2 in.-long piece is to be cut at 90 fpm with a feed of 0.010 ipr. The number of revolutions per minute $N = 4 \times 90/1 = 360$ rpm. The time $T = 2.06/0.010 \times 360 = 0.57$ min. In this case the approach and overtravel is assumed to be 0.06 in.

Questions

1. Name and describe the major units of lathes.

2. What movements does the tool have on a lathe? How are they obtained?

3. From where does the power feed come on a lathe? How much is it varied?

4. How is the carriage moved for cutting threads on a lathe? For other operations?

5. How is the size of a lathe designated?

6. What is an engine lathe?

7. How does a toolroom lathe differ from an engine lathe?

8. Describe a duplicating lathe.

9. Describe a production lathe.

10. What are lathe accessories and attachments?

11. What are the features of a three-jaw universal chuck?

12. What is the advantage of an adjustable chuck?

13. How is a four-jaw independent chuck operated? What are its advantages and disadvantages?

14. What is a combination chuck?

15. For what purposes are air or hydraulic chucks used?

16. Describe a drill chuck.

17. What is a collet chuck? How is it used?

18. How does a center rest differ from a follower rest?

19. Describe a taper attachment.

20. What is plain or straight turning? What is chuck work?

21. How is taper commonly designated? What is the amount of a Morse taper? Jarno taper?

22. In what four ways may tapers be cut on a lathe?

23. For what work is the lathe best suited?

24. How does cost vary with tolerance held in lathe work?

Problems

1. A taper 6 in. long has a large diameter of 2.0625 in. and a small diameter of 1.500 in. What should be the setting of the taper attachment in inches per foot to machine this taper?

2. The large diameter of a piece measures 0.9375 in., the small diameter 0.4375 in. The taper is 5 in. per ft. What is the length of the taper?

3. A taper of 5/8 in. per ft is to be cut on a piece 18 in. long. How much should the tailstock be set over if that method is to be used?

4. What is the nominal diameter at the small end of a No. 0. Morse taper? Of a No. 7. Morse taper?

5. A piece of aluminum is to be cut at 300 fpm. One eighth-inch of stock is to be removed to leave a finished surface of 5 in.-diameter. The length of cut is 4 in. and the feed is 0.025 ipr. What is the cutting time?

6. A finish cut for a length of 10 in. on a diameter of 2 in. is to be taken in cast iron with a speed of 150 fpm and a feed of 0.007 ipr. What is the cutting time?

7. A piece 4 in. in diameter is to be cut off by a tool fed at 0.005 in. per rev. The lathe is set at 100 rpm. How long should the cut take?

8. A workpiece 10 in. in diameter is to be faced down to a 4 in.-diameter on the end. The lathe is equipped with an electronic device that controls

the spindle speed and maintains the cutting speed at 200 fpm for the diameter the tool is cutting at any instant. The feed is 0.015 ipr. What should be the time for the cut?

9. If the spindle speed for the workpiece described in Prob. 8 is set to give a speed of 200 fpm at 10 in.-diameter and is not changed during the cut, what is the time required for the cut?

10. A lathe has a 2 hp motor and costs $3000. It is to be depreciated in 10 years, and 10% of its cost is charged each year to cover interest, insurance, and taxes. Thus the annual charge for this machine is $600. If the shop works 300 days a year, the machine must show a return above other expenses of $2 a day to pay for itself.

Another lathe that will take workpieces of the same size has a 10 hp motor and costs $6000. On the same basis as for the other machine, what must the daily return to pay for this one be?

Each machine is 75% efficient, so the first is able to deliver 1.5 hp to the tool point and the second 7.5 hp. For the material to be cut one horsepower is required at the tool point to remove one cubic inch per minute. Labor and other overhead costs are $4 per hr.

Mostly light work is done that does not require over 1.5 hp but some heavy cutting is required on which can be expended an average of 4.5 hp if available. If that power is not available, the work will have to be done more slowly. What amount of the heavy cutting, in cubic inches of stock removal per day will justify the investment in the larger lathe? What does this mean in cutting time on the two lathes?

Reference

How to Run a Lathe, South Bend Lathe Works, South Bend, Ind., 1947.

CHAPTER 19

Automatic Turning Machines

Out of the simple lathe, more complex machines have evolved that are efficient for producing duplicate parts in quantities. They do work faster and require less skill and labor than the engine lathe. A basic feature of such machines is that once they are set, the tools can be applied to the work repeatedly without having to be reset for each cut. On some machines a number of or all tools cut at once. Some machines require constant attention but only call for skill when being set up. Others need little attendance once put into operation.

As machines are made more automatic, they become more complex. To minimize complexity, automatic turning machines are made to specialize on certain kinds of work.

The common types of production turning machines are automatic lathes, turret lathes, automatic turret lathes, and single spindle and multiple spindle automatic bar and chucking machines. They differ in the extent to which they are automatic and in the kinds of work each type can do.

AUTOMATIC LATHES

Automatic lathes have the basic units of simple lathes; bed, headstock, tool slides, and usually a tailstock. In addition, an automatic lathe has a mechanism to conduct the tools respectively through all the steps

Fig. 19–1. A view of a job on an automatic lathe. The inset shows how the tools cut. (Courtesy Sundstrand Machine Tool Co.)

of a cycle without operator attention once the machine has been set up. A view of the working zone of an automatic lathe is given in Fig. 19–1. The workpiece is rotated between centers. The tools are carried on blocks on the front and rear slides. The front slide is traversed along the bed, and the tools in this case make straight cuts along the workpiece, retract at the end of the cut, and are withdrawn to the starting position. They can also be arranged, if desired, to make tapered or curved cuts. The rear tool slide normally feeds the tools toward the center of the workpiece for facing, necking, grooving, and forming but can be given a sideways movement to relieve the tools at the end of a cut. On going to or from a cut but not cutting, the tools are traversed at 250 ft per min. They may be made to dwell in desired positions.

Most automatic lathes perform basically similar functions, but different features are found in various makes. Some have an overhead slide and tool block above the workpiece to carry additional tools. On some, both the front and rear tool slide have longitudinal and cross feeds.

Some models of automatic lathes are for chuck work and do not have a tailstock, but have in its place a platen or slides to carry more tools for end-working operations such as boring. Most have one spindle, but one make has three spindles and accommodates three workpieces that are cut simultanueously by tools mounted on one tool slide.

Principles of operation. Automatic lathes are rigid and powerful producers as indicated by the statistics of several typical models in Table 19–1.

TABLE 19–1. STATISTICS OF SEVERAL TYPICAL MODELS OF
AUTOMATIC LATHES

Size [1]	Weight (lb)	Rated power at motor (hp)	Approx. price ($)	Manufacturer
12 × 24	7,000	20	16,000	A
12 × 33	7,900	30	16,000	B
24 × 36	15,000	50	43,000	A

[1] Size is designated by nominal swing over tool slides and maximum distance between centers in inches.

Automatic lathes are mostly suited for work done between centers but are used also for chuck work that requires few cuts. They are particularly competitive with tracer-type lathes, which are easy to set up. Automatic lathes are not easy to change from one job to another. For instance, speeds and feeds are not changed by shifting levers, as on an engine lathe, but by removing and replacing change gears. Set-up time may run from one quarter to several hours, as compared to a few minutes on an engine lathe. Careful scheduling to run similar jobs in succession can save change-over time.

Although set-up is lengthy, the automatic lathe is at an advantage when cutting because it is fast and often able to make up for time lost in set-up in less than 100 pieces. It normally has a number of tools acting at once utilizing full power capacity, in contrast to the use of a single tool on an engine or tracer lathe. The operator needs only load and unload and occasionally check the machine after it has been set up, and these machines are often equipped with automatic loading devices. One operator customarily takes care of two or more automatic lathes.

To be effective, an automatic lathe must be tooled well, with quick devices such as air chucks. Cutting tools are provided to cover as much of the accessible area as possible, and each tool is designed for the shape and size to suit its purpose best. Tool blocks and holders must be selected wisely. A universal tool block will serve on many jobs and its cost per job is low. The tools held by it must be adjusted on the machine and that adds to set-up time. On the other hand, cutting tools can be mounted and preset off the machine on a special or solid tool block and are ready to go to work when the block is placed on the machine. Each such block can be applied to relatively few jobs, and its cost per job is high. For short run but repeated jobs, master workpieces to which the tools can be set save set-up time.

TURRET LATHES

On a turret lathe all the tools for a particular operation can be mounted, preset, and presented to the work repeatedly as needed. An operator must give full time to the machine because he must start each movement. More skill is needed to set up than to run the machine after set-up. Sometimes a set-up man on a higher pay scale attends to several machines, and several operators at a lower scale keep the machines going.

Some turret lathes are designed and equipped for working on barstock and are called *bar-type* machines. The name of *screw machine* or *hand screw machine* has been used for such machines, particularly in the smaller sizes.

The name turret lathe alone ordinarily applies to a horizontal machine, which represents an outgrowth from the simple lathe. A similar development has arisen from the vertical boring machine and has resulted in the vertical turret lathe described in Chap. 26.

The two main types of horizontal turret lathes are the *ram type* and *saddle type.*

Ram-type turret lathes. A turret lathe is so named because it has a hexagonal turret in place of a tailstock. A ram-type turret lathe carries this turret on a ram as shown in Figs. 19–2 and 19–3. The ram slides longitudinally on a saddle positioned and clamped on the ways of the bed. Tools in their holders are mounted on the faces of the turret, and the tools on the face toward the headstock are fed to the work when the ram is moved to the left. When the ram is withdrawn, the turret indexes, and the next face, called a station, is positioned to face of the headstock.

A ram is lighter and can be moved more quickly than a saddle but lacks some rigidity. Because of convenience and speed, the ram-type construction is favored for small- and medium-sized turret lathes where the ram does not have to overhang too far.

Two types of headstocks are the *electric head* and the *all geared head.* In an electric head a multiple speed electric motor drives the spindle directly at high speeds up to 3000 rpm. The turret lathe of Fig. 19–2 has an all geared head with a speed *preselector* dial and lever. This enables the operator to select the speed for the next cut while waiting for a cut to be finished. As soon as one cut is done, the operator pushes the starting

Fig. 19–2. A view from the operator's position of the working parts of a ram type turret lathe tooled for a bar job. (Courtesy Jones and Lamson Machine Co.)

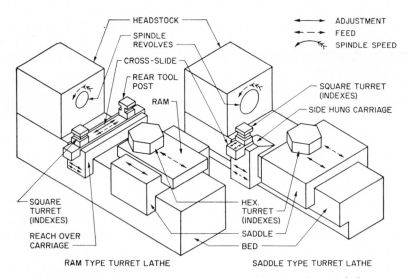

Fig. 19–3. Principal parts and movements of horizontal turret lathes.

lever, the speed changes and the next cut can start at once. Modern machines usually offer from 6 to 12 spindle speeds.

A *reach over* or *bridge type* carriage across the entire bed is commonly found between the saddle and headstock on a ram-type turret lathe. On the carriage is the cross-slide with a quick hand-indexed four station turret tool holder on the front end and a holder for one or more tools at the rear. Heavy single-point tools are clamped in these holders and fed to the work by movement of the carriage along the bed and the cross movement of the slide.

A *plain* cross-slide is entirely hand operated, but the *universal* kind is power fed also and is more common. The ram usually has power feed in addition to hand feed. Nine feeds are available on a typical line of turret lathes.

The cross-slide can be positioned accurately by means of a cross-screw and micrometer dial. Individual stops for each tool station can be set to throw out the power feed and limit the longitudinal movement of the ram or carriage. In this way the movement of any tool along the workpiece can be precisely controlled and repeated readily for as many workpieces as desired.

Fig. 19–4. A saddle type turret lathe set up for chuck work. (Courtesy Gisholt Machine Co.)

Saddle-type turret lathes. The hexagonal turret of a saddle-type turret lathe is carried directly on a saddle that slides lengthwise on the bed as depicted in Figs. 19–3 and 19–4. This construction is favored for large turret lathes because it provides good support for the tools and the means to move the tools a long way when necessary. The saddle is moved toward the headstock by hand or power to feed the tools to the work, and the turret is automatically indexed when the saddle is withdrawn.

The turret is fixed in the center of the saddle on some machines. On others it may be moved crosswise. This helps reduce tool overhang for machining large diameters and is helpful for taper or contour boring and turning.

Most saddle-type turret lathes have the *side hung type* of carriage that does not extend across the entire top of the bed and allows larger pieces to be swung. This means the rear tool station on the cross-slide is lost.

The cross-slide and carriage usually are both power and hand fed. The cross-slide is adjusted by a micrometer dial and screw. Stops are provided to throw out the feeds and position the tools longitudinally for any of the stations of either square or hexagonal turret.

Turret lathe sizes. The size of a turret lathe is designated by a number that indicates the diameter of workpiece that can be swung and the diameter of bar that can be passed through the hole in the spindle. Machines of different makes with the same size number may vary somewhat in capacity.

TABLE 19–2. Specifications and Performance Record ° of
Three Models of Turret Lathes

Size no. and type	Capacity [1] (in)	Weight (lb)	Power (hp)	Best time per piece (min)	Actual prod. per 8 hr day (pcs)	Price ($)	Net annual savings
4-Ram type	2 –9½–18⅛	3700	15	2.96	143	17,000	676
3-Ram type	1½–7 –15⅜	3030	10	3.18	137	13,500	796
3-Electro-Cycle	1½–7 –15⅜	4730	7½	3.20	147	15,500	702

[1] Bar diameter—swing over cross-slide—swing over bed.
° Based partly upon report of E. L. Murray, "Economics of Tooling and Lathe Selection," *The Tool Engineer*, Nov. 1953.

Some of the considerations besides size that are of importance in selecting a turret lathe are indicated in Table 19–2. Three sizes of machines were considered for the production of a steel shaft in moderate quantities. The largest and most powerful machine could remove the stock the fastest and was found able to turn out a piece in the shortest time, 2.96 minutes. That alone was not enough, because the No. 3 Electro-Cycle machine was able to turn out the most pieces in an eight hour day. Although the Electro-Cycle machine is basically a ram-type turret lathe, it is arranged for partial automatic operation and causes less operator fatigue during the day. Even so, the largest daily production did not designate the best choice. The job had previously been run on a machine that was due for replacement. The annual labor savings for each of the machines of Table 19–2 compared with the old machine were calculated. The biggest producer of course showed the biggest saving. Then the net savings were ascertained by subtracting the annual charges on the investment from the labor savings, and the result was that the machine with the least daily production promised the largest annual net savings because it cost the least.

Tools and attachments. Collets and collet chucks are commonly used for barstock, and hand and power chucks for individual pieces, on turret lathes. Essentially the same kinds of single-point tools, form tools, and multiple-point tools such as drills, reamers and taps are used on turret lathes as on engine lathes. Single point tools generally are heavier.

Convenient devices are made specifically for holding and adjusting cutting tools singly and in groups on the hexagonal turrets. This equipment is available commercially in many standard forms and sizes and is fully described in manufacturers catalogs. A few typical kinds are presented here. Some equipment is intended for bar work, other for chucking work, but much is fitted for both kinds of service.

Barstock generally is supported by the tailstock center on an engine lathe but that usually is not feasible on a turret lathe, especially when cuts are taken from the hexagonal turret. *Box tools* support overhanging bars that are being turned, faced, chamfered, or centered from the hexagonal turret. Rollers or a crotch bear against and back up the work surface opposite the cutting tool. The *single-cutter turner* of Fig. 19–5(A) is an example of a box tool. Other models are arranged to carry several turning bits, a facing bit, or a center drill.

The *quick-acting slide tool* of

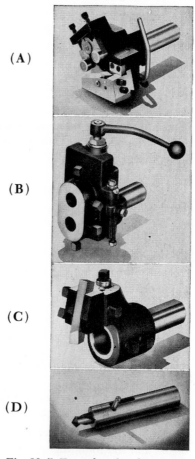

(A)

(B)

(C)

(D)

Fig. 19–5. Examples of tooling equipment for bar work. (A) Single cutter turner. (B) Quick acting slide tool. (C) Adjustable knee tool. (D) Combination stock stop and starting drill. (Courtesy The Warner and Swasey Co.)

Fig. 19–5(B) is designed to hold round shank single-point tools and boring bars for fast recessing and facing cuts on both bar and chuck work. The slide that carries the cutting tools moves ½ in. with a quarter turn of the handle. The *adjustable knee tool* of Fig. 19–5(C) can be set up quickly for turning combined with drilling, boring, or centering on short pieces. The *combination stock stop and starting drill* is a two purpose tool that saves one turret face and one index. A typical set of bar equipment is illustrated in Fig. 19–2.

Chucking work often involves a greater range of diameters and more tool overhang than bar work. The chucking set-up of Fig. 19–4 contains several characteristic tools. *Multiple turning heads* carry *cutter holders* and *boring bars* on the turret faces in line with the machine spindle. A *stationary pilot bar*, like the one in Fig. 19–4, is attached to the headstock and slips into the bushings and gives extra support to the turning heads. It can be heavy and strong because it does not add to the load on the turret. *Piloted boring bars*, like those shown, slip into and are guided and reinforced by an *internal* or *center pilot* in the machine spindle.

Planning turret lathe operations. Time is the major item of cost in a turret lathe operation. This includes the time to set up the machine, and make the actual cuts. The following principles are guides to obtaining low costs. They apply also to other kinds of operations and machine tools.

A large part of set-up time is that spent in mounting and adjusting the cutting tools. These costs may be minimized by using universal tooling and maintaining a permanent set-up on a turret lathe. To do this, large and heavy tools that perform basic functions on most operations are permanently mounted in their logical order on the turret. All these tools are not needed for every job, but then the turret may be back- or skipped-indexed. In most cases the extra indexing time is less than would be taken to remove the tools and change them around on the turret. The lighter tools are rearranged in various combinations on the heavy toolholders for various jobs. Recommendations for proven permanent set-ups for various classes of work and sizes and types of machines are available from turret lathe manufacturers.

Work handling time depends partly upon the raw material, but its selection is based upon several factors. Barstock is easily held and pieces can often be completed and cut off in one operation. A casting or forging may require that less stock be removed but calls for the cost of a pattern or die and the founding or forging operations. As an example, a part can be cut from barstock at a cost of $10 per piece. The cost of 5 pieces is $50 and for 25 pieces is $250. If the part is cast, a pattern must be made at a cost of $25. Molds can be made and the pieces cast for $2 each. The machining charge to finish the castings is $5 each. To make 5 pieces by casting and machining costs $60; for 25 pieces, $200. Obviously barstock is preferable for 5 pieces; and castings for 25 pieces.

Work handling time also depends upon the selection of collets, chucks, and fixtures. For average work in small or moderate quantities, standard holding devices are best with special jaws, arbors, and single fixtures added as justified. Special fixtures can pay for themselves on single jobs where the parts are otherwise hard to hold and are made in fairly large quantities.

Machine handling time consists of time to index and position the tools and set the speeds and feeds. More time is required to advance from step to step in an operation and it is harder to keep up a fast pace on a large machine than on a small one because of the heavier masses that must be moved. The effect of this on one operation is illustrated by the case described by Table 19–2.

Parts like collars, spacers, and gear blanks can be machined in groups with turning, drilling, boring, reaming and cutting off done on all pieces in one group at each setting. In that way the machine movements per piece are less than if the pieces are done individually.

Fig. 19–6. Multiple internal and external cuts from the hexagonal turret combined with a cut taken by a tool in the square cross slide turret on a turret lathe. (Courtesy The Warner and Swasey Co.)

Machine handling time is reduced by taking combined and multiple cuts to save indexing. Cutting time is also reduced. A *combined cut* is one where tools in both the hexagonal turret and square cross-slide turret are made to cut at the same time. A *multiple cut* is one where two or more tools are applied at the same time from one turret station. An example of combined and multiple cuts is given in Fig. 19–6.

Internal cuts are almost always made by tools in the hexagonal turret and are planned and set up first for an operation. Provision must be made for the proper order of internal cuts, for instance for drilling before boring and boring before reaming a hole.

Tolerance down to 0.001 in. per in. and finishes as fine as 60 microinches rms are practicable on turret lathes, but the more exacting the requirements, the more the cost. One cut may suffice to hold a tolerance of 0.010 in., but as a rule two cuts are needed for a tolerance between 0.005 and 0.010 in., and three cuts for tolerance less than 0.005 in., with corresponding surface requirements.

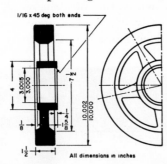

Fig. 19–7. Three turret lathe methods of increasing complexity for machining the illustrated cast iron flywheel. (A) A simple method with a minimum of special tools for producing the piece in two chuckings. (B) Requires two chuckings but represents a method suitable for most turret lathe operations for parts of this kind. (C) Requires only one chucking and represents tooling that is an extension and refinement of that proposed for Method (B).

(From E. L. Murray, "Economics of Tooling and Lathe Selection," *The Tool Engineer,* Nov. 1953, p. 51.)

Economics of tooling. Machines are like men in that without tools they can do nothing; but the better their tools, the more efficiently they work. On the other hand, tools cost money, and money can be spent for them only if they earn a profit. These principles apply to all processes, all kinds of machine tools, and all tools, but they will be illustrated and applied for turret lathe tooling, the case at hand, by Fig. 19–7 and Table 19–3.

Three methods are shown for tooling the cast iron flywheel in Fig. 19–7 on a turret lathe. Method A is the simplest and requires only standard tools but two operations. Method B also calls for two operations but is faster. It requires more tools and set-up time. Method C produces the part in one operation with the highest cost for tooling and set-up time but is the fastest producer after set-up.

TABLE 19–3. COMPARISON OF THREE TURRET LATHE TOOLING METHODS

(Illustrated in Fig. 19–7)

Cost item		Method A	Method B	Method C
Tooling cost	{ Standard tools ($)	895	1245	2118
	{ Special tools ($)	95	233	1568
Time to machine one piece (min)		13.6	9.0	6.5
Set-up time per lot (hr)		2.6	3.2	3.4
Hourly cost (set-up or prod.) ($/hr)[1]		4.26	4.31	4.41
Set-up cost per lot ($)		11.08	13.79	14.99
Production per 48 min hr (pcs/hr)		3.5	5.3	7.4
Cost per piece[2] (dollars/pc)		1.22	0.81	0.60
For total of[3] 300 pieces	{ Cost of special tools ($/pc)	0.32	0.78	5.23
	{ Cost of production ($/pc)	1.54	1.59	5.83
For total of[3] 3000 pieces	{ Cost of special tools ($/pc)	0.03	0.08	0.52
	{ Cost of production ($/pc)	1.25	0.89	1.12
For total of[3] 9000 pieces	{ Cost of special tools ($/pc)	0.01	0.03	0.18
	{ Cost of production ($/pc)	1.23	0.84	0.78
For lot size[4] of 5 pieces	{ Total of 300 pcs ($/pc)	3.76	4.35	8.83
	{ Total of 3000 pcs ($/pc)	3.47	3.65	4.12
For lot size[4] of 50 pieces	{ Total of 300 pcs ($/pc)	1.76	1.87	6.13
	{ Total of 3000 pcs ($/pc)	1.47	1.17	1.42
For lot size[4] of 500 pieces	{ Total of 3000 pcs ($/pc)	1.27	0.92	1.15
	{ Total of 9000 pcs ($/pc)	1.25	0.87	0.81

(1) Standard tools written off over 8000 hours.
    Overhead rate $2.50 per hr for all methods.
    Hourly labor rate $1.65 per hr.
(2) Not including cost of special tools nor set-up cost.
(3) Not including set-up cost {   Charges for interest, insurance, taxes and maintenance not
(4) Includes set-up cost   {   included for simplicity.

The analysis of the costs in Table 19–3 shows that for low production or a small lot size, the simple tooling at least cost is the most economical. As lot size and production increase, more complex tooling is justified. In many cases, several proven ways are available to do a job, and a given rate of production and a specific lot size are required. One way to solve the problem is to calculate the cost for each alternative for the required conditions, as is done for the cases illustrated by Table 19–3. The alternative that shows the lowest total cost is the best for the purpose. This much work is not necessary for the common situation wherein only two alternatives need to be considered. In such a case the important factors are the differences in cost between the two alternatives, and the problem can be solved by means of a simple formula which will now be explained.

If two methods or tools are considered for a specified production rate or lot size, the cost factors that must be taken into account are the number of pieces (N) to be made; the direct savings (s) in dollars per piece of one method over the other; the overhead rate (t) expressed as so many dollars per dollar of direct saving; the extra amount (I) in dollars invested in tools; the capital charges, (A) for interest, (B) for insurance and taxes, (D) for depreciation, (M) for maintenance, all as annual percentage rates of the investment; and the extra set-up cost (Y) in dollars per year of one method over the other. This last factor (Y) is the product of the number of lots run per year times the extra set-up cost per lot.

The principle which is the basis for comparing any two tooling methods can be stated in common sense terms as follows: a tool or tooling method that requires a larger investment should be selected instead of one requiring a smaller investment only if the annual amount saved by the more costly tooling is at least equal to the annual cost of the extra investment and any extra set-up charges. This principle may be written as a mathematical formula in the following form:

$$Ns(1 + t) = I(A + B + D + M) + Y \qquad (19\text{–}1)$$

This formula may be applied to the data of Table 19–3 to show how it is used. The question may be asked, what is the lowest production requirement that justifies the more expensive tooling for Method C instead of Method B, for 10 set-ups per year? The answer is obtained by solving for N in Eq. (19–1). The overhead rate (t) is already included in the hourly rate of Table 19–3.

For the first solution, it will be assumed that the interest, insurance, tax and maintenance rate may be ignored. Special tools are normally depreciated in a year. Standard tools are charged to overhead. The figures for Eq. (19–1) from Table 19–3 are

$$N(0.81 - 0.60) = [(1568 - 233) \times 1] + 10(14.99 - 13.79)$$

and

$$N = \frac{1335 + 12}{0.21} = 6414 \text{ pieces per yr}$$

to justify Method C over Method B.

Now let it be assumed that the interest rate is 10%, insurance and tax rate 5%, and maintenance rate 10% per year. Then

$$N \times 0.21 = 1335(0.10 + 0.05 + 1.0 + 0.10) + 12$$

and

$$N = \frac{1335 \times 1.25 + 12}{0.21} = 8004 \text{ pc per yr.}$$

AUTOMATIC BAR AND CHUCKING MACHINES

A machine that moves the work and tools at the proper rates and sequences through a cycle to perform an operation on one piece without the attention of an operator is commonly called an automatic. Strictly speaking, the machine is a semi-automatic if an operator is required to unload and load the machine and start each cycle. Often an operator can do this for several machines in a group. Workpieces may come to a fully automatic machine on a conveyor or an operator may load a magazine or hopper at intervals. Automatic machines are widely used for drilling, boring, milling, broaching, grinding and other operations, and examples of them are given in this text. The automatic machines described in this chapter are those for turning and allied operations.

Automatic machines for internal and external operations on barstock have been called *automatic screw machines* for years but the name of *automatic bar machines* is now preferable because screws are seldom made on them any more. Their counterparts for individual pieces are *automatic chucking machines.*

Automatic bar and chucking machines may be classified as single spindle or multiple spindle, with a number of variations in each class. Several typical kinds will be described.

Single-spindle automatic bar machines. The single-spindle automatic machine of Fig. 19–8 is made in four sizes to handle barstock up to 1½ in.-diameter and turn lengths up to 2 in. A 5 hp motor drives the 1 in.-diameter bar capacity machine that weighs around 3500 lb and costs about $13,000. It has a spindle speed range from 25 to 3025 rpm, with a choice of one of 16 high forward speeds and one of 12 low speeds, forward or reverse, for any set-up.

Barstock is fed through the revolving spindle of the machine of Fig. 19–8 by feed fingers at the start of each cycle of an operation. The stock is located by butting against a swing stop or turret stop and is gripped in a collet. The cutting tools are mounted on a six station turret and on front and rear cross-slides. The turret indexes around a horizontal axis and is moved to and from the work on a slide actuated by a disk cam

Fig. 19–8. A No. 2G single spindle automatic bar or screw machine.
(Courtesy Brown and Sharpe Mfg. Co.)

at the right-hand end of the machine. Two disk cams on the front feed shaft move the cross-slides. Special cams are made for each different job.

Feed shafts run along the front, rear, and right end of the bed of the machine of Fig. 19–8. They carry clutches, dog carriers, and cams that actuate the machine movements. The shafts revolve at constant speed regardless of the speed of the spindle and may be stopped at any time to stop the action of the tools. Dogs on disks on the front feed shaft engage clutches on the rear feed shaft at preset intervals. Power is applied through the clutches to change or reverse the spindle speed, feed the stock, and index the turret. Each of these functions takes only a fraction of a second, always at the same fast rate. Only one half-second is needed to index the turret of the machine shown in Fig. 19–8.

The automatic bar machine of Fig. 19–8 is designed so that tools can act independently or together and non-cutting movements can be over-lapped to minimize operation time. A swing stop for locating stock leaves all six turret stations available for cutting tools. The turret may be double indexed to save time where only two or three turret tools are needed. A large number of standard toolholders and other tools, similar to those on turret lathes, are available. A variety of standard and special attachments enable the machine to do such auxiliary operations as screw slotting, burring, cross drilling and milling.

Various other single-spindle automatics are available to handle work from minute parts like watch staffs to bars 7¾ in. in diameter and chuck work up to over 12 in. in diameter. These automatics have essentially the same movements and do work similar to that described, but the actual mechanisms vary somewhat with each make of machine.

Fig. 19–9. A view of the working zone of a Swiss type automatic screw machine. (Courtesy George Gorton Machine.)

Swiss-type automatic. The tool head of a type of machine that oper-ates on somewhat different principles from other bar machines is shown in Fig. 19–9. This machine is intended for stock from 0.020 to 7⁄16 in. in diameter. The barstock is held and rotated by the headstock spindle behind the tool head. The headstock is made to slide lengthwise by a cam and feeds the rotating barstock through a hard bushing in the center of the toolhead. Synchronized cams actuate adjustable linkages that bring the tools in as needed to turn, face, form and cut off the workpiece from the bar as it emerges from the bushing.

The cutting action on the Swiss type of machine is confined close to the support bushing, so that small tolerances can be held and good finishes obtained. Tolerances of 0.0002 to 0.0005 in. are common. The machine does step, straight, taper, back and form cutting and with an attachment can perform centering, drilling, and reaming. Tools are simple and adjustments easy. All necessary tools work at once and a piece is finished in one pass, making the time short for most work.

Single-spindle automatic chucking machines. An *automatic turret lathe* has a headstock, turret, and cross-slide on a bed and in its major parts looks like a hand turret lathe. However, hand controls are absent, and the action of the machine is governed by drum cams in the base. The turret is indexed and its slide reciprocated, cross-slides feed to and from the work, and speeds and feeds are changed for each step as desired, all automatically.

Fig. 19–10. A single spindle automatic chucking machine. (Courtesy Warner and Swasey Co.)

The working end of a different design of single spindle automatic chucking machine with chip guard removed is shown in Fig. 19–10. The main tool turret on this machine above the work spindle has five faces for toolholders and tools. Each face is indexed in turn to working position. The turret then moves lengthwise to feed the tools at that station to and from the workpiece. The two cross-slides below the work spindle can be made to feed at the same time as any turret station.

The conventional types of automatic machines described in this chapter are all basically cam motivated. Other kinds will be discussed in Chap. 35 on automation. For most of the cam controlled machines, new cams must be made for each different job. The automatic machine depicted in Fig. 19–10 is different because it does not require cam changes. On it the actions from a permanent set of cams are modified for each movement as desired by setting trip dogs that select speed, feed, and length of cutting stroke. On some similar fixed cam machines, variations in the action are obtained by adjusting the linkage between cam and slide. These arrangements save tooling and set-up cost. In same cases, ideal conditions may be obtained only by making cams specifically for a job, and then the replaceable cam machines are at an advantage for long runs.

Multiple-spindle automatics. Automatic bar and chucking machines are built with four, five, six, and eight spindles. Bar-type machines are rated by the largest diameter of stock that can be fed through the spindles. Some take bars over 2½ in. in diameter. As an example of specifications, a six-spindle automatic that takes round bars up to 1 in.-diameter, has a 10 hp motor, weighs 15,000 lb and costs around $25,000. The capacity of a chucking machine is the diameter of work that can be swung over the tool slides.

A cut-away view from the rear of a six spindle automatic bar machine is shown in Fig. 19–11. The opening in the center of the machine is where the tools and work go. The workpiece spindles are arranged on a circle in a large drum or spindle carrier on the right of the opening. Each work spindle carries a bar of stock, revolves continuously, and is moved from station to station as the carrier indexes. The spindle carrier is indexed smoothly by a modified Geneva mechanism and is locked in position between indexing periods. Each piece is machined in stages as it proceeds from station to station, and one piece is finished and cut off at each index.

End-working tools are mounted on the end tool slide in the middle of the opening. The end tool slide does not index but moves lengthwise to feed its tools to and from the workpieces. The end-working tools are carried on separate slides on some machines and can be fed at different rates.

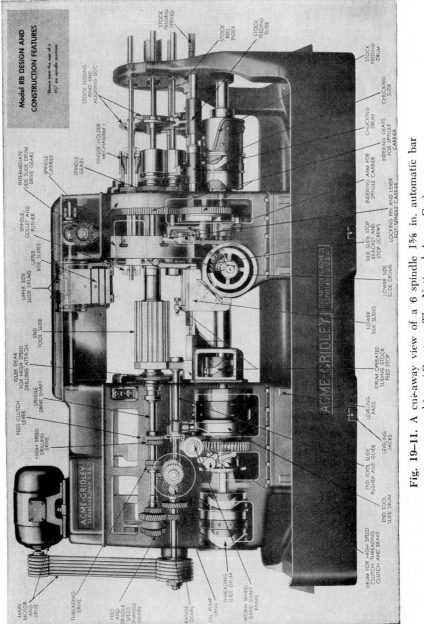

Fig. 19–11. A cut-away view of a 6 spindle 1⅝ in. automatic bar machine. (Courtesy The National Acme Co.)

Side- or cross-slides for forming and cut-off tools are mounted next to the spindle stations and move radially to and from the workpieces. Cross-slides on some machines have a longitudinal as well as radial motion with respect to the work for relieving, contour turning, and grooving.

On most machines the spindles are indexed only one station at a time, and a bar is fed forward or pieces are loaded at only one station. Some six- and eight-spindle machines double index, and two pieces are completed at each index.

Tooling and operation. An example of tooling for a multiple-spindle automatic bar machine is given in Fig. 19–12. Combined and multiple cuts are taken wherever feasible. The machine actually operates on several pieces at once. The time to make one piece on a single indexing machine is the time for the longest cut plus the idle time. The idle time is that taken to move the tools rapidly to and from the work and index the spindle. Typical idle times are 2 sec. for a 1 in. machine, 2.25 sec for 1⅝ in., and 2.3 sec. for 1¾ and 2¼ in., machines.

Every effort is made to shorten the long cuts and minimize the cutting time on a multiple-spindle automatic. This may be done by dividing parts of a long cut among two or more spindles. For instance, a 2 in. length may be turned for a distance of one inch at one station and the rest of the way at a second station. The drilling of deep holes may be divided in the same way. The disadvantage of dividing cuts is that the cuts cannot be made exactly to match each other when made at different spindle positions.

Tooling attachments and accessories increase the area of application and productivity of automatic turning machines. Attachments are added to revolve drills, reamers, or taps to increase or decrease the relative speeds between the tools and work and accelerate operations. Attachments are available for such auxiliary operations as milling, slotting, and cross drilling, right on the machine. Quick mounting and preset tool blocks and toolholders can do much to save on set-up and down time for changing tools. As has been shown, if the time for mounting and replacing tools can be shortened, a shorter tool life is economical. With a shorter tool life, cutting speeds can be increased with a corresponding increase in production.

Tolerances considered economical for multiple-spindle automatic are of the order of 0.002 to 0.004 in. for turning or forming a diameter; 0.005 to 0.010 in. between two shoulders; 0.010 in. on an overall length directly from a stock stop, or 0.005 in. by facing at cut off; and 0.001 in. for size of a reamed hole. Typical attainable runout tolerances are 0.002 in. total indicator reading (tir) between diameters machined at the same station; 0.006 in. tir between surfaces machined at different stations; and 0.005 in.

tir between a machined surface and the original stock surface. Closer tolerances than those quoted can be and are held, even to 0.0005 in., but the smaller the tolerance the slower and more expensive the operation.

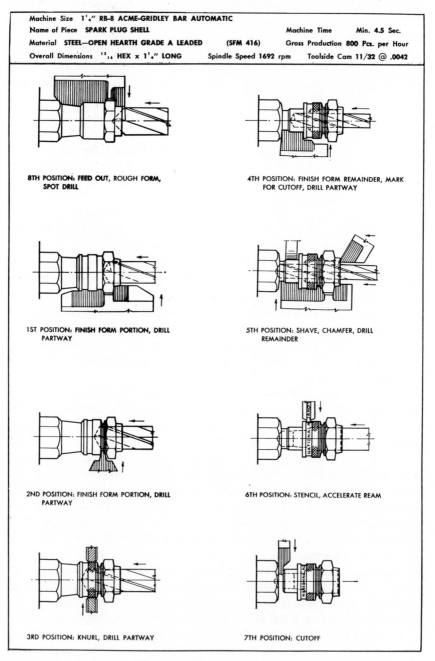

Machine Size   1'₄" RB-8 ACME-GRIDLEY BAR AUTOMATIC
Name of Piece   SPARK PLUG SHELL   Machine Time   Min. 4.5 Sec.
Material   STEEL—OPEN HEARTH GRADE A LEADED   (SFM 416)   Gross Production 800 Pcs. per Hour
Overall Dimensions   ¹³⁄₁₆ HEX x 1'₄" LONG   Spindle Speed 1692 rpm   Toolside Cam 11/32 @ .0042

8TH POSITION: FEED OUT, ROUGH FORM, SPOT DRILL

4TH POSITION: FINISH FORM REMAINDER, MARK FOR CUTOFF, DRILL PARTWAY

1ST POSITION: FINISH FORM PORTION, DRILL PARTWAY

5TH POSITION: SHAVE, CHAMFER, DRILL REMAINDER

2ND POSITION: FINISH FORM PORTION, DRILL PARTWAY

6TH POSITION: STENCIL, ACCELERATE REAM

3RD POSITION: KNURL, DRILL PARTWAY

7TH POSITION: CUTOFF

Fig. 19–12. A tool layout for an eight spindle automatic bar machine.
(Courtesy The National Acme Co.)

490

This is particularly important with multiple-spindle automatic operations where the investment is large and the equipment must be kept producing at the highest possible rate to be economical. For that reason, it generally is preferable to do small tolerance jobs on single-spindle than on multiple-spindle machines.

If run at the same speed, a multiple-spindle automatic is a faster producer than a single-spindle automatic because all its tools work at once. However, the mechanism necessary for a multiple-spindle machine may hinder it from turning as fast as a single-spindle machine can with small pieces or soft materials like brass. Single-spindle automatics can be indexed faster, and that is an advantage when few cuts are taken and cutting time is short as compared to idle time. Single-spindle automatics are available for larger work than can be done on multiple-spindle machines.

A multiple-spindle automatic is economical only when it can turn out parts faster than a single-spindle automatic, and enough parts must be produced to justify the larger investment and longer set-up time of the multiple-spindle equipment. A rule of thumb is that a multiple-spindle automatic is not justified for a job unless it can be kept busy for four or more days.

Questions

1. Why are there different kinds of automatic turning machines?

2. Describe a typical automatic lathe and how it works.

3. What are the competitive advantages and disadvantages of automatic lathes?

4. What can be done to make automatic lathe operations economical?

5. What are the two main types of horizontal turret lathes? Describe each and tell how they differ.

6. What can be done to achieve low costs in a turret lathe operation?

7. What are combined and multiple cuts?

8. What basic principle determines whether a tool should be selected for a job?

9. Describe a typical single-spindle automatic bar machine and what it does.

10. Describe a Swiss-type automatic and tell how it differs from other single-spindle automatics.

11. Describe a typical single-spindle automatic chucking machine.

12. What are the two main types of cam controlled automatics and what are the advantages of each?

13. How does a multiple-spindle automatic operate?

14. Compare single-spindle to multiple-spindle automatics.

15. Why can single-spindle machines hold small tolerances better than multiple-spindle machines?

MATERIAL: 3135 STEEL

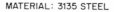
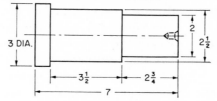

Fig. 19–13. Sketch of a workpiece.

Problems

1. The workpiece sketched in Fig. 19–13 is to be turned to 2 and 2½ in.-diameters from 3 in.-diameter barstock. One horsepower is required to remove a cubic inch of material per minute.

   Two machines are available for doing the job. Each has excess capacity, so overhead charges will be the same on whichever machine the job is done. Labor rate is $2.25 per hr. All but set-up and cutting time will be the same on both machines.

   One machine is an engine lathe with a tracer attachment and a 10 hp motor. A template costs $2 and set-up takes 10 minutes.

   The other machine is an automatic lathe with a 20 hp motor. A tooling set-up for this job costs $5 and set-up time is 30 minutes.

   Each machine is 80% efficient and is capable of removing material at a rate equivalent to its horsepower capacity.

   Find: (a) which machine should be selected for one lot of 5 pieces,
   (b) which machine should be selected for one lot of 100 pieces,
   (c) the least number of pieces that should be run on the automatic lathe in 10 lots during a year. Ignore charges for interest, insurance, taxes, and maintenance.

2. A piece can be turned on a tracer lathe in 4 minutes. The template costs $6 and set-up time is 15 minutes. The part can also be done on an automatic lathe in 2.5 minutes. Tooling cost is $75 and set-up time 45 minutes. Labor and overhead is $8 per hr on either machine. The rate for interest is 10%, for insurance and taxes 5%, and for maintenance 15%.

   (a) If only one lot of parts is to be made, how large a lot should be run on the tracer lathe?

(b) If 5 lots are to be run during a year, what is the lowest annual amount of production that justifies the use of the automatic lathe?

3. A workpiece can be held in a chuck on a turret lathe, but if a special fixture that costs $50 is provided, loading time is shortened by ½ min per piece. The composite rate for interest, insurance, taxes, and maintenance is 20%. Set-up time is not changed. The rate for labor and overhead is $6 per hr. For how many pieces is the fixture justified?

4. Ten thousand of the flywheels of Fig. 19–7 are to be machined in lots of 1000 pieces during one year. Disregard interest, insurance and tax, and maintenance charges. Should tooling method B or C be selected? How much is saved?

5. Four thousand pieces at 500 pieces to the lot are to be run to make the flywheel of Fig. 19–7. Interest is 10%, insurance and taxes 5%, and maintenance negligible. What tooling method should be selected?

6. The labor and overhead rate on an automatic bar machine is $0.207 per minute. For the tool taking the major cut in an operation, the tool life-speed relationship is $VT^{0.125} = 146$. Fifteen minutes are required to regrind the tool which cost $32 new and can be ground 50 times. Originally 20 min were required to change the tool when dull, but this time was reduced to ½ min by means of a quick change toolholder that enabled the tool to be preset off the machine.

The machine has ample power to allow the speed to be increased to any extent justified. What increase in production can be expected from the use of the quick-change holder?

References

Murray, E. L., "Economics of Tooling and Lathe Selection," *The Tool Engineer,* Nov. 1953, p. 51.

"Production Handbook" for *Warner and Swasey Turret Lathes,* The Warner and Swasey Co., Cleveland, 1956.

20

Economics of Process Planning

The choice of a method or process for machining a part determines largely the machine tool needed. On the other hand, the selection of a machine tool for an operation determines within limits how the operation is to be done. A decision to machine a flat face by revolving a workpiece points to the use of a turning type of machine. Conversely, if a person decides to machine a face by putting a piece on a lathe, he most likely intends to revolve the workpiece. Thus, in effect the principles that govern machine tool selection also are basic to machining process selection. These principles will be discussed in this chapter and illustrated mostly by reference to machines of the lathe family because those have been described. However, the principles apply just as much to all other kinds of machine tools, machines, and processes, and as the other types of machines are described, the factors that concern their selection will be included.

The choice of a machine tool must take into account: (1) the size and shape of the workpiece, (2) the work material, (3) the accuracy and surface quality required, (4) personal preferences, and (5) the quality of parts and the sizes of lots required. Usually a number of machine tools can do a job, but the one that will do the job at the lowest cost when required is the one to be chosen.

Cost is a matter of dollars and cents and in the final analysis must be estimated and calculated. Of the number of machine tools that might conceivably do a job, most can be eliminated without detailed estimates of their costs, since they are too small or too large, too weak, or in some other ways obviously deficient. The costs of the remaining few can then be ascertained to determine which tool is the best for the job. First, in the following discussion, the general considerations of dimensional size, strength and power, and performance characteristics that lead to the initial selection will be discussed. Then the principles of estimating and comparing actual costs will be presented.

GENERAL CONSIDERATIONS IN MACHINE TOOL SELECTION

Size and capacity. The dimensions that designate the size of a machine tool generally specify the size of the largest workpiece that can be handled. If enough pieces of one kind are to be produced to keep a machine busy practically all the time, a size just able to take the part might well be chosen. For instance, for pieces to be made from 1½ in. barstock, an automatic bar machine with 1½ in. collet capacity would be favored. On the other hand, if only a few pieces of a particular size are to be made, the general purpose machine selected for them might likely be larger so it would be adaptable to other jobs as well. Thus pieces from 1½ in. bar stock would probably be turned on lathes with 12 in. or larger swing, because lathes of that size would be found in a job shop for the run of medium size parts.

The size and capacity required may dictate particular features for a machine tool. As an example, small- and medium-size parts are turned on horizontal lathes but short pieces that have to be crane loaded are commonly machined on vertical lathes, called boring mills.

Other dimensions of a machine that may have to be considered are the directions and lengths of movements of tools to assure that the surfaces to be cut can be covered; the clearances for the tools that must be used; and the provisions for the holding device.

The dimensions of the various sizes of a machine suitable for a particular job may be ascertained from the manufacturer's catalog. By comparison with the requirements of the job, the proper size can be selected.

Strength and power. The rigidity and strength of a machine tool is not easy to calculate but for reputable machine tools is in keeping with the rated power capacity. Thus, a light machine usually has a smaller motor than a heavier one. In general, a machine tool is designed to resist the forces arising from cuts at rated power. Thus, the power required in an operation must be a major consideration in selecting a machine tool. The machine must have enough power, but too much is wasteful.

Ways of calculating the power needed at the cutting zone were explained in Chap. 17. A convenient way of estimating power is to multiply the rate of metal removal in cubic inches per minute by the unit power in horsepower per cu in. per min. The unit power varies with the work material, type of operation, rake angle of the cutting tool, size of cut, and speed, but mostly with the first two. Accordingly, average values of unit power, like those given in Table 20–1, may be used to estimate the power requirements of common operations.

TABLE 20–1. AVERAGE VALUES OF HORSEPOWER PER CUBIC INCH PER MINUTE OF STOCK REMOVAL FOR SOME COMMON MATERIALS AND MACHINING OPERATIONS

Workpiece material	Turning	Drilling	Milling	Shaping
Aluminum	0.2	0.5	0.6	0.3
Brass	0.2	0.5	0.7	0.3
Cast iron (soft)	0.3	0.6	0.8	0.4
Cast iron (hard)	0.5	0.9	1.0	0.6
Steel (soft)	1.0	1.2	1.5	1.0
Steel (medium)	1.4	1.6	1.9	1.4
Steel (hard)	2.0	2.0	2.2	2.0

(header: ————Machining operation————)

Some loss in power can be expected in any machine tool, so the power at the motor must be more than that at the cutting zone. An efficiency of 80% is a fair estimate for average conditions.

As an example, a ⅝ in.-diameter drill is to cut medium-soft steel at 550 rpm and 0.007 ipr feed. The estimated power at the drill

$$P_D = \left(\frac{5}{8}\right)^2 \times \frac{\pi}{4} \times 0.007 \times 550 \times 1.6 = 1.9 \text{ hp.}$$

The motor power should be $1.9/0.8 = 2.4$ hp.

An estimate of power is likely to be based on ideal experimental conditions. In actual production, tools become dull, the operator may choose to run at higher speeds and feeds than anticipated, and the work material may vary in hardness and stock allowance. This means that if a machine tool is loaded to capacity on a job for maximum economy under ideal conditions, it may be as much as 50% or more overloaded at other times. Actually that is a common experience, and good machine tools are built intentionally to stand overloads. One leading machine tool manufacturer as an example recommends:

"Rated capacity for continuous operation.

"25% over rated capacity for normal operation.

"50% over the rated capacity for intermittent operation, five minute maximum period. Minimum idle time between cuts should equal ⅕ the cutting time.

"75% over the rated capacity for intermittent operation, one minute maximum period. Minimum idle time between cuts should equal the cutting time."

Frequently the situation is that a machine meets all other requirements or happens to be available but has a limited power rating. The problem then is to determine the speed and feed at which the job may be run. As an example, a depth of cut of 0.109 in. is required to reduce a $1\frac{1}{2}$ in.-diameter to $1\frac{9}{32}$ in.-diameter at 216 fpm in medium-soft steel. The lathe has a $7\frac{1}{2}$ hp motor and is 80% efficient. The permissible rate of metal removal

$$Q = 7.5 \times 0.8/1.4 = 4.3 \text{ in.}^3 \text{ per min} = f \times 0.109 \times 12 \times 216.$$

The feed rate should be $f = 0.015$ ipr.

More precise results may be obtained from the detailed formulas of Chap. 17 as expressed in the chart of Fig. 17–9. If points on that chart are selected for a cemented carbide tool, an SAE 1020 steel of 200 Bhn, a tool life of 180 min, a depth of cut of 0.109 in., a machine of $7\frac{1}{2}$ hp, and efficiency of 80%, an economical speed of 216 fpm and feed of 0.018 ipr are indicated, comparable to the results obtained by the simpler method. These are the speed and feed shown for element 7 that calls for the heaviest cut in Table 20–1.

Other considerations. Among other factors that need to be considered in machine tool selection are the accuracy and surface finishes which a machine is capable of producing, the removal of hard material or large amounts of stock, the skill available and required to operate the machine, personal likes and dislikes, and availability. Most of these factors are not as basic as others but in some cases may be decisive. A few examples will be given. If fine surface finishes and small tolerances must be held, they often are obtainable only on grinding equipment. Grinding also is the only means of cutting some hard substances but is not well suited to remove large amounts of stock from any substance. In a situation where skill to set up automatic machines is not available, operations might have to be simplified and spread over the other simpler types of machines. Often in a shop, a machine that is available will be selected for a job rather than buying another or waiting for one that is already overloaded.

HOW COSTS ARE ESTIMATED AND COMPARED

As the result of the general considerations just described, a person may be able to eliminate all but one size of two or more types of machines from consideration for an operation. It then becomes necessary to estimate and compare the costs.

THE MONARCH MACHINE TOOL COMPANY
SIDNEY, OHIO, U.S.A.

TURNING DATA SHEET No. 104

HANDLING TIME

RECHUCK OR PLACE BETWEEN CENTERS — LENGTH IN INCHES

TIME IN MINUTES

Avg. Diam. In Inches	2	4	6	8	10	12	14	16	18	20	24	28	32	36	40	44	48	52	56	60	72	84	96	108
3/4	.10	.10	.10	.10	.10	.12	.14	.14	.16	.16	.18	.18	.20	.20	.24	.28	.32	.36	.40	.45	.58	.71	.84	.97
1	.10	.11	.12	.15	.18	.21	.24	.25	.28	.29	.32	.33	.36	.37	.42	.47	.52	.57	.62	.68	.81	.94	1.07	1.20
1¼	.14	.16	.18	.22	.26	.30	.34	.36	.40	.42	.46	.48	.52	.54	.60	.66	.72	.78	.84	.91	1.12	1.33	1.54	1.75
1½	.18	.21	.24	.29	.34	.39	.44	.47	.52	.55	.60	.63	.68	.71	.78	.85	.92	.99	1.06	1.14	1.38	1.66	1.94	2.22
2	.22	.26	.30	.36	.42	.48	.54	.58	.64	.68	.74	.78	.84	.88	.96	1.04	1.12	1.20	1.28	1.37	1.64	1.91	2.18	2.45
2¼	.26	.31	.36	.43	.50	.57	.64	.69	.76	.81	.88	.93	1.00	1.05	1.14	1.23	1.32	1.41	1.50	1.60	1.90	2.20	2.50	2.80
2½	.30	.36	.42	.50	.58	.66	.74	.80	.88	.94	1.02	1.08	1.16	1.22	1.32	1.42	1.52	1.62	1.72	1.93	2.53	3.13	3.73	4.33
2¾	.34	.41	.48	.57	.66	.75	.84	.91	1.00	1.07	1.16	1.23	1.32	1.39	1.50	1.61	1.72	1.83	1.94	2.16	2.76	3.36	3.96	4.56
3	.38	.46	.54	.64	.74	.84	.94	1.02	1.12	1.20	1.30	1.38	1.48	1.56	1.68	1.80	1.92	2.04	2.16	2.39	2.99	3.59	4.19	4.79
3½	.42	.51	.60	.71	.82	.93	1.04	1.13	1.24	1.33	1.44	1.53	1.64	1.73	1.86	1.99	2.12	2.25	2.38	2.52	3.12	3.72	4.32	4.92
4	.44	.56	.66	.78	.90	1.02	1.14	1.24	1.36	1.46	1.58	1.68	1.80	1.90	2.04	2.18	2.32	2.46	2.60	2.75	3.35	3.98	4.55	5.15
4½	.48	.61	.72	.85	.98	1.11	1.24	1.35	1.48	1.59	1.72	1.83	1.96	2.07	2.22	2.37	2.52	2.67	2.82	2.98	3.58	4.18	4.78	5.38

PLACE AND REMOVE - HAND - ELECTRIC - AIR - 3 OR 4-JAW CHUCK — LENGTH IN INCHES

TIME IN MINUTES

Avg. Diam. In Inches	2	4	6	8	10	12	14	16	18	20	22	24	26	28	30	32	34
5	.52	.66	.80	.94	1.08	1.22	1.36	1.50	1.64	1.78	1.92	2.06	2.20	2.34	2.48	2.62	2.76
5½	.56	.71	.86	1.01	1.16	1.31	1.46	1.61	1.76	1.91	2.06	2.21	2.36	2.51	2.66	2.81	2.96
6	.60	.76	.92	1.08	1.24	1.40	1.56	1.72	1.88	2.04	2.20	2.36	2.52	2.68	2.84	3.00	3.16
6½	.64	.81	.98	1.15	1.32	1.49	1.66	1.83	2.00	2.17	2.34	2.51	2.68	2.85	3.02	3.19	3.36
7	.68	.86	1.04	1.22	1.40	1.58	1.76	1.94	2.12	2.30	2.48	2.66	2.84	3.02	3.20	3.38	3.56
7½	.72	.91	1.10	1.29	1.48	1.67	1.86	2.05	2.24	2.43	2.62	2.81	3.00	3.19	3.38	3.57	3.76
8	.76	.96	1.16	1.36	1.56	1.76	1.96	2.16	2.36	2.56	2.76	2.96	3.16	3.36	3.56	3.76	3.96
8½	.80	1.01	1.22	1.43	1.64	1.85	2.06	2.27	2.48	2.69	2.90	3.11	3.32	3.53	3.74	3.95	4.16
9	.84	1.06	1.28	1.50	1.72	1.94	2.16	2.38	2.60	2.82	3.04	3.26	3.48	3.70	3.92	4.14	
9½	.88	1.11	1.34	1.57	1.80	2.03	2.26	2.49	2.72	2.95	3.18	3.41	3.64	3.87	4.10		
10	.92	1.16	1.40	1.64	1.88	2.12	2.36	2.60	2.84	3.08	3.32	3.56	3.80	4.04			
10½	.96	1.21	1.46	1.71	1.96	2.21	2.46	2.71	2.96	3.21	3.46	3.71	3.96				

Use Place & Remove Time & Factor

	Fac-tor
Face Plate and Centers with Dog	.8
Face Plate and Centers with Driver	.7
Chuck and Center	1.2
Chuck and Steady Rest	1.5
Chuck and Steady Rest and Center	1.7
Air Arbor—Thread or Stud	1.0
	Min.
Pcs. On and Off Thread Arbor—Long	.50
Tighten & Loosen Headstock Center	.20
Split Bushings use in P. & R.—Add	.05
Minimum Time to P. & R. Work Between Centers	.20
Arbor Press In & Out, Add to P.& R.	.30
Pcs. In & Out of Fixtures—On or Off Table—Small	.15

Fig. 20–1. Standard elements of handling time for lathes. (Courtesy The Monarch Machine Tool Co.)

	1.00	1.26	1.52	1.78	2.04	2.30	2.56	2.82	3.06	3.34	3.60	3.86	4.12			Medium	.30
11	1.00	1.26	1.52	1.78	2.04	2.30	2.56	2.82	3.06	3.34	3.60	3.86	4.12			Large	.50
11½	1.04	1.31	1.58	1.85	2.12	2.39	2.66	2.93	3.18	3.47	3.74	4.01				Extra Large	.80
12	1.08	1.36	1.64	1.92	2.20	2.48	2.76	3.04	3.30	3.60	3.88					Tighten Nut and Bolt	.20
13	1.12	1.41	1.70	1.99	2.28	2.57	2.86	3.15	3.42	3.73	4.02					Tighten Clamp 1 Nut or Bolt	.25
14	1.16	1.46	1.76	2.06	2.36	2.66	2.96	3.26	3.54	3.86						Tighten Clamp 2 Nut or Bolt	.40
15	1.20	1.51	1.82	2.13	2.44	2.75	3.06	3.37	3.66	3.99						Clamp On & Off 1 Nut or Bolt	.50
16	1.24	1.56	1.88	2.20	2.52	2.84	3.16	3.48	3.78	4.12						Clamp On & Off 2 Nut or Bolt	.70
17	1.28	1.61	1.94	2.27	2.60	2.93	3.26	3.59	3.90							Jack Moved to P. & R. Piece	.60
18	1.32	1.66	2.00	2.34	2.68	3.02	3.36	3.70	4.02							Clean Chips Off Job	.30
19	1.36	1.71	2.06	2.41	2.76	3.11	3.46	3.81								Adjust Set Screw	.10
20	1.40	1.76	2.12	2.48	2.84	3.20	3.56	3.92								Place & Remove Shim in Fixture	.05
21	1.44	1.81	2.18	2.55	2.92	3.29	3.66	4.03								Nut Arbor—Add to P. & R.	.50
22	1.48	1.86	2.24	2.62	3.00	3.38	3.76										
23	1.52	1.91	2.30	2.69	3.08	3.47	3.86									Add one (1) minute for hoist on piece over 35 pounds.	
24	1.56	1.96	2.36	2.76	3.16	3.56	3.96									(lbs.= D² × length × .22)—Solid piece.	
Over	1.60	2.01	2.40	2.83	3.24	3.65	4.06									Tubing or like pieces—Factor .5	

Double above times for Independent 4-Jaw Chuck—Includes ordinary indicating.

TOOL ADJUST—MEASURING¹—SPECIAL ALLOWANCES

Short Operations by Stock Diameter

	¾″	1¼″	2″	3″	4″	5″	7″	10″	15″	Over
Spot Drill or Center	.10 ·	.15	.20	.25	.30	.35	.40	.45	.50	.55
Chamfer—Bevel—Radius—Neck—Recess	.05	.10	.15	.20	.25	.30	.35	.40	.60	.80

Use these Material Factors with above operations, S.A E 1020, 1112, Cast Iron, Brass - 1.00 — Machine Steel, Bronze, Tubing - 1.50 — Tool Steel - 2.00

Measuring Times by Outside-Inside Diameters or Lengths

	½″	1″	2″	3″	4″	5″	7″	10″	15″	Over
Scale Short Length	.10	.10	.15	.15	.15	.20	.20	.25	.30	.35
Scale Long Length (over 4 feet)	.35	.35	.40	.40	.50	.50	.60	.70	.80	.90
V-Gauge—Calipers	.20	.20	.25	.25	.30	.30	.40	.50	.60	.70
Thread Gauge Male by I. D. Female by O. D.	.10	.15	.20	.25	.35	.45	.65			
Plug Gauge by I. D.	.05	.05	.10	.20	.30	.30	.40	.50	.60	.70
Taper Gauge Male by O. D. Female by O. D.	.20	.25	.30	.35	.40	.45	.50	.60	.70	.80
Bevel Protractor	.20	.20	.20	.30	.30	.30	.40	.50	.60	.70
Depth Micrometers by Length of Depth	.15	.20	.25	.30	.35	.40				
Micrometrs and Verniers (X2 on inside mikes)	.05	.10	.15	.20	.25	.30	.40	.50	.75	1.00
Height Gauge	.10	.10	.15	.15	.20	.20	.25	.25	.30	.30

Tool Adjust By Stock Diameters

	¾″	1¼″	2″	3″	4″	5″	7″	10″	15″	Over
Hexagon Turret or Cross Slide	.10	.15	.17	.20	.25	.27	.30	.35	.40	.45
Tailstock (Hole Diameter)	.20	.30	.40	.50	.60					

Tool Adjust on Work Supported on Both Ends—By Length

	6″	12″	18″	24″	30″	36″	48″	60″	72″	Over
Cross Slide	.10	.15	.20	.25	.30	.35	.40	.45	.50	.55

Form No. M-251 3M-9-45

Fig. 20-1 (Cont.)

All costs that vary must be considered and for convenience may be divided into direct costs, indirect or overhead costs, and capital costs. The direct cost that varies most from machine to machine is labor, which is usually calculated by multiplying the time required for an operation by a labor rate. Thus, the time to set up and perform an operation must be estimated to find its direct cost. Other direct costs such as for power and material do not vary much for the same job and are not included as a rule. Overhead costs are commonly calculated by multiplying the operation time by an overhead rate. Capital costs are determined by distributing the major machine and tool costs on an hourly basis or among the pieces produced.

The parts of productive time. The total time required to perform an operation may be divided into four parts. They are:

1. *Set-up time.* This is the time required to prepare for the operation and may include time to get tools from the crib and do paper work as well as to arrange the tools on the machine.
2. *Man or handling time.* This is the time the operator spends loading and unloading the work, manipulating the machine and tools, and making measurements during each cycle of the operation.
3. *Machine time.* This is the time during each cycle of the operation that the machine is working or the tools are cutting.
4. *Down or lost time.* This is the unavoidable time lost by the operator because of breakdowns, waiting for the tools and materials, etc.

Set-up, man, and down time. Set-up time is performed usually once for each lot of parts. It should therefore be listed separately from the other parts of the operation time. If 30 minutes are required for a set-up and only ten pieces are made, an average of 3 minutes of set-up time must be charged against each piece. On the other hand, if 60 pieces are made from the same set-up, only ½ minute is charged per piece. Thus a prorated set-up time may be very misleading because it depends so much on lot size.

Both set-up and man time are estimated from previous performance on similar operations. All work on a particular type of machine tool consists of a limited number of elements, selected and arranged to suit each operation. These elements may be standardized, measured, and recorded. That is the essence of the subject of Time Study, a large field in itself. Space does not permit a detailed treatment of that subject in this text. An example of handling time standards for lathes is given in Fig. 20–1.

The time to perform an operation also includes time for personal needs of the operator, time to change tools, etc.

The actual amount of down time that will occur in a specific operation can scarcely be predicted. Some operations will run smoothly, others will be beset by troubles. The best estimate that can be made is based upon the average amount currently lost in the plant. For a comparison between two operations, the assumption is that both will be subject to the same down time, so that part of the cost is not included as a rule.

Machine time. The way to calculate machine or cutting time for turning operations was explained in Chap. 18. The basic relationship for any operation is that the cutting time in minutes is equal to the distance the tool is fed in inches divided by the feed in inches per minute.

The distance a tool is fed to make a cut is the sum of the distance the tool travels while cutting to full depth plus its approach distance plus its overtravel. The *approach* is the distance a tool is fed from the time it touches the workpiece until it is cutting to full depth. Approach distance for a drill is the length of its point, which is about one-fourth the diameter of a standard drill. The approach of most single-point tools is negligible. *Overtravel* is the distance the tool is fed while it is not cutting. It is the space over which the tool idles before it enters and after it leaves the cut. Overtravel usually is from $\frac{1}{32}$ to $\frac{1}{4}$ in.

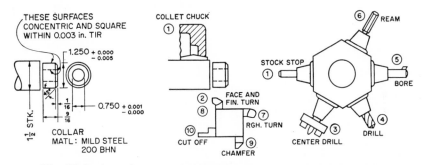

Fig. 20-2. A workpiece and a turret lathe tool layout to make it.

How operation time is estimated. The workpiece in Fig. 20–2 may be made on an engine lathe or on a turret lathe with the tool layout shown. To illustrate the details of estimating operation time and as a basis for further comparison, Table 20–1 contains figures compiled for both the engine lathe and turret lathe operations. The speeds and feeds selected are customary ones for the operations and tools. A check of the heaviest cut, that of element 7, was made against the power of the machine in a previous example in this chapter. The values for standard time for the engine lathe were taken from Fig. 20–1 and for the turret lathe from a similar table for that machine tool.

TABLE 20–1. Comparison of Elemental Times on 14 in. Engine Lathe and #4 Turret Lathe

No.	Element Designation	fpm	Cutting time rpm	ipr	min	Minutes Standard time Engine lathe	Turret lathe
1.	Advance & position bar					0.20	0.12
2.	Face end—set tool (1)					0.16	0.12
	1/32 deep cut	216	550	0.010	0.16		
3.	Center drill—set tool (2)					0.20	0.12
	Cut to 3/16 diam.		1200	hand	0.15		
4.	Drill—set tool (2)					0.20	0.13
	⅝ diam. × 11/16 deep cut	90	550	0.007	0.23		
5.	Bore—set tool (3)					0.36	0.13
	0.742/0.747 diam. × ⅝ dp. cut	138	700	0.007	0.14		
6.	Ream—set tool (2)					0.20	0.13
	0.750/0.751 diam. × ⅝ dp. cut	39	200	0.031	0.11		
7.	Rough turn—set tool (1)					0.26	(with No. 4)
	1 9/32 dia. × ¾ lg. cut	216	550	0.018	0.09		
8.	Finish turn—set tool (1)					0.25	(with No. 5)
	1.250/1.245 diam. × ⅝ lg.	275	700	0.010	0.13		
9.	Chamfer—set tool (1)					0.15	0.13
	1/16 × 45°	230	700	hand	0.10		
10.	Cut off—set tool (1)					0.25	0.13
	Cut to 9/16 thick	65	200	0.004	0.35		
11.	Break edges					0.25	0.20
12.	Check (Every piece on lathe, every 5th piece on turret lathe)					0.40	0.10
	Handling time					2.88	1.31
	Applicable cutting time					1.46	1.37
	Cycle time					4.34	2.68
	Set-up time					15	75
	Teardown and cleanup					5	5
	Total per lot					20	80

TABLE 20–1. (Cont.)

No.	Includes on lathe	On turret lathe
1.	Place and adjust tool on cross-slide (includes 0.10 min to measure if dimensional)	Index square turret and position tool
2.	Place tool in tailstock and adjust	Index hex. turret, advance tool to work, and start feed
3.	Place and adjust tool on cross-slide	Index hex. turret, advance tool to work, and start feed

For element 5, bore, the standard time for the lathe of 0.36 min includes "tool adjust 0.16 min" and "measure I.D. 0.20 min". The tool is preset to cut to size on the turret lathe, and the standard elemental time for that machine is only 0.13 min to "index hexagonal turret, advance tool to work, and engage feed." The total length of cut includes 1/16 in. overtravel, and the cutting time = $0.69/(700 \times 0.007) = 0.14$ min.

On the 10 hp turret lathe, element 7 has a total time of 0.22 min and can be performed entirely within the cutting time of 0.23 min of element 4. The value of 0.09 min for cutting time in element 7 is therefore not applied to total cutting time on the turret lathe.

For element 8, the handling time on the turret lathe of 0.13 min can be performed during the cutting time of 0.14 min for element 5.

For element 3, center drill, feed is by hand and machine time is not calculated. Instead, a value is obtained for "spot drill or center 0.15 min" from Fig. 20–1.

The set-up time on the lathe was calculated from the following elements:

TABLE 20–1. (CONT.)

Check-in on job .... 1.00 min
Study blueprint 1.00
Trip to tool crib 5.00
Handle 8 tools @ 0.4 min 3.20
Handle 4 measuring instruments @ 0.4 min 1.60
Install chuck 3.00

$\qquad$ _Total_ $\quad$ 14.80 min

Teardown and cleanup consists of these elements:

Sign out .... 1.00 min
Remove & clean 8 tools @ 0.3 min 2.40
Clean 4 measuring instruments @ 0.4 min 1.60

$\qquad$ _Total_ $\quad$ 5.00 min

The set-up time on the turret lathe is estimated in the same way but is larger than for the lathe because elements must be included to mount the tools, adjust them, and set the stops to get the cuts to size.

This estimate does not include time for personal needs of the operator, changing tools, delays, etc. In a comparison between machines, the time for such items usually can be expected to be about the same for both machines and often is ignored. One way to include it is to allow a fixed amount for each hour. Thus the productive hour may be considered to consist of only 50 minutes, for example.

Comparison of engine lathe and turret lathe. The operating differences between engine lathes and turret lathes are illustrated in Table 20–1. To produce 5 pieces of the part shown in Fig. 20–2 takes a total of 41.70 minutes or 8.34 minutes per piece on the engine lathe as compared with 93.40 total minutes or 18.68 minutes per piece on the turret lathe. For 100 pieces the total time is 454 minutes or 4.54 minutes per piece on the engine lathe but only 348 total minutes or 3.48 minutes per piece on the turret lathe. If the labor and overhead rates and capital costs are nearly the same on both machines, and they usually are for two machines like these, the comparison of the operation times tells which machine is more economical for a required number of pieces. This comparison bears out the principle that the engine lathe is usually economical for a few pieces, but for larger numbers the turret lathe shows lower costs.

Equal cost points. In the comparison of two machine tools, the equal cost point for an operation is at the quantity at which the total and unit costs are the same for both machines. One of the machines is the more economical for a smaller quantity, and the other for a larger quantity. A typical situation of this sort is shown in Fig. 20–3.

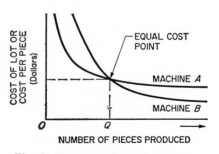

Fig. 20–3. A typical equal cost situation.

Let Q stand for the number of pieces produced at the equal cost point for two machine tools, A and B. Subscripts A and B indicate the following factors applicable to each machine.

P_A or P_B = number of pieces produced per hour.

S_A or S_B = number of hours of set-up and tear down.

L_A or L_B = labor rate in dollars per hr.

O_A or O_B = overhead rate in dollars per hr.
          (not including machine depreciation).

E_A or E_B = cost of special tools and equipment chargeable to the job, in dollars.

D_A or D_B = depreciation rate on standard items in dollars per hr.

R_A or R_B = composite rate = $L + O + D$.

For the equal cost quantity,

$$\left(\frac{Q}{P_A} + S_A\right)(L_A + O_A + D_A) + E_A = \left(\frac{Q}{P_B} + S_B\right)(L_B + O_B + D_B) + E_B$$

or

$$\left(\frac{Q}{P_A} + S_A\right)R_A + E_A = \left(\frac{Q}{P_B} + S_B\right)R_B + E_B.$$

The left side is the cost of producing Q pieces on machine A, which for the equal cost quantity must equal the cost for Q pieces on machine B, represented by the right side. The solution for the equal cost quantity is

$$Q = \frac{P_A P_B(S_B R_B + E_B - S_A R_A - E_A)}{P_B R_A - P_A R_B} \qquad (20\text{-}1)$$

As an example, this may be applied to the case described in Table 20-1, for which the rate of production is 11.52 pieces per 50 min hr on the engine lathe and 18.69 pieces on the turret lathe. Assume the composite rate to be \$6 on the engine lathe and \$6.50 on the turret lathe. No special equipment is required for either machine. Then

$$Q = \frac{11.52 \times 18.69(1.33 \times 6.50 - 0.33 \times 6)}{18.69 \times 6 - 11.52 \times 6.50} = 39 \text{ pieces.}$$

Thus the engine lathe is the more economical for lots of up to 39 pieces, and the turret lathe for larger lots.

Comparison of turret lathes and automatics. A turret lathe is a hand operated machine and for some operations may be the most practical choice for almost any number of pieces. Such a situation might occur for workpieces requiring quite deep drilling, intricate forming, or abnormal thread length where constant operator attention would be necessary to avoid trouble. However, most operations can be done equally well on a turret lathe or automatic and should be put in the machine that gives the lowest cost for the number of pieces to be made.

TABLE 20–2. A COMPARISON OF MACHINE COSTS

	Ram-type turret lathe with standard tools	Ram-type turret lathe with special tooling	Single-spindle automatic with proper tooling	Multi-spindle automatic with proper tooling
Cost of machine—($)	6500.00	6500.00	10750.00	17325.00
Cost of standard tools—($)	1234.75	59.50	750.00	750.00
Total cost of standard items—($)	7734.75	6559.50	11500.00	18075.00
Annual depreciation on 15 yr basis of std. items—($ per yr)	515.65	437.30	766.67	1205.00
Over 2000 hr/yr—Depreciation ($ per hr)	0.258	0.219	0.383	0.603
Composite rate (1)—($ pr hr)	4.26	4.22	3.63	3.85
Composite rate—($ per min)	0.0710	0.0703	0.0605	0.0642
Set-up time—(hr) (estimated)	2.5	2.5	3.5	6.0
Total set-up cost per lot (2)—($)	10.65	10.55	15.33	27.62
Cost of special tools (3)—($)	197.00	2616.70	350.00	700.00
Cost of special tools and set-up—($)	207.65	2627.25	365.33	727.62
Operation time per piece—(min) (estimated)	6.5	4.0	3.0	1.0
Production per 50 min hr—(pcs. per hr)	7.69	12.5	16.67	50.0
Cost per piece (without set-up)—($ per pc.)	0.555	0.338	0.218	0.077

Notes: 1. Labor rate is $1.50 per hr on hand turret lathe but is $0.75 per hr on automatics where one man attends to two machines. Overhead rate (not including depreciation) is $2.50 per hr.

2. Labor rate is $1.50 per hr for set-up time on all machines.

3. Special tools are depreciated and charged against one lot.

Basic data obtained from E. L. Murray, "Machine Tool Selection in the Turning Field," *The Tool Engineer,* June, 1949. (For simplicity, the relatively small items of interest, insurance, and taxes are not included.)

A comparison of the relevant costs to make a typical part on a turret lathe, a single-spindle automatic, and multiple-spindle automatic is given in Table 20–2.

This table shows that the single-spindle automatic is more economical than the turret lathe with special tooling at any level of production. That is because the single-spindle automatic not only produces faster but also has a lower composite rate and tooling cost than the special tooling set-up on the turret lathe. On the other hand, the single-spindle automatic produces faster but requires more tooling and set-up cost than the turret lathe with standard tools. Accordingly, when tooled simply, the turret lathe is the more economical for a few pieces.

Formula (20–1) tells the number of pieces for the equal cost point for turret lathe with standard tools and the single-spindle automatic. At this level

$$Q = \frac{16.67 \times 7.69 \ (365.33 - 207.65)}{16.67 \times 4.26 - 7.69 \times 3.63} = 468 \ \text{pieces.}$$

For 468 pieces or less, the turret lathe is more economical. For more in a lot, the single-spindle automatic is preferred. The equal cost point for the multiple- and single-spindle automatics is

$$Q = \frac{50 \times 16.67 \ (727.62 - 365.33)}{50 \times 3.63 - 16.67 \times 3.85} = 2580 \ \text{pieces.}$$

For more than 2580 pieces, the multiple-spindle automatic should be chosen.

Special considerations. The analysis that has just been made has been based upon the assumption that all the machines are standard general-purpose units that can be kept busy with other jobs when not needed for the job under consideration. On this basis, the costs of the machines and standard tools in Table 20–2 are distributed over the total normal number of working hours and added to the other items of depreciation. That would not be sufficient if the automatic machine could not be used for other jobs and had to be paid for in its entirety from the savings realized from the one job under consideration. This is the general case of the special machine that is built to do a specific operation on one or a few different parts and is not suited for other operations or other parts.

In this analysis, the costs of interest, insurance, and taxes are neglected. This simplifies calculation and does not make an appreciable difference in the answer. Some methods of analysis that are more refined and advanced take these factors into account but are not necessary for our purposes.

Formula (20–1) may be used to find the equal cost quantity when a special machine is involved, but the factors have somewhat different values. This may be illustrated by assuming that machine B can be utilized to make the part under consideration, but that there is no other work that can be put on it.

One case arises when machine A is the turret lathe with standard tools and can be kept busy when not on this job. Machine B is the single-spindle automatic and has no use other than for this job. In that case, the value of the special tools and equipment, E_B, includes \$11,500 + \$350 = \$11,850. The composite rate, R_B, is \$3.25 instead of \$3.63 because it includes only labor and overhead without any depreciation. Because set-up time is a small part of the cost and no change-over is necessary, the set-up rate may be considered the same as R_B with no appreciable error. In that case

$$Q = \frac{16.67 \times 7.69 \ (3.5 \times 3.25 + 11,850 - 2.5 \times 4.26 - 197)}{16.67 \times 4.26 - 7.69 \times 3.25} = 32,400 \text{ pc}$$

Another case is the comparison of the standard turret lathe with special tools and the single-spindle automatic that can be used only for this job. For that case

$$Q = \frac{16.67 \times 12.5 \ (3.5 \times 3.25 + 11,850 - 2627.25)}{16.67 \times 4.22 - 12.5 \times 3.25} = 64,300 \text{ pieces.}$$

From a comparison of the turret lathe with special tools and the multiple-spindle automatic, also considered a special machine, the equal cost quantity is found to be

$$Q = \frac{50 \times 12.5 \ (6 \times 3.25 + 18,775 - 2627.25)}{50 \times 4.22 - 12.5 \times 3.25} = 59,000 \text{ pieces.}$$

These comparisons indicate that under the circumstances the turret lathe with standard tools is the economical choice for a small quantity, the turret lathe with special tools is economical for moderate quantities, and the multiple-spindle automatic is preferable for any quantity over 59,000 pieces. The single-spindle automatic does not seem to have a place in this situation. Before, when all the machines were considered standard, the turret lathe with special tooling was not found to be economical, and the single-spindle automatic was the choice for medium lot sizes.

A rule of thumb. A large manufacturer of both turret lathes and permanent cam automatics has proposed a simplified form of Formula (20–1) for average conditions based upon his extensive experience. The assumptions made are:

1. The labor rate for set-up and operation is \$1.50 per hr for both types of machines.
2. Factory overhead except for machine depreciation is really not appreciably different for the two types of machines and is omitted.

3. Hourly depreciation is $0.40 for hand turret lathes and $1.175 for automatics.
4. The cost for special tools and equipment is the same on either type of machine, and is omitted.
5. Set-up time on an automatic averages three times as long as on the hand operated turret lathe and hourly production is on the average three times as much on the automatic as on the turret lathe.

On the basis of these assumptions, the equal cost quantity

$$Q = \frac{3P_A^2 \ (3S_A \times 2.675 - S_A \times 1.90)}{3P_A \times 1.90 - P_A \ 2.675} = 6S_A P_A. \qquad (20\text{-}2)$$

Questions

1. Is the general-purpose machine tool with a size capacity just large enough usually selected for a workpiece? Why?

2. What should the size capacity of a special- or single-purpose machine tool be in relation to the size of part it is intended to handle?

3. What kinds of pieces are machined on vertical lathes or boring mills?

4. What is one method of estimating the power required for an operation?

5. Why is the power at the motor of a machine tool likely to be considerably higher than that estimated at the tool point?

6. Is it permissible to overload a machine tool?

7. What are some particular considerations important in machine tool selection?

8. How are labor and overhead costs usually calculated?

9. Into what four parts may the time to perform an operation be divided? Describe these parts.

10. What is the basic relationship for calculating cutting time?

11. How do the engine lathe and turret lathe compare as far as quantity of production is concerned? Why?

12. What does an equal cost point show in the comparison of two machine tools?

13. When might a turret lathe be preferable to an automatic machine, even for large quantities?

14. Why is a comparison between standard general-purpose machines different from a comparison between special- and standard-purpose machines?

15. What is a rule of thumb way of telling whether a job should be put on a hand turret lathe or an automatic?

Problems

1. Calculate the cutting time for the starter pinion gear blank shown in Fig. 20–4. Assume a cutting speed of 200 fpm for cemented carbide tools and 60 fpm for high-speed steel tools (except for reaming). Barstock size is 2½ in.

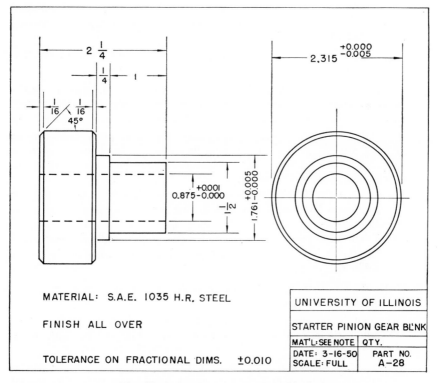

MATERIAL: S.A.E. 1035 H.R. STEEL

FINISH ALL OVER

TOLERANCE ON FRACTIONAL DIMS.   ±0.010

UNIVERSITY OF ILLINOIS

STARTER PINION GEAR BL'NK

MAT'L: SEE NOTE	QTY.
DATE: 3-16-50	PART NO.
SCALE: FULL	A-28

Fig. 20–4. A starter pinion gear blank.

2. Estimate the total cycle time to turn out one of the gear blanks of Fig. 20–4 on a 14 in. engine lathe with a 7½ hp motor.

3. Estimate the total cycle time to turn out one of the gear blanks of Fig. 20–4 on a No. 5 ram-type turret lathe with a 10 hp motor.

4. It estimated that it takes 21 minutes to set up and teardown and 10 minutes for each piece like Fig. 20–4 on a 14 in. engine lathe. Set-up and teardown is estimated to be 85 minutes and each piece 6 minutes on a No. 5 turret lathe. The rate for labor and overhead is $8 per hr on both machines. No special tools are required. What is the equal cost quantity for the two machines?

5. For the situation given in Table 20–2, what is the equal cost quantity for the ram-type turret lathe with standard tools and the same machine with special tooling?

6. If the part shown in Fig. 20–4 is made on a No. 5 ram-type turret lathe with standard tools, set-up time is 85 minutes and the cycle time 6 min per piece. The machine costs $12,000 and tools $2000, depreciated over a 15 yr period and 2000 hr per yr. Labor rate is $2 per hr and overhead (not including depreciation) is $4 per hr.

   If $1500 of special tools are applied to the job, the cost of standard tools is reduced to $1000, and the time per piece to 5 minutes. Set-up time is not changed.

   What is the equal cost quantity between the standard tooling and special tooling arrangements?

7. The part shown in Fig. 20–4 can be made on a 2½ in. capacity single-spindle automatic bar machine in 4.5 min. The machine costs $13,500, standard tools $900, and special tools $400. Set-up time is 3 hours. The labor rate on set-up is $2 per hr, but otherwise is $1 per hr because one operator attends more than one machine. The overhead rate, except for depreciation, is $4 per hr. This machine can be used for other work whenever it is not busy with the job.
   (a) What is the equal cost quantity for the single-spindle automatic and the turret lathe with standard tooling for which costs are given in Prob. 6?
   (b) What is the equal cost quantity for the single-spindle automatic and the turret lathe with special tooling for which costs are given in Prob. 6?

8. If the single-spindle automatic bar machine described in Prob. 7 has no use other than for this part,
   (a) what is the equal cost quantity to justify use of the single-spindle automatic in preference to the hand operated turret lathe with standard tooling?
   (b) What is the equal cost quantity to justify the use of the single-spindle automatic in preference to the hand turret lathe with special tooling?

9. The part shown in Fig. 20–4 can be made on a 2⅝ in. capacity six-spindle automatic bar machine in 1.5 min. The machine costs $28,115, standard tools $3300, and special tools $2400. Set-up time is 7 hr. The labor rate for set-up is $2 per hr, but otherwise is $1 per hr because one operator attends more than one machine. The overhead rate, except for depreciation, is $4 per hr. The machine can be used for other work when it is not busy with this job.
   (a) What is the equal cost quantity for the six-spindle automatic and the turret lathe with special tooling for which costs are given in Prob. 6?

(b) What is the equal cost quantity for the six-spindle automatic and the single-spindle automatic described in Prob. 7?

10. If the six-spindle automatic bar machine described in Prob. 9 cannot be used for other work, what quantity must be produced on it to justify its selection?

References

Doyle, L. E., *Tool Engineering: Analysis and Procedure,* Prentice-Hall, Inc., Englewood Cliffs, N. J., 1950.

Principles of Machine
Tool Design

All machine tools serve a common purpose, to cut and form materials, and all are dependent upon certain principles. These principles govern the designs that enable the machine tools to

(1) produce precise results repeatedly,

(2) apply forces and power as required,

(3) do their work in an economical manner.

The principles in each of these areas and the ways they are applied will be discussed in this chapter. All of the practical designs that carry out the principles cannot be illustrated in the space available, but typical and basic ones will be described. The reader will then be in a position to recognize the applications of the principles as he observes and studies various types of machine tools. The principles and applications cited here will be the ones common to most machine tools. Others of more limited scope will be brought out in connection with the machine to which they pertain.

PRECISION

Modern machine tools are marvels of near perfection. Consider a lathe producing round pieces to a tolerance of 0.002 in. That is expected performance; yet it means that the machine maintains a relationship between a whirling workpiece and gliding tool within 0.001 in. on a side and does it over and over again. That dimension is less than half the thickness of a human hair.

To turn to a tolerance of 0.001 in. on a side, the tool first must be adjusted to within 0.0005 in. of exact size. Such a minute amount can scarcely be seen, and the machine has to magnify it to reveal it to the crude vision of the operator. Then as metal is slashed away with tremendous force, the machine must guide the tool along a firm course and hold the workpiece steady so that neither deviates from the other by more than 0.0005 in.—and this is not close work. Tolerances smaller than 0.0001 in. are held in some operations.

Errors in the work done by a machine tool are caused by: (1) inaccuracy in its construction, (2) deflection, (3) wear, (4) thermal expansion, (5) dirt, and (6) human laxity. Good design and operation of a machine tool depend upon observing principles that keep errors small. Evidences of these principles are found in the structural members, the bearings and guide-ways for straight and rotary motions, the micrometer scales, and the standards of construction of all good machine tools.

Fig. 21–1. A part of a planer bed. (Courtesy Rockford Machine Tool Co.)

Structural members. An evident feature of all major machine tool members is rigidity. This is illustrated by the view of the base or bed for a planer in Fig. 21–1. The same general characteristics of deep and well braced sections are found in other units. The components of standard machine tools made in lots are most often cast, but some, and especially special units, are built up by welding steel plates and sections together.

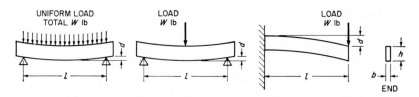

Fig. 21–2. Scheme of deflection of typical machine tool members.

The main purpose of rigidity in machine tool design is to keep deflections small. The principles of mechanics reveal that a member like one of the beams depicted in Fig. 21–2 under a load W deflects an amount

$$d = KWl^3/bh^3. \tag{21-1}$$

The constant K depends upon the material and kind of support. The other symbols are explained in Fig. 21–2, and their units are in inches. Deflection decreases in proportion to the cube of the depth of a section in the direction in which a force is applied. For that reason, machine tool sections like the bed of Fig. 21–1 are deep in the directions of the main forces to resist deflection. Also they are heavily ribbed and wide to take forces from other directions.

Machine tool members are designed not only to be rigid, but to have the most rigidity with the least possible weight. One reason, of course, is that a machine has to be moved, at least from where it is made to where it is used. Another reason is to minimize the effects of vibration.

For a simple case, any object with a single degree of freedom has a natural frequency in cycles per second of $W_n = \sqrt{k/m}$. The factor m is the mass of the structure and k is proportional to the stiffness of the object. Thus, the stiffer the member and the less its mass, the higher is its natural frequency.

A high natural frequency is desirable because it is less excited by the usual disturbances. As has been pointed out, metal cutting is inherently cyclic and vibratory. It tends to induce vibrations in machine tools and to cause chatter. Vibrations may also be set up by other actions, such as the running of gears. The farther the natural frequency of a machine member is from the exciting frequency, the smaller the intensity is of the vibration induced in the member. For the best effect, the natural frequency should be higher than the induced frequency. Thus if a machine member is to be least susceptible to vibration, its structure should be as rigid and as light in weight as possible. This explains why machine tool members are designed like the bed of Fig. 21–1 with thin deep sec-

tions, adequate cross ribbing, and many hollow spaces. The aim, in effect, is to approach as near as possible to hollow box or cylindrical sections which have the most rigidity against forces from different directions or against twisting.

Stiffness can be increased and natural frequency raised by making a member shorter, supporting it more fully, or making it from stiffer material. The first two of these means are manifest in the design of many machine tool members. The third merits further discussion. Traditionally gray cast iron has been the material used for most major machine tool members because of its low cost. Cast iron also has good vibration dampening qualities; its internal structure tends to absorb energy and to cause induced vibrations to die out quickly.

In recent years the trend has been to steel castings and weldments. Steel is stronger and stiffer and can be stressed more highly than cast iron with less to no more deflection. At sufficiently high stresses, steel has a dampening capacity equal to or better than cast iron. Also, because of stiffness, steel can offer a higher natural frequency. Kronenberg has reported tests that showed a cast iron lathe bed subject to vibrations of undesirable intensity between 60 and 180 cycles per sec at spindle speeds of the machine from 200 to 600 rpm. A comparable steel bed showed excessive vibrations at frequencies of 90 to 120 cps, corresponding to speeds of 300 to 400 rpm. Thus the steel bed was affected over a narrower range and exhibited a more effective dampening capacity.

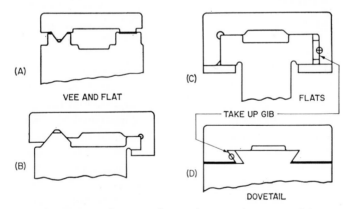

Fig. 21–3. End views of several types of ways or slides.

Bearings and guide-ways. Straight line motion in a true path is obtained from most machine tools by having precisely finished guide-ways of one member slide along those of another member. A way may be flat or vee shaped; the latter acts as a guide in two directions. A table will slide on the two vee ways on top of the planer bed of Fig. 21–1. End views of vee and flat ways are shown at *A* and *B* in Fig. 21–3. A vee has the advantage of not becoming loose as wear takes place but may ride up a little on the side with a large side thrust. The ways so far described are limited to horizontal movements. Two types suited for vertical mounting are shown at C and D in Fig. 21–3. Looseness is taken up in a slide of that sort by tapered adjustable inserts called *gibs*. Ways with rollers or balls move easily and are put on some machine tools but cost much more for the same precision and load bearing capacity as plain slides.

A few heavy machine tools have plastic inserts for ways. Chips imbed in these and do not cause severe scoring. Most ways are cut in cast iron, but in recent years the trend has been toward hardened steel inserts or flame hardening of cast steel.

Movements along precise paths are obtained from machine tool ways because the ways themselves are true. Hardened ways are ground. Soft cast iron ways are machined and then hand scraped to match precise straight edges. This procedure is the basis for the precision in all machine tools.

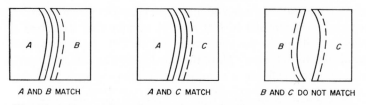

A AND *B* MATCH   *A* AND *C* MATCH   *B* AND *C* DO NOT MATCH

Fig. 21–4. Two surfaces that match a third will not match each other unless they all are true flat planes.

Two pieces B and C in Fig. 21–4 may have surfaces matching piece A, but will not match each other unless all three surfaces are true planes. Straight edges and surface plates are made originally on this principle in sets of three. They are compared, after being machined, by coating them lightly with red lead or prussian blue and rubbing them together. High spots that show contact are removed by selectively hand scraping away minute amounts of metal. This leaves other high spots. This process is repeated until enough high spots are obtained on each surface to simulate true planes. Surfaces precisely at right angle may be obtained in a similar way.

The bearing ways of a machine tool are scraped to desired straightness, alignment, and amount of bearing by first comparing them with master surfaces until the desired degree of truth is achieved; then mating ways are finished to match each other.

Machine tool looseness. Because of the looseness that must exist between sliding members, more than elastic deflection takes place in machine tools. If a force in the positive direction of Fig. 21–5 is applied to a machine tool member in a neutral position, a movement is found to take place as represented by line *OA*. When the force is released, the member does not return to point *O*, but rather to point *B*. A negative force can be expected to cause a negative movement to point *C*, and so on. With slides free enough for feeding and adjusting a member, deflection movements under normal loads may amount to a fraction of a thousandth to several thousandths of an inch.

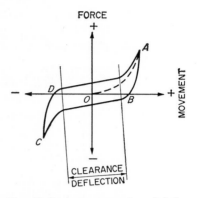

Fig. 21–5. A representation of deflection of machine tool members.

Comparable movements in the form of vibrations and chatter can be expected to occur from varying applied forces.

Universal and general-purpose machine tools usually have many slides and adjustable members. As a result they lack some rigidity and are not capable of taking cuts as heavy and fast as special-purpose and high-production machines, which are designed with as few connections as possible for sturdiness but are limited in flexibility and are harder to adjust.

Even though the ways on the base or bed of a machine tool are made straight and parallel, they will become untrue if the structure is placed on an uneven foundation and allowed to sag. This is particularly true of large and long machines like planers, but all machines need to be well supported. The bed of Fig. 21–1 has levelling jack screws at intervals along each side at the bottom, which is typical. The bed is intended to stand on these levelling screws. Levelling is done with a precision spirit level applied to finished surfaces along and across the ways. The straightness of a long bed may be checked by stretching a wire lengthwise and sighting along the wire with a microscope mounted on a bracket guided by the ways.

Spindles. The members that revolve workpieces or cutters on machine tools are called *spindles.* They have to be sturdy and well supported in true bearings to avoid deflection and runout as much as possible. In recent years the trend has been away from sleeve-type sliding bearings except in heavy service where the highest degree of accuracy is required. Thus, large grinding wheel spindles mostly run in sliding bearings, although they usually are some form of rocker shoe type rather than plain sleeve bearings. Most machine tool spindles today run in anti-friction bearings. Roller bearings, usually tapered, are used

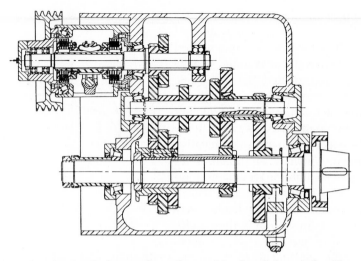

Fig. 21–6. The layout of an all geared headstock for a lathe. The sliding gears on the spindle, at bottom, and pulley shaft are shifted by three levers on the outside of the headstock to give twelve spindle speeds. (Courtesy Rockford Machine Tool Co.)

for heavy service at low and moderate speeds. A typical spindle design is shown in Fig. 21–6. Ball bearings run freely, stand up at high speeds, and are favored for light service. For the highest precision, ball bearings are preloaded and selected in matched sets to minimize runout.

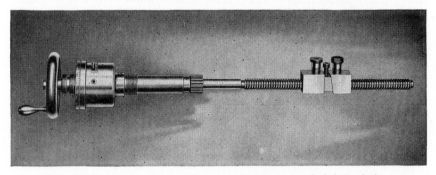

Fig. 21–7. A cross screw with nut and micrometer dial for a lathe. (Courtesy The American Tool Works Co.)

Precision adjustment. The common way of precisely adjusting the position of a slide on a machine tool is through a screw and nut. A cross screw for a lathe is illustrated in Fig. 21–7. This screw is attached to the carriage and restrained from moving lengthwise but is free to turn in bearings. The nut shown on the screw is fastened to the cross-slide and moves along as the screw is turned. On the left end of the screw is the handwheel and the micrometer dial, normally graduated to indicate 0.001 in. increments. The screw is also the means to feed the cross-slide by power, as evidenced by the pinion in the middle of the shaft.

When in good condition and properly used, a micrometer screw on a good quality machine tool can be expected to indicate increments of movement corresponding to the dial graduations. However, necessary clearance between screw and nut, wear, and deflection can cause a reading on a micrometer dial to differ appreciably from an actual movement. To correct for the looseness, or *backlash* as it is called, an operator always makes sure that the dial is turned in the same direction at the end of an adjustment as it was turned to reach the starting point.

A few machines have vernier scales, sometimes read with a microscope, to measure movements of slides. These are slower to read than micrometer dials. Other more precise measuring devices will be described in connection with jig boring machines.

Thermal distortion. Machine tool members get hot during operation, and the temperature rise is not uniform as a rule. This means that some members expand more than others, and alignments and settings change. This is most noticeable during the first two hours of operation of a machine tool, and usually conditions become stable after equilibria of temperatures are reached. An example is cited by Kronenberg of a turret lathe running at 1000 rpm. During the first hour the temperature rose about 30°F in the headstock, and the spindle moved 0.002 in. upward and 0.007 in. sideward. During the second hour, spindle movements were 0.0004 in. up and 0.0001 in. to the side.

Some remedial measures for thermal expansion are found in machine tool designs. These include heater elements in housings to maintain working temperatures and the use of low-expansion alloys. For the most part, the effects of thermal expansion must be corrected by good operating practice. Machines for precision operations may be turned on well before starting time in a plant and kept running during breaks and lunch periods. Adjustments are made by the operator as temperature rise causes change during operation. Much can be done by assuring proper bearing adjustments and lubrication.

Standards of construction. The standards of accuracy for engine lathes recognized by most manufacturers are shown in Fig. 21–8. A study of these standards will reveal the alignments and limits held in the construction of good quality machine tools. The accuracy of a machine tool cannot be represented by one or a few numbers but depends on many measurements. Sheets of test standards like those illustrated are prepared by reputable manufacturers of all kinds of machine tools, and each machine is tested against the standards.

RECOMMENDED STANDARDS

TEST	TOOL ROOM LATHES	12 TO 18 INCL. ENGINE LATHES	20 TO 36 INCL. ENGINE LATHES
1 BED LEVEL - TRANSVERSE DIRECTION	WHEN USING PRECISION LEVEL, BOTH READINGS TO BE WITHIN .0005 IN 12 INCHES	WHEN USING PRECISION LEVEL, BOTH READINGS TO BE WITHIN .0005 IN 12 INCHES	WHEN USING PRECISION LEVEL, BOTH READINGS TO BE WITHIN .001 IN 12 INCHES
2 BED LEVEL - LONGITUDINAL DIRECTION	WHEN USING PRECISION LEVEL ALONG BED MAXIMUM READING TO BE WITHIN .0005 IN 12 INCHES	WHEN USING PRECISION LEVEL ALONG BED MAXIMUM READING TO BE WITHIN .0005 IN 12 INCHES	WHEN USING PRECISION LEVEL ALONG BED MAXIMUM READING TO BE WITHIN .001 IN 12 INCHES
3 TAILSTOCK WAY ALIGNMENT	MAXIMUM READING ALONG LENGTH OF BED .0005 IN 48 INCHES	MAXIMUM READING ALONG LENGTH OF BED .00075 IN 48 INCHES	MAXIMUM READING ALONG LENGTH OF BED .001 IN 48 INCHES
4 SPINDLE CENTER RUNOUT	TOTAL INDICATOR READING 0 TO .0004	TOTAL INDICATOR READING 0 TO .0005	TOTAL INDICATOR READING 0 TO .00075
5 SPINDLE NOSE RUNOUT	TOTAL INDICATOR READING 0 TO .0003	TOTAL INDICATOR READING 0 TO .0004	TOTAL INDICATOR READING 0 TO .0006
6 CAM ACTION OF SPINDLE	TOTAL INDICATOR READING WITH INDICATOR ON REAR SIDE OF TEST PLATE 0 TO .0003	TOTAL INDICATOR READING WITH INDICATOR ON REAR SIDE OF TEST PLATE 0 TO .0005	TOTAL INDICATOR READING WITH INDICATOR ON REAR SIDE OF TEST PLATE 0 TO .00075

RECOMMENDED STANDARDS

TEST	TOOL ROOM LATHES	12 TO 18 INCL. ENGINE LATHES	20 TO 36 INCL. ENGINE LATHES
7 SPINDLE TAPER RUNOUT	TOTAL INDICATOR READING AT END OF 12 INCH TEST BAR 0 TO .0006 AT END OF SPINDLE NOSE 0 TO .0003	TOTAL INDICATOR READING AT END OF 12 INCH TEST BAR 0 TO .0008 AT END OF SPINDLE NOSE 0 TO .0004	TOTAL INDICATOR READING AT END OF 12 INCH TEST BAR 0 TO .00125 AT END OF SPINDLE NOSE 0 TO .0006
8 HEADSTOCK ALIGNMENT - VERTICAL	HIGH AT END OF 12 INCH TEST BAR 0 TO .0005	HIGH AT END OF 12 INCH TEST BAR 0 TO .001	HIGH AT END OF 12 INCH TEST BAR 0 TO .001
9 HEADSTOCK ALIGNMENT - HORIZONTAL	AT END OF 12 INCH TEST BAR 0 TO ±.0003	AT END OF 12 INCH TEST BAR 0 TO ±.0005	AT END OF 12 INCH TEST BAR 0 TO ±.0008
10 TAILSTOCK SPINDLE ALIGNMENT - HORIZONTAL	FORWARD AT END OF SPINDLE WHEN FULLY EXTENDED 0 TO .0005	FORWARD AT END OF SPINDLE WHEN FULLY EXTENDED 0 TO .0005	FORWARD AT END OF SPINDLE WHEN FULLY EXTENDED 0 TO .0005
11 TAILSTOCK SPINDLE ALIGNMENT - VERTICAL	HIGH AT END OF SPINDLE WHEN FULLY EXTENDED 0 TO .0005	HIGH AT END OF SPINDLE WHEN FULLY EXTENDED 0 TO .0008	HIGH AT END OF SPINDLE WHEN FULLY EXTENDED 0 TO .0015
12 TAILSTOCK TAPER ALIGNMENT - HORIZONTAL	END OF 12 INCH TEST BAR 0 TO ±.0005	END OF 12 INCH TEST BAR 0 TO ±.0008	END OF 12 INCH TEST BAR 0 TO ±.0015

RECOMMENDED STANDARDS

TEST	TOOL ROOM LATHES	12 TO 18 INCL. ENGINE LATHES	20 TO 36 INCL. ENGINE LATHES
13 TAILSTOCK TAPER ALIGNMENT - VERTICAL	HIGH AT END OF 12 INCH TEST BAR 0 TO .0005	HIGH AT END OF 12 INCH TEST BAR 0 TO .0008	HIGH AT END OF 12 INCH TEST BAR 0 TO .0015
14 VERTICAL ALIGNMENT OF HEAD & TAIL CTRS.	HIGH AT TAILSTOCK 0 TO .0008	HIGH AT TAILSTOCK 0 TO .001	HIGH AT TAILSTOCK 0 TO .0015
15 LEAD SCREW ALIGNMENT (READINGS FOR BASE LENGTH BED TAKEN WITH LEAD SCREW STATIONARY. ADD .001 INCH FOR EACH ADDITIONAL 4 FEET OF BED LENGTH)	PARALLEL WITH WAYS 0 TO .004 HORIZONTAL 0 TO .004 VERTICAL ALIGNMENT OF HALF NUT HORIZONTAL OR VERTICAL 0 TO .006	PARALLEL WITH WAYS 0 TO .006 HORIZONTAL 0 TO .006 VERTICAL ALIGNMENT OF HALF NUT HORIZONTAL OR VERTICAL 0 TO .006	PARALLEL WITH WAYS 0 TO .006 HORIZONTAL 0 TO .006 VERTICAL ALIGNMENT OF HALF NUT HORIZONTAL OR VERTICAL 0 TO .008
16 LEAD SCREW CAM ACTION	MAX. .0003	MAX. .0004	MAX. .0005
17 CROSS SLIDE ALIGNMENT	TO FACE HOLLOW OR CONCAVE ONLY ON 12 INCH DIAMETER 0 TO .0005	TO FACE HOLLOW OR CONCAVE ONLY ON 12 INCH DIAMETER 0 TO .001	TO FACE HOLLOW OR CONCAVE ONLY ON 12 INCH DIAMETER 0 TO .001
18 FACE PLATE RUN OUT	ON DIAMETER 0 TO .001 ON FACE AT NOMINAL DIAMETER 0 TO .001	ON DIAMETER 0 TO .001 ON FACE AT NOMINAL DIAMETER 0 TO .0015	ON DIAMETER 0 TO .0015 ON FACE AT NOMINAL DIAMETER 0 TO .002

RECOMMENDED STANDARDS

TEST	TOOL ROOM LATHES	12 TO 18 INCL. ENGINE LATHES	20 TO 36 INCL. ENGINE LATHES
19 CHUCK - RUN OUT	FACE AND PERIPHERY .003 FACE OF STEPS .003 BAR TEST 3" FROM END OF JAW. BAR DIA. SAME AS HOLE .003	FACE AND PERIPHERY .003 FACE OF STEPS .003 BAR TEST 3" FROM END OF JAW. BAR DIA. SAME AS HOLE .003	FACE AND PERIPHERY .004 FACE OF STEPS .004 BAR TEST 3" FROM END OF JAW. BAR DIA. SAME AS HOLE .004
20 COLLET CHUCK - RUN OUT	ONE INCH FROM SPINDLE 0 TO .001	ONE INCH FROM SPINDLE 0 TO .001	ONE INCH FROM SPINDLE 0 TO .001
21 LATHE MUST TURN ROUND WITH WORK MOUNTED IN CHUCK	.0003	.0004	.0008
22 LATHE MUST TURN CYLINDRICAL WITH WORK MOUNTED IN CHUCK	.0008	.0015	.002
23 LATHE MUST TURN CYLINDRICAL WITH WORK MOUNTED BETWEEN CENTERS	.0004	.0008	.001
24 LEAD SCREW - LEAD PER FT.	±.001	±.0015	±.002
LEAD IN ANY 4"	±.0004	±.0005	±.0007
25 BACK LASH ON CROSS FEED SCREW	.004	.004	.005
ON COMPOUND REST SCREW	.004	.004	.005

Fig. 21–8. Standards of accuracy as recommended by the Lathe Group of the National Machine Tool Builders Association.

POWER DRIVES

A primary function of a modern machine tool is to deliver the required power to the metal cutting zone with little or no exertion on the part of an operator. Most modern machines are driven by individual electric motors run at 1200, 1800, or 3600 nominal rpm. Multiple vee belt drives from the motor to the first drive shaft of the machine predominate, although chain drives are found on some heavy equipment. At one time machine tools were driven in groups from a large engine or motor through line shafts and belts. The individual drives of today are slightly more expensive but more flexible, permit better plant layout and changes, help maintenance, and allow better lighting.

Two general types of power transmissions to give the speeds and feeds desired in machine tools are: (1) mechanical, and (2) hydraulic or pneumatic.

Mechanical drives. Rotary motion is transmitted predominately by mechanical means for economy and reliability. This is generally through hardened and ground gears for more than fractional horsepower drives, as typified by the lathe headstock design of Fig. 21–6. The gears in that headstock slide into mesh. Another common design has pairs of gears, usually helical, already in mesh and engaged by clutches. In addition, multiple-speed motors may be used. The simplest arrangement is to shift gears or engage clutches directly through levers on the outside of the gear case. A faster and more convenient means found on some machines is to select speeds or feeds by setting a single dial or pointer. This sets a valve and actuates hydraulic pistons to shift the gears or changes motor speeds. Also while the machine is cutting at one speed, the next speed can be preselected.

Speeds are commonly varied in geometrical progression; each speed is multiplied by a constant to get the value of the next higher one. For example, if the lowest speed is 12 rpm and the constant ratio is 1.5, the next speed is $12 \times 1.5 = 18$ rpm, the third speed is 27 rpm, and so on. Thus, speeds are always proportional and have small numerical differences in the low ranges.

Belts and stepped pulleys are popular for fractional horsepower drives because they are simple and cheap. Belts are preferred for precision and high-speed drives, such as in a grinding machine workhead and wheelhead because they run smoothly, and the slightly uneven action of gears tends to leave marks on fine finished surfaces.

A continuously variable speed or feed rather than adjustments in steps is sometimes needed. The elements of a stepless variable speed drive are portrayed in Fig. 21–9.

The flange on the left side of each pulley can be moved. When the upper flange moves to the right, the lower moves to the left and vice versa.

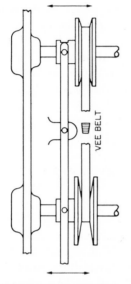

VEE BELT

Lever moved to vary pulley widths and belt positions.

Fig. 21–9. A diagram of a stepless variable speed device.

Three principle types of mechanical devices are used commonly to transform rotary motion to straight line or reciprocating motion. One is the pinion and rack that has been described for the lathe; another is the screw and nut described earlier in this chapter; and the third is the crank that will be described in connection with the mechanical shaper.

Hydraulic drives. In some, but not all cases, hydraulic drives are more expensive to make, operate, and service than mechanical drives. The motors for rotary hydraulic drives particularly are complex, expensive, and not common. Hydraulic drives offer several advantages that have made them popular in recent years for straight line and reciprocating motions. The reasons are:

1. A hydraulic drive is smooth and reverses without shock. Thus hydraulic drives are found on most reciprocating grinding machine tables because they contribute to good surface finish.

2. A hydraulic drive stops when pressure reaches a preset maximum and tool breakage is less likely than with a mechanical device that surges relentlessly to the end of its stroke. This is one reason hydraulic drives are preferred for fragile and expensive broaching tools.

3. A hydraulic drive is infinitely variable for speed and feed within its range, and the length and position of stroke it gives is easily adjusted.

4. Faster reverse and acceleration rates are possible with hydraulic drives because of less inertia and the cushioning effect of the fluid. On the other hand, a mechanical drive is easier to reverse accurately, particularly at high and varying speeds and loads.

Variable speed or feed is a primary requisite for most machine tools, with something near full driving force available over the full range. Essentially there are two basic types of hydraulic drives that fulfill this need. Each type has many variations but only a basic form of each will be presented here. One is called the *throttle type* and is built around a pump that delivers liquid at a constant rate. The other type has a *variable delivery* pump.

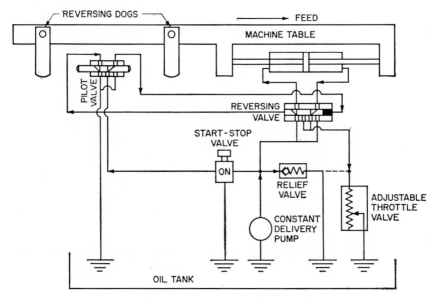

Fig. 21–10. An elementary constant delivery hydraulic system.

The circuit diagram of Fig. 21–10 is for a system with a pump that delivers a constant volume of oil. As much of the fluid as is needed flows through a reversing valve to one end of the machine table cylinder. The rest of the oil is passed back to the oil tank through the relief valve. As the oil under pressure pushes the piston along to move the table, it forces oil out of the other end of the cylinder through the reversing valve and throttle valve to the tank. The resistance of the variable throttle valve determines the rate of oil flow and the feed rate of the machine table.

The circuit in Fig. 21–10 is set for the machine table to move to the right. When the left hand dog reverses the pilot valve, oil will be admitted to the left end of the reversing valve and will push the plunger of that valve to the right. The oil flow to the cylinder will be reversed, and the table will feed to the left. To stop the action altogether, the start-stop valve is opened to allow all the oil from the pump to discharge freely to the tank.

Details of the designs of the components are not shown. A number of different types are available, and space does not permit describing them here. If the proper components are selected, a circuit of the type shown in Fig. 21–10 can be made to maintain a preset feed rate over most of the range of loads for which it is designed. For light loads, such as driving a grinding machine table, a circuit like that of Fig. 21–10 is adequate and normally used, but it is inefficient from a power standpoint. At other than maximum feed rate, part of the oil is being pumped under pressure through the relief valve, and that energy is wasted.

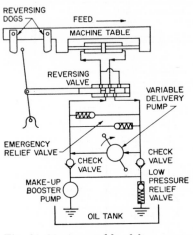

Fig. 21–11. A variable delivery circuit.

Pumps are available that can be adjusted to deliver an infinitely variable quantity of oil at a constant pressure within capacity. Such pumps are more complex and expensive than constant delivery pumps. A typical circuit utilizing a variable delivery pump is depicted in Fig. 21–11. The amount of oil delivered and the rate of feed are varied by adjusting the pumps. No excess oil is pumped, except for a small amount of slippage and leakage, and this system is more efficient than a constant delivery system. Even so, in many cases the difference is not large, and the saving in operating costs alone does not justify the more expensive equipment.

The booster pump puts oil into the circuit to make up for that lost by leakage. The circuit shown in Fig. 21–11 is what is called a *locked circuit,* because the table will feed at the rate set no matter what direction the load is acting on the table. The circuit of Fig. 21–10 can also be made locked to a certain extent, but not as completely under the heaviest loads as the circuit of Fig. 21–11. A fully locked circuit is needed to control heavy cuts and is normally used for hydraulic planers and milling machines.

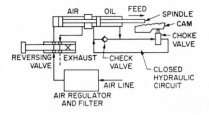

Fig. 21–12. An air-hydraulic circuit.

Pneumatic drives. Compressed air is already available in most plants and can be put to work with rather inexpensive equipment. Air flow is fast, but the use of compressed air has several disadvantages that limit it to light service. Pressures available are usually not high. A compressed air system by itself is hard to control because

of the compressibility of the air. Feeds or speeds are inclined to vary too much as the load changes and the equipment may not stop and reverse within desired limits.

Air is widely used for work clamping devices and feeding small machines such as drill presses. In the latter capacity, an air driven but hydraulically controlled circuit like that shown in Fig. 21–12 mitigates some of the shortcomings of air. With the reversing valve in the position shown, air is admitted behind the piston. The spindle advances first at fast rate with the choke valve open. When the cam closes the choke valve, the oil flow from the right cylinder is throttled, and then a slow feed rate is maintained. With the reversing valve plunger moved to the left, the pistons return at a rapid rate because the oil is bypassed through the check valve.

MACHINE TOOL ECONOMY

Major aspects of the design of a machine tool that determines its economy are: (1) the operating controls, (2) provisions for safety, (3) facilities for changing jobs, (4) means of maintenance of accuracy, and (5) unit construction. These considerations explain important features of many machine tools and will be discussed now.

Machine tool controls. Essentially the means for controlling and adjusting a machine tool must enable the operator to work fast with a minimum of fatigue. One way is to eliminate the operator partially or entirely. Means of doing that are explained in connection with automatic machines. However, automatic operation is not warranted for much work, and most machine tools require full attention of an operator. Even so most machines have power feeds and movements to save effort. Fast movement, called *rapid traverse,* is commonly provided to save time between cuts.

The controls on a well designed machine tool are arranged so the operator does not have to move nor exert himself any more than absolutely necessary. All unnecessary motions are eliminated; the need to move the body about is minimized; necessary motions are kept as short and simple as possible; both hands are kept busy and moving; and motions of the eyes are minimized. The diagram on the left of Fig. 21–13 illustrates that an operator in a fixed position can conveniently make motions within a certain space. The boundaries of the work space have been determined for normal people and are specified in reference- and hand-books. As indicated by the composite photograph on the right of Fig. 21–13, the controls of a well designed machine tool are placed within the maximum normal working area.

Short motions are easier and faster than long ones. Thus finger movements are preferable to hand movements, and so on. Accordingly, machine controls should require as short movements as possible consistent

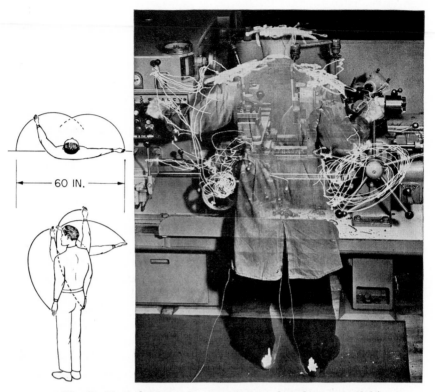

Fig. 21–13. A diagram of a person's normal working area (left). The operator's movements on a well designed turret lathe are delineated by light paths on a time exposure (right). (Photo courtesy The Warner and Swasey Co.)

with adequate leverage. Sufficient mechanical advantage must be provided because controls must not be hard to move and tiring. Handles should be proportioned to the natural grasp of the operator.

The machine operation depicted in Fig. 21–13 requires the continuous use of both hands with only limited body and practically no foot movements. The dial that is set to select speeds is on the headstock near eye level for ready vision.

On some machine tools it is convenient for the operator to take different stations for different kinds of work, and duplicate sets of controls may be provided for convenience. An example of this is seen in general-purpose milling machines that often have controls at the front and on one side behind the table. Limitations in present day designs make it necessary for the operators to stand when attending most machine tools, although less fatigue is experienced when sitting.

Unfortunately, the principles that have been pointed out have been disregarded in machine tool design in too many cases. An understanding of the principles should help a person evaluate and understand the arrangement of controls on any particular machine.

Safety. Safety is provided on machine tools by:
1. *Safeguarding the point of operation.* If possible, provision should be made so the operator does not need to put his hands into the working area of the tools. For that purpose, mechanical loading devices often are justified for high-production operations. Guards or cages are commonly built around a danger zone. For low production, the operator commonly must reach into the working zone to load workpieces and make adjustments when tools are not cutting. To reduce the danger, provisions may be made so that the machine cannot be started until both hands are withdrawn. One way is to require the operator to depress two buttons or levers at the same time, one with each hand.
2. *Safeguarding controls and machine mechanisms.* Starting levers may be placed up out of the way of ordinary motions or covered by guards so they are not tripped by falling objects. Gear case covers or working area guards may be interlocked with the power source of the machine so the machine will not start when the cover guards are off.
3. *Guarding moving parts and power transmissions.* An evident feature of present day machines is that covers and guards completely enclose all shafts, belts, gears, etc., largely as a safety precaution.

Changing of jobs. In connection with the machine tools of the lathe family, features were described that made engine lathes and even turret lathes easy to change over from one job to another. As an example, speeds and feeds are easy to change. In contrast, it was pointed out that to change speed or feed on an automatic turning machine commonly requires that a cover be removed from a gear case and pick-off gears be changed. This illustrates a basic principle for all types of machine tools. General-purpose machine tools are made easy to change from one job to another, not only in changing speeds and feeds but also in making all necessary adjustments. However, the construction necessary for this restricts the general-purpose machine to be a slower producer than a corresponding special-purpose machine after a set-up has been made.

One reason a general-purpose machine is slow has already been explained. That is because it has more components, is not as rigid, and cannot cut as fast. Another reason a general-purpose machine is a slow producer is that the operator must spend time manipulating the controls and adjustments for each piece. In contrast, an automatic machine may have dogs or cams to govern the actions. Time is required for set-up, but once that is done, the machine can get along without the operator's attention.

Accessories and attachments are important adjuncts to adapt machine tools to various jobs and reflect an extension of the design of each machine. Typical adjuncts of this kind are described along with the basic machines.

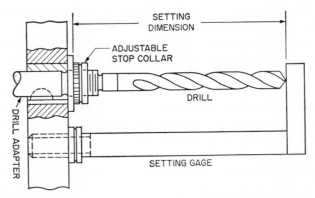

Fig. 21–14. A gage for presetting a drill in its adapter.

The tools are normally set to cut to size on a general-purpose machine by making adjustments by means of micrometer dials. Quite commonly with the equipment furnished, on a special-purpose or automatic machine the tools must be set by a cut-and-try procedure which is slow. Adjustable tool adapters and special presetting gages help to change tools faster. An example of one is given in Fig. 21–14. The drill and adapter are placed in the gage, and the stop collar on the adapter is adjusted to the setting dimension. Then when the drill and adapter are placed on the holder on the machine tool, the stop collar positions the drill to cut to the correct depth.

Maintenance of accuracy. The chief value of a machine tool lies in its accuracy. To preserve this, protection and lubrication of the bearings and guideways are important.

The type of lubrication system used for a machine tool depends upon the need, and often different systems may be used on different parts of a machine. The four most common types of systems are:

1. A fully automatic system, usually a pump continually forcing oil through tubes or holes to the bearings. This is an expensive system but efficient for heavy duty. Examples of its application are in the lubrication of plain sleeve bearings for large grinding wheel spindles and the ways under heavy reciprocating tables. Often such a system is interlocked with the power supply so that the main drive motor will not start until ample lubricating oil is assured to the bearings.

2. Semi-automatic and intermittent systems such as splash, oil ring, and metering arrangements. These generally are moderate in cost and satisfactory for all but severe services.

3. Manual single-shot system, conventionally a hand operated plunger that forces a shot of oil from a reservoir through tubes or holes to desired bearing areas. This is a popular means of distributing lubrication to miscellaneous bearing areas requiring only periodic attention.

4. Various single-shot devices such as sight feed oilers, oil cups, etc. These are the traditional and cheapest means but require individual attention, and some may be overlooked.

Lubrication may help wash away dirt and chips that damage bearings and ways, but the best protection in that respect is a cover or enclosure. As has been pointed out, modern machine tools are well covered for operator safety, but covers are important also to protect the bearings. Covers for ways range from spring steel to impregnated fabric strips and from telescopic metal guards to fabric bellows. Instead of covers, wipers of plastic, leather, bronze, or other materials may be used to clear off the ways as a table is traversed along them.

Fig. 21–15. A special machine made from units of a small drill press on a special base for the specific task of facing the ends of a die cast aluminum motor housing. (Courtesy New Jersey Zinc Co.)

Unit construction. When typical machine tools are described in this text, reference is made to the major components or units such as the base, headstock, or saddle. This is intentional because machine tools are normally made up of such distinct units and are designed on that basis. Aside from other considerations, unit construction is particularly economical for building special-purpose machine tools. A large proportion of machine tools are made for specific purposes by modifying standard machine to a larger or smaller extent. This can be done by adding, substituting, or altering one or a few components instead of building an entirely special machine for each purpose, which would be much more expensive. For example, a tracer lathe is commonly constructed by substituting a tracer attachment for the regular saddle of a standard engine lathe. An example of a special-purpose machine made largely from drill press components is shown in Fig. 21–15.

Questions

1. What are the causes of errors in metal machining?

2. What dimension is most important to the rigidity of a machine tool member?

3. Why is it desirable that a machine tool member have a high natural frequency?

4. What makes the frequency of a member high?

5. What are the desirable proportions of machine tool members and why?

6. What are the relative advantages of iron and steel for major machine tool components?

7. How is accurate straight line motion obtained on a machine tool?

8. How are truly flat and straight surfaces obtained?

9. Describe how a machine tool member deflects under varying and reversing loads.

10. Why must machine tools be kept level?

11. What types of spindle bearings are used for machine tools, and in what type of service is each used?

12. How are precise adjustments made on a machine tool?

13. What effect does heat have on a machine tool and what can be done about it?

14. Why are individual motor drives preferred for modern machine tools?

15. Describe a common drive for rotary motion.

16. In what steps are machine tool speeds usually provided?

17. Why are hydraulic drives popular for straight line or reciprocating motion?

18. Describe the two basic types of reciprocating hydraulic drives and explain their advantages and disadvantages.

19. What are the advantages and disadvantages of pneumatic drives?

20. What principles apply to the arrangement of controls on a machine tool?

21. How is safety provided on machine tools?

22. Why is a general-purpose machine a slow producer?

23. What provision may be made to change tools faster?

24. Describe four common types of lubrication systems found on machine tools and explain for what type of service each is used.

25. What is unit construction and what are its advantages?

Problems

1. A design for a machine-tool member calls for a depth of 6 in. Under a given load the deflection is 0.001 in. If everything else remains the same and the depth is increased to 24 in., what should the deflection be under the same load?

2. When the gibs on a milling machine were fully tightened and a force of 1000 lb was applied, the table moved 0.0003 in. but returned to its original position when the force was released. Then the gib tightening screws were loosened one turn as recommended by the manufacturer for normal operation. Upon application of a 1000 lb load in each direction, the total displacement was found to be 0.0015 in. Draw a deflection-force loop for this situation, showing the approximate points for various conditions.

3. A setting gage like the one shown in Fig. 21–14 costs $36. It must be paid for in a year's operation plus a charge for interest, insurance, and taxes of 15%. Maintenance on the device is negligible.

    A drill on an automatic machine must be removed and replaced by a sharp one for every 500 pieces. With the setting gage, the time to make the change is ½ minute. Without the gage, one minute is needed for the change. The direct labor rate on the machine is $2 per hr and overhead is $6 per hr.

(a) What quantity of production justifies purchase of the setting gage?
(b) Should a setting gage be ordered if only 50,000 pieces are to be made?
(c) Should a setting gage be ordered for a lot of 500,000 pieces?

References

ASTE, *Tool Engineers Handbook*, McGraw-Hill Book Co., Inc., New York, 1959.

CHAPTER 22

Drilling and Allied Operations

The kinds of operations to be considered at this time are those concerned mostly with the opening, enlarging, and finish cutting of holes from a small fraction of an inch to a few inches in diameter.

ALL TOOLS ROTATE AND FEED DOWNWARD

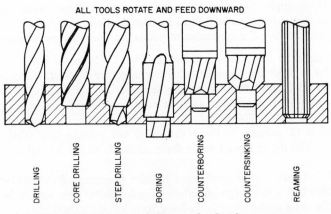

DRILLING   CORE DRILLING   STEP DRILLING   BORING   COUNTERBORING   COUNTERSINKING   REAMING

Fig. 22–1. Common drilling and related operations.

The common types of operations under consideration are illustrated in Fig. 22–1. *Drilling* is the easiest way to cut a hole into solid metal. It is also done to enlarge holes and then may be called *core drilling* or *counter drilling.* When a hole of two or more diameters is cut by one drill, the operation is called *step drilling*.

Boring is the enlarging of a hole, sometimes with the implication of producing a more accurate hole than by drilling. Enlarging a hole for a limited depth is called *counterboring*. If the depth is shallow so the cut leaves in effect a finished face around the original hole, it is called *spot-facing*. The cutting of an angular opening into the end of a hole is *countersinking*, also loosely termed *chamfering*. *Reaming* is also a hole enlarging process but its purpose specifically is to produce a hole of accurate size and good surface finish, and stock removal is small.

Tapping is often done along with the other operations performed, but it will be discussed along with the other thread cutting operations.

The tools and not the workpieces are revolved, and usually fed, in most of the operations taken up in this chapter.

Fig. 22–2. A straight shank two lipped twist drill (top). A tapered shank two lipped twist drill (next to top). A four flute core drill (next to bottom). A subland drill (bottom). (Courtesy Chicago-Latrobe Twist Drill Works.)

DRILLS, BORING TOOLS, AND REAMERS

Twist drills. The most common form of metal-working drill is characterized by helical grooves or *flutes* as shown in Fig. 22–2. Those with three or more flutes cannot start holes but only can enlarge holes previously drilled or cored. They are called *core drills*, sometimes spiral reamers or core reamers.

A *multicut drill* makes holes of two or more diameters as in step drilling in Fig. 22–1. It can also drill, counterbore, and countersink within limits. A standard drill ground in that way is called a *step drill*. Drills specifically made for the purpose are named *subland drills*. Since a multicut drill gives two or more surfaces in one pass it is desirable for quantity production although it costs more than a standard drill.

The fluted portion of a drill is its *body*. The *point* is the cutting end. The drill is held and driven at the *shank* on the other end. The shank may have a Morse taper and driver tang or may be straight.

Drill sizes and materials. The size of a drill designates the nominal diameter of its body and the hole it is intended to produce. Standard drills are available in *numbered, lettered, fractional inch* and *millimeter* sizes.

Fractional size drills come in $\frac{1}{64}$ in. steps up to $1\frac{3}{4}$ in. and larger steps above that to $3\frac{1}{4}$ in. diameter. Numbered and lettered size drills are from 0.0135 in. to 0.413 in. in diameter in between the fractional sizes so there is only a few thousandths of an inch difference between one drill size and the next in that range. The size of a drill is generally stamped on the shank, just behind the flutes. Drill lengths vary with diameter and many sizes are available in short and long lengths.

Carbon tool steel drills have a low first cost and have a place for occasional usage but must be run slowly. High-speed steel drills are the most popular and have good strength. Drills tipped with cemented carbide are economical for high production but are expensive and must be handled carefully to avoid breakage.

Drill angles and edges. The body and point of a drill must have certain features for efficient performance. These are designated in Fig. 22–3. Actual cutting is done by the *cutting lips* or *edges* that correspond to the cutting edges of a single-point tool. The cutting lip relief angle is ordinarily 12° to 15° at the outside and increases toward the center. This relief angle must always be larger than the lead angle of the path of the cutting edge as the drill is revolved and fed into the work. This angle increases from the outside to the center of the hole. The *helix angle* of the flutes corresponds to and is governed by the same factors as the rake angle of a single-point tool. An average value is about 30°, but helix angles from about 18° for hard materials to 45° for soft materials are used.

The *point angle* between the cutting edges is 118° for average work but is given different values for specific purposes. For example, a point angle of 136° is suitable for hard manganese steel, but only 60° for wood and fiber.

It is particularly important that the cutting edges or lips be of equal length and lie at equal angles from

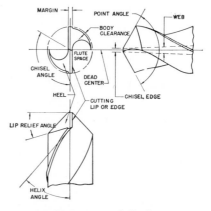

Fig. 22–3. Twist drill elements.

the axis of a drill. Otherwise the drill receives severe punishment and cuts a hole too large or distorted, as indicated by Fig. 22–4. As narrow a chisel edge as feasible is desirable to keep down the thrust of the drill.

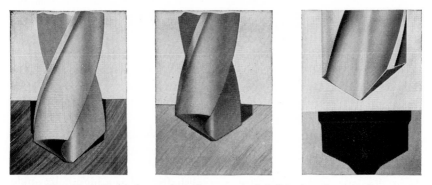

Fig. 22–4. Bad holes resulting from unequal drill lip lengths or angles. (Courtesy Cleveland Twist Drill Co.)

The *body clearance* on all but very small drills leaves a narrow *margin* or strip at full nominal diameter along the edge of each flute. This reduces rubbing between drill and hole and allows cutting fluid to reach the point of the drill. Also, the body decreases a few thousandths of an inch in diameter from the point to the shank to keep down rubbing.

Spiral point drill. The conventional chisel point on drills is inefficient because it gives the effect of a large negative rake angle ($-50°$ or more is typical) at the center of the cut where the speed is quite low. The chisel point tends to extrude rather than cut metal. The spiral point drill illustrated in Fig. 22–5 gives some improvement. The straight cutting edge on each side ends in a small radius at the center. This line and

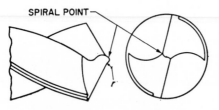

Fig. 22–5. A spiral point drill.

curve combination is the generatrix for forming the heel on a spiral behind the cutting edge. The result is a true point that holds the drill to position at the start of a cut, helps prevent runout and oversize holes, and contributes to better cutting action with lower thrust forces.

Drill sharpening. A twist drill is sharpened by grinding the heel behind the cutting edge on the point, never the outside diameter. Skilled mechanics may grind chisel point drills off hand with passable results; but generally machine ground drills cut faster, last longer, and produce more accurate holes. A special machine is required to sharpen spiral point drills. In principle, a drill grinder is a grinding stand with an attachment to hold the drill at the correct angle and swing it with respect to the grinding wheel, or vice versa, to grind the heel behind the cutting edges on the point. A means is also provided to true the wheel.

Deep hole drills. Deep holes are difficult to drill. Chips are difficult to get out of the hole; it is not easy to get the fluid to the point of the drill; and the drill tends to runout too much. These conditions must be corrected in drilling such parts as gun barrels, crankshafts, camshafts and hollow spindles. Certain procedures help, such as revolving both workpiece and drill and withdrawing the drill often, but specific drills for the purpose are often necessary.

For a diameter over ¾ in., a drill with oil holes between the flutes and a supply of high-pressure oil helps wash out chips and cool the drill point.

A *crankshaft* drill is a special twist drill for deep holes smaller than ⅜ in.-diameter, such as oil holes in crankshafts. It has a high helix angle, a thick web, and a point ground with a secondary clearance on the heel to thin the web at the point and break up the chips.

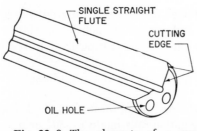

Fig. 22–6. The elements of a gun drill.

Deep holes requiring smooth finish and minimum runout are drilled with single flute-single edge *gun drills* like that depicted in Fig. 22–6. These are operated at relatively high speeds and low feeds. The workpiece preferably is revolved, and oil is forced through a hole and emerges from the end of the drill to wash out chips and provide cutting fluid. Deep holes may be reamed after drilling to improve finish. Gun drilling is mostly done on horizontal drilling machines specifically designed to accommodate the long drills and workpieces.

Fig. 22–7. Typical boring, counterboring, and spotfacing tools. A solid taper shank counterbore with integral pilot (left). (Courtesy The Standard Tool Co.) An interchangeable counterbore or spotfacer and pilot. The cutter can be removed easily from the driver and re-placed with another (middle). (Courtesy Ex-Cell-O Corp.) A special multi diameter boring cutter for machining 8 surfaces in one operation (right). (Courtesy Eclipse Counterbore Co.)

Boring tools. A boring tool meant to revolve has several cutting edges or blades to balance the cutting forces. Typical boring tools, commonly called *counterbores* or *counterboring tools,* are shown in Fig. 22–7. The same kinds of tools are also used for spotfacing and in that role are called *spotfacers.*

An example of a special boring tool, one for machining eight surfaces in one operation, is also shown in Fig. 22–7. The blades for the different cuts are staggered to facilitate grinding to resharpen the edges.

Countersinking tools or *countersinks* are similar to counterboring tools except that their blades are ground at an angle to do countersinking as illustrated in Fig. 22–1. Included angles of 45°, 60°, 82°, and 90° are common.

Usually a counterboring or countersinking tool has a pilot on one end to guide the tool in the hole previously drilled.

Reamers. Reamers are made in a number of styles to suit various purposes. They may be hand or machine driven, for roughing or for finishing work, have integral shanks or be attached to holders, be solid or have inserted blades that may be expanded or adjusted, have straight or helical flutes, and have straight, tapered, or other shapes.

20 in. Man-Au-Trol spacer costs about $12,000. Over the years of its life, the cost for each piece done on the spacer is small; but it normally would not be profitable unless a large amount of work were available to keep it busy.

Fixtures and jigs. A fixture is a device that holds and locates a workpiece. Strictly speaking, conventional work holding devices such as chucks and vises are fixtures, but mostly the name is given to single-purpose holding devices. Fixtures are mostly associated with lathes, shapers, planers, millers, broaches, and grinders.

A jig not only holds and locates a workpiece but also guides the cutting tool. That is particularly desirable in drilling because the point of the drill tends to wander unless it is guided when a hole is started. Multiple point boring tools and sometimes reamers need to be guided.

Workpiece location has a particular meaning. A free body in space has six degrees of freedom; three represented by coordinate axes of translation and three by rotation about those axes. A piece is fully located when definitely restricted in all six degrees of freedom. This occurs only if the piece is held against three points in one plane, two in a second plane, and one in a third plane, with the planes preferably perpendicular to each other. Full restriction is not always desirable, as for instance when a piece must be left free to rotate between centers. Thus fewer than six locating points are supplied in some cases. A basic feature of any jig or fixture is that it provides the locating surfaces or points against which all pieces of one kind can be precisely located.

Fig. 22-22. A jig to line bore six holes in a master rod for an aircraft engine. (Courtesy Swartz Tool Products Co.)

The simplest kind of jig is a template that fits a part and has holes to guide one or more drills. More elaborate jigs have locating and clamping details to hold the workpiece in relation to the jig plate. The jig plate is the essence of the jig, is made of soft steel, and has accurately located holes bored in it. Hardened bushings, inserted in the plate to withstand wear, do the actual guiding of the drills, reamers, etc. *Slip* or *removal bushings* are convenient where tools of different sizes are to be used in one hole.

Jigs have many forms. Two are illustrated in Figs. 22-13 and 22-22. Economical fixtures and jigs for small quantities are made by putting special jaws on standard vises and chucks.

body, which is hollow and has several slots running part way along the flutes. A tapered threaded pin expands the body.

An *adjustable reamer,* as depicted in Fig. 22–9, has inserted and replaceable blades locked to the body. The blade seats are tapered so the diameter of the reamer is increased by moving the blades forward.

Fig. 22–9. An adjustable shell reamer. (Courtesy Cleveland Twist Drill Co.)

As shown by Fig. 22–10, the teeth of a reamer have angles corresponding to and governed by the same factors as those of a single-point tool as explained in Chap. 16. The true rake behind the end chamfer where a machine reamer does most of the cutting depends upon whether the teeth are straight or helical as well as upon the nominal rake angle shown in the figure. Practical specifications can be obtained from reamer manufacturers or reference-books.

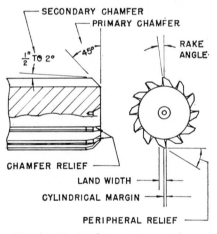

Fig. 22–10. Machine reamer angles.

Fig. 22–11. An adjustable blade hollow mill. (Courtesy Gairing Tool Co.)

Hollow mill. Short diameters, like a boss, can be turned by a revolving tool called a *hollow mill.* One is illustrated in Fig. 22–11. Hollow mills are also used with the stock revolving on machines of the lathe family. The blades are pitched and sharpened so that they cut on their inner corners and front edges. The work enters the hollow space in the body of the tool.

DRILLING MACHINES

Drilling machines are made in many forms and sizes. Portable or hand drills are well known. The drilling machines commonly used for precision metal working are known as drill presses. Representative types will be described.

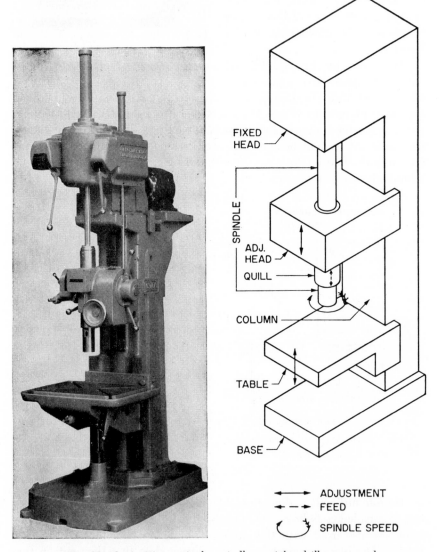

Fig. 22–12. A 25 in. single spindle upright drill press and a diagram of its principal parts. (Photo Courtesy The Fosdick Machine Tool Co.)

Vertical drill presses. The general-purpose *standard upright drill press* of Fig. 22–12 has the main features of most vertical drill presses. A column rises from the base and carries a table for the workpiece and a spindle head. The table is raised or lowered manually by an elevating screw in this case, and can be clamped to the column for rigidity. Some tables are round and can be swiveled. On vertical drill presses with round columns, the tables generally can be swung out from under the spindle so workpieces can be mounted on the base.

The spindle that takes the cutting tools revolves in the non-revolving quill which is fed up or down. Some machines have only hand feed, but this one also has 9 power feed rates from 0.005 to 0.043 in. per rev. Machines like this may be equipped with a positive leadscrew for tapping and a spindle reversing mechanism. As a rule an adjustable stop is provided to limit the depth of travel of the quill and, with power feed, to disengage the power at a definite depth or reverse the spindle rotation for tapping. The spindle of the machine in Fig. 22–12 has a No. 4 Morse taper hole. As a rule the larger the machine, the larger the tapered hole, but the smallest machines often have a drill chuck attached permanently to the end of the spindle.

The spindles of fractional horsepower drill presses are usually driven by vee belts on stepped pulleys. Larger ones, like that of Fig. 22–12, have gear transmissions. In this case 12 speeds from 60 to 1500 rpm are available. Some drill presses have motors wound for several speeds.

A *bench-type drill press* is a light machine for small work. Light drill presses, bench and upright, that are hand fed so the operator can feel the resistance met by the drill are called *sensitive drill presses*. They are advantageous for feeding small drills to avoid breakage.

Very small holes must be drilled on highly sensitive presses with spindles running quite true at high speeds, in one design in vee bearings. The action of the drill is watched through a microscope. Holes less than 0.001 in. in diameter have been drilled, and diameters around 0.005 in. are common in the instrument and watch industries.

Production drill presses are sturdily built for heavy work and simple in design, but in overall appearance look like other upright drill presses. They are intended for long runs on specific jobs and are not easy to change from one job to another.

Sizes of drill presses. The size of a vertical drill press may be designated in several ways. The most common designation is the diameter in inches of the largest disk or workpiece in which a center hole can be drilled on the press. Other designations are the diameter of the largest drill the press is designed to drive in cast iron or steel and the Morse taper number in the spindle hole. Table 22–1 shows typical specifications for several popular sizes of drill presses.

TABLE 22–1. Some Typical Vertical Drill Press Specifications

Type	Diameter workpiece	Size Diameter drill	Morse taper no.	No. speeds	No. spindles	Hp	Wt. (lb)	Cost ($)
Bench hand feed	14	½	2	4	1	½	150	150
Upright hand feed	24	1	2 or 3	6	1	1	1650	2000
Upright hand feed gang style	24	1	2 or 3	6	2	1 ea.	3000	3100
Upright power feed	25		4	12	1	5 to 7½	3500	5500
Upright power feed	30		4	12	1	5 to 7½	4350	6500

Fig. 22–13. A production job on a two spindle gang drill press has a jig clamped to the table under each spindle. Quick change chucks are mounted on the spindles, and the tools are held in quick change collets. An air line is arranged with a nozzle to blow the chips away from each jig. (Courtesy Consolidated Machine Tool Corp.)

Multi-spindle drill presses. A *gang drill press* is the equivalent of two or more upright or production drill presses in a row with a common base and table. A production job under spindles of a gang drill press is shown in Fig. 22–13. Gang drills are advantageous for production to do several operations on a part or for machining several parts at one time.

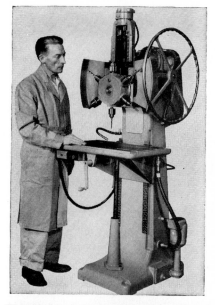

Fig. 22–14. A turret drill press. (Courtesy Burg Tool Mfg. Co.)

Fig. 22–15. A multiple spindle drilling machine for drilling 50 holes in a gear case. (Courtesy Baush Machine Tool Co.)

A *turret drill press*, illustrated in Fig. 22–14 has a number of spindles on a turret so that different tools can be indexed into position quickly. The ram that carries the turret feeds the tools to the workpiece on the table below.

A *multiple-spindle drill press* has a cluster of spindles on one or more heads for a part having a number of holes and produced in large quantities. These machines range in size from small ones powered by a few horsepower to massive ones driven by as much as 50 hp. The one in Fig. 22–15 has a 28 hp drive, drills 50 holes in each part, and produces 20 parts per hr. Some of the more elaborate machines have heads and spindles in more than one position to operate on a workpiece from several directions or upon several stations, each holding a workpiece.

Radial drill presses. Radial drills are convenient for heavy workpieces that cannot be moved around easily or are too large for other kinds of drill presses. A *plain radial drill*, like the one in Fig. 22–16, has a base and column that carries an arm. The arm can be raised or lowered and swung around the column. The head can be moved along the arm, and the spindle it carries can thus be positioned in a circle with a radius about as large as the length of the arm. All adjustments can be locked once the spindle is positioned. The drill spindle is fed up and down by hand or power.

The size of a radial drill press is given in feet and designates the

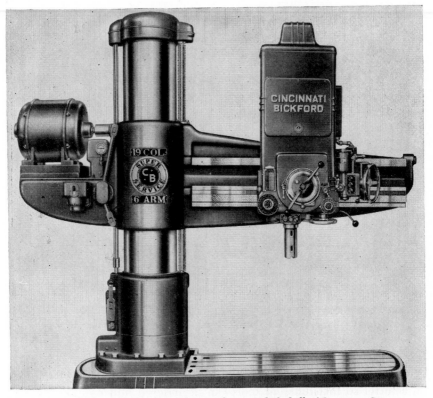

Fig. 22–16. A 6 ft. arm, 19 in. column radial drill. (Courtesy Cincinnati Bickford Tool Co.)

radius of the largest disk in which a center hole can be drilled with the head at its outermost position on the arm. Some makers also specify the diameter of the column in inches.

A small radial drill with a 4 ft arm and 9 in.-diameter column weighs 4500 lb, has a No. 4 Morse taper spindle hole, is driven by a 3 hp motor, and costs around $7500. A large size has a 12 ft arm and 26 in.-diameter column.

DRILLING MACHINE ACCESSORIES AND ATTACHMENTS

Toolholders and drivers. The essential purpose of all toolholders for drilling machines is to make the tool run true with the tapered hole in the machine spindle. Straight shank tools may be held by a drill chuck, as on a lathe, or by a split collet. If of the right size, the tapered shank of a tool may be placed directly in the tapered hole of the machine spindle. If the tapered shank is smaller than the tapered hole, a *taper shank socket*, with inside and outside tapers, is used. A short socket is shown in Fig. 22–17. The cross slot takes the tang of the tapered shank tool and allows a wedge (called a *drift*) to be used to push the tool out of the socket when the two are to be separated.

A *floating driver* is a toolholder with its two ends somewhat loosely coupled to allow a reamer or tap to follow a previously drilled or bored hole. An *adjustable extension assembly* is a form of taper socket adapter that can be adjusted for length. It is the means whereby drills of different lengths can be used together on a multiple spindle head.

A *quick-change chuck* and *quick-change collets* allow tools to be taken off and put on the spindle of a drill press while it is running. Two are shown in Fig. 22–13.

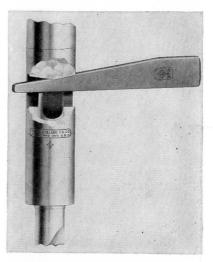

Fig. 22–17. A taper shank sleeve or shell socket. (Courtesy Cleveland Twist Drill Co.)

Multiple-spindle drill heads. A standard single-spindle drill press can be converted to a multiple-spindle machine, within limits by attaching a multiple-spindle head to the machine spindle. Some of these heads are made for specific purposes and have their spindles in fixed positions. On others, like the one in Fig. 22–18, the locations of the spindles can be changed.

Work-holding devices. If a drill or other tool catches in a hole, it can twirl a workpiece not properly fastened, and that is dangerous with all but small drills. A workpiece may be kept from turning by an obstruction placed in its way, or it may be clamped to the table by bolts and straps.

Vee blocks make good casual supports and locators for round pieces. A workpiece may be clamped to an angle plate. A universal angle plate has a T-slotted surface that can be tilted and swivelled and then secured.

A typical vise of the kind commonly used to hold work on drill presses is shown in Fig. 22–20. Its open construction allows a drill to pass through the work. Many vises are actuated by cams or toggles and are quicker.

A three jaw chuck, like the one used on lathes, may be mounted on a base with the jaws up to hold pieces for drilling. The base often contains an indexing mechanism so that holes can be spaced and drilled at equal intervals on a circle.

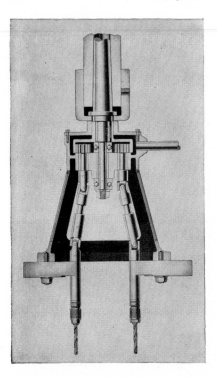

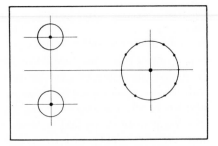

Fig. 22–19. A layout for drilling three holes.

Fig. 22–18. A cross section of a portable and adjustable multiple spindle drill head. (Courtesy Baush Machine Tool Co.)

The location of holes. The means used to locate holes depend first upon the number of workpieces required. If one or a few pieces are to be drilled, the holes may be located by layout, transfer, or use of a hole spacer. More accurate methods of locating holes will be described for jig boring machines. For larger quantities of pieces, the use of jigs on drilling machines is economical.

Fig. 22–20. A typical drill vise. (Courtesy Atlas Press Co.)

Layout consists of drawing lines on a workpiece and centerpunching for the locations of the holes in the manner indicated in Fig. 22–19. A drill, usually one of small diameter, is started in the centerpunch mark. This method requires little extra equipment but is slow and can normally be depended upon to locate a hole only within 0.005 to 0.010 in. of true position.

If holes are to run through two mating parts, they may be drilled in one of the parts first. Then the two parts are assembled together and clamped, and the drill guided in the holes already drilled to complete the holes in the second part. This is the *transfer* method of hole locations. In this way holes between the two parts can be matched as precisely as in any other way.

Fig. 22–21. A 30 in. by 20 in. hole spacing device on a radial drill for positioning holes in a workpiece. (Courtesy Bullard Co.)

Hole spacer. A hole spacer, like the *Man-Au-Trol spacer* in Fig. 22–21, has a table that slides on a saddle. The saddle slides along the other coordinate on a base. A workpiece is located on the table under a drill press spindle. The table is moved hydraulically to a predetermined position when the operator turns a selector dial that gives thirteen selections. The saddle is located independently in the same way to 20 positions. The table and saddle positioning stops are set initially for a job by precision measurements.

A hole spacer can be set up in about the time required to lay out one piece and after that is capable of repeating quickly. A workpiece is located with less than 0.001 in. error in successive positions on a hole spacer. The accuracy of hole locations depends then upon how much the drill runs out. On the other hand, a hole spacer is expensive. The 30 ✕

20 in. Man-Au-Trol spacer costs about $12,000. Over the years of its life, the cost for each piece done on the spacer is small; but it normally would not be profitable unless a large amount of work were available to keep it busy.

Fixtures and jigs. A fixture is a device that holds and locates a workpiece. Strictly speaking, conventional work holding devices such as chucks and vises are fixtures, but mostly the name is given to single-purpose holding devices. Fixtures are mostly associated with lathes, shapers, planers, millers, broaches, and grinders.

A jig not only holds and locates a workpiece but also guides the cutting tool. That is particularly desirable in drilling because the point of the drill tends to wander unless it is guided when a hole is started. Multiple point boring tools and sometimes reamers need to be guided.

Workpiece location has a particular meaning. A free body in space has six degrees of freedom; three represented by coordinate axes of translation and three by rotation about those axes. A piece is fully located when definitely restricted in all six degrees of freedom. This occurs only if the piece is held against three points in one plane, two in a second plane, and one in a third plane, with the planes preferably perpendicular to each other. Full restriction is not always desirable, as for instance when a piece must be left free to rotate between centers. Thus fewer than six locating points are supplied in some cases. A basic feature of any jig or fixture is that it provides the locating surfaces or points against which all pieces of one kind can be precisely located.

Fig. 22–22. A jig to line bore six holes in a master rod for an aircraft engine. (Courtesy Swartz Tool Products Co.)

The simplest kind of jig is a template that fits a part and has holes to guide one or more drills. More elaborate jigs have locating and clamping details to hold the workpiece in relation to the jig plate. The jig plate is the essence of the jig, is made of soft steel, and has accurately located holes bored in it. Hardened bushings, inserted in the plate to withstand wear, do the actual guiding of the drills, reamers, etc. *Slip* or *removal bushings* are convenient where tools of different sizes are to be used in one hole.

Jigs have many forms. Two are illustrated in Figs. 22–13 and 22–22. Economical fixtures and jigs for small quantities are made by putting special jaws on standard vises and chucks.

Jigs are economical for locating holes to be machined in parts made in quantities.

Whether the layout method, a hole spacer, or a jig should be used in any particular case depends upon the factors related by Eq. (19–1), the same as for any other tooling problem. For instance, suppose ten holes are to be drilled, bored, reamed, tapped, etc. in a piece and the work takes one hour. A jig costs $450 and will be depreciated in one year with a combined rate of 25% for interest, insurance, taxes, and maintenance. It costs $3 to set up the hole spacer and after that the charge for its use is $1 per hr. Overhead costs do not change. For how many pieces in one lot is it economical to make a jig and release the hole spacer for other work? In this case

$$N \times 1 = 450 \times 1.25 - 3 = 559.5 \text{ pieces.}$$

A jig should be provided for 560 pieces or more.

DRILLING PERFORMANCES

Accuracy. The degree of accuracy obtainable in hole location depends largely upon the method, as has been explained. Accuracy of hole size is another matter, dependent largely upon the tools and the way they are used. A drilled hole cannot be held closely to a specified diameter. Under average conditions it may be said that practical drilling tolerances range from 0.002 in. for a $\frac{3}{16}$ in.-diameter to 0.010 in. for 1 to 2 in.-diameter. Boring generally gives appreciably better results. A multiblade boring tool will produce a large number of holes within 0.001 to 0.002 in. of a specified size. A fluted reamer properly used and removing a limited amount of stock can be expected to produce holes repeatedly within 0.001 in. above its own size. As a rule, the best results are obtained only from the use of several tools in succession.

The degrees of surface finish obtainable from drilling and related operations are indicated in Fig. 15–37.

Feeds and speeds. The speed at which a drill, boring tool, or reamer should be run depends upon the same consideration as for other tools, explained in Chap. 17. In general, the proper peripheral cutting speed of a drill is about the same as for a single-point tool under comparable circumstances.

The feed of a drill is the distance it advances in one revolution. Feeds depend mostly upon what the drill will stand, determined by its size and the work material. As a general guide, the Cleveland Twist Drill Co. recommends "a feed of 0.001 to 0.002 in. per rev for drills $\frac{1}{8}$ to $\frac{1}{4}$ in., 0.004 to 0.007 for drills $\frac{1}{4}$ to $\frac{1}{2}$ in., 0.007 to 0.015 for drills $\frac{1}{2}$ to 1 in., and 0.015 to 0.025 for drills larger than 1 in. Alloy and hard steel should generally be drilled at a lighter feed than given above while cast iron, brass, and aluminum may usually be drilled with a heavier feed than given above."

Boring and similar tools are run at about the same speeds and feeds as drills, sometimes slightly less. As a rule, reaming must be done at low speeds and high feeds for best results. Speeds of 50 to 75% of drilling speeds and feeds 200 to 300% of drilling feeds for rose reamers and 300 to 500% for fluted reamers are recommended.

Estimating machining time and power. A hole 1 in. in diameter is drilled through a cast iron piece 3 in. thick. A H.S.S. drill with a surface speed of 50 fpm revolves at about 200 rpm. At a feed of 0.015 in. per rev, the feed rate of the drill is $200 \times 0.015 = 3.0$ in. per min. The distance the drill is fed in this case is the sum of the length of the hole of 3 in., an overtravel assumed to be $\frac{1}{8}$ in., and approach of $\frac{1}{4}$ in.; a total distance of $3\frac{3}{8}$ in. The time for the cut equals $3.375 \div 3 = 1.13$ minutes. Power may be estimated as explained in Chaps. 17 and 20.

Drilling operations compared with others. Drilling, boring, and reaming can be done on other machines such as lathes, boring machines, and milling machines. However, drilling machines are best for many such jobs because they are simple and their cost is low. Drilling machines can be tooled at moderate cost to do most high-production drilling and related operations as accurately as needed and more rapidly than on other machines. Often considerable savings can be realized by combining operations, such as drilling of several holes.

Drilling machines are economical for small as well as large quantities. Because of their simplicity, drilling machines are easy to set up and operate for work for which they are suited. A drill press can be adjusted and changed over quickly from one job to another. Work must be done on a lathe, boring machine, or milling machine around one axis at a time; adjustments are slow, and appreciable time is required to change from one axis to another. In contrast, tools can be changed quickly, work can be shifted around rapidly, and settings can be altered easily on a drill press to machine holes of different sizes in various positions. A radial drill is convenient for large pieces because it can save moving them. Work that is hard to revolve on a lathe is usually done easier on a drill press.

A drill press is at a disadvantage in some cases. A hole may be machined more economically on a lathe in the same set-up with outside surfaces, and more accurately with respect to those surfaces, than separately on a drilling machine where the external cuts cannot be taken conveniently. Also, a drill press does not offer the most accurate means of locating holes unless enough pieces are required to justify expensive tooling.

Questions

1. Define drilling, core drilling, counter drilling, and step drilling.

2. Define boring, counterboring, spotfacing, and countersinking.

3. What does reaming entail?

4. Sketch a twist drill and name its principal parts.

5. What means are used to drill deep holes?

6. Name and describe the principal kinds of reamers.

7. Describe and designate the principal units of a vertical drill press.

8. What is the difference between a gang drill press and a multiple drill press? For what are they of value?

9. Describe a radial drill press. For what is it used?

10. What are a taper shank socket, floating driver, adjustable extension assembly, and quick change collet?

11. How may work be held on a drill press?

12. Describe four ways of locating holes in drill press operations. When is each method used?

13. What determines the accuracy of the size of a hole made in a drilling operation?

14. How do drill presses compare with other machines able to do the same kind of work in small quantities?

15. Why are drilling machines advantageous for drilling operations on work done in large quantities?

Problems

1. A bearing cap must have four holes of ½ in.-diameter drilled in it. If these holes are drilled one at a time, each piece takes three minutes. The labor rate is $2 per hr and overhead on the machine $5 per hr.

A four-spindle drill head for the job costs $350 and will do each piece in one minute but has no other use. The labor rate is $2 per hr, but overhead on the heavier machine required is $5.50 per hr. A composite rate of 25% is required for interest, insurance, taxes, and maintenance of special tools. The depreciation period is one year. Set-up cost is negligible.

For how many pieces is it economical to get a four-spindle drill head?

2. A workpiece must have 10 holes finished in it. Layout time is ½ hr per piece; the same time is required to set up the hole spacer for the job. To finish the holes requires one hour for each piece, not counting layout or set-up. The labor rate is $2 per hr, the machine rate is $5 per hr, and the hole spacer rate is $2 per hr. How large a lot should be put on the hole spacer, if either method gives the results desired?

3. A part may have a hole located for drilling by layout. If a jig is provided, ½ minute is saved for each piece. Labor rate is $2.40 per hr, which means a savings of $0.02 per piece. The overhead rate on the labor saved is 100%. Set-up time is no more with than without the jig. The combined rate for interest, insurance, taxes, and maintenance is 35%. The cost of the jig is $100.

    (a) How many pieces must be made in one lot to make the jig worth-while?

    (b) How many pieces must be made on the jig in one lot each month to earn the cost of the jig in 2 years?

    (c) How many pieces must be made on the jig in one lot each year to save its cost in 2 years?

4. If one lot of 3000 pieces is to be made under the conditions described in Prob. 3, how much is it justified to spend for a jig?

5. The cost for the use of a hole spacer is $2 per hr. A part with seven holes can be machined in 15 minutes with either the hole spacer or the jig. Set-up time is 10 minutes more with the hole spacer. Labor and over-head rate is $4 per hr. A jig costs $125 and is depreciated in one year. The combined rate for interest, insurance, taxes, and maintenance is 35%. For how many pieces is it economical to use the hole spacer?

6. A jig for machining a part with three holes costs $100. Machining time is 12 minutes. The other conditions are the same as in Prob. 5. For how many pieces is it economical to make a jig rather than to use a hole spacer?

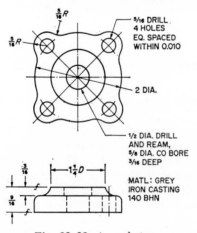

Fig. 22–23. A workpiece.

7. Write a list of the steps or unit operations required to machine all the holes in one piece shown in Fig. 22–23. Specify the machine and tools to use.

8. Write a list of the steps or unit operations required to machine 5000 pieces shown in Fig. 22–23. A four-spindle drill head is available. Specify the machines and tools required.

9. Estimate the cutting time for the operation and the power of the machine for Prob. 7.

10. Estimate the cutting time for the operation and the power of the machine for Prob. 8.

References

Oxford, C. J., Jr., "Mechanics of Drilling," *The Tool Engineer,* May, 1954, p. 145.

Woodcock, Frederic L., *Design of Metal Cutting Tools,* McGraw-Hill Book Co., Inc., New York, 1948.

23

Shaping and Planing

Both shaping and planing are intended primarily for flat surfaces, horizontal, vertical or at an angle as indicated in Fig. 23–1, but can be arranged for machining curved surfaces and slots. Short internal surfaces can also be shaped.

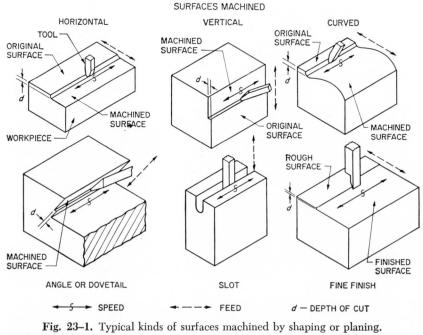

SURFACES MACHINED

HORIZONTAL   VERTICAL   CURVED

TOOL

ORIGINAL SURFACE

MACHINED SURFACE

ORIGINAL SURFACE

MACHINED SURFACE

WORKPIECE

MACHINED SURFACE

ORIGINAL SURFACE

ROUGH SURFACE

MACHINED SURFACE

MACHINED SURFACE

FINISHED SURFACE

ANGLE OR DOVETAIL   SLOT   FINE FINISH

◄─*S*─► SPEED   ◄─ ─ ─► FEED   *d* — DEPTH OF CUT

Fig. 23–1. Typical kinds of surfaces machined by shaping or planing.

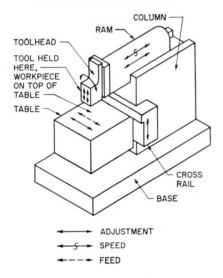

TOOLHEAD

TOOL HELD
HERE,
WORKPIECE
ON TOP OF
TABLE

TABLE

RAM

COLUMN

CROSS
RAIL

BASE

Fig. 23–2. A 24 in. standard horizontal crank operated push cut shaper and a diagram of its principal parts and movements. (Photo Courtesy The Cincinnati Shaper Co.)

ADJUSTMENT

SPEED

FEED

Shaping and planing differ with respect to action and workpiece size. In shaping, the tool is reciprocated over the workpiece surface, while in planing, the workpiece is moved past the tool, in both cases at cutting speeds. In shaping a horizontal surface the workpiece is fed, but for shaping vertical and inclined surfaces and in all planing, the tool is fed an increment for each stroke in a direction perpendicular to the cutting speed.

Because of the necessary structure of the machine, shaping is limited to small and moderate size workpieces.

In most shaping and planing operations, cutting is done in one direction only. The return stroke represents lost time. Thus these processes are slower than milling and broaching, which cut continuously. On the other hand, shaping and planing use single-point tools that are less expensive, are easier to sharpen, and are conducive to quicker set-ups than the multiple point tools of milling and broaching. This makes shaping or planing economical as a rule to machine one or a few pieces of a kind.

SHAPING

Horizontal shapers. A horizontal shaper typified by Fig. 23–2 has a horizontal ram that reciprocates at cutting speed. A cutting tool is carried on the toolhead on the front of the ram. The length and position of the stroke of the ram is adjustable so that the tool can be set to cover any part of the maximum stroke of the shaper and need not travel any more than necessary for each job. The slide that carries the tool on the toolhead can be swivelled to and clamped at any angle in a vertical plane on the front of the ram. An application of the adjustment is illustrated in Fig. 23–3. The slide can be adjusted by a micrometer dial or fed by hand or automatically in the direction to which it is swivelled. The available movement is limited because the slide is short. The cutting tool, normally in a tool post, is fastened to a clapper box on the front of the tool slide. The clapper box is pivoted and swings to allow the tool to lift and ride loosely over the work on the return stroke. This eases the pressure on the tool and prevents marring the work surface.

A cross rail mounted on ways on the front of the column of a horizontal shaper is adjustable up or down. The work table rides crosswise on the rail and can be adjusted or fed manually or automatically. Feed takes place just before the beginning of each stroke. The power feed is activated by the ram driving mechanism.

A *plain* or *utility shaper* is a light shaper with a plain adjustable table. *Standard, heavy duty,* or *production shapers* are heavy and rugged and are characterized by an adjustable table supported at its front end, as in Fig. 23–2.

A *universal shaper* has a table that can be swivelled around two horizontal axes in addition to horizontal and vertical adjustments.

All the shapers described so far push the tool away from the column

Fig. 23–3. A view of the toolhead and clapper box swivelled on a shaper to machine an inclined surface. (Courtesy The Cincinnati Shaper Co.)

to cut. In contrast, a *draw cut shaper* cuts towards the column. It can be built with a long stroke and take heavy cuts and is made in the larger sizes. Draw cut shapers are intended for heavy duty and are correspondingly expensive.

Among other less common types of shapers is a *travelling head shaper* that has a box-shaped bed with two tables. The ram is carried by a saddle that moves crosswise to position the ram with respect to each table in turn. A *double head shaper* has two rams to work on two workpieces at a time mounted on a table.

Vertical shapers. A vertical shaper or *slotter* has a vertical ram and normally a rotary table as illustrated in Fig. 23–4. On some machines the ram is inclinable up to 10° from the vertical, which is useful for cutting inclined surfaces. The rotary table can be indexed accurately or rotated continuously by hand or power. It moves on a saddle that slides on the bed and has horizontal adjustments and feeds in two directions.

The horizontal table of the vertical shaper is easy to load. The cir-

Fig. 23–4. A 20 in. hydraulic vertical shaper or slotter machining an internal keyway. (Courtesy Rockford Machine Tool Co.)

cular plus the two straight line motions of the table permit easy machining of circular, convex, concave, and other curved surfaces. Slots or grooves can be accurately spaced around a workpiece.

The vertical design of this shaper requires a minimum of floor space and makes possible a convenient grouping of controls. The operator can readily control and observe the work being done. The tool enters the work from the top and can be guided to a line thereon with relative ease.

Shaper drives. Several types of drives are built for shaper rams, and the name given to a shaper frequently denotes the kind of drive it has. One kind is through a *mechanical crank*, another is *hydraulic*. Typical hydraulic circuits are described in Chap. 21. A less common kind is the *gear drive*, in which a rack on the ram is driven by a spur gear. A shaper with that drive may be called a *geared shaper*.

The mechanism of a typical crank-operated shaper is shown in Fig. 23–5. Power goes from the motor to a pulley through vee belts and passes through a clutch and gear transmission to the pinion that drives the large

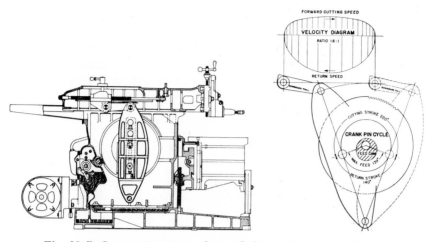

Fig. 23–5. Cross section views of a crank driven shaper and a diagram of the crank mechanism. (Courtesy The Cincinnati Shaper Co.)

bull gear in the middle of the column. The bull gear's speed is varied by shifting gears in the transmission.

The bull gear in the middle of the column in Fig. 23–5 rotates clockwise at a uniform rate. A block on a crankpin that travels in a circle on the bull gear slides in a slot in the crank and causes it to reciprocate. The crank may be identified by its near elliptical shape. It is pivoted at the bottom and is connected at the top to the ram through a link.

As depicted by the diagram on the right in Fig. 23–5, the direction of movement of the crank changes when the centerline of the crank is tangent to the circular path of the crankpin on the bull gear. The crankpin is positioned in or out radially on the bull gear from an external control to change the length of stroke. For a constant bull gear speed, the ram speed changes with the radial setting of the crankpin. When the ram moves forward on the cutting stroke, the driving pin moves through an arc of 220°. On the return stroke, the pin travels through only 140° of arc. Thus the ram travels much faster and takes less time on the return stroke than on the forward or cutting stroke. This *quick return motion* saves time when the tool is not cutting.

The relative advantages and disadvantages of mechanical and hydraulic drives in general, explained in Chap. 21, apply to shapers. The benefit of a quick reversal and uniform cutting speed is illustrated by a comparison for a 40 fpm nominal cutting speed and 10 in. stroke. Under those conditions a hydraulic shaper was reported able to make 31 strokes per min and a mechanical shaper 18.7 strokes per min.

Sizes of shapers. The size of a shaper designates its longest nominal cutting stroke. Thus, a 24 in. shaper has ram travel enough to drive a tool across a 24 in.-long surface, sometimes a little more. On most horizontal shapers, the table can be fed crosswise a distance at least as large as the stroke. That means a 24 in. shaper usually is capable of machining a plane surface at least 24 × 24 in. square. Horizontal shapers range from bench models with strokes of 7 or 8 in. to heavy duty machines with strokes of 72 in. The feasible size of the overhanging ram limits the largest size of shapers.

TABLE 23–1. Specifications of Medium-Size Shapers

Type	Nominal size (in.)	Drive	Speed range	No. of speeds	Feed range (ips)	No. of feeds	Motor (hp)	Wt. (lb)	Price ($)
Plain, horizontal ⎱	24	Mech.	10–129	8	0.010–0.170	11	7½	6,720	9,000
Standard ⎰	24	Hydr.	10–100	Inf.	0–0.100	Inf.	7½	5,400	8,000
Vertical 28 in.-diam. table	20	Hydr.	10–60	Inf.	0–0.106	Inf.	7½	14,000	23,000

Shaper tool and attachments. The single-point tools used on horizontal shapers are much like lathe tools, except that shaper rake angles may be slightly less, particularly for hard materials. High-speed steel is the most common cutting tool material for shaping, but shockproof grade carbides are in wide use, especially for hard materials. A *tool lifter* is a device that automatically raises the tool to clear the work on the return stroke. It is particularly desirable for use with carbide tools.

Index centers like those that will be described for milling machines have uses for spacing shaper cuts around workpieces.

Profiling and duplicating attachments are added to shapers to make them capable of reproducing surfaces of curvature. A finger or follower is arranged on a bracket attached to the toolhead so that it travels over a master surface as the tool passes over the workpiece. As the finger rises and falls in tracing the master surface, the tool is raised and lowered in unison by hydraulic means and reproduces the master profile on the workpiece.

Shaping operations. Workpieces are commonly clamped to the table or held in a vise on a shaper. Small quantities normally do not justify fixtures. Forces are preferably directed against the fixed jaws of a vise for rigidity. A tool should travel lengthwise over a surface if possible. In that way fewer strokes are needed, and less time is lost in return strokes.

Copper, brass, or lead strips called *false jaws* are inserted at the sides of a rough piece as in Fig. 23–6(A) to protect the vise jaws. A surface can be shaped square with another by locating against the fixed jaw as in Fig. 23–6(B). To machine the top parellel with the bottom, a workpiece is held down firmly by *hold downs,* as in Fig. 23–6(C). These are thin tapered strips tilted at an angle.

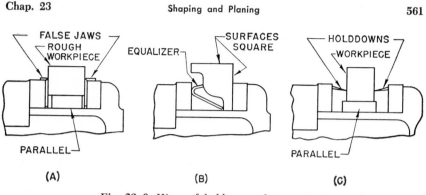

FALSE JAWS
ROUGH
WORKPIECE
EQUALIZER
PARALLEL

(A)

SURFACES
SQUARE

(B)

HOLDDOWNS
WORKPIECE
PARALLEL

(C)

Fig. 23–6. Ways of holding work in a vise.

A common practice is to scribe the outline of a surface along its edges on a workpiece and adjust the shaper tool to the line to machine the desired surface. The tool is adjusted to cut an irregular surface by the operator manipulating the controls.

Very small tolerances can be held on a shaper if sufficient skill and care are exercised by the operator. These may be of the order of 0.001 in. or less on dimensions and 0.001 in. in 6 in. for squareness and parallelism. However, more usual and economical tolerances are 0.003 to 0.005 in. on dimensions and 0.002 to 0.003 in. in 6 in. for squareness and parallelism.

Estimating shaping time and power. The cut speed of a single-point tool on a shaper should be about the same as on a lathe under comparable conditions. For a given length of stroke, l, in inches, the number of strokes per minute, N, must be selected to give the required cut speed, V in fpm. The average cut speed is a little less than the highest cut speed.

The cutting stroke occupies only a part of each full stroke. The proportion varies with different shapers, but a common ratio shown in Fig. 23–5 of 1.6 to 1 for duration of cutting stroke to return stroke will be used as an example. With that ratio, the tool moves at the average cut speed during $\frac{1.6 \times 100}{1.6 + 1} = 61.5\%$ of the full stroke. The time for a full stroke is $1/N$ min, and for the cutting stroke $0.615/N$ min. Distance is equal to velocity multiplied by time, or

$$l = 12V \times \frac{0.615}{N}, \quad \text{and} \quad N = 7.4 \frac{V}{l} \qquad (23\text{–}1)$$

As an example, a machine steel surface 10 in. long is to be shaped with a H.S.S. tool at 80 fpm. The shaper should be set as near as possible to $7.4 \times (80/10) = 59.2$ strokes per min.

It is well to remember that long strokes and high speeds together impose a strain on a shaper because of the large forces of reversal and should be avoided. An example of that is a 24 in. stroke at 100 strokes per min giving an average surface speed of 324 fpm. Most shapers are not capable of delivering cutting speeds as high as those used in turning aluminum, for example.

The feed on a shaper should be as heavy as the machine, workpiece, or tool will stand and as will not give too rough a surface. Table 23–2 shows average feeds for cast iron and machine steel as a guide. Higher or lower feeds may be selected to suit particular situations. The feed may be reduced to ½ or ⅓ for irregular surfaces. grooves, and cutting off. The finer the feed the better the finish. Softer materials allow higher feeds, and harder materials require lower feeds. A rigid set-up permits a heavier cut than a weak one. A feed as high as ¼ in. per stroke may be desirable for a broad nose finishing tool, and one as fine as 0.005 in. per stroke for a sharp point tool.

TABLE 23–2.

Type of cut				Roughing		Finishing	
Depth or manner of cut	¹⁄₁₆	⅛	¼	Tool head feed	¹⁄₃₂	Tool head feed
Feed (in. per stroke)	0.06	0.04	0.03	.02	0.02	0.01

For an example of estimating the cutting time, a machine steel surface 10 in. long and 5 in. wide is to be shaped at 60 strokes per min. The depth of cut is ⅛ in. and the feed 0.04 in. per stroke. The feed rate is $0.04 \times 60 = 2.4$ in. per min. If ¼ in. overtravel is assumed, the distance the work is fed is 5¼ in., and the machine time is $5.25 \div 2.4 = 2.2$ minutes.

In the foregoing example, the average cutting speed for a 10¼ in. stroke is $60 \times 10.25/7.4 = 83$ fpm. The average rate of metal removal is $0.04 \times ⅛ \times 83 \times 12 = 5.0$ cu in. per min. For a unit power consumption of one hp per cu in. per min indicated in Table 20–1, 5.0 hp are expended at the tool point. For a machine efficiency of 75%, 6.7 hp are required at the motor.

Shaping compared with other operations. Other machine tools are able to cut and remove stock faster than shapers, but shapers are favored for many short run jobs because of several advantages they offer. A shaper can be put to many uses in a shop and can easily be changed from one job to another. Set-up time for many jobs is less on a shaper than on other machines. Practically all work can be done with simple and inexpensive tools. This is exemplified by a curved surface that would require a special form tool if machined by another method such as milling but can be shaped by a single-point tool. Even if a form tool is used on a shaper, it can be made and sharpened more easily than a multiple-tooth milling cutter or broach.

A shaper is convenient for cutting inclined surfaces. On the other machines, such as the milling machine, fixtures and attachments often are needed to machine inclined surfaces. Frail workpieces can sometimes be shaped with ordinary set-ups because the cutting forces are not large, whereas extra supports would be needed on other machine tools.

PLANING

The planer. The *planer* or *planing machine* carries the work on a massive table, fully supported by a heavy bed, like the one in Fig. 21-1, and capable of sustaining heavy loads. The table slides on ways on the bed. Most planers cut in one; some, in both directions. Tee slots and holes are provided for bolts, keys, and pins for holding and locating workpieces on the finished table top.

The common type of planer illustrated in Fig. 23-7 has two heavy housings, also called columns and uprights, at about the middle of the bed, with one on each side of the table. These carry the horizontal cross rail that can be raised or lowered and then clamped in place. The columns and rail carry the toolheads. Those on the side slide up and down; those on the cross rail slide horizontally.

A planer toolhead normally can be swivelled on its base, called the saddle, up to about 60° of each side of its neutral position. The plate that swivels carries a slide that has a clapper box on the end for mounting the tool. The clapper allows the tool to rise from the workpiece on the back stroke like on a shaper. The clapper box can usually be swivelled about 20° in each direction to place the tool in advantageous positions as needed. Many planers have air or hydraulic tool lifters that automatically swing the clapper block out for each return stroke to save the tools.

Planer drives and feeds. Some planers have hydraulic drives, with locked variable delivery circuits. The maximum table speed depends upon the service for which the machine is designed and may be from 50 to 300 fpm on different machines.

Modern planers with mechanical drives are powered by variable speed, reversing, d-c motors. A motor generator set powered from an a-c supply furnishes adjustable voltage d-c to the motor of the machine. The main drive motor ordinarily has a speed range characteristic in the ratio of 3:1 or 6:1. With the adjustable voltage feature, the speed range ratio can be raised to 30:1. Thus the realizable speed range of the motor is normally from 40 to 1200 rpm with practically a constant horsepower delivered over the range of 500 to 1200 rpm, and the torque constant at lower speeds.

The power is carried from the motor to the table through a set of reduction gears housed in the bed. The last gear in the series is a bull gear that meshes with a rack fastened to the underside of the table.

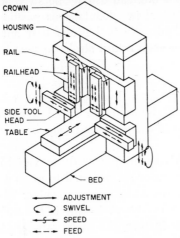

CROWN
HOUSING
RAIL
RAILHEAD
SIDE TOOL
HEAD
TABLE
BED

→ ADJUSTMENT
↻ SWIVEL
←s→ SPEED
←--→ FEED

Fig. 23–7. A 48 in. by 48 in. by
16 ft. double housing planer with twin
helical gear drive and a diagram of its
principal parts. (Photo Courtesy The
Cincinnati Planer Co. Div. Giddings
and Lewis Machine Tool Co.)

The gear ratio of a mechanical planer is defined as the number of
turns the motor shaft makes to drive the table one foot. Gear ratios vary
from 4 to 12½, and each planer is made with a specific ratio. The higher
ratios are put on heavy duty machines. If the gear ratio is 4 and the
motor speed range 40 to 1200 rpm, the table speed range is 10 to 300 fpm.
With a gear ratio of 8 and the same motor, another planer has speeds from
5 to 150 fpm but twice as much table pull at any specified speed.

Adjustable dogs bolted to the side of a planer table trip a switch or control valve to reverse the table at the end of the desired stroke. If not reversed as intended, a heavily loaded planer table might very well run off the end of the bed and cause considerable damage. Most planers have a safety device to take care of just such an emergency. Among these devices are hydraulic bumpers. Another form has cutting tools bolted to the underside of the table to bite into replaceable stop blocks fastened to the bed.

Feed on a planer is intermittent and is the distance in inches the tool is moved for each stroke of the workpiece. One means is through a ratchet mechanism actuated by table reversal. Each toolhead can be fed horizontally or vertically as shown in Fig. 23–7. The tool may also be fed at an angle by swivelling the toolhead and feeding the tool slide. The feeds to the various heads are independent of each other. A typical feed range is 0.01 to 1 in. per stroke.

Fig. 23–8. An openside hydraulic planer with a workpiece on the table extending beyond the rail. (Courtesy Rockford Machine Tool Co.)

Types of planers. The *standard* or *double housing planer* that has been described is capable of heavy service. An *openside planer*, like the one in Fig. 23–8, has a housing only on one side of the bed. The other side is open so that extra wide work can hang over the side of the bed, sometimes supported on an auxiliary rolling table alongside. Small sizes of openside planers are also called *shaper planers*. A *divided* or *latching table planer* has a table in two sections. They may be coupled together for long work or separated so the work on one table may be set up while that on the other is machined.

The *planer-type milling machine* is a cross between the planer and milling machine and is described in Chap. 24. A *planer-type grinder* has a grinding head in place of one or more of the conventional toolheads on the rail.

A *plate planer* is a special-purpose machine for squaring and bevelling the edges of steel plates for armor, ships, or pressure vessels. One edge of the plate is held down and machined by a tool traversed on a carriage along the front of a machine.

When workpieces are too heavy or bulky, the tools may be moved more readily than the work. That is the basis for the design of the *pit planer* on which the workpiece is mounted on a stationary table. Columns carrying the cross rail and toolheads ride on long ways on both sides of the table.

Sizes of planers. The size of a standard planer is designated by the distance between the vertical housings in inches, the height from the top of the table to the rail in its uppermost position in inches, and the maximum length of table travel in feet. The length of travel is often the length of the working area of the table. The size of an openside planer is designated by comparable figures, but the first specifies the distance from the column to the tool in its outmost positions. Sometimes when the first two figures are the same, they are expressed by one quantity, such as $42^x \times 10'$ for $42'' \times 42'' \times 10'$.

Planers range in size from 24 in. with 42 in. stroke to 16 ft $\times$ 16 ft by 60 ft long. Specifications of several common sizes are given in Table 23–3.

TABLE 23–3. Specifications for Several Planers

Model	Size	Type of drive	Main motor (hp)	Weight (lb)	Price ($)
Openside	$24'' \times 36'' \times 10'$	Hydr.	20	26,200	27,000
Openside	$42'' \times 42'' \times 10'$	Hydr.	60	53,500	55,000
Double housing	$42'' \times 42'' \times 10'$	Hydr.	60	56,500	60,000
Double housing	$48'' \times 48'' \times 10'$	Mech.	50/100	70,000	90,000
Double housing	$72'' \times 72'' \times 12'$	Mech.	100/150	110,000	120,000

Planer tools and attachments. Single-point cutting tools of the same general shapes, materials, and angles as lathe and shaper tools are used on planers but for the most part are heavier and larger because the planer normally takes deep cuts at heavy feeds. Round nose tools are favored for roughing, but sharp point tools are necessary to get into corners, such as in dovetails. Various arrangements of gangs of tool bits in a holder are widely used. Finishing tools may have cutting edges up to 1½ in. wide set carefully parallel to the surface cut.

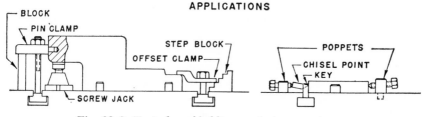

Fig. 23–9. Typical workholding methods on a planer.

Most workpieces are clamped directly to the table on a planer. Some typical arrangements are depicted in Fig. 23–9. Sometimes work is held in a vise or vises fastened to the table top. Occasionally fixtures may be justified by the quantity of pieces to be machined. Set-up time can be saved by loading one set of fixtures while a duplicate set holds pieces being planed. *Set-up plates* fit the table top, and one is loaded off the machine while another is on the table with work being machined.

Many sizes and shapes of surfaces may be reproduced by planing by use of a hydraulic duplicating attachment. A special rail head carries a tracer finger and cutting tool. During each stroke the finger rides over a master surface. As the finger rises and falls, the tool is raised and lowered hydraulically the same way and cuts a profile on the workpiece like that on the master.

Planing operations. Efficient set-up practice is probably the most important phase of planer operation. It has been said that a planer is more difficult to set up than any other machine tool, in spite of the fact that it is a relatively simple machine in itself. Large and intermittent forces varying in direction must be forestalled. Workpieces are bulky and heavy but must be precisely and safely located and fastened, and each job is almost a new problem.

To get the most out of a planer, as many tools as possible must be used for each job, and each tool must be held securely with a minimum of overhang. A number of workpieces may be placed side by side or in rows to utilize the tool heads fully.

The large work commonly done on planers is not expected to be machined as closely as smaller work done on other machines, such as shapers. Tolerances of 0.005 to 0.010 in. are considered practicable, although smaller tolerances are realizable with care and skill.

Estimating planing time and power. A planer tool is usually set to rough a surface to about 0.005 in. above size. The depth of cut depends upon the amount of stock to be removed and frequently is as much as 1¼ in. and more. An average feed is ⅛ to ¼ in. for roughing, but may be more or less to suit conditions.

For fair finishes, only two cuts may be taken. For fine finishes, three cuts are customary, with 0.001 to 0.002 in. of stock taken off by the final cut. Broad nose finishing tools for cast iron are fed ¼ to 1 in. per stroke at speeds of about 40 fpm for high-speed steel and 200 fpm for carbides. Feeds up to ¼ in. per stroke are recommended for finishing steel.

Planing tools are governed by the same factors and economically can stand the same speeds as other single point tools but the actual speeds and feeds in planing operations are often limited by sizes of the workpieces and machines. The strength of the workpieces or the pull of the machines may limit the feed. However, cuts are generally heavy in planing, and for a large cut, the speed must be decreased to maintain an economical tool life. Thus operating speeds tend to be lower for planing than some other operations. The speed may be limited for a heavy cut by the power of the machine especially with several tools cutting at once. In general, both cutting and return speeds should be lower for heavy workpieces because of their inertia. On the other hand, full advantage should be taken of the capacities of the tools and machine when the workpiece or cut, or both, are light. Speeds and feeds used in practice are given in Table 23–4 to serve as a guide.

TABLE 23–4. RECOMMENDED SPEEDS AND FEEDS FOR PLANING

| Material | H.S.S. | Speed (ft per min) | | Feed (ips) |
		Nonferrous alloy	Cemented carbide	
Aluminum	100–200 ⎫	At maximum table speed		0.03–0.09 ⎧
Brass and Bronze	50–150 ⎭			0.03–0.09 ⎩
Cast iron ⎫ and ⎬ Steel ⎭	50–100	100–150	150–300	0.03–0.12
	30–60	75–125	100–200	0.12–1.00

The return stroke speed may be from about one to four times as high as the cutting speed. For an average ratio of 2½ to 1, Eq. (23–1) becomes

$$N = 8.6\frac{V}{l} \qquad (23\text{–}2)$$

The cutting time for planing is calculated from the number of strokes per minute, the feed in inches per stroke, and the distance the tool is fed in inches, in the same way as described for shaping.

The horsepower per cubic inch per minute of stock removal may be comparable to that required on a shaper for light cuts. Metal removal is more efficient for heavy cuts usually taken on a planer. One leading manufacturer uses the constants of 0.25 hp per cu in. per min for cast iron, 0.5 for machine steel, and 0.15 for bronze.

Planing compared with other operations. Planers generally are capable of performing the same basic operations as shapers and milling machines. Because they offer full support, planers can be made to take large, bulky, and heavy workpieces or numbers of pieces at one time. Although the planer is not as suitable as the shaper for small- and medium-size parts done one or a few at a time, it often is better when enough parts are required so that a number can be done at one time or when heavy cuts can be taken. The components of a planer are massive and rigid, and heavy cuts and feeds are feasible.

Planing with single-point tools generally is conceded to be a slower cutting operation than milling with multiple-point tools. However, the planer has a definite place in metal machining because both the machine and tool are relatively low in first cost and upkeep. As a rule, the planer offers more machine capacity at the same cost as a milling machine, or the same capacity at less cost. If a part can be planed almost as fast as it can be milled, a planer may be more desirable because of the low cost of grinding the tool bits. For a typical operation, enough planer tool bits could be ground in about an hour for a 24 hour operation. Several hours would be spent in grinding milling cutters for the same operation.

Questions

1. How are shaping and planing alike and how do they differ?

2. What are the advantages and disadvantages of shaping and planing as compared to other operations?

3. Describe a horizontal shaper.

4. What is a draw-cut shaper?

5. Describe a vertical shaper.

6. What are the common kinds of shaper drives?

7. Discuss the relative advantages and disadvantages of hydraulic and mechanical shaper drives.

8. What does the size of a shaper designate?

9. What are false jaws and why are they used?

10. What are hold-downs and what purpose do they serve?

11. What limits the size and practical cutting speeds of shapers?

12. For what work are shapers favored and why?

13. Describe a double housing planer.

14. Describe the typical forms of planer table drives.

15. What is the gear ratio of a planer and how does it affect the table speed?

16. Name and describe the principal types of planers.

17. How is the size of a planer designated?

18. How is work held on a planer?

19. In what ways are planers economical?

Problems

1. List the steps and describe the set-ups and tools needed to shape one piece depicted in Fig. 23–10. The rough casting has ⅛ in. stock on all surfaces. Normal operation tolerances are satisfactory.

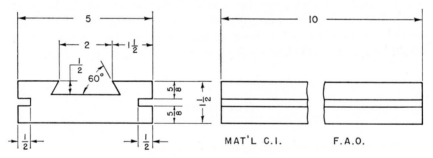

Fig. 23–10. A slide block.

2. For an average cutting speed of 100 fpm, what should be the theoretical number of strokes per minute on a shaper with a cutting to idle stroke ratio of 1.8:1 and a length of stroke of (a) 3 in. (b) 5 in. (c) 8 in. (d) 15 in.?

   Would it be likely that you would be able to get a cutting speed of 100 fpm for all these lengths of stroke on a 24 in. shaper?

3. For a 12 in.-length of stroke on a shaper with a cutting to idle stroke ratio of 1.8:1, how many strokes per minute are required for a cutting speed of (a) 55 fpm (b) 50 fpm (c) 75 fpm (d) 100 fpm?

4. A cast iron surface 1½ × 10 in. is to be rough shaped with a depth of cut of ⅛ in. The shaper ratio is 1.6:1. Estimate the cutting time and power required for the cut.

5. The top of a mild steel plate 9×20 in. is to be finish shaped with the removal of $\frac{1}{32}$ in. of metal. The shaper ratio is 1.6:1. Cutting speed is 100 fpm with a H.S.S. tool. Estimate the cutting time and power required for the cut.

6. A mechanical planer with a gear ratio of 4:1 has a table pull of 13,200 lb at speeds from 10 to 125 fpm. Above 125 fpm the pull diminishes as speed increases, to 5500 lb at top speed of 300 fpm. What is the range of motor speeds and what power is delivered? If this motor is put on another planer with a gear ratio of 5:1, what should be the table speeds and how much pull should be available?

7. What are the relationships corresponding to Eq. (23–2) when the forward to return stroke ratios are 2:1, 3:1, and 4:1?

8. A cast iron machine tool bed weighing 10 tons is to be machined on a planer. As much as ¾ in. of stock must be removed on the largest surface that is 12 ft long and 8 in. wide. Two other surfaces of the same length and with the same stock removal may be machined at the same time, but are not as wide. Cemented carbide tools are to be used. The planer can deliver 75 hp to the cut. What cutting speed and feed should be used?

   For what return stroke and what number of strokes per minute should the planer be set?

   Estimate the cutting time for the roughing operation.

   Estimate the cutting time for the finishing operation.

9. A mild steel plate has a top surface 24×56 in. to be planed with a stock removal of ⅛ in. Two cemented carbide tools are to be used at once. Specify the number of strokes per minute. The machine has a 50 hp motor. Estimate the time for a single cut to remove all the stock.

10. One quarter inch of stock is to be removed from a cast iron surface 42×48 in. in two passes. Two roughing tools will be used at once. All tools are cemented carbide. A speed of 12 fpm and feed of ¼ in. for both roughing and finishing have been selected. Estimate the cutting time for the operation.

11. Twenty slide blocks like the one shown in Fig. 23–10 are to be machined on a planer. Specify the size of planer suitable for the job. Describe the steps and arrangements needed to machine these pieces.

References

Tool Engineer Handbook, McGraw-Hill Book Co., Inc., New York.

Treatise on Planers, Cincinnati Planer Co., Cincinnati.

CHAPTER 24

Milling

Flat or curved surfaces, inside or outside, of almost all shapes and sizes can be machined by milling. Common milling operations are depicted in Fig. 24–1. As a rule the workpiece is fed into or past a revolving milling cutter that usually has a number of teeth all taking intermittent cuts in succession. Less commonly, the rotating cutter is fed into the workpiece.

As indicated in Fig. 24–1, the same kind of a surface can often be milled in several ways. For instance, plane surfaces may be machined by slab milling, side milling, or face milling. The method for any specific job may be determined by the kind of milling machine used, the cutter, or the shape of the workpiece and the position of the surface.

MILLING CUTTERS AND DRIVERS

Kinds of milling cutters. Many kinds and sizes of cutters are needed for the large variety of work that can be done by milling. Many standard cutters are available, but when they are not adequate, special cutters are made. The principal types of standard cutters are identified in Fig. 24–2. A cutter is often named for the kind of milling operation it does.

Milling cutters are made of various diameters, lengths, widths, and numbers of teeth. Milling cutters may be of the *solid, tipped* or *inserted tooth* types with the same materials as for single-point tools. Large

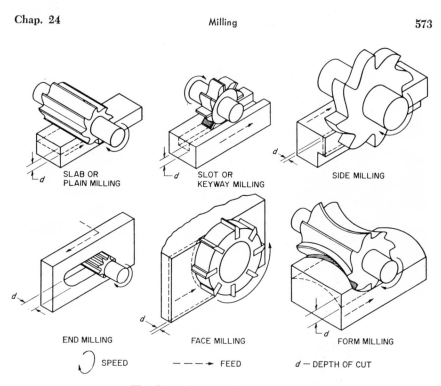

SLAB OR
PLAIN MILLING

SLOT OR
KEYWAY MILLING

SIDE MILLING

END MILLING

FACE MILLING

FORM MILLING

SPEED   — — — → FEED d — DEPTH OF CUT

Fig. 24–1. Some milling operations.

cutters commonly have teeth of expensive material inserted and locked in place in a soft steel or cast iron body, like the face milling cutter of Fig. 24–2.

The simplest type of special milling cutter is a *fly cutter*. It consists of a bit held in an arbor as in Fig. 24–3 or in a heavy disk that acts like a flywheel. Such a cutter is easy to form and can be made to do accurate work but is slow in operation. Fly cutters are used chiefly for form milling where only a few pieces are to be made. For milling larger quantities of a particular form, a special multi-tooth cutter is made.

Teeth of milling cutters. The teeth of a milling cutter have cutting edges and angles related to the edges like other cutting tools. The names of the surfaces or elements and angles of a plain milling cutter given in Fig. 24–4 are typical.

A *shaped* or *formed profile cutter*, also called a *profile ground cutter*, has a cutting edge of the desired form on each tooth with a narrow land behind the edge as in Fig. 24–4. Straight cutters are mostly of this kind, like the plain milling cutters in Fig. 24–2. This land is ground to sharpen the cutter, and it may be difficult to reproduce the original contour on a form cutter, although some form cutters are of this kind and machines are available for grinding them.

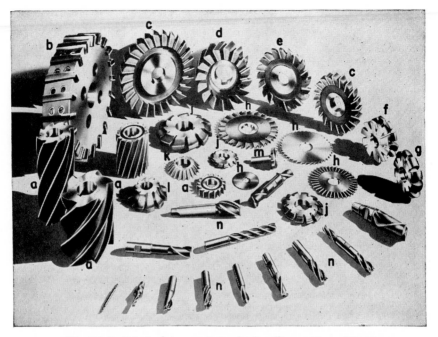

Fig. 24–2. Principal types of standard milling cutters. (Courtesy Brown and Sharpe Mfg. Co.) **a.** Plain milling cutters. **b.** Face milling cutter. **c.** Side milling cutters. **d.** Shell end mill. **e.** Staggered tooth side milling cutter. **f.** Concave cutter. **g.** Convex cutter. **h.** Metal slitting saws. **j.** Involute gear cutters. **k.** Angular cutter. **l.** Corner rounding cutter. **m.** Woodruff keyseat cutter. **n.** End mills of various types.

A *form* or *cam relieved cutter,* also called a *face ground cutter,* has a cutting edge of the desired form around each tooth and also the same profile in radial or parallel planes behind the cutting face. Examples shown in Fig. 24–2 are the concave, convex, involute gear, and corner rounding cutters. The cutter is sharpened by grinding the same amount from the faces of all teeth. Form-relieved cutters are relatively easy to sharpen, and their teeth may be reground until they become too frail to withstand the cutting load.

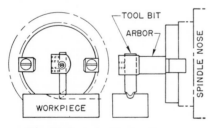

Fig. 24–3. A sketch of a flycutter.

Cutters with inserted teeth are exemplified by the diagram of Fig. 24–5 for one type of face mill. The teeth cut mostly on the nose chamfer edge. Both axial and radial rake determine the *true rake angle* in a plane perpendicular to the cutting edge. Negative rake angles are common for cemented carbides or oxides to cut steel because they help reduce the

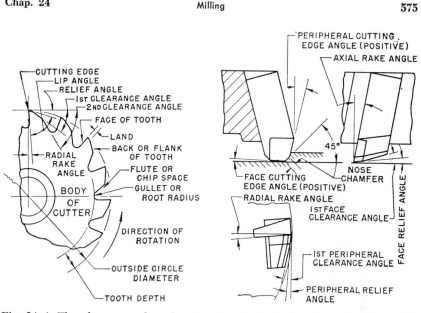

Fig. 24–4. The elements and angles of the teeth of a plain milling cutter.

Fig. 24–5. Angles of a typical face mill.

shock on the cutting edges. Face milling cutters usually are bolted on the machine's spindle nose.

Detailed recommendations for milling cutter tooth angles for various applications are given in reference- and hand-books.

Arbors, collets, and adapters. A variety of holders and drivers is needed to accommodate the many sizes and types of milling cutters. These are known as milling machine arbors, collets, and adapters.

The hole in the spindle of a modern milling machine has a taper of 3½ in. per ft at the cutter end. This is known as a National Machine Tool Builders Association taper and exists in several standard sizes.

A cutter with a center hole is held by a *milling machine arbor* like those illustrated in Figs. 24–7 and 24–13. The cutters are clamped and keyed on the straight portion, and the tapered end of the arbor is held in the hole of the machine spindle. A draw bar holds the arbor in the spindle. A short arbor is available for shell end and small face milling cutters held close to the machine spindle. It is sometimes called a *shell end mill arbor.*

Collets and *adapters* serve to adapt taper shank cutters or drivers to the taper in the end of the hole of a milling machine spindle. An adapter usually has an outside NMTBA standard taper and a smaller inside taper. Collets usually but not always have sticking tapers, such as Brown and Sharpe (½ in. per ft) or Morse tapers (⅝ in. per ft), inside and outside.

A *quick-change adapter* and *quick-change collets* provide means to change tools quickly and conveniently on the spindle of a milling machine.

A *spring chuck* or *collet holder* may be mounted on a milling machine spindle to hold wire, rods, and straight shank tools.

MILLING MACHINES

Many types of milling machines serve in various ways in industry. Some kinds are best for general-purpose work, others are suited for repetitive manufacturing, and some are ideally arranged for special jobs. In general, milling machines may be classified as general-purpose, production, planer-type, and specialized millers.

General-purpose milling machines. The *knee and column milling machine* for general purpose work has the characteristics designated by Fig. 24–6. This type of machine is capable not only of doing straight milling of plane and curved surfaces but also gear and thread cutting, drilling, boring, and slotting when suitably equipped.

The *plain* knee and column-type milling machine of Fig. 24–6 has a horizontal hollow spindle in the column to drive cutters. The knee is mounted on the column and can be adjusted or fed up and down. The saddle on top of the knee can be adjusted or fed to or away from the column. The work table can be adjusted or fed lengthwise on top of the saddle in the third coordinate direction. Feed may be by hand or power. The overarm extending from the top of the column carries supports for cutter arbors. Braces are available to tie the arbor supports and overarm to the knee for added rigidity.

A *universal* knee and column milling machine is like a plain type except that the table can be swivelled in a horizontal plane. This is especially helpful for milling a helix as shown in Fig. 24–7. The saddle is made in two parts. The upper part swivels on the lower and carries the table with it, to a limit of about 45°. The leadscrew that feeds the table is arranged so that a geared drive can be taken from it to drive a dividing head on the table. Some universal type machines have additional features. On one the knee can be swivelled to tilt the table end over end and an auxiliary spindle head on the side of the column can be swivelled to almost any angle.

A *vertical* knee and column milling machine has a vertical head and spindle as indicated in Fig. 24–6 but the same feeds and adjustments as the plain machine. On some models the head can be moved up and down, and on others it can be swivelled around a horizontal axis.

Knee and column-type milling machines can be arranged to do any kind of milling and are relatively easy to change from one job to another

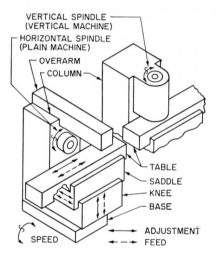

VERTICAL SPINDLE
(VERTICAL MACHINE)

HORIZONTAL SPINDLE
(PLAIN MACHINE)

OVERARM

COLUMN

TABLE

SADDLE

KNEE

BASE

ADJUSTMENT

SPEED   FEED

Fig. 24–6. A diagram of movements and a picture of a No. 2 plain knee and column type milling machine. (Photo courtesy of Cincinnati Milling Machine Co.)

but are not able to mill parts repetitively as fast as production-type machines. General-purpose milling machines are not able to take the heaviest cuts because of a certain amount of unavoidable looseness in the joints between major units and weakness from overhanging members. They are relatively slow to manipulate because the operator must give attention to a number of separate controls needed to govern all the available movements, adjustments, and selections.

Fig. 24–7. A No. 2 universal knee and column milling machine
with a dividing head and helical milling attachment set up for cutting
a helical gear. (Courtesy Brown and Sharpe Mfg. Co.)

Production milling machines. *Production* or *manufacturing milling
machines* are designed to remove metal rapidly and to require a minimum
of attention from the operator. They are not as easy to adapt to various
jobs as knee and column millers. For instance, adjustments are provided
in three coordinate directions, but feeds are often available in only one
direction and seldom in more than two directions. As a result, each
workpiece must be held in a particular position to be milled. Versatility
is not so important because production millers are intended for long runs
where set-up changes are not frequent and special fixtures and cutters
are often justified to hold workpieces and adapt the machine to specific
jobs.

Production milling machines are made in several styles. Some small
models have knees, but the most common construction is on a heavy bed
that forms a base for the major units and by which the table is fully supported. They are sometimes called *bed-type milling* machines. As many
units as possible are securely tied together. The construction is rigid to

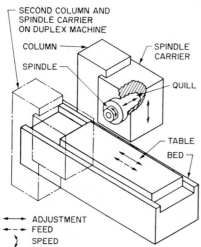

SECOND COLUMN AND
SPINDLE CARRIER
ON DUPLEX MACHINE

COLUMN

SPINDLE CARRIER

SPINDLE

QUILL

TABLE

BED

ADJUSTMENT
FEED
SPEED

Fig. 24–8. A dia-
gram of the principal
parts and movements
and a picture of a No.
2–24 plain bed type
production milling ma-
chine. (Photo Courtesy
Cincinnati Milling Ma-
chine Co.)

withstand heavy cuts. The operator is aided because the controls are
simple and the action often automatic.

Simple hand-operated millers are common among the smaller production machines. They are suited for light cuts, like slotting the heads of
screws. As the name implies, the table is fed by hand through a handwheel or lever, but the cutter is driven by a motor.

The characteristics of a typical medium size bed-type production milling machine are illustrated in Fig. 24–8. The only feed movement is the lengthwise feed of the table. Dogs on the front of the table are set to trip plungers to direct the table through each cycle of the operation. The table may be fed in either or both directions. In a typical cycle, the table carries the work rapidly to the cutter, proceeds at slow feed, reverses at the end of the cut, and withdraws quickly. The spindle is started at the beginning and stopped at the end of each cut automatically. Once the machine has been set up, all the operator has to do to control it is to start each cycle by pushing a lever on the front of the bed.

The spindle of the machine illustrated in Fig. 24–8 is carried in a quill in the spindle carrier and is adjustable crosswise over the table. The spindle carrier is adjustable vertically on a column attached to the bed. After adjustment, these units are clamped in position. Some machines of this kind are built with spindle carriers having controlled up and down movements.

A production miller with one spindle carrier is called a *plain* machine. A *duplex* machine has two opposed spindle carriers as indicated in the diagram of Fig. 24–8. A rail may be placed across the columns and a third or fourth spindle carrier mounted vertically on it over the table. This type machine is considered a special type.

Fig. 24–9. A No. 56–60 plain tracer controlled hydromatic production type milling machine. (Courtesy Cincinnati Milling Machine Co.)

Tracer-controlled production milling machines mill curved and irregular surfaces in moderate to large quantities. A typical job is shown in Fig. 24–9. A roller on a tracer control valve rides on a template bolted to the rear of the table and causes the cutter to cut in a path corresponding to that of the template.

Not all production millers have reciprocating tables. *Continuous millers* have rotary tables; some horizontal, others vertical. Workpieces are clamped in a series of fixtures around the table as each passes the operator's position. The revolving table carries the workpieces past one or more cutter spindles where the milling is done.

In addition to the common machines described to define the specific types, other models are available with various characteristics of both general-purpose and production millers.

Milling machine sizes. The most prevalent but not sole way of designating the size of a knee and column milling machine is by a number that indicates longitudinal table travel. Letters may accompany the numbers to indicate certain models. The usual numbers for sizes and corresponding dimensions are

Numbers	1	2	3	4	5	6
Table travel, in.	22	28	34	42	50	60

A common way of designating the size of a production-type milling machine is by a series of letters or numbers. The first one or two numbers or letters designate the manufacturer's model and the remainder the table travel in inches. Thus 2–24 and M–24 specify type or size 2 of one maker and M of another; both with a nominal length of table travel of 24 in.

Machines of a nominal size are built in light-, medium-, and heavy-duty models, with corresponding differences in power. This is indicated for several milling machines in Table 24–1. Also, standard machines provide wide ranges of speeds and feeds. Typical specifications for a No. 2 general-purpose milling machine call for 16 speeds from 25 to 1500 rpm and 16 feeds from ½ to 32 ipm.

TABLE 24–1. Specifications of Several Milling Machines

Type			Nominal size	Motor (hp)	Weight (lb)	Price ($)
Knee & column	Plain		2	3	3,600	11,000
" "	"		2	5	4,600	13,000
" "	"		2	10	8,000	19,000
" "	"		3	10	7,000	17,000
" "	Universal		3	10	7,500	19,000
" "	Vertical		3	10	8,000	21,000
" "	Plain		5	20	15,300	33,000
Production	Plain		2–24	5	5,600	15,000
"	"		5–60	25	19,000	30,000

Planer-type milling machines. A planer-type milling machine looks like and has comparable movements to a double housing planer, except that the table customarily feeds at a slow rate and spindle carriers for rotating cutters take the places of the planer toolheads. These machines are designed to handle large workpieces.

Special-purpose milling machines. Some milling machines are made for special kinds of work. In this class are duplicating machines, cam millers, and planetary millers. Others are built for specific single jobs.

Among duplicating machines, *profilers* are capable of duplicating external or internal profiles from templates in two dimensions. *Duplicators* reproduce forms in three dimensions. Some are hand-operated; others are power fed and are capable of copying any form of surface within the range of the machine entirely automatically after being set up. Some have several spindles and can reproduce the same form on several workpieces at one time.

Duplicators are commonly used to make forging dies, form dies, steel molds, etc. and often are called *die sinking machines.* A hand-operated machine on which a form is being duplicated is shown in Fig. 24–10. The

Fig. 24–10. A form being duplicated by hand manipulation. (Courtesy Geo. Gorton Machine Co.)

tracer finger is held in a bracket attached to the spindle head and is moved up and down in unison with the cutter spindle quill. The operator is controlling this movement with his left hand. His right hand grasps a lever that moves the table in a horizontal plane. The master form and workpiece are clamped to the table.

Cam millers produce disk cams. The profile of the cam is cut on a slowly revolving workpiece by an end mill positioned by a master cam revolving in unison with the workpiece.

Planetary millers do internal and external circular form and thread milling. They are convenient for cumbersome pieces because the work does not move. Instead, the cutter rotates about its axis and also is made to travel in a circular path.

Special milling machines are often built to do specific jobs quickly and efficiently when production is large enough to justify the initial cost. For example, machines may be made with a number of cutter spindles, spindles in various special positions or at odd angles, or unusual movements or cycles.

MILLING MACHINE ATTACHMENTS

Many standard attachments are available to make milling machines easier and faster to operate and increase the variety of jobs that can be done. They may be divided into two general classes. One class includes those for positioning and driving cutters. The other includes attachments for positioning and holding work.

Cutter driving attachments. Attachments are commonly put on horizontal spindle milling machines to hold and drive cutters with their axes inclined or swivelled from the conventional position. This puts the cutters into positions for milling helical gear teeth, racks, cams, and surfaces, grooves, or holes at all angles in workpieces that cannot conveniently be reached otherwise. A popular type is the universal high-speed milling attachment of Fig. 24–11 that can be swivelled 360° in a plane parallel to and 45° either way in a plane normal to the machine column face. The attachment shown is driven by the machine spindle as are many others, but some have their own driving motors.

Work holding devices. Work must be held securely for milling. When one or a few pieces are to be milled, a workpiece may be fastened and located on the table by tee bolts, strap clamps, blocks, etc. as is done on shapers, planers, and drill presses. Set-up in this way is slow and not even feasible for many kinds of work such as gear cutting. Devices used to make work positioning easy are vises, chucks, fixtures, index bases, circular tables, and index and dividing heads.

Fig. 24–11. A universal high speed milling attachment and end mill and dividing head with helical milling attachment on a plain knee and column type milling machine for end milling a cam track. (Courtesy The Cincinnati Milling Machine Co.)

Fig. 24–12. A plain milling vise with special jaws for holding an irregular workpiece. (Courtesy The Cincinnati Milling Machine Co.)

A *vise* is the most common holding device found on milling machines. A *plain vise* is depicted in Fig. 24–12. Other kinds can be swivelled or tilted but are not as rigid.

Many vises are opened and closed by a screw like that in Fig. 24–12, but faster acting cam and toggle devices are often used. Air or hydraulic operated vises are economical for quantity production.

The vise jaws that make contact with the work are held on by screws and are removable. Standard jaws for general-purpose work have flat faces. Special jaws of various shapes are often made and applied to hold specific workpieces milled in quantities. This is illustrated in Fig. 24–12. Special jaws on a standard vise are cheaper than a whole special fixture.

Universal chucks like those used on lathes are employed to hold work either on the table or spindle of a milling machine.

Fixtures were introduced and defined along with jigs in Chap. 22. They are widely used to hold and locate parts milled in moderate to large quantities. Fixtures are mounted on the table of the machines in Figs. 24–9 and 24–13. A fixture may save time and money in operation by holding a workpiece in a desired position to make attachments or a difficult set-up unnecessary; by providing full support to a workpiece so that heavy cuts can be taken and better pieces and less scrap are made because deflection and distortion are eliminated; and by making unloading and loading the workpieces easier and quicker. A fixture usually is good for only one operation and is justified only when it can save enough on that operation to pay for its cost. The worth of a fixture may be estimated by Eq. (19–1).

Fig. 24–13. An index base with duplicate fixtures on the table of a plain hydromatic milling machine. (Courtesy The Cincinnati Milling Machine Co.)

An *index base* is essentially a swivel table with two stops positioned 180° apart. Fixtures are mounted on each end of the attachment as depicted in Fig. 24–13. While pieces at one end are being milled, the operator loads the fixture at the other end. This is known as *index base milling*. Some bases are indexed manually, others mechanically.

A *circular milling attachment* or *rotary table* is a round table that can be turned about its axis on a base. It is set down on the reciprocating table of a conventional milling machine. Some rotary tables are turned or indexed by hand; others are power driven from the feed drive of the machine. Cuts may be made at desired intervals around a workpiece on the table by indexing. Circular arcs may be milled, and other curves obtained by combining the circular motion with the linear machine feeds. Fixtures may be placed around a rotary table so one is loaded while others carry pieces past the cutter as the table rotates, in what is called *rotary* or *continuous milling*.

Dividing heads. A *dividing* or *index head* is a mechanical device for dividing a circle accurately into equal parts. This is called *indexing*. A common indexing device for milling machines is the *universal dividing head* shown in Figs. 24–7 and 24–11.

Direct indexing is done by means of a plate on the front of the spindle of the head. The plate has equally spaced notches or holes in one or more circles. The number of divisions available is limited to the hole circles on the plate.

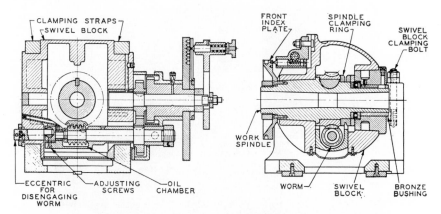

Fig. 24–14. Sections through a universal dividing head to show the indexing mechanism. (Courtesy The Cincinnati Milling Machine Co.)

Plain or *simple indexing* is done through a single train of gears. The sections of a universal dividing head of Fig. 24–14 show a worm turned by gears and a crank on the side of the head. The worm is engaged with a worm wheel around the spindle. Forty turns of the crank are needed to turn the work spindle of this head one full revolution; five turns on some heads. A pin in the crank handle registers in holes in a plate fixed to the side of the head. The plate and crank can be seen in Figs. 24–7 and 24–11. The holes are arranged in circles, and a different number is cqually spaced in each circle. Standard plates on one make of dividing head have holes that make it possible to index all numbers up to and including 60 and many higher numbers.

The number of turns of the crank of a dividing head required to index the work one division is equal to the ratio of the dividing head (40 for example) divided by the number of equally spaced divisions required for one full turn of the workpiece.

As an example, a dividing head with a 40:1 ratio is to be used to cut a gear having 36 teeth. The crank must be turned $40 \div 36 = 1\frac{4}{36} = 1\frac{1}{9}$ turns to index from one tooth space to the next on the gear. If the index plate has a circle with 18 holes, the crank must be advanced $18 \times \frac{1}{9} = 2$ spaces after each full turn.

The dividing head has been called a jewel among machine tools because of its precision. Plain indexing is commonly done on standard heads with an error from setting to setting on the work of less than one minute of arc. This is equivalent to 0.0015 in. on the circumference of a 12 in.-diameter circle or one part in 25,410.

Several means are available for indexing numbers not obtainable with standard plain indexing, especially large numbers. One of these is *differential indexing*, an arrangement whereby a suitable train of gears is installed between the spindle of the dividing head and a jackshaft that turns the side indexing plate. Thus when the crank is turned and causes the spindle to turn, the plate is rotated and the actual distance the crank is moved from one hole to another depends upon the displacement of the plate. A *wide range divider* has two sideplates and cranks, one that turns the spindle with a 40:1 ratio and another that furnishes an additional 100:1 ratio. This provides indexing from 2 to 400,000 divisions. An *astronomical dividing head attachment* has three plates and cranks arranged to divide a circle into degrees, minutes, and seconds.

A *helical milling* or *lead attachment* is mounted on the end of a milling machine table, as in Figs. 24–7 and 24–11, to provide a drive from the table leadscrew to the dividing head to cut helical gears, worms, threads, twist drills, etc. The attachment drives the jackshaft that causes the index plate to turn. The crank, engaged with the plate, turns and causes the spindle of the dividing head to revolve. The lead of a helix cut on a milling machine is equivalent to the distance the table advances while the dividing head spindle makes one full revolution. The lead is varied by means of change gears in the driving attachment.

Linear indexing may be done on a general-purpose milling machine for such jobs as cutting rack teeth by means of the table leadscrew dial or a *rack indexing attachment*. That unit consists of a gear or slotted plate connected to the leadscrew through change gears and indexed by a pin.

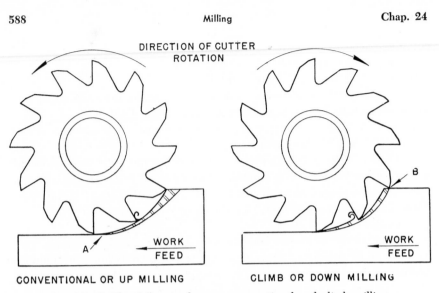

Fig. 24–15. The difference between conventional and climb milling.

MILLING OPERATIONS

Performance. Two styles of peripheral milling are depicted in Fig. 24–25. *Conventional* or *up milling* is the more common because the cutter is opposed by the feed of the work and the effect on the machine is more even. It is harder on cutters because each tooth tends to rub rather than to take a bite as it enters the cut; pronounced feed marks are left on the work surface; and forces tending to lift the work are high when the depth of cut is over about ⅛ in. In contrast, each tooth enters the work with a substantial bite in *climb* or *down milling*. The cut is cooler, cutters last longer, feed marks are smaller, and the work is held down. However, the cutter tends to pull the workpiece along. The average milling machine has too much backlash in the leadscrew and nut and allows the cutter to draw the workpiece ahead and take bites that are too large. Damage is likely to result unless the workpiece and fixture are strong and backlash is eliminated as it is on hydraulic and some mechanical machines.

Tolerances of less than 0.001 in. can be held when milling a few pieces at a time with sufficient care and skill. However, tolerances of 0.002 to 0.005 in. are more practicable and economic for production milling.

Planning for economical milling. Set-up often accounts for most of the time to mill one or a few pieces of a kind. Time can be saved where a variety of work is milled by planning and scheduling the jobs so that similar parts are milled in succession.

Cutting time is saved when two or more cutters are put to work at the same time. *Gang milling* is done with two or more cutters on one arbor, as in Figs. 24–12 and 24–13. If side milling cutters machine two sides of a workpiece at the same time, the operation is called *straddle milling.*

Simple milling involves the loading and milling of one piece at a time. Other arrangements can save time for a quantity of pieces. For *string* or *line milling,* two or more pieces are held in a row. Cutting time is saved because the cutter can be entering one piece as it is leaving another. Savings can be realized by means to allow the operator to load at one station while the machine is cutting at another. One such arrangement is called *reciprocating milling* and employs fixtures at both ends of the table. The operator loads the fixture at one end while work at the other end is being milled. Other arrangements for the same purpose are *index base* and *rotary milling,* already described in connection with the attachments used.

Speed, feed and depth of cut. Substantially the same factors determine economical speeds for milling cutters as for single-point tools. As a start, the recommendations of Table 17–1 may be applied to milling. Specific cutting speeds for milling cutters in various circumstances are given in hand-books. The cutting speed is the speed at the periphery of the cutter. The cutter rpm is calculated in the same way as for the workpiece in turning.

Basic milling feed is the distance the workpiece advances in the time between engagements by two successive teeth. This is called feed per tooth in units of inches per tooth or ipt. However, the machine feed rate is given in inches per minute and is equal to the feed in ipt times the number of teeth in the cutter times the number of rpm of the cutter.

Feed per tooth should be as high as possible for fast cutting, but the heavier the feed per tooth, the greater the load on the cutter teeth, workpiece, holding device, and machine. A large face mill will withstand a greater feed per tooth than a small end mill. A light feed may have to be chosen for a fragile workpiece. The rigidity and power of a milling machine may limit the rate at which stock can be removed. A heavier feed is possible in soft materials than in hard or tough metal. Practical feed rates in ipt are given in hand-books for many situations. Table 24–2 gives recommendations for average conditions.

One cut is enough for most jobs, but rough and finish cuts are required to produce the best surface finishes and hold small tolerances. The depth of a roughing cut should be as much as the cutter, machine, and work will stand, and in most cases is the full amount of stock on a surface minus that needed for finishing. One sixteenth inch or less is normally left for finishing.

TABLE 24–2. RECOMMENDED FEEDS IN IPT FOR H.S.S. CUTTERS UNDER
AVERAGE CONDITIONS

			Type of cutter			
			Slotting		Form-	
	Face	Helical	and	End	relieved	Slitting
Material	mill	mill	side mills	mill	cutter	saw
Aluminum and						
alloys	0.022	0.018	0.013	0.011	0.007	0.005
Cast iron (Bhn):						
Soft (150–180)	0.016	0.013	0.009	0.008	0.005	0.004
Medium (180–220)	0.013	0.010	0.007	0.007	0.004	0.003
Hard (220–300)	0.011	0.008	0.006	0.006	0.003	0.003
Steel:						
Soft	0.012	0.010	0.007	0.006	0.004	0.003
Medium	0.010	0.008	0.006	0.005	0.003	0.003
Hard	0.004	0.003	0.003	0.002	0.002	0.001

Feeds are generally at least 20% higher for carbide cutters. For finishing cuts, the feed may be reduced to improve the finish. Based upon recommendations by Cincinnati Milling Machine Company.

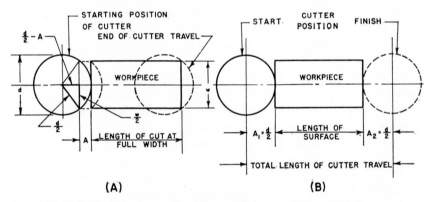

Fig. 24–16. (A) Approach of face mill for roughing cut. (B) Approach of face mill for finishing cut.

Estimating milling time and power. The approach of a milling cutter may be an appreciable part of the length of cut. A face mill taking a roughing cut is normally stopped when it has just cleaned the surface as indicated by Fig. 24–16(A). The approach shown at the beginning of the cut can be calculated from the right triangle having sides $d/2$–A, $w/2$, and $d/2$. It is $A = d/2 - \sqrt{(d^2 - w^2)/4}$. However, if the diameter of the cutter is only a little larger than the width of the surface, the approach is $d/2$ for practical purposes. For a finishing cut, a face mill is passed entirely over a surface so that its trailing edge can get in a full wiping action. Thus, the approach for finishing is equal to d.

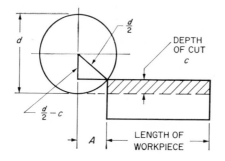

Fig. 24-17. Approach of plain or slot milling cutter.

The approach of a cutter milling a flat surface or a slot occurs from the first contact until full depth of cut is reached, as depicted in Fig. 24-17. It can be calculated from the right triangle shown and is $A = \sqrt{cd - c^2}$.

The cutting time in minutes is the quotient of the total length of cutter travel in inches divided by the feed in inches per minute.

The rate of metal removal in cubic inches per minute for milling is the product of the width of cut in inches times the depth of cut in inches times the feed in inches per minute. An empirical formula proposed by the Cincinnati Milling Machine Company that takes into account the effect of the rate of metal removal Q in cubic inches per minute upon power consumption in milling is that horsepower

$$P = P_u Q^{3/4} \tag{24-1}$$

The factor P_u is the unit horsepower per cubic inch per minute. Some average values are given in Table 20-1. They apply mostly to face milling. Power may be about 25% to 50% higher for cutters that cut mostly on their peripheries, such as plain milling cutters.

Milling compared with other operations. Any surface that is accessible can be milled. This means that milling machines are to some extent competitive with all other machine tools. However, when the work is to be revolved, a milling machine can be used but is seldom selected for the job because machines of the lathe family are inherently more efficient for such purposes.

Milling machines are capable of machining holes and locating them with a fair degree of accuracy, to tolerances of 0.001 to 0.002 in. A milling machine is economical for doing such work in small quantities without extra equipment. If the holes do not need to be located accurately, a drill press will do the job more quickly and easily. For large quantities, the milling machine is usually slower and not able to compete with the use of jigs on drilling machines or with production boring machines.

Jig boring machines are necessary where holes must be located more precisely than can be done with milling machines. Really large pieces require the capacity and range of horizontal boring machines, beyond that of most milling machines.

Flat, straight, and many curved and irregular surfaces can be shaped, planed, or broached as well as milled. The advantages of shapers and planers, particularly for one or a few pieces, were pointed out in Chap. 23. Broaching is more economical than milling in many cases for large quantities but is at a disadvantage in other cases as explained in Chap. 25.

Grinding is capable of producing to closer tolerances and finer finishes than milling. However, grinding is not generally an economical means for removing much stock, and surfaces are commonly milled before being ground.

Questions

1. What kind of work can be done by metal milling?

2. Name and describe the principal kinds of milling cutters.

3. What is a fly cutter and what is its purpose?

4. Sketch a typical milling cutter tooth and name its elements.

5. Name and describe the common cutter holding devices on milling machines.

6. Describe the principal characteristics of general-purpose milling machines.

7. What are the relative advantages and disadvantages of knee and column- and bed-type milling machines?

8. Describe a typical production-type milling machine.

9. Describe a planer-type milling machine.

10. How is the size of a standard milling machine designated?

11. What are profilers and duplicators?

12. What is a planetary miller and how does it work?

13. Describe a typical cutter driving attachment.

14. How are workpieces held on milling machines?

15. What is plain or simple indexing and how is it done?

16. What means are available to index higher numbers than possible with standard plain indexing?

17. How can a helix be milled?

18. Define conventional and climb milling and state the advantages of each.

19. Define and state the reasons for gang milling, straddle milling, simple milling, string milling, index base milling, rotary milling, and reciprocating milling.

20. When is a milling machine more economical than a shaper, planer, or broaching machine?

Problems

1. A form for which standard cutters are not available must be milled on the top of a workpiece 6 in. long. A fly form cutter can be ground in one hour from a piece of high-speed steel worth $0.50. With it, the workpiece can be fed at ½ in. per min. A special form cutter having 12 teeth costs $75. With it the feed is 6 in. per min. Overtravel and approach are one inch in both cases. Labor and overhead is worth $8 per hr. For how many pieces can the special form cutter with 12 teeth be justified?

2. If a fixture is made for a milling operation, in which pieces are now held in a vise, one-quarter minute can be saved for each piece made. The fixture will cost $50, and the cost of interest, insurance, taxes, and maintenance is 25% altogether. No extra set-up time is required for the fixture. The hourly rate for labor and overhead in the plant is $8. For how many pieces is the fixture justified?

3. An operation with conditions described in Prob. 2 takes 3 minutes floor to floor time without the fixture. The need for a vertical milling attachment can be eliminated by use of the fixture. The cost of this attachment is $0.50 per hr, and the device can be put to work elsewhere if not needed on this operation. Under those circumstances, how many pieces justify the cost of a fixture?

   What is the most that should be paid for a fixture if only 1000 pieces are to be run?

4. Specify the number of turns, the number of holes in the circle, and the number of spaces to index the following divisions on a universal dividing head with a 40:1 ratio.
   (a) 120, (b) 100, (c) 96, (d) 75, (e) 48, (f) 34, (g) 30, (h) 26, (i) 24, (j) 18, (k) 15, (l) 13, (m) 9.

5. The table leadscrew of a milling machine has a lead of 0.250 in. Thus, that is the amount the table advances each time the screw makes one revolution. The ratio between the jackshaft and spindle of a dividing head placed on the table is 40:1. That means the jackshaft must turn 40 times to turn the dividing head spindle once.

It is desired to cut a helix with a lead of L inches with the equipment just described. Derive an expression for the gear ratio R that must be provided between the table leadscrew and dividing head jackshaft.

What should the gear ratio be for an L of (a) 1 in., (b) 5 in., (c) 10 in., or (d) 25 in.?

6. A surface 4½ in. wide by 10 in. long is to be rough milled with a depth of cut of ¼ in. by a 16-tooth cemented carbide face mill 6 in. in diameter. The material is medium-hard cast iron.

   Estimate the cutting time and the power required at the cut.

7. The cutter described in Prob. 6 is used for a finishing cut of ⅟₁₆ in. depth on the surface. The speed is increased 25% and the feed decreased 25%. What is the time required for the finishing cut? How much power is needed at the cutter?

8. A high-speed steel helical milling cutter with 12 teeth is 4 in. in diameter and 5 in. long. It is used to mill a soft steel surface 3 in. wide by 9 in. long with a depth of cut of ¾ in. A cutting speed of 100 fpm is selected. What is the cutting time and how much power is required?

9. If the cutter described in Prob. 8 takes a finishing cut ⅟₁₆ in. deep on the surface at the same speed and feed, what time is required and what power is consumed?

10. A ½ in. wide slot by 4 in. long through a piece of medium steel 1 in. thick is to be widened to ¾ in. Its other dimensions are to remain the same, and radii are allowed at the ends. What time is required to do the operation with a ¾ in.-diameter H.S.S. end mill having 8 teeth? The cutting speed is 75 fpm and the feed 0.002 ipt. How much power is required?

11. A piece shown in Fig. 23–10 is to be milled from a rough casting having ⅛ in. of stock on all surfaces. Normal operation tolerances are satisfactory. List the steps that must be taken to mill one piece. For each step, specify the machine and cutter to be used and how the workpiece is to be held.

12. A lot of 100 pieces like the one shown in Fig. 23–10 is to be milled from rough castings having ⅛ in. of stock on all surfaces. Describe the operations necessary to do the work. For each operation specify how the work is to be held and the machine and cutter are to be used.

13. An operation is to be performed to machine the sides and bottom of the dovetail grooves on a number of parts of the kind shown in Fig. 23–10. Set-up time is 20 min on a shaper and 30 min on a milling machine. The direct time to machine each piece on the shaper is 14 min, and on the miller is 11 min. Labor costs $1.50 per hr. The charge for the use of the shaper is $3 per hr and for the milling machine $3.50 per hr.

   (a) What is the quantity below which the shaper is more economical and above which the miller is more economical?

   (b) Which machine would you choose for 5 pieces? For 25 pieces?

14. A machine shop has two machines available for a job. One is a 48 × 48 × 10 double-housing planer that originally cost $50,000, is depreciated over a 20 year period, and is operated about 6000 hr per yr. The charge for the use of the machine is $0.85 per hr, and labor and overhead in addition are charged at $8 per hr.

The other machine is a 48 × 48 × 10 double-housing planer milling machine that cost $105,000. The charge for the use of the planer milling machine is $1.97 per hr in addition to the labor and overhead cost of $8 per hr.

To machine the workpiece under consideration takes 10 hr on the planer and 8.5 hr on the milling machine. The cutting tools consumed cost $25 for the planer and $55 for the miller for each piece.

(a) Which machine should be selected to machine one piece?

(b) Which machine should be selected for 5 pieces?

References

The Milling Machine and Its Attachments, Kearney and Trecker Corporation, Milwaukee, 1945.

A Treatise on Milling and Milling Machines, The Cincinnati Milling Machine Company, Cincinnati, 1951.

25

Broaching

In broaching, a tool with a series of teeth called a *broach* is pushed or pulled over a surface on a workpiece as depicted in Fig. 25–1. Each tooth takes a thin slice from the surface. Broaching of inside surfaces is called *internal* or *hole broaching;* of outside surfaces, *surface broaching.* Typical internal broaching operations are the sizing of holes and cutting of serrations, straight or helical splines, gun rifling, and keyways.

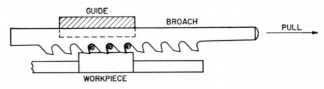

Fig. 25–1. The way a broach works.

BROACHES

Types of broaches. Almost every broach is designed to do a specific job in a certain way. Typical forms are shown in Fig. 25–2. Some are intended to be pulled, others pushed, and still others to be held, either on a movable ram or in a fixed position. Some machine inside surfaces, others outside. A broach may be made in one piece, called *solid,* or assembled or *built up* from *shells, replaceable sections,* or *inserted teeth.*

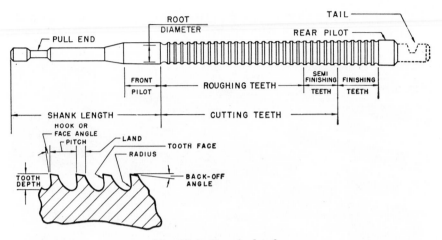

Fig. 25–3. Broach details.

The enlarged section of broach teeth in Fig. 25–3 reveals features like those of other cutting tools. The *back-off angle* corresponds to the relief angle of a single-point tool, and the *hook* or *face angle* to the rake angle. A hole broach is sharpened by grinding the tooth face. Surface broaches with curved shapes may be sharpened the same way, but others are ground on the back-off angle land.

The teeth of a broach may be staggered, or offset as indicated in Fig. 25–4, to enable each tooth to take a deep and effective but narrow cut. This makes a broach somewhat longer.

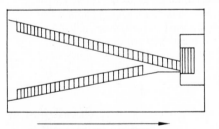

DIRECTION OF TRAVEL

Fig. 25–4. The arrangement of a progressive surface broach.

Most broaches are made from high-speed steel, ground after hardening. Cemented carbide is used, especially for surface broaches, for high production and for finishing broaches.

Broach pullers and fixtures. Many surface broaches are mounted on holders bolted to the face of a ram, but some surface broaches and all pull broaches must be connected to the end of a ram by a *puller* or *puller head*. Several common pullers and broach shanks to fit them are shown in Fig. 25–5.

The *threaded puller* of Fig. 25–5(A) *and the key-type puller* in Fig. 25–5(B) are simple and inexpensive but relatively slow. The *automatic puller* of Fig. 25–5(C) is favored for large production uses, especially on machines with broach elevators and automatic handling equipment. When the sleeve on this puller is pushed backward by hand or by striking a stop, the puller accepts or releases the broach shanks.

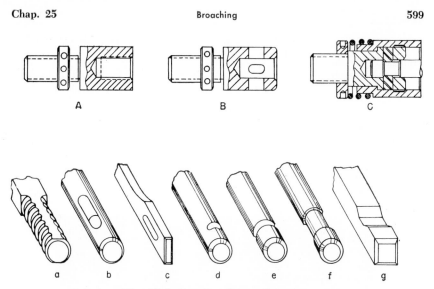

Fig. 25–5. Broach pullers and shanks.

Fixtures generally are justified for holding workpieces being broached because production is large. Broaching fixtures are simple in comparison with those of other processes; one may even be just a plate to bear the part and with a hole to pass the broach. Broaching forces generally tend to stabilize the part in the fixture but are large, and fixtures must be strong.

BROACHING MACHINES

Broaching machines may be classified as (1) broaching presses, (2) pull broaching machines, (3) surface broaching machines, and (4) continuous broaching machines. Typical machines of these types will be described.

Broaching presses. Presses are used mostly for internal push broaching, such as hole sizing and keyway cutting. Push broaches must be short, and each cannot remove much stock. On the other

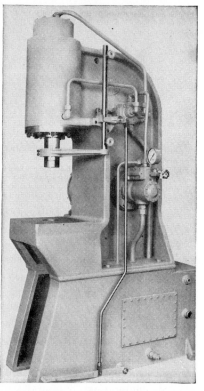

Fig. 25–6. A 15-ton hydraulic arbor press with guided ram and a controlled ram speed for broaching. (Courtesy Greenerd Arbor Press Co.)

hand, the tooling is usually simple, and operations can be set up and changed over easily.

Hand and hydraulic arbor presses are popular for push broaching because they are simple and inexpensive and can be readily used for many other operations such as assembling, bending, and staking. Hydraulic arbor type presses specifically equipped for broaching, like the one in Fig. 25–6, are called *push broaching machines* and range in capacity from ¼ to 35 tons. On a machine of this kind the workpiece is placed on the table, sometimes in a simple fixture, under the vertical ram that pushes a short broach through the work.

Fig. 25–7. An internal helical spline being broached on a horizontal pull type broaching machine. (Courtesy Colonial Broach Co.)

Pull broaching machines. In a pull broaching machine the broach is pulled by a drawhead actuated by a hydraulic piston and cylinder. One type of such machines pulls horizontally; another vertically. These machines are used mostly for internal broaching but do some surface broaching.

The working zone of a horizontal pull broaching machine is shown in Fig. 25–7. The workpiece is located in and pressed against a cup centered in the machine face plate at the back of the picture. The shank of the broach is passed through the initial opening in the workpiece and attached to the puller that draws it completely through the opening.

A horizontal broaching machine offers convenient access to any part of the machine. Heavy broaches do not have to be raised and lowered. A long stroke is feasible but more floor space usually is needed for a horizontal machine as compared with a vertical broach.

Commonly vertical broaching machines are arranged to pull broaches

either downward or upward, although some do both. The action of a

vertical *pull-down broaching ma-*
chine is depicted in Fig. 25–8. The
broaches are grasped and pulled
from below the table. Large and
irregular pieces can be loaded somewhat more easily than on pull-up
machines. Fixtures can be used to
hold the locations of broached holes
in relationship with external surfaces of parts. Application of cutting fluid is natural and effective.

The broaches on a *vertical
pull-up broaching machine* start
from below the table and, as they
are pulled upward through the
parts, press the workpieces against
the underside of the table. At the
end of the stroke the parts are freed
to fall down a chute, and motions
are saved for the operator.

Fig. 25–8. A view of a set up on a
vertical pull down broaching machine.
(Courtesy The Oilgear Co.)

Surface broaching machines. A surface broaching machine has its

Fig. 25–9. A 25-ton horizontal double acting surface broaching
machine for finishing surfaces of an automobile cylinder head. (Courtesy The Cincinnati Milling Machine Co.)

Fig. 25–10. A 15-ton vertical single ram broaching machine with 54 in. stroke. A hydraulically operated fixture is carried on the table. (Courtesy The Cincinnati Milling Machine Co.)

broaching tools attached to a ram or rams forced in a straight path along guideways past the workpiece. On some machines the rams move horizontally, on others vertically. *Horizontal surface broaching machines* take heavy and bulky workpieces and provide long strokes. Some are single acting, but the one in Fig. 25–9 has two sets of broaches mounted on its ram and cuts in both directions. Two fixtures, one for each direction of cut, are integrated with a waist-high roller conveyor and are loaded alternately.

A *vertical single-ram surface broaching machine* (Fig. 25–10) has a ram that carries the broach downward for the cut and then returns to top position. The table in front of the ram slide carries the fixture for the workpiece, is moved into cutting position just before the ram descends, and is withdrawn for unloading and loading as the ram ascends.

A *vertical double-ram surface broaching machine* is equivalent to two single-ram machines because it has two ram and fixture sets side by side. One ram goes down with its fixture in cutting position. At the same time the other returns while its fixture is unloaded and loaded. Operation can be practically continuous.

Continuous broaching machine. A *horizontal continuous broaching machine* is different from the machines previously described because the broaching cutters on it remain stationary while the workpieces held in fixtures are carried past the cutters.

A series of fixtures are mounted on a chain drive. One is shown at the loading position in Fig. 25–11. The pieces are released and discharged down a chute at the other end of the machine. Parts are broached as rapidly as they can be loaded.

One type of *rotary continuous broaching machine* is somewhat like a rotary miller. It has a slowly revolving round table carrying a group of fixtures in a circle. Workpieces loaded in the fixtures are carried past stationary broaches and may be ejected automatically thereafter.

Fig. 25–11. The loading station of a horizontal continuous broaching machine. (Courtesy The Foote-Burt Co.)

Sizes of broaching machines. The size of a broaching machine is designated by the length of stroke in inches and the force in tons that can be applied to the broach. Thus a 42-10 machine has a 42 in. stroke with a 10 ton nominal pull. Specifications of several common sizes of broaching machines are given in Table 25–1.

BROACHING OPERATIONS

Planning for economical broaching. The skill in broaching is built into the tools and is exercised in setting up the equipment. After that the operation of the machine is mere routine. How well the operation goes depends upon the design and set-up of the tools.

TABLE 25-1. SPECIFICATIONS OF SEVERAL BROACHING MACHINES

Type	Stroke (in.)	Rated pull (tons)	Broaching speed (fpm)	Return speed (fpm)	Motor (hp)	Weight (lb)	Price ($)
Broaching press	27	12	25	41	15	4,300	5,000
Horizontal pull	48	10	15 to 28	45	15	5,400	8,000
"	66	15	17 to 32	60	20	12,400	12,000
Vertical pull-up	30	10	19 to 32	65	15	10,300	18,000
Vertical surface:							
Single ram	42	10	11 to 25	44	15	10,000	17,000
Double ram	42	10	19 to 32		20	17,500	25,000

The cutting time in a broaching operation is short, and the loading and unloading time takes an appreciable part of the total time. Thus labor saving and motion economy are important considerations. For production of large quantities of pieces, the machines often have several work stations or pull a number of broaches at once, broach handling is done automatically, and fixtures are made quick acting to save operation time.

Surfaces that run in the same direction on a workpiece, especially if they are contiguous, can generally be broached at the same time. As many surfaces on a part as possible should be broached in one operation.

Although most broaching operations are completed in one pass, some are arranged for repeated cuts to simplify the design of the broach and save tooling expense where small or moderate quantities only are needed. The teeth of a gear or spline may be broached all together or one or a few at a time. A comparatively simple broach can be made to cut one or a few tooth spaces. After one pass, the gear blank is indexed, and more of its teeth are cut. Successive passes are made until all the teeth are finished.

Where several similar parts are made in one plant in small or moderate quantities, arrangements may be made to broach them all economically with the same tooling. A machine tool manufacturer makes a variety of dogs of different sizes and shapes, but all have the same size integral key on one face. Broaching equipment has been designed to take any of the dogs, and all are broached on the key and face, although none alone is produced in sufficient quantity to justify the cost of broaching equipment.

Broaching performance. The size of a broaching machine for an operation depends largely upon the design of the broach to do the job. The cutting length of the broach determines the length of stroke. The number of teeth cutting at one time and the depth each cuts determine the pull.

Each tooth of a broach can remove only a few thousandths of an inch of stock. The teeth must be spaced far enough apart to allow room for chips, but several teeth need to be in contact with the workpiece at any time for uniform action. The total amount of stock that must be removed from a surface determines the number of teeth needed and consequently the length of the broach for a feasible tooth spacing and depth of cut. Desirable values for these factors are given in tool design books.

Material is best broached when it has a hardness between 10 and 35 Rockwell C. Harder material wears broach teeth rapidly, but material as hard as 45 Rockwell C is broached successfully. Too soft material is difficult to cut cleanly.

In typical practice, it has been found feasible to broach irregular and intricate shapes to tolerances of ±0.001 in. from locating surfaces. Tolerances of ±0.0005 in. can be held between two or more surfaces cut at the same time. A 30 microinch rms finish can be obtained consistently if the material properties do not vary.

Estimating broaching time. Broaching is done at comparatively slow cutting speeds. Most high-speed steel broaches are not run over 30 fpm, but return stroke speeds may be 40 fpm or more. Broaching with cemented carbides is done at 100 to 200 fpm.

The cutting time in a broaching operation is the quotient of the length of stroke in inches divided by the cutting speed in inches per minute. For example, a stroke of 48 in. at 24 fpm is required. The cutting time is $48/(24 \times 12) = \frac{1}{6} = 10$ seconds. The return stroke may be calculated in the same way on the basis of the return speed of the broach but may not add to the operation time if unloading and loading can be done at the same time. Other elements of time in a broaching operation are starting and stopping time, commonly two seconds, and loading and unloading time which depends upon the nature of the work and fixture.

Broaching compared with other operations. The work done by broaching can also be done in other ways. Under certain conditions, broaching is preferable to other operations, but under other conditions broaching is either unfeasible or disadvantageous.

The main advantage of broaching is that it is fast. With properly applied broaches, fixtures, and machines, more pieces can be turned out per hour by broaching than by any other means. Little skill is required to perform a broaching operation after it has been set up, and automation is easily arranged. The tool cost per piece is low. A broach does not need to be sharpened or changed often and has a long life because speeds are low, each tooth makes contact only once and for a short time with each workpiece, and a broach does not overheat. Roughing and finishing can be and often are done by one broach. Good finish and accuracy are obtainable over the life of a broach because roughing and finishing are done by separate teeth. The finishing teeth remove little stock and stay in good condition. Cutting fluid is readily applied where it is most effective because a broach tends to draw the fluid into the cut.

Broaching has disadvantages as well as advantages. A broach usually does only one job and is expensive to make and sharpen. Special fixtures often are needed. All this adds up to a relatively heavy investment for each operation.

Special precautions may be necessary in founding or forging to control variations in stock or extra operations to remove excess stock may have to be added before broaching to protect the broach. These add to the overall cost of manufacturing.

Some of the limitations of broaching are enough to make it impracticable for certain work. A surface cannot be broached if it has an obstruction across the path of broach travel. For instance, blind holes and pockets normally are not broached. Frail workpieces are not good subjects for broaching because they are not able to withstand the large forces imposed by the process without distorting or breaking. Surfaces that run in the same general directions often can be broached at the same time, but surfaces not so related must be broached separately as a rule. For instance, a hole and a perpendicular face may be machined in one operation on a lathe or boring machine but require two passes in broaching. The lines left on a surface lie in the direction of broach travel. Thus for instance, broaching is not capable of producing a circular pattern in a hole if such a finish is required.

When broaching can be done, it is selected in preference to other processes if the amount it saves is more than able to pay for the cost of the equipment. The amount saved by broaching depends upon the saving per piece and the number of pieces required. The saving per piece may be relatively large in some cases, as, for instance, in machining small diameter but long holes with splines or keyways. In such cases, broaching may be economical for small or moderate quantities. For work that can be done readily in other ways, runs of 100,000 or more pieces are often necessary if broaching is to be considered.

Questions

1. What is broaching?
2. Describe a hole broach and name its principal elements.
3. How is a broach pulled?
4. What are the main types of broaching machines?
5. What is a broaching press and how is it used?
6. What are the different kinds of pull broaching machines and what are their relative advantages?
7. Describe the various kinds of surface broaching machines and the advantages of each.
8. How does a continuous broaching machine operate?
9. How is the size of a broaching machine designated?
10. By what means is economy achieved in broaching?
11. What determines the length of stroke and pull required in a broaching operation?
12. When is broaching economical and when is it not feasible?

Problems

1. With an assumed 80% efficiency, how much is the motor overloaded when the machine of Table 25–1 is loaded to its maximum rated capacity, in the case of: (a) the broaching press, (b) the 48 in. horizontal pull broaching machine, (c) the 66 in. horizontal pull broaching machine, (d) the vertical pull-up broaching machine, (e) the 42 in. vertical single-ram surface broaching machine, and (f) the 42 in. double-ram surface broaching machine?

2. The roughing section of a broach is to remove 0.125 in. from a steel surface 8 in. long and 2 in. wide. Each tooth takes a 0.005 in. deep cut. The pitch of the teeth is given by the formula that pitch $= 0.35$ $\sqrt{\text{length of surface}}$. How long should the roughing section be? What pull must the broaching machine exert if the chip pressure is 600,000 lb per sq in. of chip area? What power is required for a broaching speed of 24 fpm?

3. A 54 in. stroke is required for the operation described in Prob. 2. The time to unload and load a fixture is 0.10 min and to index the machine 0.03 min. What is the cycle time per piece on
   (a) a single-ram surface broach with a return speed of 40 fpm?
   (b) a double-ram surface broach?

4. A 24/48 pitch internal involute spline with 36 teeth and a pitch diameter of 1.500 inch is to be cut in steel in a hole 2 in. long. This can be done on a gear shaper in 5 min per piece. Tooling costs $200. The cost for use of the gear shaper is $0.65, overhead is $4, and labor is $2 per hr. Set-up time is 1 hr per lot. The spline can be broached with an operation time of ½ min. The cost of tooling including the broach is $1500. The cost for use of the broaching machine is $1, overhead is $4, and labor is $1.50 per hr. Set-up time is ½ hr per lot. For what quantities of pieces should each machine be used?

5. A cast iron housing has a surface 4½ in. wide by 6 in. long from which ⅛ in. of stock is to be removed. On a milling machine the feed is 48 in. per min and the time per piece is 0.30 min complete. The surface can be broached in 0.25 min per piece on a double-ram surface broaching machine.

   The cost for the machine, overhead, and labor is $8 per hr on either machine. Set-up time is the same on both. Tooling for milling costs $350, and for broaching $2500. What annual rate of production justifies the use of the broaching machine?

References

Broaching Practice, National Broach and Machine Co., Detroit, 1953.

Manual of Broaching, Detroit Broach Co., Detroit, 1948.

Boring Operations and Machines

Several kinds of machine tools are called boring machines because they are used largely for locating and finishing holes. Most of them also do related operations like drilling, reaming, threading, and facing, and some do turning and milling. Outside of boring, many of these machines have little in common with each other. They may be divided into four commonly recognized classes of horizontal boring mills, vertical boring and turning machines, precision boring machines, and jig boring machines. The machines in these groups and the operations they do are the ones to be described.

HORIZONTAL BORING MILLS

Horizontal boring mill is the common name for the *horizontal boring, drilling and milling machine*. Machines of this kind do drilling, boring, reaming, threading, facing, milling and allied operations on large work-pieces.

Table-type horizontal boring mill. The table type is the most common horizontal boring mill, so named because work is carried on a table that is adjusted and fed by hand or power lengthwise and crosswise with respect to the bed of the machine. The heavy cylinder block on the large horizontal boring mill of Fig. 26–1 is supported also on a small auxiliary table added to the machine.

Fig. 26–1. A 6-in. table-type horizontal boring, drilling, and milling machine with an auxiliary saddle and table. A boring bar is rotated between the spindle and backrest block for boring the bearings in a large cylinder block. (Courtesy Lucas Machine Div., The New Britain Machine Co.)

The cutting tools are guided and revolved by a spindle in the headstock of a horizontal boring machine. The spindle revolves in a quill or sleeve and can be fed in or out of the headstock. The headstock or spindle head is carried on ways on a vertical column bolted on one end of the bed of the machine and can be moved up or down.

Long and heavy boring bars cannot be supported by the headstock spindle alone. An outboard support is provided by a backrest or end support shown in Fig. 26–1. This is a column clamped to the ways and having a block that is raised or lowered by a screw in unison with the headstock. A bushed hole in the block in line with the machine spindle supports the outer end of the boring bar.

Other horizontal boring mills. The column that carries the headstock of a *floor-type horizontal boring mill* is mounted on a base that slides on runways. A workpiece is placed on floor plates alongside the runways. Whereas the work is moved past the spindle of a table-type machine, the spindle is traversed on the runways past the workpiece by a floor-type machine. That is easier if the workpiece is quite large.

A *portable horizontal boring mill* consists of a column and headstock on a base. The entire machine is picked up by a crane, carried to the work, and placed in a convenient position for the job to be done. Portable boring mills are essential for assemblies like huge turbo-generators and ships.

The *planer-type horizontal boring mill* has a table like that of a planer. The headstock and its column and the end support are movable on runways toward and away from the table. The table is fully supported on the bed in all positions, and the machine has the advantage of giving full and rigid support to the long and heavy workpieces.

Planer-type machines with two or more headstocks and columns, and even a cross rail between columns, are called *multiple-head horizontal boring, drilling, and milling machines.* They look like and do much the same work as double housing planers or planer-type milling machines.

Sizes of horizontal boring machines. The size of a horizontal boring mill is designated by the diameter of its spindle in inches. Specifications of several typical machines are given in Table 26–1. A typical table-type machine with a 5 in.-diameter spindle has 45 speeds in a standard range from 7.5 to 457 rpm and 18 feeds from 0.005 to 0.250 in. per rev.

TABLE 26–1. Specifications of Several Horizontal Boring Machines

Type	Spindle diameter (in.)	Table or machine travel (in.)	Motor (hp)	Weight (lb)	Cost ($)
Table	3	24	10	25,000	40,000
Table	5	36	25	40,000	70,000
Floor	8	72	50	105,000	180,000
Planer	7	60	40	150,000	225,000

Tools and attachments. Drills, reamers, taps, and milling cutters of all kinds and sizes are commonly used on horizontal boring mills. Boring bars range from small stub bars to some many feet in length and as large in diameter as the machine spindle. One or more single-point tools are commonly used on a boring bar, especially for general-purpose work.

The *star feed facing head* and the *continuous feed facing and boring head* are spindle attachments for facing or recessing cuts. A single-point cutter is fed outward, intermittently on the star head or continuously on the other head, as the attachment is revolved with the spindle.

Horizontal, vertical, and tilting rotary tables like those for milling machines are used for many operations on horizontal boring machines.

VERTICAL BORING AND TURNING MACHINE

A vertical boring and turning machine is like a lathe set on the end of its headstock so that the face plate or chuck is in a horizontal position. The face plate then becomes a revolving table. These machines do essentially the same work and use similar or the same tools as lathes but are easier to load with large and heavy pieces. Bulky pieces can be fully supported as well as rotated. The operator can observe the actions of the tools from several positions.

Fig. 26–2. A 36-in. vertical turret lathe taking cuts with the turret and side head. (Courtesy The Bullard Co.)

Vertical turret lathe. Vertical boring machines of smaller sizes commonly have an indexable turret on a ram above the table like the one in Fig. 26–2. They have all the movements of horizontal turret lathes. In addition the turret ram slide is mounted on a crossrail, and the turret can be adjusted or fed across as well as to and from the work. Just above and to the right of the table is a side head with a four-station square turret with movements comparable to those of the square turret on a horizontal turret lathe.

Most vertical turret lathes are hand operated but some are semi-automatic. The latter type of machine will go through a preset cycle. All the operator has to do is unload and load the workpieces after set-up.

Vertical boring mill. A vertical boring mill is like a vertical turret lathe but has no turret head. Normal equipment includes two ram heads on a cross rail and one or two side heads. A job on such a machine is shown in Fig. 26–3. Each ram can be swivelled to set and feed the ram at an angle. Each ram carries a non-indexing tool post.

Fig. 26–3. An 84-in. vertical boring mill set up to face and bore large castings. (Courtesy Danly Machine Specialties Co.)

Vertical boring mills mostly are larger in size than vertical turret lathes. These large machines handle essentially round and symmetrical workpieces like reduction gear housings, turbine casings, and locomotive tires. They do facing, boring, turning, grooving, etc., generally with conventional single-point tools.

Vertical multiple-spindle chucking machines. A vertical multiple-spindle chucking machine, like the one in Fig. 26–4 has a number of stations, each with a chuck on the end of a vertical spindle, at which work is done simultaneously for large quantity production. The cutting tools are carried on vertical slides around a central column above the working stations and are fed to the workpieces when the spindles revolve. One station is for unloading and loading workpieces. At the end of each cycle,

Fig. 26–4. A 16–23-in. 8-spindle vertical chucking machine. (Courtesy The Bullard Co.)

Replaceable sections, teeth, or shells make a broach easier to repair and, in some cases, easier to make initially.

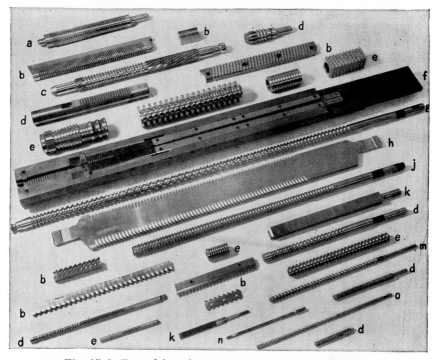

Fig. 25–2. Typical broaches. (Courtesy Continental Tool Works, Ex-Cell-O Corp.) **a.** Combination hole sizing and involute spline push broach. **b.** Broach sections. **c.** Spiral spline hard gear pull broach. **d.** Push broaches. **e.** Broach shells. **f.** Broach inserts assembled in holder. **g.** Rotary cut pull broach for round hole. **h.** Slotting broach. **j.** Hole sizing and spline cutting pull broach. **k.** Flat broaches. **m.** Spline pull broach. **n.** Keyway broach. **o.** Combination hole cutting and burnishing broach.

A *burnishing broach* makes a glazed surface in a steel, cast iron or nonferrous hole. Burnishing teeth are rounded and do not cut but compress and rub the surface metal.

Details of broaches. A hole broach depicted in Fig. 25–3 is gripped by a puller at the *shank* end. The *front pilot* centers the broach in the hole before the teeth begin to cut. The first group of teeth remove most of the stock and are called *roughing teeth*. The *finishing teeth* of a new broach are all the same size and must have the shape required of the finished hole. As the first finishing teeth become worn, those behind take up the function of sizing. The *rear pilot* supports the broach after the last tooth leaves the hole. A broach handled automatically has a *tail.*

the tools are retracted, and all chucks are indexed to succeeding stations. A finished piece is produced at each index in the time of the longest single operation plus a few seconds for indexing. Some machines have two spindles at each station, and others double index to produce two pieces at each index. Drilling, boring, turning, facing, threading or grooving can be done on forgings, castings, or cut-off bar stock.

Sizes of vertical boring machines. The size of a vertical boring machine is designated by the diameter of its table or chuck, and that is nominally the largest diameter that can be swung on the machine. Vertical turret lathe sizes are commonly under 100 in. The sizes of vertical boring mills go up to above 20 ft. Specifications of several machines are given in Table 26–2.

TABLE 26–2. SPECIFICATIONS OF SEVERAL VERTICAL BORING MACHINES

Type	Size (in.)	Std. speeds		Std. feeds		Motor (hp)	Weight (lb)	Cost ($)
		No.	Range (rpm)	No.	Range (.001 ipr)			
Vertical turret lathe	36	16	5.7–172	16	2.5–500	30	30,000	60,000
	74	16	1.4–68	12	10–500	40	66,000	90,000
Vertical boring mill	54	16	2.6–72	16	3–750	40–60	55,000	80,000
	12 ft	16	0.6–22.5	16	4–750	60	170,000	190,000
Vertical multiple-spindle chucking machine	10 in.– 6 sp	49	56–503	81	2.5–62.5	30	33,000	80,000

PRECISION PRODUCTION BORING MACHINES

Precision production boring machines make use of single-point tools to machine surfaces rapidly, precisely, and repetitively. They are capable consistently of holding tolerances of a few ten-thousandths of an inch and finishing surfaces of 10 to 20 microinches rms or better. As their name implies, they are used basically for boring, but also are arranged for facing, turning, grooving, and chamfering. The work they do can also be done on general-purpose machines, such as the lathe, but the precision boring machines are more efficient where large quantities of parts are produced because they operate semi-automatically.

A popular type of standard precision production boring machine that is simple but can be adapted for many jobs with special tooling for each job is depicted in Fig. 26–5. The table in the center moves lengthwise and can be made to traverse, dwell, or reverse at any point in its stroke. Some machines have a bridge at one end; this one has bridges at both ends spanning the table and carrying the boring heads.

For some jobs, the boring bars are mounted on the table, and the workpieces are revolved by chucks or fixtures on the boring heads. The fixture on the table in Fig. 26–5 holds two workpieces. When the preset

Fig. 26–5. A view of the work station of a double end horizontal precision production boring machine with tooling for machining 10 surfaces on a pump body. (Courtesy The Heald Machine Co.)

operation cycle is started, the table advances to the left for boring and facing. When that is done, the table traverses to the right. The heads on the right-hand bridge bore and face both pieces. Then the table returns rapidly to its original position and stops.

A machine of the type described has a rated capacity of an 8 in.-diameter bore and 18 in. stroke with feeds from $\frac{1}{4}$ to 20 in. per min, is driven by a 2 hp motor, weighs 6600 lb, and costs around $11,000.

Entirely special precision boring machines of many kinds are constructed for particular purposes where the output is sufficient to justify the cost. An example of such a machine is the one in Fig. 26–6 for boring all the cylinders at once in an engine block.

JIG BORING

Precision hole location. The accuracy required for the location of holes varies from $\frac{1}{32}$ in. commonly needed for clearance holes to a few ten-thousandths of an inch for holes in exacting production parts, such as those for aircraft engines, and many jigs, fixture, dies, and gages. The method selected to locate a hole or holes depends upon the accuracy required and the number of pieces to be made.

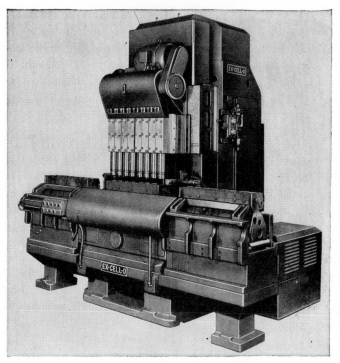

Fig. 26–6. A special precision production boring machine for boring all the cylinders in an engine block at one time. (Courtesy Ex-Cell-O Corp.)

The accurate location of holes calls for three steps. The first is to establish the positions of the holes, the second is to cut the holes, and the third is to check the results.

The positions of holes may be established by layout, transfer, buttoning, and coordinate location. The location of holes by layout and transfer was described in Chap. 22 in connection with drilling operations. Layout is not a precision method. The transfer method by jigs is adequate for almost any degree of precision but generally can be justified only for producing parts in quantities.

Buttoning is the name of a method using toolmakers' buttons. These are accurately sized hollow cylinders with squared ends. A button is clamped by a screw to the workpiece and adjusted with precision measuring tools to the position desired for a hole. The workpiece is then mounted on the face plate of a lathe with the button protruding. The workpiece is shifted until a dial indicator shows the button running true. The workpiece is secured, the button removed, and the hole is bored in the same spot. Holes may be located by this method to within 0.0005 to 0.001 in. of true location. No expensive equipment is needed, but the method is time consuming.

Coordinate location is done by moving a workpiece from a reference point through measured distances in coordinate directions. Ways of doing this with the hole spacer on the drill press, the milling machine, and the horizontal boring machine have been described. On such machines, holes can be located within 0.001 to 0.005 in. of their true positions without extra attachments. Coordinate location is also done on jig boring machines, but the means of measurement are refined, and location may be achieved within 0.0001 to 0.0005 in.

After the position of a hole has been established, the way it is cut determines whether accurate location as well as size ensues. Where a truly positioned and round hole with an accuracy of less than 0.0005 in. is required, drilling followed by several cuts with a single-point boring tool is the only means of insuring it. Faster methods may be used if more tolerance is permitted. For tolerances between 0.0005 and 0.001 in., a multiple-point boring tool or end mill followed by a sizing reamer will do. Where tolerances of several thousandths of an inch are permissible, a hole may be spotted, drilled undersize, and reamed.

Grinding is a positive way of correcting positional errors and finishing holes in hardened materials. Other abrasive methods are not effective in positioning holes.

Jig boring machines. A jig boring machine looks like a vertical milling machine. Most jig borers in the United States are of the openside construction like the one in Fig. 26–7. The vertical spindle revolves and moves up and down with its quill in a bracket clamped to the front of the column and adjustable for height. The table is mounted on a saddle on the bed and can be moved lengthwise or crosswise. Large pieces on the table can extend out on the sides or front, and the operator has ready access to the work.

Another style of jig borer has its table sliding lengthwise directly on the bed. Two columns, one at each side in the middle of the bed, support a cross rail that carries the vertical spindle head. The head is moved across the table and the spindle is fed vertically.

A jig boring machine like the one in Fig. 26–7 with 16 × 30 in. table and 24 in. table travel weighs about 8000 lb and costs around $27,000. A complete set of tools and accessories may cost another $8000 to $10,000. A comparable vertical milling machine of good quality costs about $21,000. Jig boring machines are costly because they are built to insure the utmost accuracy through extra rigidity, low thermal expansion, and precise means of measuring distances. The spindles of most machines run in preloaded antifriction bearings. The spindle housing may be cast of Invar iron with a low coefficient of expansion. A wide range of speeds is available so that cuts may be taken quickly. Measurements are made and workpieces positioned in different ways on different makes of ma-

Fig. 26–7. (A) A jig boring machine that employs measuring instruments. (Views B and C on page 620.)

chines. The four basic measuring devices on jig boring machines are micrometer leadscrews, graduated scales and microscopes, end measuring instruments, and the Electrolimit measuring system.

All jig borers have leadscrews and graduated dials for moving their tables, but the screws are not always depended upon for precise measurements and table settings. The best screws are made with an error of no more than 0.0002 in. in 16 in. The screws and other parts are subject to wear and deflection in service. The use of screws alone has been found satisfactory for small jig boring machines, but the errors become too much in large machines.

Corrections are made for the errors in long screws by a compensating device on some Swiss jig boring machines. A cam with a profile representing the errors to a large scale is fitted to the side of the table. The cam follower through a linkage shifts a pointer so that it always points

Fig. 26-7. (B) The arrangement of the measuring instruments.

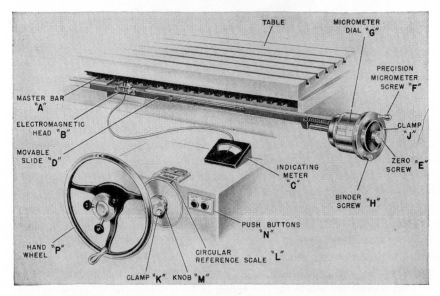

Fig. 26-7. (C) An electrical device for precision measurement on the jig boring machine. (Pratt and Whitney Photo from Pratt and Whitney Division, Niles-Bement-Pond Co., W. Hartford, Conn.)

to true readings on the leadscrew dial. Machines of this kind can be manipulated rapidly because the leadscrews serve to move the table as well as to provide measurements.

Measurements are made on some jig borers by means of accurate vernier scales that are read by microscopes.

The jig boring machine of Fig. 26–7 is equipped with end measuring instruments, which are rods of even inch lengths made to gage block accuracy. An inside micrometer is adjusted for decimal parts of an inch. The end measures and micrometer are placed in a trough between an adjustable stop on the table and a 0.0001 in. dial indicator at the outer end of the trough. The table is locked in the first position, measuring instruments are inserted, and the table stop is adjusted to set the dial indicator to zero. A hole may be bored in that position. To locate the next hole, the measuring instruments are changed an amount equal to the distance to be moved, and the table is moved until the dial indicator again registers zero. The same procedure is followed to set the saddle for cross movements. The effects of deflection and wear are minimized by the end measuring system, but the system by itself is not fast.

A jig boring machine equipped with the Electrolimit measuring system has a master bar attached to the table and beneath that a movable slide with an electromagnetic head as depicted in Fig. 26–7(C). Projections on the master bar are magnetized with magnetic centers one inch apart within an accumulated tolerance of 0.0002 in. in the full length of the bar. Movements in inch increments of the projections past the electromagnetic head are indicated by the meter, which shows when the head and a projection are aligned. For increments of less than one inch, the head is positioned by the precision micrometer screw and dial on the right to within 0.0001 in.

Some models of jig borers are arranged so that the operator merely sets a series of dials to cause the end measures to fall into place or to position the Electrolimit system and thus obtain a desired table setting. This makes the machine fast to operate. Such machines are also available with automatic control of table and saddle location, speeds and feeds, depths of cut, and tool changes as directed by punched cards or tape with repetition for any number of parts.

Jig boring operations. Jig boring machines are used for accurate toolmaking, manufacturing of exacting parts in small and moderate quantities, and for close limit inspection. Although the jig borer is thought of mainly for machining holes, it often is used for light milling.

A jig boring machine and its accessories represent a large investment, and a well paid operator is essential to get the best out of the machine. Even so, the machine is capable of producing results usually attainable only by buttoning or from using other machines, such as millers, with expensive extra equipment. Also, the jig boring machine achieves these results at the lowest cost when enough work is available to keep the machine busy. To get the most out of the machine, several principles that will be discussed must be observed.

A variety of work is usually done on a jig boring machine, and much more time is consumed for set-up and changeover than for cutting. Thus, important saving in time can be realized from tools and accessories that make manipulation of the machine quick and easy. These include brackets for quick attachment of indicators, a spindle centering microscope, proving bars, and auxiliary rotating and tilting tables.

Generally adjustments in workpiece position can be made more easily than the tools can be changed on a jig borer. Also changing of tools adds a certain amount of error. Consequently a desirable procedure is first to make all roughing cuts and then the finishing cuts on all holes in a workpiece.

Jig boring is done from coordinate location, and a workpiece drawing should be dimensioned the same way, like the example of Fig. 26–8. The

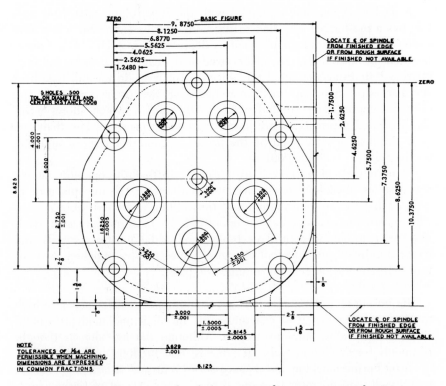

Fig. 26–8. An example of the way to dimension a part for jig boring. (Pratt and Whitney Photo from Pratt and Whitney Division, Niles-Bement-Pond Co., W. Hartford, Conn).

coordinate basic dimensions enclosed by rectangles are those the operator uses to set the measuring instruments.

Temperature changes are important in working to small tolerances on a jig borer. These may result from the handling of measuring instruments, the actions of cutting tools, or heat from motors, pumps, and moving parts. Care must be taken constantly to control temperatures, by allowing for heat dissipation and maintaining constant room temperature.

Jig grinding machines. A jig grinder is like a jig borer except that the spindle head of the machine carries a high-speed grinding spindle that revolves in a planetary fashion. Jig grinders are capable of finishing holes in hard materials, such as hardened steel, to a degree of accuracy equal to that of jig boring machines in soft materials and are used for finishing operations.

Questions

1. Describe a table-type horizontal boring mill and its movements and tell how its size is designated.

2. What are the principal types of horizontal boring mills and for what is each suited?

3. Describe a vertical turret lathe and its advantages.

4. Describe a vertical boring mill and its uses.

5. Describe a type of vertical boring machine used for quantity production.

6. What are precision production boring machines and what do they do?

7. What are the three steps needed to locate holes accurately?

8. By what four methods may the positions of holes be established?

9. What is buttoning and when is it used?

10. What is coordinate location and what accuracy is obtainable from it?

11. What cutting procedure is necessary to position and size a hole within less than half a thousandth of an inch?

12. Describe a typical jig boring machine.

13. Why are jig boring machines expensive?

14. Describe and compare the four basic measuring devices on jig boring machines.

15. What kind of work does a jig boring machine do, and how does it compare with competitors?

16. What may be done to make jig boring economical?

17. What is a jig grinding machine?

Problems

1. The times taken for operations at the stations of a six spindle vertical chucking machine are (1) unload and load 10 sec, (2) 9 sec, (3) 12 sec, (4) 13 sec, (5) 11 sec, and (6) 8 sec. Indexing time is 3 seconds. What is the production in a 50 min hr?

2. To be justified in a certain plant, a jig boring machine must show a savings of $4000 per yr. It is estimated that on the average, about one fourth of the time now spent in locating holes by buttoning can be saved by jig boring. Labor and overhead are considered worth $8 per hr. How many hours of work per year should be available for this jig boring machine to justify its purchase?

3. A jig for a job will cost $450. The operation can be done with the jig in 4 minutes and on a jig borer without a jig in 12 minutes for each piece. Set-up time is the same either way. The labor and overhead rate on the drill press with the jig is $6 per hr and on the jig boring machine $8 per hr. A composite rate for interest, insurance, taxes, and maintenance is 20%. For how many pieces is the jig justified?

References

Handbook for Horizontal Boring, Drilling and Milling Machines, Giddings and Lewis Machine Tool Company, Fond Du Lac, Wisconsin, 1947.

CHAPTER 27

Sawing and Filing

Metal is removed in sawing and filing by the action of many small teeth. Saw teeth act in a narrow line, and a saw can sever a sizable chunk of material with a minimum of cutting. If a piece of metal is removed by milling, for instance, a large part or all of it may have to be reduced to chips. The same piece may be cut off or out by a saw acting on only a small part of the material. Thus, in many cases work can be done faster and with less power by sawing than by other methods of metal cutting, and material can be saved.

The teeth of a file act over a wide surface and progress slowly. Their cutting effect can be watched and controlled. Thus, filing is suited for finishing irregular surfaces and surfaces hard to reach with other kinds of cutting tools. Filing is limited to removing small amounts of soft materials.

Saws and files have been used as hand tools since ancient times because they require little force and power, but they also are machine driven today. Power driven hack saws, circular saws, and band saws are employed to cut off pieces of bar stock, plates, sheets and other shapes of metal. Versatile band saw machines have been developed for cutting out cavities or pieces of intricate shapes with a minimum waste of material and time. Reciprocating and continuous filing machines are available for rapid and accurate finishing of plain and irregular surfaces in small quantities.

SAWS AND FILES

Saws. Three common kinds of metal-cutting saws are hack saws, circular cold saws, and band saws. Although different in overall form, they all contain a series of cutting teeth that operate in the same basic way. The important features of a saw are: (1) material, (2) tooth form, (3) tooth set, (4) tooth spacing, and (5) size.

Most good grade saws are made from alloy or high-speed steels. Some circular saws have teeth with cemented carbide tips or inserts.

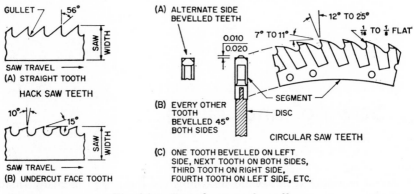

Fig. 27–1. Typical saw tooth profiles.

Saw teeth have rake and clearance angles corresponding to single-point tools as shown by the typical profiles of teeth for hack saws and circular cold saws in Fig. 27–1. Circular saw disks may be solid, may carry segments, each with several teeth, or may have inserted individual teeth. The teeth of band saws for general metal cutting are like those of other solid saws, but many other forms are available for other materials and specific operations. Among these are scallop-edge band saw blades for cloth, spiral saw blades for paper, and diamond tooth blades for ceramic and vitreous materials.

Saw teeth are offset to the side to make the cut wider than the thickness of the back of the blade to prevent rubbing. The width of the saw cut is called the *kerf*. Three common types of saw settings are shown in Fig. 27–2. The wave tooth is suited for fine tooth spacing. Circular saws, and sometimes other kinds, have alternately high and low teeth and straight and bevelled teeth like the ones in Fig. 27–1. These forms help break up the chips, distribute the load, and allow some teeth to take finishing cuts. Tooth spacing or pitch has an important influence upon saw performance as explained in Fig. 27–3. The spaces between the teeth are needed for the chips removed during a cut. Some band saws have as

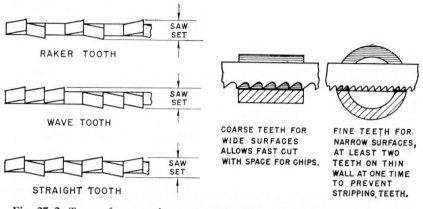

Fig. 27–2. Types of saw tooth sets.   **Fig. 27–3.** The significance of saw tooth spacing.

many as 32 teeth per in. Fourteen teeth per inch is considered fine for hack saws. Coarse band and hack saws may have as few as two teeth per inch. The pitch may run from 0.20 in. for small circular saws to 2 in. on large diameter saws for soft materials.

Hack saws are straight blades from $\frac{1}{32}$ to $\frac{1}{8}$ in. thick, $\frac{5}{8}$ to $2\frac{1}{2}$ in. wide, and 12 to 32 in. long. The heavier the cut, the larger the blade. Most band saws are welded in continuous loops and generally run from 0.020 to 0.060 in. thick and $\frac{1}{16}$ to 1 in. in width. The narrower blades are required to cut small radii. Circular cold saws are disks from $\frac{1}{32}$ to $\frac{1}{4}$ in. thick and 8 to 36 in. in diameter. The outside diameter must be large enough to enable one side to pass through the work.

Files. Files are identified by: (1) method of application, (2) class, (3) cut, (4) pitch, and (5) size.

The common file with a tang is usually operated by hand, with a wooden handle over the tang. Such files may be used on a die filing machine like the one in Fig. 27–10. The file is reciprocated across the work, with pressure applied on the forward stroke and released on the return stroke.

Continuous filing is done with a band file, which is made up of a series of short file segments. Each segment is fastened near its leading end by a clip to a flexible steel band so that it can pass freely over the wheels on which the band runs. Each file segment is interlocked and fits snugly with the segment behind it so that the cutting action is not interrupted. The ends of the band are connected by a latch so they can be fastened together to make a continuous loop. Band filing is easier than hand filing to remove much stock. A final touch may be given by a hand file.

The cross-sectional shape of a file determines its *class*. About 20 shapes are recognized as standard. The principal shapes are rectangular (called flat), square, part round (half round), round, oval, and triangular (three cornered).

The *cut* of a file designates the way the teeth are cut. A *single-cut* file has single rows of parallel teeth across its face at an angle with its axis. A *double-cut* file has two rows of teeth crossing each other, one row finer than the other. Each tooth of a *rasp cut* file is formed by itself by a single punch mark. A *vixen cut* is a milled cut with large knifelike teeth, often curved across the face of the file.

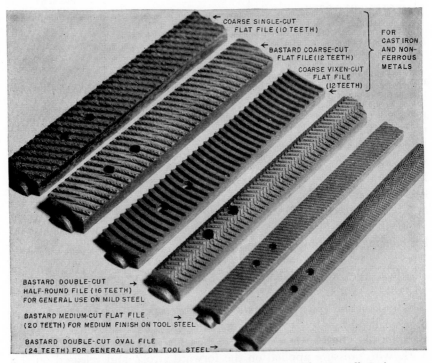

Fig. 27–4. Typical band file segments. (Courtesy The Do All Co.)

Files are graded according to the pitch or spacing of the teeth. Descriptive terms that refer to the pitch, from wide to close spacing, are rough, coarse, bastard, second cut, smooth, and dead smooth. Some files are designated by a series of numbers from the coarsest, no. 00, 0, and 1 through 8, the finest. No relationship between the descriptive name or number and the number of teeth per inch is universally accepted.

Several typical band file segments of various shapes, cuts, and pitches are shown in Fig. 27–4.

Coarse files remove metal rapidly; fine files give good finishes. Medium files offer a compromise between rapid metal removal and finish. Files most commonly used for ferrous metals are flat or half round; double or single cut; in bastard, second cut, and smooth grades. Files should have deeply cut teeth for chip clearance for nonferrous metals and non-metals.

Hand files are available in many sizes from a small fraction of an inch wide and 2 in. in length to over 1 in. wide and 14 in. long, not including the tang. Band files are commonly ¼, ⅜ and ½ in. wide.

SAWING AND FILING MACHINES

Power hack saw machines. A power-driven hack saw machine drives a blade back and forth through a workpiece, pressing down on the cutting stroke and releasing the pressure on the return, as a person does in using a hand hack saw. Many are crank driven; the large ones often are hydraulically driven. A quick return saves time. Force to feed the saw may be from gravity or springs regulated by a ratchet mechanism, a positive feed screw, or a hydraulic drive which can be controlled well for fragile workpieces.

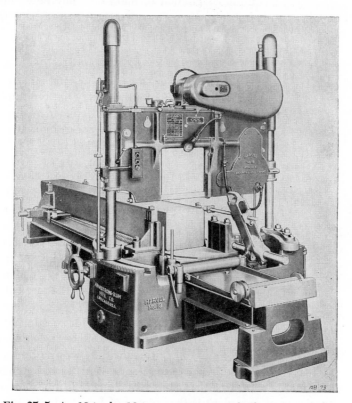

Fig. 27–5. An 18-in. by 18-in. capacity power hack sawing machine. (Courtesy Armstrong-Blum Mfg. Co.)

Work is usually held in a vise on the bed of a hack sawing machine. The frame of the machine shown in Fig. 27–5 can be swivelled for angular cuts. The machine stops automatically at the end of a cut. Production-type machines are arranged to feed, measure and cut off a series of pieces automatically from one or more bars. Specifications of several general-purpose hack sawing machines are given in Table 27–1.

TABLE 27–1. SPECIFICATIONS OF SEVERAL HACK-SAWING MACHINES

Capacity (in.)	Type	Weight (lb)	Cost ($)
6 × 6	Dry cut	225	350
6 × 6	Heavy duty—single speed	1,325	1,600
24 × 24	Large size	16,000	26,000

Because the stroke is intermittent, hack sawing is not a rapid method of cutting off stock, but the machines are simple in design and easy to change from job to job, to operate, and to maintain. Alloy and high-speed steel blades commonly used are not expensive but have long lives. On an average job a continuous circular or band saw may be ⅓ or more faster than a hack saw, but in many cases the overall cost of hack sawing is less and in some cases is only ⅓ to ¼ as much.

Fig. 27–6. A circular sawing machine that uses a cold saw to cut stock up to 4 in. square or round. (Courtesy The Motch and Merryweather Machinery Co.)

Circular saw machines. A circular saw machine cuts off stock with a rotating saw. One type utilizes a cold saw, as depicted in Fig. 27–6, mounted on a carriage with hand, air or hydraulic feed.

Workpieces are usually clamped in a vise or V fixture, one or more at a time, for cold sawing. On manual models, the stock is pushed against a stop and clamped, and the saw is fed by hand. Other models are semi- and fully-automatic in operation. Some also chamfer or center the pieces that are cut off.

Cold sawing is a continuous and fast method for cutting off and leaves a smooth and accurate milled surface with few or no burrs, which may save work in subsequent operations. A 6 in.-diameter steel bar can easily be cut off in a minute. The typical experience of one plant is that pieces of bar stock can be cut off with a tolerance in length of 0.003 in. and a finish equal to or better than that obtained from a cut-off tool on a lathe.

Another kind of circular saw is the friction saw. It has a smooth or nicked outer edge and is run at 10,000 to 25,000 sfpm. The heat of friction softens the metal of the workpiece in contact with the disk, and the soft metal is rubbed away. Only a small amount of the saw is in contact at any instant, and the rest is cooled as it travels around to enter the cut again. Teeth do not have to be kept sharp on the saw. Friction sawing is fast but leaves a heavier burr and a less accurate surface than tooth cutting does.

Abrasive disks, like the one shown in Fig. 27–7, also are used for cutting off stock. As the name implies, an abrasive disk is a thin flexible grinding wheel. It runs at speeds as high as 15,000 sfpm and is usually carried on a swinging frame. Abrasive sawing is advantageous for hard materials and fast for thin and simple sections.

Fig. 27–7. An abrasive cut-off wheel mounted on a high speed swing frame machine. (Courtesy The Carborundum Co.)

TABLE 27–2. Specifications of Several Circular Sawing Machines

Type	Rated capacity (in.)	Weight (lb)	Cost ($)
Cold saw	4 in.-diam. workpiece	3,500	10,000
Friction saw	⎰24 in.-diam. blade	3,000	5,000
	⎱58 in.-diam. blade	17,000	20,000
Abrasive	5 × 12 in. light-walled formed shapes and sprues	2,200	4,000

Band saw machines. A continuous saw blade or band runs over the rims of two wheels on a band saw machine. Horizontal band saw machines, like the one in Fig. 27–8, do cut-off work. The saw is carried on a frame and is fed downward through the workpiece clamped in a vise on the bed. A machine like the one shown weighs 1950 lb and costs around $2400.

Vertical band saw machines are used for cutting off pieces but in addition are widely used for cutting outside and inside shapes of all kinds for tool-, jig-, fixture-, die-, and gage-making and the production of

Fig. 27–8. A 12 by 16 in. capacity horizontal metal cutting band saw.
(Courtesy Wells Manufacturing Corp.)

small intricate parts. For inside cutting, the band is cut, passed through a drilled hole, and butt welded together. An example of sawing an opening inside a piece is given in Fig. 27–9. A machine with 26 in. clearance between band and frame weighs about 2500 lb and costs about $4500.

Contour band sawing machines are adaptable to other operations. A continuous band of file segments or stones may be put in place of the band saw. Friction sawing is done on high-speed machines with bands having dull teeth.

Band saws are continuous and faster but more expensive than hack saws for cutting off. In many cases they are as fast and cut as accurately as circular saws, particularly through thin sections and for weak work-pieces, and cost less. One manufacturer guarantees a tolerance of 0.002 in. per in. of width of cut-off face for his products. Contour sawing care-fully done can be held to a ±0.003 in. tolerance. Band saws are thin and cut away less stock than other saws.

Die sawing and filing machines. Machines like the one in Fig. 27–10 simulate the hand action of sawing, filing, and stoning. The tool is held

Questions

1. What economy does sawing give?

2. For what is filing used and why?

3. Describe the important features of the three types of saws.

4. Describe the important features of files.

5. How does a power hack saw operate, and what are its advantages and disadvantages?

6. Describe cold sawing and its merits.

7. What is friction sawing, and what does it offer?

8. Describe abrasive disk sawing and its uses.

9. Describe the two types of band sawing machines and the work they do.

10. How do band sawing machines compare with other types of sawing machines?

Problems

1. The pitch of the teeth is 0.23 in. on an 18 in.-diameter circular cold saw. It is fed at a rate of 0.002 in. per tooth and revolves at 60 sfpm. How long will it take to cut through a 5 in.-diameter steel bar? What is the maximum power consumption at one horsepower per cubic inch per minute of stock removal? The kerf of the saw is ¼ in.

2. The cold sawing machine to do the operation described in Prob. 1 has an overhead rate of $2 per hr. A hack saw will cut off the same piece in 5 min and has an overhead rate of $0.50 per hr. Each machine stands idle for 1 min while the operator gets the stock and loads it. Which machine would you select for the job and why?

3. A cold circular saw is needed for general work that should keep it busy for the full 2000 hr per yr that the plant operates. It is estimated that the saw will be cutting 80% of the time and removing material at an average rate of 5 cu in. per min with a ³⁄₁₆ in.-wide kerf. The machine costs $5000, and $500 a year is needed to amortize its cost.

   To do the same work on a horizontal band saw will require about 25% more cutting time, and therefore two machines are needed. Each costs about $3000, and the annual cost of two is $600. Labor and overhead cost will be the same for either kind of saw. The band saw cuts up about only half as much material in making each cut, and the stock saved is considered worth $0.05 per lb. Which sawing machine would you recommend and why?

References

Emerson, Chas., "How To Cut Off Metals," *American Machinist*, Aug. 13, 1956, p. 133.

CHAPTER 28

Abrasives, Grinding Wheels, and Grinding Operations

ABRASIVES

Abrasives are hard substances used in various forms as tools for grinding and other surface finishing operations. They are able to cut materials too hard for other tools and give better finishes and hold closer tolerances than can be obtained economically by other means on most materials.

Abrasives may be used as loose grains, in grinding wheels, in stones and sticks, and as coated abrasives. When applied properly, abrasives remove metal by cutting it into chips just like other metal cutting tools, but the chips generally are so small that they must be magnified to be seen.

Common abrasives. The principal abrasive substances are:

1. aluminum oxide, chemically Al_2O_3, known by such trade names as *Alundum* and *Aloxite*.
2. silicon carbide, SiC, known by such trade names as *Carborundum* and *Crystolon*.
3. diamond, a form of pure carbon.

636

Other abrasive substances exist but aluminum oxide and silicon carbide, illustrated in Fig. 28–1, are by far the most widely used. They are made in a number of varieties, and each variety has a distinct combination of properties that makes it most efficient for certain applications. The important properties of an abrasive material are: (1) hardness, (2) toughness, and (3) resistance to attrition.

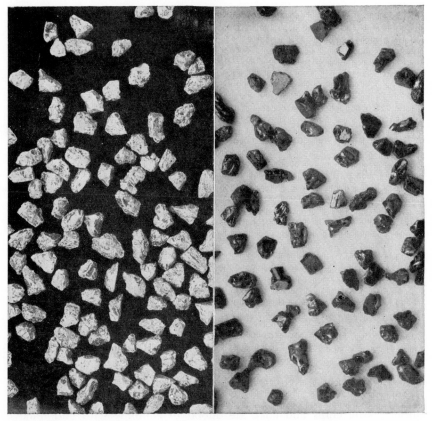

(A)   (B)

Fig. 28–1. (A) Aluminum oxide abrasive grains. (B) Silicon carbide
abrasive grains. (Courtesy Norton Co.)

Hardness is the ability of a substance to resist penetration. An abrasive must be hard to penetrate and scratch the material on which it works. The greater the difference in hardness between an abrasive and the work material, the more efficient the abrasive. The diamond is the hardest known substance. If its hardness is designated by 80, then the hardness of silicon carbide may be represented approximately by 25, aluminum oxide by 20, cemented carbide by 18, hard steel by 8, and common glass by 4. Silicon carbide and aluminum oxide are considerably harder than, and therefore suitable abrasives for, most materials.

Abrasive grains deteriorate in service by relatively large pieces of the crystals breaking off and by the loss of fine particles, flattening and dulling the edges. The first action is called *fracture;* the second, *attrition.* The toughness or body strength of an abrasive grain is a measure of its resistance to fracture. The ability of a grain to remain sharp depends upon its resistance to attrition. This latter is partly related to hardness but also to the chemical affinity between the abrasive and the material it penetrates, particularly with high pressures and temperatures. An abrasive may have a high attrition resistance with one material and a low resistance with another material of about the same hardness as the first.

Manufacture of abrasives. Natural abrasives were all that were available until about the beginning of this century. Impure aluminum oxide occurs naturally as corundum and emery. However, such natural abrasives lack uniformity and reliability and have been replaced largely by manufactured abrasives. Most diamond abrasives still are natural, although artificial ones are becoming important.

Silicon carbide does not appear in nature but is made from sand, coke, sawdust, and salt, mixed together and piled around a carbon electrical conductor. A wall of uncemented bricks is built around the mass, and a heavy current is passed through the electrode. A temperature around 4200°F is reached to make the silicon of the sand combine with the carbon of the coke to form SiC. The sawdust burns and leaves pores to let the gas escape. The salt helps remove impurities. After the process has run its course, the furnace is cooled and the outside removed. The core of loosely knit silicon carbide crystals is broken into individual grains.

Aluminum oxide abrasive is derived from an ore called bauxite, which is mainly aluminum hydroxide. The ore is calcined to drive off excess water and then exposed to high temperatures in an arc-type electric furnace. Iron chips and coke are added to combine with and remove impurities. The refined aluminum oxide comes out of the furnace in a large lump called a pig. It is crushed and rolled into small grains, treated magnetically to remove ferrous impurities, and washed.

Varieties of the abrasives with different degrees of toughness and friability are produced by modifications of the refining processes or additions of various minor substances.

Grain size. Abrasive grains are sorted into various sizes for a uniform and dependable product. This is done by passing the grains through screens in mechanical sieving machines. The size of a grain is designated by the mesh of the screen through which it just passes. Thus, a grain of 20 grit passes through a mesh of 20 *openings per linear inch* but will not go through the next smaller screen. Standard screened grain sizes for aluminum oxide and silicon carbide run from 4 to 220 grits. Finer sizes, called flours, are segregated by flotation methods.

GRINDING WHEELS

Properties of grinding wheels. A grinding wheel is made of abrasive grains held together by a *bond*. These grains cut like teeth when the wheel is revolved at high speed and is brought to bear against a workpiece. The properties of a wheel that determine how it acts are the kind and size of abrasive, how closely the grains are packed together, and the kind and amount of bonding material.

The principal bonds are vitrified, silicate, resinoid, rubber, and shellac bonds.

A *vitrified bond* is a clay bond melted to a glass-like consistency. It can be made strong and porous for heavy grinding and is not affected by water, oils, acids, or other than extreme temperatures. Most grinding wheels have vitrified bonds. Their strength and rigidity helps to control size and finish.

Fig. 28–2. A few typical grinding wheels. (Courtesy The Carborundum Co.)

A *silicate* bond is essentially water glass hardened by baking. It holds the grains more loosely than a vitrified bond and gives a cooler cut. Large wheels can be made more easily with a silicate bond.

A *resinoid bond* is a synthetic organic or plastic compound. It is strong and fairly flexible, can be run at high speeds, and is cool cutting.

A *rubber bond* is composed of fairly hard vulcanized rubber, and is dense. This bond makes strong and flexible wheels that can be made very thin.

A *shellac bond* helps produce high finishes on such products as cam shafts and mill rolls. It cuts cooly on hardened steel and thin sections.

The *grade* of a grinding wheel is a measure of how strongly the grains are held by the bond. The bonding material in a wheel surrounds the individual grains and links them together by connectors called *posts*, as illustrated in Fig. 28–3. The sizes and strengths of the posts depend upon the kind and amount of bonding material in a wheel. The ability to hold its abrasive grains is called the *hardness* of a grinding wheel. A hard wheel holds its grains more tenaciously than a soft wheel. A wheel that is too hard for a job keeps its grains after they have become dull. A wheel that is too soft loses grains before they have done full duty. Hard-

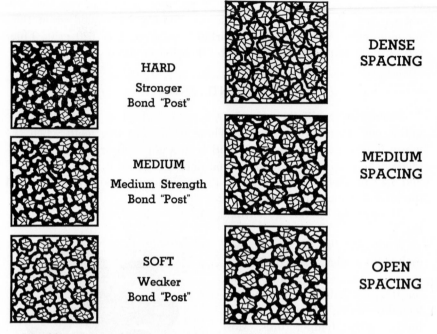

Fig. 28–3. An explanation of the meaning of wheel grade. (Courtesy The Carborundum Co.)

Fig. 28–4. An explanation of the meaning of wheel structure. (Courtesy The Carborundum Co.)

ness of the wheel should not be confused with hardness of the abrasive grains themselves.

The *structure* or *spacing* of a grinding wheel refers to the relationship of abrasive gains to bonding materials and of those two elements to the voids between them. The meaning of structure is illustrated in Fig. 28–4. The spaces in a grinding wheel provide room for chips to escape during a cut and for cutting fluid to be carried into a cut.

Grinding wheels are marked with symbols that designate their properties. A typical wheel marking and an explanation of its meaning are shown in Fig. 28–5. Each letter or number in a certain position in the sequence designates a particular property. All grinding wheel manufacturers use substantially the same standard wheel marking system. However, properties of wheels are determined to a large extent by the ways the wheels are made. The processes vary from one plant to another, and wheels carrying the same symbols but made by different manufacturers are not necessarily identical.

Wheel shapes and sizes. A few typical grinding wheel shapes are shown in Fig. 28–2. The nine grinding wheel shapes recognized as standard include straight cylinders, with or without recesses in their sides, and

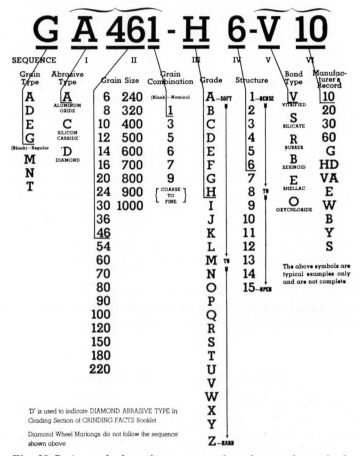

Fig. 28–5. A standard marking system chart for grinding wheels.
(Courtesy The Carborundum Co.)

others described as tapered two sides, straight cup, flaring cup, dish, and saucer. Other shapes may be obtained as specials.

The principal dimensions that designate the size of a grinding wheel are the outside diameter, width, and hole diameter. Standard wheel shapes are made in certain sizes only, but the variety is large.

Disk wheels are abrasive disks cemented or bolted to steel disks and are stronger for grinding from the side of the wheel than straight wheels alone. Side grinding wheels known as *built-up, segmental,* or *sectored wheels* are composed of bonded abrasive blocks held in a chuck or fastened to a metal disk by wedges, steel bands, wire, or bolts. They are easier to make than solid wheels for diameters over 36 in. and cut cooly because they cut intermittently.

Mounted wheels and points are small grinding wheels, usually a fraction of an inch in diameter, with attached shanks. They are commonly used at high speeds on portable grinders for burring, removing excess material from dies and molds, grinding in recesses and crevices, and for small holes.

Manufacture of grinding wheels. Vitrified grinding wheels may be made by the puddling, tamping, or pressing processes. Pressed wheels are the most dense and puddled wheels the least dense. First clay and abrasive are machine-mixed thoroughly. In the puddling process, water is added, and the mixture is poured into molds. For pressed wheels, the dry or semi-dry mixture is placed in molds and squeezed in hydraulic presses. The same type of mixture is compressed less but still firmly in the tamping process. At this stage, the wheels are baked and dried. The puddled wheels must be trimmed to size.

Grinding wheels are vitrified by being fired for several days at high temperatures, like pottery. When hard, the wheels are trued, their arbor holes are bushed with babbit metal or lead, and large wheels are balanced.

Other kinds of wheels are made by processes associated with the particular bonding agents. In general, the ingredients are mixed, molded, and heated as required. The finished wheels are sized, balanced, and graded.

OTHER ABRASIVE PRODUCTS

Silicon carbide and aluminum oxide abrasive grains are bonded into *sticks* and *stones* of various types and sizes. They are used for honing, touching up edges of cutting tools, and cleaning, polishing, and finishing dies, molds, and jigs.

Coated abrasives. Coated abrasives are made of abrasive grains, adhesive, and backing. The adhesive may be glue or resin and holds the grains together and to the backing, which is commonly paper or cloth. Common sandpaper is a well known form. Cloth with aluminum oxide abrasive is used mostly on metals. It is available in sheets, rolls, strips, belts, sleeves, cones, and disks of various sizes.

Polishing wheels. Flexible wheel bodies of cloth, leather, or wood, depending upon the work, are coated with adhesive and rolled in abrasive grains of uniform sizes, coarse for roughing and fine for finishing. After the adhesive, glue or cold cement, has dried, the abrasive layer is cracked by pounding to make it resilient. The resulting polishing wheels, like those in Fig. 28–6, are revolved at surface speeds around 7500 sfpm. After its grains have become dull and worn off, a polishing wheel is stripped and recoated.

GRINDING OPERATIONS

Work done by grinding. Grinding is done on surfaces of almost all conceivable shapes and materials of all kinds. Grinding may be classified as nonprecision or precision, according to purpose and procedure. *Nonprecision grinding,* common forms of which are *snagging* and *off-hand grinding,* is done primarily to remove stock that cannot be taken off as conveniently by other methods from castings, forgings, billets, and other rough pieces. The work is pressed hard against the wheel, or vice versa. The accuracy and surface finish obtained

Fig. 28–6. Polishing wheels. (Courtesy Norton Co.)

are of secondary importance. *Precision grinding* is concerned with producing good surface finishes and accurate dimensions. The wheel or work or both are guided in precise paths.

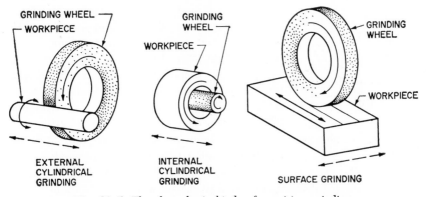

Fig. 28–7. The three basic kinds of precision grinding.

The three basic kinds of precision grinding shown in Fig. 28–7 are *external cylindrical grinding, internal cylindrical grinding,* and *surface grinding.* Variations of each of these will be described in connection with grinding machines.

Grinding is able to produce accurate and fine surfaces because it works through small abrasive cutting edges, each of which takes a tiny bite. On the other hand appreciable quantities of material can be removed by grinding because a large number of cutting edges are applied at high frequency. For instance, about 39,000,000 cutting points act in a minute when a 46 grit wheel, 18 in. in diameter and 2 in. wide, is revolved with a surface speed of 5000 fpm.

The factors of cost. Grinding is done to remove material and expose surfaces of definite shapes; flat or round, straight or curved. The latter function is of more concern in precision grinding, which must create fine finishes and accurate dimensions. The costs that must be borne to achieve the purposes of grinding are those of time, labor and overhead, wheel wear, and power.

When abrasive grains cut, they become dull like other cutting tools. When they are dull and rounded, abrasive grains rub, create excessive heat which can ruin the work surface, and smear the metal. The ideal condition is for the abrasive grains to break down as soon as they become dull, thereby presenting new sharp edges, or to be released from the wheel, thus uncovering fresh grains. Then the wheel remains sharp and continues to cut cleanly. This causes wheel wear, which is a definite part of cost, and can be wasteful if the grains are cast off before they do their full share of work and become dull.

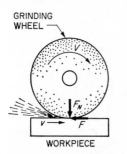

GRINDING WHEEL

WORKPIECE

Fig. 28–8. The forces exerted by a grinding wheel.

A grinding wheel exerts two components of force on a workpiece, a normal F_n and tangential F in the manner shown in Fig. 28–8. The ratio $C = F/F_n$ is called the *coefficient of grinding pull* and varies from 0.1 to 0.3 for snagging to 0.4 to 0.5 for wet precision grinding. The normal force F_n determines the rate of stock removal in non-precision grinding. As it is increased with the same wheel speed, the force F and the power increase with the stock removal. Approximately 200 lb is the heaviest load for manual application with weights. Mechanical and hydraulic means are utilized for larger forces.

An empirical formula for estimating the power needed for grinding iron and steel with a wheel running at normal grinding speed is

$$\text{horsepower } P = K\sqrt{Q}, \tag{28–1}$$

where Q is the rate of stock removal in cubic inches per minute. The following are typical values of K:

Kind of grinding operation	Snagging		Precision grinding with wheels about one inch wide		
	Floor stand	Swing frame	Surface	Internal	Cylindrical
Value of K	6	7	8.5	9.5	10.0

Power is one of the least costly items in most grinding operations. However, the energy released when power is applied is important because most of it becomes heat which can crack, check, or soften the ground surface under severe conditions.

A grinding operation is most efficient when it produces the results required with the sum of the factors of cost at a minimum. The elements of the grinding operation that determine the factors of cost are: (1) the grinding wheel and its selection, (2) the equipment and its operation (including such items as wheel speed, work speed, feed, depth of cut, cutting fluid, and wheel dressing), and (3) the workpiece and its material.

The selection of the grinding wheel. A grinding wheel may be needed to remove stock rapidly, give a high finish, or hold close tolerances. Each function calls for different properties, and no wheel can do all best. A compromise may be selected for a general-purpose wheel. A wheel suited just for the job is chosen for a production operation; quite often one wheel is needed for roughing and another for finishing. The following discussion will provide a basic understanding of what is involved in grinding wheel selection. In practice, experts should be consulted to select wheels for important jobs.

Selection of abrasive and grain size. The resistance to fracture seems about the same for silicon carbide and aluminum oxide. Silicon carbide has a low resistance to attrition when cutting steel or malleable iron, and its grains dull quickly, so aluminum oxide is preferred for that purpose. Silicon carbide performs better as a rule for grinding cast iron, brass, copper, soft bronze, aluminum, stone, rubber, leather, and cemented carbides. The reason is that silicon carbide fractures more satisfactorily in relation to the dulling of its grains, and its cutting edges are renewed as needed. However, various kinds of aluminum oxide are made, and the crystals of some kinds are relatively weak and desirable for some soft ductile materials.

If a fine finish rather than stock removal is desired, the positions of the abrasives may be reversed. A rapid dulling of the grains is desirable in some cases to produce fine finishes. Thus, silicon carbide wheels are used to get a mirror finish on hardened steel rolls, and aluminum oxide for a high finish on glass.

Diamond abrasive has physical properties for grinding far superior to other abrasives, but its cost and the cost of wheels made from it are high. Diamond wheels are used for rapidly cutting and finishing gems, ceramics, stone, and cemented carbides.

Soft materials are rough-ground with coarse grains, and hard materials with fine grains. Coarse grains take big bites in and rapidly remove soft materials. Only small bites can be taken in quite hard materials in any event, and consequently small grains are advantageous because more of them can be brought to bear on the material in a given time.

Fine grains make small scratches and generally are preferred for finishing. However, coarse grains cut fully, and moderately coarse grains are desired by some people for producing fine surface finishes to small tolerances. Surface finishes of a few microinches rms and tolerances of less than 0.0001 in. have been achieved on grinding jobs with fast cutting wheels of 60 to 80 grit.

Fine-grain wheels can be trued to thin sections and hold up better at corners and edges than coarse-grain wheels. An example is found in thread grinding, where fine-grain wheels are desirable to hold the shapes required for the roots of thread.

Selection of wheel bond, grade, and spacing. Hard, tough materials dull abrasives rapidly and require soft grinding wheels that release the grains readily when they become dull. Hard wheels are suitable for soft material. On the other hand, hard wheels exert high pressure and tend to chatter, which is detrimental to good surface finish.

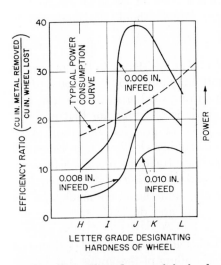

Fig. 28-9. The influence of the hardness of grinding wheels upon the efficiency ratio and power consumption in a centerless grinding operation. (As reported by John A. Mueller, "How to Select the Best Grinding Wheels," *The Tool Engineer,* Feb., 1955, p. 91.)

A common measure of wheel performance is the *efficiency ratio* or *volume ratio,* which is the number of pounds (or cubic inches) of metal removed in a given time divided by the pounds (or cubic inches) of wheel loss. This may be plotted from tests for a series of wheels of the same type but of different grades for a specific operation, as in Fig. 28-9. One grade generally shows the highest ratio for a given set of conditions. If one of the variables of the operation, such as the infeed in Fig. 28-9, is changed, different curves result, and the peaks of the curves are at different levels. If wheel wear alone is to be considered, the best wheel for a job is the one at the highest point. Wheel wear is important because of wheel cost in all operations. Also, in precision grinding wheel wear affects wheel shape, and a wheel that wears rapidly and nonuniformly must be retrued often. This takes time, interrupts production, and is expensive.

Commonly a wheel that does not have the highest volume ratio for a job is faster and can show a total cost less than the wheel that is at the top of the curve. Power consumption and the heat generated increase with grade hardness, and that may be harmful to the work. Experts recommend that the best wheel to use for a job is the softest grade that performs satisfactorily.

Grain spacing provides the openings for chips between grains during a cut. An open spacing or structure is desirable for a large area of contact and heavy roughing cuts in soft materials because it permits the grains to work at their fullest depths and provides good chip clearance space. If the face of a wheel tends to become loaded with metal, its structure is too dense for the work it is doing.

When the grains cannot bite deeply, as in grinding hard materials, chip clearance is secondary and a dense spacing is desirable so that many grains can act at once. Dense spacing is also necessary to produce scratches close together for fine finishes. A wheel with dense spacing holds its shape well and contributes to dimensional control.

Balancing the grinding wheel. Grinding wheels, particularly large high-speed ones, must be balanced to produce good finishes. A wheel is mounted on the machine and trued before it is balanced. A conventional wheel mount for a straight wheel fits into the hole of the wheel and has two flanges that clamp against blotting paper rings against the sides or in the recesses of the wheel. Weights attached to one flange can be shifted for balancing. Most large wheels are balanced statically off the machine like automobile wheels. Grinding wheel mounts are available that automatically balance the wheels in a few seconds while running on the machine.

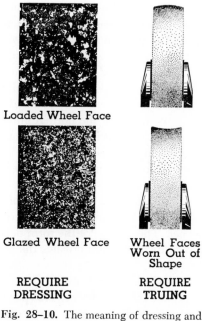

Loaded Wheel Face

Glazed Wheel Face

Wheel Faces Worn Out of Shape

REQUIRE DRESSING

REQUIRE TRUING

Fig. 28–10. The meaning of dressing and truing. (Courtesy The Carborundum Co.)

Dressing and truing the grinding wheel. A grinding wheel retains its true form and resharpens itself fully as it breaks down in an ideal grinding operation. The condition is only approached in most operations, and the sharpness and form of the wheel must be restored from time to time by dressing and truing as indicated in Fig. 28–10. How often a wheel must be dressed or trued depends upon the type of work, the fitness of the wheel, and the skill of the operator. For internal grinding, the wheel is not uncommonly trued for each piece. For some high-production precision external cylindrical grinding jobs, the wheels may run for days without being dressed.

When metal particles become imbedded and fill the spaces around the surface grains, the wheel face is said to be *loaded*. Ductile materials and dense wheel structure particularly engender that condition. When the abrasive grains become dull and cease to cut efficiently because their edges are rubbed off, the wheel face becomes *glazed*. Dressing is done to restore the cutting action of the wheel by fracturing and tearing away the dull grains to expose fresh cutting edges or clear away the imbedded material. *Truing* is done to create a true surface on a wheel. The act of truing a wheel dresses it also.

Steel cutters, abrasive sticks, and small abrasive wheels are relatively inexpensive and are popular tools for dressing grinding wheels. They may be pushed against and wiped across the face of the wheel by hand or attached to holders on the machine.

Diamonds unsuited for gems are mostly used for truing wheels for precision grinding. A single large stone or a group of small ones in a setting may be used. Light cuts of less than 0.001 in. must be taken with a coolant to avoid overheating and damaging the stone. Continued use of a dull diamond makes for dull grains and a poor cutting wheel. Diamond tools are accurately fed and traversed for precision truing, in most cases by means of the normal movements of the machines. For that purpose a standard grinder usually has an attached diamond tool holder, like the ones in Figs. 29–9 and 29–10. Truing attachments for straight surfaces, angles, radii, and almost any other form are available for addition to any grinding machine.

Crush dressing is a method of truing and dressing a grinding wheel by means of a hard roller pressed against the slowly revolving grinding wheel. The reverse of the form desired on the wheel is given to the roller, which displaces and crushes the surface grains and imprints the form on the wheel.

Crush dressing is often more economical than diamond truing, especially for intricate forms. Sharper crystals are left by crush dressing, and that means cleaner and cooler cutting. Diamond truing is generally more accurate and can be made to produce better surface finishes.

The theory of grinding. The effects of the principal variables in a grinding operation can be seen by analyzing the grinding action depicted in Fig. 28–11. The grinding wheel rotating in the direction shown with a surface speed of V fpm is assumed to have n grains per linear inch in a narrow band around its periphery. The average spacing from grain to grain is $1/n$. After one grain passes point A, the time until the next grain reaches the same point is $T = 1/(12Vn)$ minutes. During that time the workpiece is revolving with a surface speed of v fpm, and a point on its periphery advances from A to B, a distance $AB = 12vT = v/Vn$. The chip removed in that time is represented by the area $CEAB$. The maximum chip thickness $t = \overline{EB}$ largely determines what happens to the grinding wheel. The area EAB is small and may be closely approximated by a triangle EAB with the angle $EAB = \alpha + \beta$. Then the maximum chip thickness

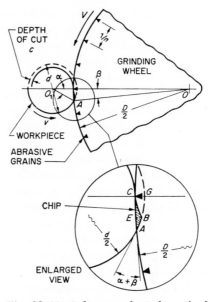

Fig. 28–11. A diagram of grinding wheel action.

$$\overline{EB} = t = AB \ \sin \ (\alpha + \beta) = (v/Vn) \ \sin \ (\alpha + \beta). \quad (28\text{–}2)$$

The triangle O_1OA in Fig. 28–11 has one side $D/2 + d/2 - c$, a second side $\dfrac{D}{2}$, and a third side $\dfrac{d}{2}$. By the law of cosines,

$$(D/2 + d/2 - c)^2 = (D/2)^2 + (d/2)^2 - 2(D/2)(d/2) \ \cos \ [\pi - (\alpha + \beta)] \quad (28\text{–}3)$$

also

$$\sin \ (\alpha + \beta) = \sqrt{1 - \cos^2 \ (\alpha + \beta)} = \sqrt{1 - \cos^2 \ [\pi - (\alpha + \beta)]} \quad (28\text{–}4)$$

If Eqs. (28–3) and (28–4) are combined and solved, and terms containing c^2 are neglected because c is quite small, it is found that

$$\sin \ (\alpha + \beta) = 2\sqrt{c[(1/d) + (1/D)]}. \quad (28\text{–}5)$$

If this result is substituted in Eq. (28–2),

$$t = (2v/Vn) \ \sqrt{c} \ \sqrt{(1/D) + (1/d)}. \quad (28\text{–}6)$$

This relationship is based on several approximations but is substantially the same as the exact expression that can be obtained for t for each type of grinding. Experience and experiments have shown that the force acting on a grain increases or decreases with the grain depth of cut t, although not necessarily in proportion. An increase in the grain depth of cut causes the forces to increase and the grains to fracture or break away sooner, and the wheel acts softer. Conversely, a decrease in the grain depth of cut makes the wheel act harder. Thus Eq. (28–6) reveals at least qualitatively how the variables in a grinding operation should be arranged for efficient performance.

The grain depth of cut must be small in precision grinding to make light scratches and leave a fine finish. Even in non-precision grinding, the grain depth of cut cannot be huge or the grains would be overwhelmed. From Eq. (28–6) it is evident that the wheel speed must be high. For most materials grinding wheels are run as fast as they safely can; vitrified wheels up to 6500 sfpm, and resinoid, rubber, and shellac wheels from 9000 to 15,000 sfpm. The speed does need to be low to grind a few materials like titanium and zirconium, to keep the temperature down and avoid excessive surface chemical interaction.

For a small grain depth of cut, the workpiece velocity, v, in Eq. (28–6), should not be high and the depth of cut, c, should be shallow, especially for fine surface finishes. For external cylindrical grinding, workspeeds vary from 30 sfpm for hardened steel, which the abrasive cannot cut deeply, 50 to 100 sfpm for average work, to as high as 150 sfpm in some cases. For average internal grinding, surface speeds of 150 to 200 sfpm are advocated. Work speeds on surface grinders generally are less than 100 sfpm. A depth of cut of 0.001 to 0.004 in. is customary for roughing when precision grinding, and less than 0.001 in. for finishing.

It would not be reasonable to expect that exactly the best wheel would be readily available for every grinding job. Equation (28–6) reveals in which direction each variable can be changed to modify the action of the wheel. As a wheel wears to a smaller diameter and its surface speed decreases with the same number of revolutions per minute, the wheel acts softer. The surface speed of the workpiece is increased to make the wheel act softer and decreased for harder action. A deeper cut causes a wheel to act softer, and a lighter cut harder. Deep cuts and rapid stock removal call for hard wheels.

A small value of n in Eq. (28–6) corresponds to a wheel with an open structure or with its surface dressed coarsely. Such a wheel can be expected to have a soft action. This explains accepted practice of using a wheel for finishing that is of the same grade as for roughing but has finer grains more closely spaced, or the alternative of a softer wheel with the same grain size and spacing as for roughing. The first is a wheel that cuts finely but acts hard; the second can break down readily and stay sharp.

The larger the workpiece diameter, d, the smaller the effect of the factor $1/d$ in Eq. (28–6). This factor is zero for surface grinding and negative for internal grinding.

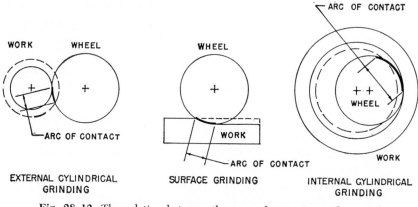

EXTERNAL CYLINDRICAL
GRINDING

SURFACE GRINDING

INTERNAL CYLINDRICAL
GRINDING

Fig. 28–12. The relation between the type of operation and area of contact in grinding with the periphery of a wheel.

The area of contact. An expression could be derived for the arc of contact *CEA* in Fig. 28–11, and it would show the same thing as Fig. 28–12, that the length of the arc is dependent mainly upon the diameters of wheel and workpiece and the depth of cut. The arc is shortest for cylindrical grinding, longer for surface grinding, and longest for internal grinding. Surface grinding with the side of a wheel gives full contact. A large wheel has a longer arc of contact than a small wheel. A deep cut means more contact than a shallow cut. The longer the path through the material, the more the grains are subject to attrition and, for the same grain depth of cut, the harder the wheel acts. For this reason, internal grinding calls for softer wheels than external grinding with other conditions being comparable.

The area of contact is the product of the arc length times the width of contact. As the area of contact increases, the number of grains in contact with the work increases with a uniform grain spacing, and the force tending to separate the wheel from the work is increased. This affects dimensional accuracy and finish in precision grinding and indicates the need for a more open spacing.

Heat generated by grinding. Experiments have shown that it takes more energy to remove a certain amount of material by means of small chips than by large ones. This is known as the *size-effect* in metal cutting. An indication of its magnitude is

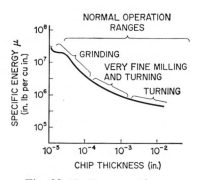

Fig. 28–13. How specific energy increases as chip thickness decreases. (As reported by N. H. Cook, M. C. Shaw, and P. A. Smith, "Practical Application of Grinding Principles," *The Tool Engineer*, Oct., 1955, p. 113.)

given in Fig. 28–13. This accounts for the fact that grinding uses more energy to remove a unit volume of material than other cutting operations; the reason being that the chips are much smaller.

A plateau occurs in the curve of Fig. 28–13 for chips less than about 30 microinches thick. These sizes correspond to the distances between the minute defects, called dislocations, that are distributed through a metal and weaken it. Within these sizes, the material is homogeneous and uniformly strong. This explains why all steels, for example, consume about the same power for fine grinding irrespective of hardness. For extremely minute chips, rubbing rather than cutting is thought to be the major factor which causes the curve to turn upward.

Most of the energy of grinding becomes heat. The bulk of the heat passes off with the chips, but some goes into the abrasive grains and some into the workpiece. Indications are that the instantaneous temperature on a surface being ground is normally 2000° to 3000°F. This may cause the temperatures to reach heights of 800°F at 0.001 in. and 600°F at 0.005 in. depths even in normal operations. In some cases, such as with rough iron castings, the surface temperature may be of little importance; in other cases, such as in grinding hardened steel, excessive temperature may ruin the workpiece by softening, burning, rehardening, or cracking the surface material. In such cases care must be exercised to keep the temperatures down.

Research has shown that the temperature T of a surface being ground is a function of the specific energy, u, and the depth of cut, c. This is

$$T = f(uc) \tag{28-7}$$

Also as indicated by Fig. 28–13, $u \cong k/t$, where t is chip thickness, so

$$T = f(c/t). \tag{28-8}$$

These relationships show that a light cut and thick chip are favorable to a low grinding temperature. A thicker chip calls for a lower amount of energy for each unit of material removed, and a light cut means that little material is removed. This results in a minimum of heat released. As was pointed out in connection with Eq. (28–6), a thin chip is desirable for good surface finish. Consequently the conditions that are favorable for producing a fine surface finish are largely opposed to those necessary to keep temperatures down and prevent surface damage.

The material and the workpiece. Three considerations are necessary to describe how hard or easy a material is to grind. These have been called grindability, finishability, and grinding sensitivity.

Grindability is a measure of the relative ease of removing material. The rate of wheel wear as indicated by the volume ratio is generally considered a satisfactory index of grindability because it generally agrees

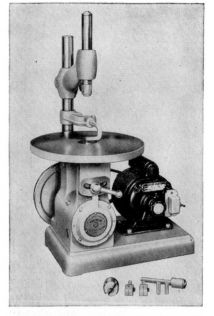

Fig. 27–9. The openings in a die block being sawed on a contour band sawing machine. (Courtesy Grob Bros.)

Fig. 27–10. A die filing machine with a 1½-in. stroke and 12-in. diameter table. (Courtesy Illinois Tool Works.)

at both ends and reciprocated up to 500 strokes a minute through a hole in the center of the table. The work on the table is applied to the tool by hand.

SAWING AND FILING OPERATIONS

Sawing and filing are cutting operations and are governed by the same considerations as other cutting operations. Speeds range from 50 fpm for harder steel alloys to 1000 fpm or more for soft materials with high-speed steel tools. Speeds and feeds for circular cold saws are comparable to those for milling cutters. The speed of a hack saw is generally specified in strokes per minute. The rate at which it penetrates the stock depends upon the feeding force applied to it, as a general rule from 10 to 50 lb for small pieces to 200 to 300 lb for large pieces. For band sawing, one manufacturer recommends feeds from 6 in. per min for ¼ in.-thick stock to ³⁄₁₆ in. per min for 6 in.-thick stock for straight cutting of machine steel with a ¼ in.-wide blade. Harder materials call for lower feeds, softer materials permit higher feeds. A wider blade cuts faster, but a narrower blade cuts to a smaller radius. Contour cutting must be done at a slow feed to produce a uniform and true curved surface.

with the evaluations made in practice. Power consumption might also be considered an index because it is an indication of the amount of heat involved, but it does not correlate with the volume ratio. The grindability of hardened tool steels has been found to decrease to a great extent with an increase in the amount of hard carbide particles present in them. The most difficult steels to grind have been reported to cause wheels to wear 200 times faster than the easiest.

Finishability is related to the relative cost of putting a fine finish on a material. In general, materials of medium grindability have been found to have the poorest finishability. Hard materials with low grindability seem to have good finishability as a rule because they dull the grains and prevent deep scratches.

Grinding sensitivity is the propensity of a material to crack or lose its surface hardness when ground. Untempered martensite in high-speed steel, excessively high-carbon content in the outermost layers of carburized steels, and retained austenite in medium- and high-alloy steels are conditions that have been shown to cause hypersensitivity. Even sensitive steels can be ground if the work is done slowly and carefully enough, but that is expensive. Corrective measures in heat treatment generally can eliminate causes of ultrasensitivity and keep costs down. Where some sensitivity still exists, control of the conditions that keep grinding temperatures down is necessary.

The condition of the rough workpiece determines much of the success of a grinding operation. Too much stock requires an unnecessary amount of time and wheel wear for grinding; too little stock may mean that a piece will not clean up before finished size is reached. A case hardened piece may be left with a soft surface if too much material is removed. Warpage and runout determine to a large extent the amount of stock that must be provided for grinding. The better the control of these factors, the more efficient a grinding operation. Typical practice is to allow stock of 0.010 to 0.0150 in. for rough and 0.002 to 0.005 in. on the diameter for finish cylindrical grinding, depending on the size of the workpiece. About half as much is left on a side for surface grinding.

Cutting fluids for grinding. Water solutions are widely used for grinding because they cool well, but water decidedly increases wheel wear. Oils lubricate the chips as well as the abrasives, and mitigate wheel loading and attrition. All fluids are helpful in removing particles but care must be taken to filter or settle out the particles so they are not recirculated.

Economy in grinding. Planning a grinding operation involves first selection of the abrasive, grain size, and bond best for the job. The extent to which a type of wheel is suited to a job is called its *grinding quality.*

Then the rate of grinding is set at the highest value possible to get the job done at the lowest cost. As typified by Fig. 28–9, a different wheel grade is the best as far as wear is concerned for each appreciable difference in grinding rate.

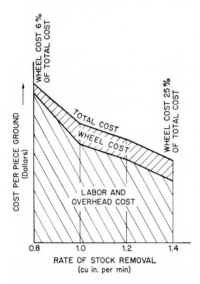

Fig. 28–14. How wheel and operating costs vary as the rate of production is increased in precision grinding.

As the rate of production is increased in a grinding operation from a low level, the wheel cost increases. At the same time the labor and overhead unit cost goes down and so does the total cost per piece, as depicted in Fig. 28–14. The production rate in a precision grinding operation can be only so fast for satisfactory accuracy and surface finish. As the rate is increased to that point, costs continue to decrease. Therefore the rate of stock removal should be set as high as the required quality of the work permits. Then the wheel grade is selected and the operation variables are arranged to do the job at the lowest cost at that rate of production.

In the case of nonprecision grinding, a minimum cost can normally be found within the limitations of the equipment. The best type wheel is selected for a snagging operation on the basis of its grinding quality. For such a type, the volume ratio M/W decreases and M increases, or vice versa, as the wheel grade is changed so that the factor $M^2/W = K_1$ is a constant for practical purposes for swing frame grinding operations, for instance. The letter M stands for the rate of production in pounds per hour, or tons per hour, or equivalent of metal removal, and W is the rate of wheel wear, usually in cubic inches per hour. A comparable term is L, the wheel life in hours, and it leads to the expression M^2L which is also used. The exponent may be different from 2 for other types of nonprecision grinding.

A comparison is then made of different grades of the same type of wheel, all applied with the same force, to find the most economical. The cost per unit of stock removal in a snagging operation is the sum of the time cost plus the wheel cost and is

$$C_H = \frac{R_H}{M} + \frac{R_K W}{M} = \frac{R_H}{M} + \frac{R_K M}{K_1}. \qquad (28\text{–}9)$$

The term R_H is the cost of labor and overhead in dollars per hour and R_K is the wheel cost in dollars per cubic inch, both constants. If this expression is differentiated with respect to M, and the derivative is set equal to zero, the result shows that minimum cost is realized in a snagging operation when the time cost is equal to the wheel cost in the form,

$$\frac{R_H}{M} = \frac{R_K M}{K_1}. \tag{28-10}$$

The minimum cost is

$$C_{HM} = 2\sqrt{\frac{R_H R_K}{K_1}}. \tag{28-11}$$

The economic situation can be illustrated by the cost figures for swing frame grinding stainless steel billets. The best type of grinding wheel for the job has a grinding quality factor $G = M_1^2 L = 0.645$. In this case M_1 is given in tons per hour. The cost of a wheel, of any grade, is $R_W = \$35.60$. The labor and overhead rate $R_H = \$3.50$ per hr. Comparable to Eq. (28-9), the total cost in dollars per ton here is

$$C_T = \frac{R_H}{M_1} + \frac{R_W M_1}{G}. \tag{28-12}$$

The results for two wheel grades are as follows:

Wheel grade	Wheel life—L (hr)	Production rate—M_1 (tons/hr)	Time cost R_H/M ($/ton)	Wheel cost $R_W M_1/G$ ($/ton)	Total cost C_T ($/ton)
Y	16.12	0.200	17.50	11.05	28.55
Z	10.17	0.252	13.90	13.90	27.80

The grade Z wheel removes stock at a higher rate but with more wheel cost than grade Y, but the time cost and total cost are less. The time cost is equal to the wheel cost in the case of grade Z, which indicates it to be the most economical grade obtainable.

Questions

1. What are the principal abrasive materials and what are their properties?

2. Describe how aluminum oxide and silicon carbide abrasives are made.

3. How is the size of an abrasive grain designated?

4. Name and describe the principal bonds for grinding wheels.

5. What is meant by the grade of a grinding wheel?

6. What is meant by the structure or spacing of a grinding wheel?

7. Describe common types and shapes of grinding wheels.

8. How are grinding wheels manufactured?

9. What are sticks, stones, coated abrasives, and polishing wheels and how are they used?

10. Describe nonprecision and precision grinding.

11. Discuss the costs that are present in a grinding operation.

12. What considerations enter into the selection of a grinding wheel?

13. What considerations influence the selection of an abrasive?

14. When are coarse grains and when are fine grains preferred?

15. What is the efficiency ratio or volume ratio, and what bearing does it have on the selection of wheel grade?

16. What considerations determine what grain spacing a grinding wheel should have?

17. How and why are grinding wheels balanced?

18. What are truing and dressing of grinding wheels, and how are they done?

19. Explain how the grain depth of cut, surface finish, and rate of wheel wear are affected by the work speed, wheel speed, wheel depth of cut, wheel diameter, and work diameter.

20. How does the length of contact between wheel and workpiece influence a grinding operation?

21. What is "size effect" and what does it mean in grinding?

22. What conditions are favorable to a low surface temperature in grinding, and why?

23. How do the conditions favorable to a low surface temperature compare with those favorable to a good surface finish?

24. What is meant by grindability, finishability, and grinding sensitivity?

25. How may grinding sensitivity be corrected?

26. What determines the proper amount of grinding stock on a workpiece?

27. What is meant by the grinding quality of a wheel?

28. How do the wheel cost and time cost vary with the grinding rate?

29. What should the rate of production be in a precision grinding operation, and why?

30. What is the economical rate of production for a snagging operation?

Problems

1. Ten pounds of metal are being removed per hour with a power consumption of 5.4 hp at the wheel in a snagging operation on a swing frame

grinder. The wheel has a surface speed of 6000 fpm and is pushed against the work with a force of 180 lb. To what amount must the normal force be raised to increase the metal removal rate to 15 lb per hr? The motor and wheel will take the increased load.

2. A motor on a floor stand grinder is delivering 5.5 hp to drive a vitrified grinding wheel at 6000 fpm to remove one cubic inch of metal per minute. The drive efficiency is 80%. If a resinoid wheel is put on the stand and driven at 9000 fpm and the same normal and tangential forces are maintained at the point of contact, what power must the motor deliver at the same efficiency? If the K factor of Eq. (28–1) for the resinoid wheel is 6.6, what rate of metal removal may be expected from that wheel?

3. Estimate the normal force that must be applied to:
   (a) remove 20 lb of metal per hr on a swing frame grinder with a resinoid wheel running at 9000 surface fpm.
   (b) grind wet at the rate of ½ cu in. per min of metal removal on an external cylindrical grinder with a vitrified wheel having a surface speed of 6000 fpm.

4. A 10 in.-diameter soft-carbon steel shaft is to be traverse ground with coolant and a wheel 2 in. wide running at 6000 fpm on a cylindrical grinder. The motor is rated at 15 hp and the machine efficiency is 80%. Machine rigidity allows a work-wheel normal force of 200 lb. What is the traverse rate permitted with a depth of cut of 0.002 in. per pass?

5. For the grinding action in Fig. 28–11, show that the length of grain path $CA = L = \sqrt{c/(1/D + 1/d)}$

6. What change in each of the following variables in a grinding operation will tend to give a finer surface finish? (a) wheel speed (b) work speed (c) grain size (d) depth of cut (e) wheel size

7. What should be the approximate properties of a grinding wheel with respect to abrasive, grain size, bond, grade, and structure for each of the following typical applications?
   (a) To commercially grind a mild steel shaft.
   (b) For snagging cast iron.
   (c) To sharpen a high-speed steel milling cutter.
   (d) To grind a 3 in.-diameter hole in a case hardened steel bushing.
   (e) To grind the top and bottom surfaces of a water hardening tool steel die block.
   (f) To cut off aluminum bar stock.

8. A type of grinding wheel selected for a swing frame grinding operation has a quality factor $G = .37$. Grade A has a life of 13.11 hr with a production rate of 0.168 tons per hr. Grade B has a life of 10.17 hr with a production rate of 0.191 tons per hr. The cost of either wheel is $35.60, and the labor and overhead rate is $3.50 per hr. Which wheel is the more economical? Is there any indication that either is the most economical available?

9. Five wheels 36 in.-diameter by 4 in. wide tried for a precision grinding operation perform as follows:

Wheel	A	B	C	D	E
Rate of production (cu in. in 8 hr)	910	526	1060	690	830
Volume rate (in.^{3} stock/in.^{3} wheel)	4.74	3.35	2.45	6.31	5.5

Wheel cost is $0.08 per cu in. and the labor and overhead rate is $8 per hr. Which would you recommend for use?

References

Lewis, K. B., *The Grinding Wheel,* The Grinding Wheel Inst., Greendale, Mass., 1951.

Grinding Machines and Methods

Grinding machines utilize grinding wheels and may be classified according to the types of operations described in Chap. 28. Thus the broad classes are precision and nonprecision grinders. The main types of precision grinding machines are external and internal cylindrical grinding machines and surface grinding machines. Certain types have been developed to do specific operations and are classified accordingly.

Space is available to describe only the basic grinding machines. Most types are available in simple hand operated models and in various semi- and fully-automatic models, as are other machine tools.

PRECISION GRINDERS

Cylindrical centertype grinders. Cylindrical centertype grinders are used for grinding straight and tapered round pieces, round parts with curved lengthwise profiles, fillets, shoulders, and faces. A simple and the original form of cylindrical grinder is a head that revolves a grinding wheel and is mounted on the cross-slide or compound rest of a lathe. These *toolpost grinders* are made to deliver from a small fraction to 10 hp and cost from 50 to several hundred dollars. They are expedient when regular grinding machines are not available.

A workpiece is usually held between dead centers and rotated by a dog and driver on the faceplate on a *plain cylindrical centertype grinder*

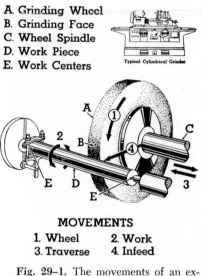

A. Grinding Wheel
B. Grinding Face
C. Wheel Spindle
D. Work Piece
E. Work Centers

Typical Cylindrical Grinder

MOVEMENTS

1. Wheel   2. Work
3. Traverse   4. Infeed

Fig. 29–1. The movements of an external cylindrical grinding machine. (Courtesy The Carborundum Co.)

as depicted in Fig. 29–1. The centers in the headstock and tailstock do not revolve because that provides the most rigid work support and accuracy between centers. Plain grinders are powerful production-type machines for work done between centers.

The headstock and tailstock of a cylindrical centertype grinder are mounted on an upper or swivel table and can be positioned along the table to suit the length of the work. The upper table can be swivelled and clamped in position on a lower table to provide adjustment for grinding straight or tapered work as desired. The amount of taper that can be ground in this way is normally less than 10° on a plain grinder, like the one in Fig. 29–2, because the table bumps the wheel head if swivelled too far.

The lower table slides on ways on the bed and provides traverse of the work past the grinding wheel. It can be moved by hand or power, within limits desired.

The grinding wheel revolves in the direction shown in Fig. 29–1 on a heavy spindle—running in close fitting bearings to prevent flutter. The grinding force is directed downward for stability. The wheelhead carries the wheel to and away from the work. The movement is called infeed and normally can be controlled to 0.0001 in. or less.

Cylindrical grinding may be done by the plunge cut or traversing methods. Similar methods are found in surface grinding. In *plunge cut grinding*, a wheel somewhat wider than the work surface is fed in as the workpiece revolves. With other factors constant, the depth of cut and rate of stock removal depend upon the rate of infeed. A work surface wider than the wheel is *traverse ground* by traversing the revolving workpiece lengthwise with respect to the wheel, or vice versa. The rate of traverse becomes one of the conditions determining the length of grain path. The radial depth of cut is determined by the amount the wheel is fed in at each reversal of the traverse. An advance along the workpiece of ¼ to ½ of the width of the wheel per revolution of the work in cylindrical grinding or per stroke in surface grinding is common. The leading portion of the wheel removes most of the stock, and the remainder cleans up the surface.

Fig. 29–2. A plain cylindrical centertype grinding machine in operation. (Courtesy Norton Co.)

Cylindrical centertype grinders capable of swinging diameters in excess of 20 in., particularly for grinding rolls for rolling mills, are called *roll grinders.* Roll grinders commonly have cambering attachments that enable them to grind accurate and reproducible curved lengthwise profiles on rolls. Rolls are often ground in that way so they become straight when deformed by high temperatures and pressures in operation.

A *universal cylindrical centertype grinder,* as illustrated in Fig. 29–3, has all the units and movements of a plain grinder, but in addition:

1. its headstock spindle may be used alive or dead, so that work can be held and revolved by a chuck as well as ground between centers;
2. its headstock can be swivelled in a horizontal plane so that any angle, even a flat plane, can be ground on a workpiece chucked on the headstock spindle;

Fig. 29–3. A 12 in. by 36 in. universal centertype hydraulic grinding machine. (Courtesy Cincinnati Grinders, Inc.)

3. its wheelhead and slide can be swivelled and traversed at any angle in the manner indicated in Fig. 29–4 so that any taper can be ground on work between centers.

Most universal grinders can be arranged for internal grinding by the addition of an auxiliary wheelhead to revolve small wheels at high speeds.

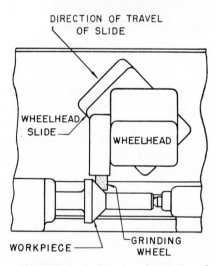

Fig. 29–4. A diagram of a universal centertype grinder arranged for grinding a steep taper.

Universal grinders can grind surfaces such as steep tapers and holes not accommodated on plain grinders but at the sacrifice of rigidity, power, and rapidity of operation. They are found in toolrooms and jobbing shops.

Sizes of cylindrical centertype grinders. The size of a cylindrical centertype grinder usually is designated by the diameter in inches and the length in inches of the largest workpiece the machine can nominally accommodate between centers. Thus a 12 in. by 36 in. centertype grinder can swing a workpiece 12 in. in diameter over the table and grind it with a new wheel. A workpiece up to 36 in. long may be mounted between centers. Specifications of several sizes of centertype grinders are given in Table 29–1.

TABLE 29–1. TYPICAL SPECIFICATIONS OF CENTERTYPE CYLINDRICAL GRINDERS

Type	Nominal size (in.)	Power (hp)	Weight (lb)	Cost ($)
Plain	6 × 18	10	6,500	19,000
Universal	10 × 24	3	5,000	15,000
Plain	14 × 72	20	15,000	35,000
Universal	18 × 72	5	11,000	27,000
Plain	28 × 192	30	75,000	125,000
Roll	60 × 288	50	160,000	220,000

Chucking grinders. Chucking grinders are designed for grinding small- and medium-diameter short parts automatically and in large quantities. Typical applications are the grinding of tapered roller bearing cone races, valve tappets, and small bevel gear shoulders and stems. The workpiece is held in a chuck, collet, or fixture.

Centerless grinders. *An external cylindrical centerless grinding machine* revolves a workpiece on top of a workrest blade between two abrasive wheels as shown in Fig. 29–5. The grinding wheel removes material from the workpiece. The workpiece has a greater affinity for and is driven at the same surface speed as the regulating wheel, which is normally a rubber bonded abrasive wheel that turns at a surface speed of 50 to 200 fpm. A typical medium-size centerless grinder equipped with an automatic loading attachment for high production is shown in Fig. 29–6.

Thrufeed centerless grinding is done by passing the workpiece completely through the space between the grinding and regulating wheel, usually with guides at both

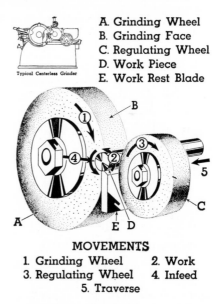

A. Grinding Wheel
B. Grinding Face
C. Regulating Wheel
D. Work Piece
E. Work Rest Blade

Typical Centerless Grinder

MOVEMENTS

1. Grinding Wheel   2. Work
3. Regulating Wheel   4. Infeed
5. Traverse

Fig. 29–5. The action of an external cylindrical centerless grinding machine. (Courtesy The Carborundum Co.)

ends, as indicated in Fig. 29–7. The regulating wheel is tilted a few degrees about a horizontal axis perpendicular to its own axis. This feeds the workpieces lengthwise. The rate of feed in inches per minute depends

Fig. 29–6. A No. 2 centerless grinder arranged for infeed grinding. (Courtesy Cincinnati Grinders, Inc.)

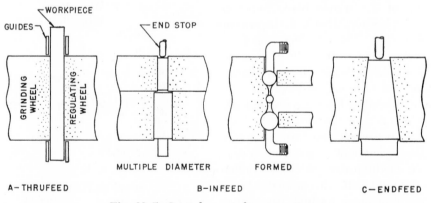

A—THRUFEED   B—INFEED   C—ENDFEED

Fig. 29–7. Centerless grinding operations.

upon the angle of inclination and speed of the regulating wheel as expressed by the relation

$$F = \pi D N \sin \alpha. \qquad (29\text{--}1)$$

D is the diameter in inches, N is the speed in rpm, and α is the angle of tilt of the regulating wheel, which may be from $0°$ to $8°$. A slow feed is necessary to remove relatively large amounts of stock within the power capacity of the machine and to produce accuracy and good surface finish.

Most thrufeed work is ground in two passes with a total stock of removal of 0.010 to 0.015 in.

Infeed centerless grinding is slower than thrufeed grinding but is necessary for a workpiece with a shoulder, head, or obstruction that prevents its passing completely through the throat between the wheels. Two examples of infeed grinding are given in Fig. 29–7. The workrest and regulating wheel are withdrawn from the grinding wheel to receive a workpiece. They are then moved toward the grinding wheel to grind the work to size.

Endfeed centerless grinding is for tapered work, as shown in Fig. 29–7(C). Either the grinding wheel or regulating wheel or both are trued to a taper. The work is fed lengthwise between the wheels and is ground as it advances until it reaches the end stop.

A popular medium-size centerless grinder takes workpieces up to 4¾ in.-diameter and wheels as wide as 8 in., is driven by a 15 hp main motor, weighs 9000 lb, and costs $17,000. A centerless grinder used for a specific job often requires special equipment or attachments for efficient operation, and that may well cost several thousand dollars more.

Comparison of centertype and centerless grinding. As a rule more time is needed to set up a centerless grinder, but the difference is not large for many simple parts. Also much can be done to minimize centerless set-up time by scheduling similar parts in successive lots over the same machine. Parts with several diameters or curved profiles usually require special equipment that is expensive and takes a long time for set-up. Therefore, such parts are not centerless ground unless produced in quite large quantities.

Centerless grinding is faster than centertype grinding because:

1. It is almost continuous, especially for thrufeed grinding, with a minimum of machine time lost for loading and unloading.
2. The work is fully supported by the workrest blade and regulating wheel and can be subjected to cuts as heavy as it will take without overheating. Plunge cuts can often be made over the entire length of a workpiece.
3. No axial thrust is present, as it is on work between centers. Long thin pieces are not so likely to be distorted.
4. The action of centerless grinding is such that each workpiece is cleaned up with the removal of the least possible amount of stock. Errors of centering are eliminated.
5. Large grinding wheels can be used and wheel wear is correspondingly small. Therefore, a minimum amount of adjustment is needed.
6. Adjustments for size are made directly on the diameter of the

workpiece, and that contributes to accurate results. If the regulating wheel and workrest blade are moved 0.001 in. toward the grinding wheel, the workpiece diameter is reduced 0.001 in.

7. A low order of skill is needed to attend to centerless grinding much of the time.

For simple parts, the saving in grinding time for only a few pieces may make up for the longer set-up time for centerless grinding. Centerless grinding has been found profitable in many places for lots less than 100 pieces, sometimes for a dozen or less. However, as a rule, centertype grinding is preferable where the work is varied, irregular in shape, or large in size, especially in small quantities.

Equation (20–1) is helpful in showing for what quantities of production a centerless grinder is economical for any particular product. As an example, an armature shaft for an electric motor is to be ground on four diameters with a stock removal of 0.010 to 0.015 in. on each surface. The shafts can be finished on a plain cylindrical centertype grinder at the rate of 125 pieces per hr, with 30 minutes required for set-up for each lot. A production rate of 150 pieces can be realized per hour with set-up time of one hour per lot on the centerless grinder. That machine must have special equipment for the job that costs $1200 and must be paid for by the first lot. The labor, overhead, and depreciation rate is $9 per hr for either machine. The equal cost quantity in this case is

$$Q = \frac{125 \times 150 \ (1 \times 9 + 1200 - \frac{1}{2} \times 9 - 0)}{150 \times 9 - 125 \times 9} = 100{,}000 \ \text{pieces.}$$

The centerless grinder is economical for this job if 100,000 or more pieces are to be produced.

Figure 29–7 indicates a principle of economical grinding for moderate and large quantities. That is to use a wide wheel or several wheels on one mount trued to take care of two or more surfaces at the same time. This is especially applicable to centerless grinding because the work is well supported for multiple cuts, but the principle is often applied profitably to all other forms of grinding.

Equation (19–1) provides the basis for ascertaining when it is economical to combine grinding operations. For example, three diameters may be ground one at a time on the stem of a bevel gear pinion, with an output of 35 pieces per hr. The combined operation produces 80 pieces per hr but requires a special wheel mount and cam for the truing attachment that costs $400 and 1½ hr more set-up time for each operation. The labor rate in the plant is $2.50 per hr with a labor dollar overhead rate of 1. A rate of 35% for interest, insurance, taxes, and maintenance is required. The number of pieces in one lot for which the combined operation is justified may be ascertained from

$$N(\tfrac{1}{35} - \tfrac{1}{80})(2.50)(1 + 1) = 400 \times 1.35 + 1.5 \times 5.$$

and, $N = 6800$ pieces, the smallest quantity for which it is economical to invest in the special wheel mount. It is presumed that the machine has the power to sustain the faster rate of production.

Internal grinders. Most internal cylindrical grinders rotate the workpiece around the axis of the hole ground. The plain or universal types hold the workpiece on a faceplate or in a fixture or chuck as in Fig. 29–8. The typical *plain internal grinder* of Fig. 29–9 can handle a variety of work efficiently on short and moderately long production runs. The workhead can be swivelled to grind a straight hole

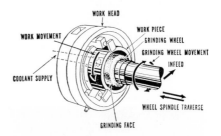

Fig. 29–8. The action of a plain or universal internal grinding machine. (Courtesy The Carborundum Co.)

or tapers up to 45° included angle. The high speed grinding wheelhead on slides is moved into and away from the hole and can be cross-fed into the work.

Fig. 29–9. A plain internal grinding machine for holes up to 7½ in. diameter by 5 in. long. (Courtesy The Heald Machine Co.)

A *universal internal grinder* is basically the same as a plain internal grinder except that the workhead is mounted on a cross-slide as is the wheelhead, and can be swivelled through a 90° angle.

One kind of internal grinder has a gap in the bed to clear large diameter workpieces. A *duplex internal grinder* has a workhead between two reciprocating wheelheads so that two opposite holes in a workpiece can be ground in alignment. An *internal and face grinder* has two wheelheads side by side. One has a small wheel to grind a hole, and the other has a large wheel to grind a face in the same set-up and square with the hole.

Fig. 29–10. A view of a centerless internal grinding machine. (Courtesy The Heald Machine Co.)

Fig. 29–11. A manually operated sizing device on an internal grinder. The workpiece is a gear located on its pitch line by pins in a sliding jaw chuck. (Courtesy Bryant Chucking Grinder Co.)

A *centerless internal grinder* revolves the workpiece in contact with three rolls as shown in Fig. 29–10. The large roll is the driver. The movements of the grinding wheel are the same as shown in Fig. 29–8. The machine grinds straight, tapered, continuous, interrupted, open end, or blind holes in all parts having finished round outside surfaces and produces a highly uniform wall thickness. The manner of holding the work lends itself well to automatic unloading and loading of pieces.

A *planetary internal grinder* is designed for parts too large or unwieldy to be rotated conveniently. The workpiece is not revolved. Instead, the grinding wheel is revolved in a planetary fashion around the axis of the hole being ground.

Internal grinder attachments and operations. Work may be held in a chuck, collet chuck, face plate, or fixture on an internal grinder. Quick acting chucks are available to provide concentricity in locating as close as 0.0002 inch. The more accurate chucks are limited in range and are expensive.

Accurate sizing is obtained in several ways. For one or a few pieces, an operator can grind a hole to size by controlling the infeed through a handwheel and dial. This is a slow process because several measurements must be made on each hole and care is necessary. The small wheels needed to get into holes wear rapidly, and slender spindles deflect appreciably. One form of sizing device that shows an operator the size of a hole being ground is depicted in Fig. 29–11. It has a finger that rides in the hole and is connected to the dial indicator by a linkage.

A *Size-matic* internal grinder is arranged to go through a routine to size each piece in production. The grinding wheel reciprocates through the hole and is fed automatically almost to size while it is roughing. In preparation for the finishing cut, the wheel is withdrawn, trued, and returned to the work. The wheel is then fed in a predetermined amount to account for wear and deflection and to grind to the desired size in the hole.

A *Gage-matic* equipped internal grinder has a mechanism that tries to insert a round plug gage in the back of the hole each time the reciprocating wheel leaves the front of the hole being ground. When the first part of the plug enters, the wheel is trued for finishing. When the whole plug enters, the correct size is indicated, the wheel is withdrawn, and the machine stops.

Sizes of internal grinders. Manufacturers commonly designate each model and size of internal grinder with a number not related to any particular dimension. The capacity may be specified by the nominal diameter of workpiece that can be swung and the maximum length of stroke of the wheel.

TABLE 29–2. Specifications of Several Typical Internal Grinders

Type	Size diam × stroke (in.)	Power (hp)	Weight (lb)	Cost ($)
Plain	12 × 16	7	6,700	17,000
Universal	18 × 30	7	8,300	26,000
Centerless	8	7	8,000	30,000

Surface grinders. Surface grinding is concerned primarily with grinding plane or flat surfaces but also is capable of grinding irregular, curved, tapered, convex, and concave surfaces.

Conventional surface grinders may be divided into two classes. One class has reciprocating tables for work ground along straight lines. This type is particularly suited to pieces that are long or have stepped or curved profiles at right angles to the direction of grinding. The second class covers the machines with rotating work tables for continuous rapid grinding.

Surface grinders may also be classified according to whether they have horizontal or vertical grinding wheel spindles. Grinding is normally done on the periphery of the wheel with a horizontal spindle. The area of contact is small, and the speed is uniform over the grinding surface. Small-grain wheels can be used, and the finest finishes obtained. Grinding with a vertical spindle is done on the side of the wheel, which may be solid, sectored, or segmental. The area of contact may be large, and stock can be removed rapidly. A crisscross pattern of grinding scratches is left on the work surface.

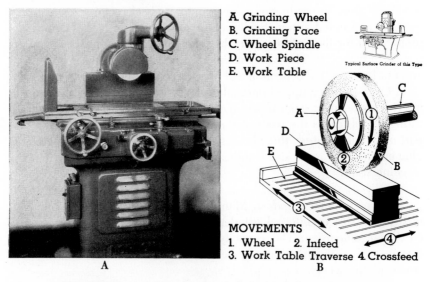

A. Grinding Wheel
B. Grinding Face
C. Wheel Spindle
D. Work Piece
E. Work Table

Typical Surface Grinder of this Type

MOVEMENTS
1. Wheel   2. Infeed
3. Work Table Traverse 4. Crossfeed

A   B

Fig. 29–12. A surface grinder with horizontal spindle and reciprocating table. (A) A 6 in. by 18 in. surface grinder with hydraulic table traverse and automatic cross feed arranged for dry grinding. (Courtesy Norton Co.) (B) Diagram of machine movements. (Courtesy The Carborundum Co.)

Surface grinders with reciprocating tables and horizontal spindles, like the one shown in Fig. 29–12, are popular for toolroom work. The size designates the working area of the table, which often holds a magnetic chuck. The workpiece is reciprocated and fed crosswise. The wheel is moved downward to the work.

One form of surface grinder with a reciprocating table and horizontal spindle has its wheel cutting on the side rather than the periphery. Work carried on the table is ground on the side rather than the top. Such machines are called *face grinders.*

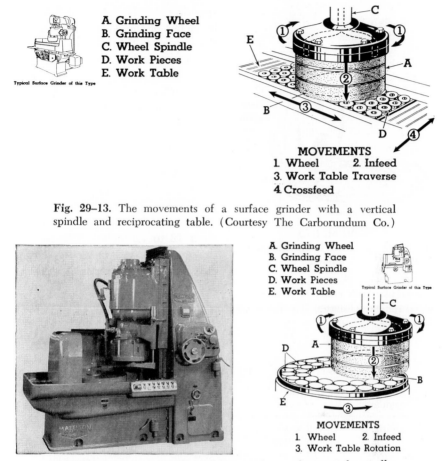

A. Grinding Wheel
B. Grinding Face
C. Wheel Spindle
D. Work Pieces
E. Work Table

Typical Surface Grinder of this Type

MOVEMENTS
1. Wheel   2. Infeed
3. Work Table Traverse
4. Crossfeed

Fig. 29–13. The movements of a surface grinder with a vertical spindle and reciprocating table. (Courtesy The Carborundum Co.)

A. Grinding Wheel
B. Grinding Face
C. Wheel Spindle
D. Work Pieces
E. Work Table

Typical Surface Grinder of this Type

MOVEMENTS
1. Wheel   2. Infeed
3. Work Table Rotation

Fig. 29–14. (A) A rotary surface grinder with vertical spindle. (Courtesy Mattison Machine Works.) (B) Diagram of machine movements. (Courtesy The Carborundum Co.)

The type of machine typified in Fig. 29–13 has reciprocating and crossfeed movements. However, in this case the vertical spindle carries a wheel that grinds with its side on the top surfaces of the workpieces.

Rotary surface grinders with vertical spindles, like the one illustrated in Fig. 29–14, usually are used for rapid production grinding. The one shown has a 25 hp wheelhead motor. The rotary table is a magnetic chuck. It can be moved under or away from the wheel for unloading and loading the work.

A rotary table surface grinder with the movements indicated by Fig. 29–15 may carry a single large piece or a number of pieces in one or more circles on its table.

Sizes of surface grinders. The capacity of a surface grinder with a reciprocating surface is commonly designated by two numbers corre-

A. Grinding Wheel
B. Grinding Face
C. Wheel Spindle
D. Work Pieces
E. Work Table

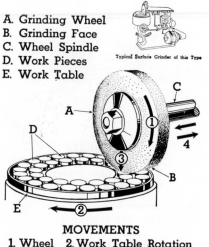

Typical Surface Grinder of this Type

MOVEMENTS

1. Wheel   2. Work Table Rotation
3. Infeed   4. Crossfeed

Fig. 29–15. The movements of a surface grinder with rotary table and horizontal spindle. (Courtesy The Carborundum Co.)

sponding to the width and length in inches of the working surface of the table. A third figure may be given to specify the largest distance in inches from the top of the table to the face of the wheel. A usual designation for a rotary surface grinder is the diameter of chuck or table. (See Table 29–3.)

Disk grinders. Disk grinders finish flat surfaces and remove stock rapidly by grinding with the sides of disk wheels ranging in diameters from 12 to 72 inches. The size of the machine designates the diameter of the wheel. Really close tolerances are not generally held in disk grinding, but production rates are high. Some machines have horizontal spindles; others vertical spindles.

TABLE 29–3. Specifications for Several Typical Surface Grinders

Type table spindle	Size (in.)	Main motor (hp)	Weight (lb)	Cost ($)
Recip. horiz.	6 × 18	1½	2,000	4,200
" "	36 × 240	30	86,000	83,000
Recip. vert.	16 × 24	5	4,400	16,000
Rotary horiz.	16 diam.	10	8,000	21,000
Rotary vert.	20 diam.	15	5,500	7,000
" "	84 diam.	100	60,000	50,000

The single horizontal spindle disk grinder of Fig. 29–16 has a disk wheel backed by a steel plate at each end of the spindle. A table at each wheel, often with a fixture added, supports work that is pressed and ground against the side of the wheel. This machine has a 20 hp motor, weighs 3725 lb, and costs about $4500.

Typical of many semi- or fully-automatic disk grinders for large quantity production is the opposed double spindle machine of Fig. 29–17. Work is fed continuously between two disks, one on each wheelhead, and is ground on two sides at the same time.

A workpiece is placed on the revolving horizontal disk on the vertical spindle machine of Fig. 29–18 and stopped against the crossbar

Fig. 29–16. A 26 in. single horizontal spindle disk grinder. (Courtesy Gardner Machine Co.)

Fig. 29–17. A 15 in. double horizontal spindle disk grinder equipped with a notched rotary carrier and inclined chute to grind small sizes of ball bearing inner races at the rate of 60 to 80 per minute. (Courtesy Gardner Machine Co.)

above the disk. This medium-size machine has a 20 hp motor, weighs 6600 lb, and costs about $6000.

Fig. 29–18. A 53 in. horizontal disk grinder. (Courtesy Gardner Machine Co.)

Thread grinders. Threads are produced by a number of methods as described in Chap. 33. They are ground for accuracy and finishes not obtainable in other ways. Tolerances are held for size to ±0.0001 in. per in. of pitch diameter and for lead within 0.0003 in. in 20 in. of length. Hard materials can be threaded more economically by grinding than by other methods. Threads may be cut and then finish ground after heat treatment, or they may be ground from solid stock.

Thread grinding is done on centertype and centerless machines. They may utilize single-rib-type or multi-rib-type grinding wheels. The first is a thin wheel with its outer edge trued to the shape of the thread space. The second is a wide wheel with grooves and ridges formed on its periphery.

Centertype thread grinders grind external or internal threads, or both. A typical machine resembles a universal centertype cylindrical grinder but has features to enable it to do its intended work. A master leadscrew is geared to the work spindle, makes the table to traverse, and causes the workpiece to turn with the proper lead as it advances. The grinding wheel is tilted to the helix angle of the thread. An attachment trues the wheel to the thread form.

A   **B**

Fig. 29–19. Two views of milling cutters being sharpened on a universal tool and cutter grinder. (A) Shell end mill. (B) Helical mill. (Courtesy The Cincinnati Milling Machine Co.)

Tool and cutter grinders. Tool and cutter grinders are used mainly to sharpen multiple-tooth cutters like reamers, milling cutters, taps, and hobs. They can also do light surface, cylindrical, and internal grinding to finish such items as jig, fixture, die, and gage details and sharpen single-point tools.

The main parts of a typical *universal tool and cutter grinder* are visible in Fig. 29–19. It has all the movements of a universal centertype grinder and in addition the wheelhead can be swivelled and raised or lowered. The machine can be set up quickly to grind the usual angles on cutters. Two examples are shown in Fig. 29–19.

Profile or contour grinders are capable of reproducing a template form on a flat or round cutter. Some can grind metal surfaces to conform to outlines drawn on paper.

A type of tool grinder adaptable to a large variety of tools, but particularly to spiral tools, as indicated in Fig. 29–20, is the *Monoset cutter and tool grinder.* The workhead spindle can be indexed and also synchronized with the table movement to grind helices. The major units are fully adjustable to enable much work to be done in one setting that otherwise would require several set-ups.

Carbide tool grinders, like the one in Fig. 29–21, are designed for grinding the faces and radii of single-point tools, especially carbide tipped tools. A tool applied to one of the wheels is supported at the desired angle on the adjacent tilted table.

Fig. 29–20. The flutes of a twist drill being ground from the solid on a Monoset cutter and tool grinder. (Courtesy The Cincinnati Milling Machine Co.)

Fig. 29–21. A medium size carbide tool grinder. (Courtesy Ex-Cello-O Corp.)

Miscellaneous grinders. Cam and camshaft grinders are essentially modifications of centertype cylindrical grinders to finish various forms of round cams, camshafts, and pistons. The headstock and footstock are on a cradle and rock to and from the grinding wheel in response to a master cam that rotates in unison with the workpiece.

Crankshaft or *crank pin grinders* resemble cylindrical centertype grinders but are implemented to grind the offset pins in the throws of crankshafts.

ROUGH OR NONPRECISION GRINDERS

Swing frame grinders. A swing frame grinder has a horizontal frame from 6 to 10 ft long suspended at its center of gravity so as to move freely within the area of operation. The operator applies the wheel on one end of the frame to the work in the manner illustrated in Fig. 29–22.

Floor-stand and bench grinders. A floor-stand grinder has a horizontal spindle with wheels usually at both ends and is mounted on a base or pedestal. Work is applied to the wheels in the manner shown in Fig. 29–23. A small size mounted on a bench is called a bench grinder. These machines are used for snagging and off hand grinding of cutting

Fig. 29–22. A swing frame grinder in operation. (Courtesy The Carborundum Co.)

Fig. 29–23. Snagging a casting on a floor stand grinder. (Courtesy The Carborundum Co.)

tools and miscellaneous parts. Polishing wheels may be run on these grinders.

Portable and flexible shaft grinders. The usual form of portable grinder resembles a portable or electric hand drill with a guard and grinding wheel mounted on the spindle. A similar purpose machine is the flexible shaft grinder that has the grinding wheel on the end of a long flexible shaft driven by a motor on a relatively stationary stand. Heavy tools of these kinds are used for roughing and snagging, and small ones for burring and die work.

Fig. 29–24. A variety belt grinder. (Courtesy Mattison Machine Works)

Belt grinders. Belt grinders are grinding and polishing machines that utilize continuous belts of coated abrasives. A belt grinder for rapid sanding of small and irregularly shaped work is shown in Fig. 29–24. It also has a spindle for abrasive rolls. Work may be applied, commonly by hand, against the open belt, sanding pulleys, platen, shaped forms, or rolls in succession to reach various curves and flat surfaces,

GRINDING COMPARED WITH OTHER OPERATIONS

Grinding commonly is not economical for removing large amounts of stock and usually is preceded by other operations that remove the bulk of the stock from rough workpieces. For example, a shaft made from one inch-diameter bar stock must have a 0.750/0.751 in.-diameter with a surface finish of 20 microinches, rms, for a length of three inches on one end. Grinding is the economical method of achieving the specifications, but to remove ¼ in. of stock by grinding would be costly. The piece is turned before it is ground.

The reason precision grinding is not economical for removing large amounts of material is that power, labor, and tool costs are high for each cubic inch of material. About 10 hp is required to grind off a cubic inch of ordinary steel per minute, whereas only about 1 hp is needed by a lathe tool. Unless a grinder is much larger and more powerful, it must take more time than a lathe, miller, broach, etc. to remove each unit of material.

Machines and techniques have been developed to make grinding of flat surfaces from the rough economical. Such work is done on rigid and powerful disk and surface grinders on castings or forgings with scaly hard skins that are difficult to cut otherwise. Grinding stock is kept small and generally is less than ⅛ in. The work often can be held on a magnetic chuck and does not need a fixture so loading time can be saved. For one case reported, SAE 4140 steel forgings were milled at the rate of 33 pieces per hr and at a cost of $0.54 per piece. On a surface grinder, 58.6 pieces were produced per hr at a cost of $0.11 per piece.

Material harder than about Rockwell C–45 can be machined efficiently only by abrasive action. Customary procedure in manufacturing hardened steel parts is to cut the material in a soft state leaving only enough stock for grinding, heat treat to the required hardness, and grind the surfaces that must be finished.

Fine finishes and tolerances less than 0.001 to 0.003 in. are more easily obtained by grinding than by non-abrasive methods. Tolerances as small as 0.0001 in. and finishes with readings as low as 10 microinches rms are regularly obtained by commercial grinding. The cost increases as the tolerances become smaller. Some grinding is done with tolerances as small as 0.00002 in., roundness and straightness within 0.00002 in., and surface finishes better than 2 microinches, but only at high cost. In many cases the smallest tolerances and finest finishes can better be obtained by lapping, honing, and Superfinishing. As indicated by Fig. 15–37, these methods normally cover ranges only exceptionally reached by grinding. They are discussed in Chap. 30.

Questions

1. Describe a plain cylindrical centertype grinder and tell what it does.

2. Describe and distinguish between plunge cut and traverse grinding.

3. What is a roll grinder and what does it do?

4. How does a universal cylindrical centertype grinder differ from a plain grinder?

5. How is the size of a cyindrical centertype grinder designated?

6. For what are chucking grinders used?

7. Describe the action of a centerless grinder. What are its advantages?

8. Describe thrufeed, infeed and endfeed centerless grinding and their applications.

9. Make a comparison of the relative merits of centertype and centerless grinding.

10. Describe plain and universal internal grinders and the work they do.

11. Describe an internal centerless grinder and tell what advantages it has.

12. What purpose does a planetary internal grinder serve and how?

13. What are several means for controlling workpiece size on an internal grinder?

14. Describe the four principal types of surface grinders.

15. What is the advantage of each kind of surface grinder?

16. What are disk grinders and what do they do?

17. What are the advantages of thread grinding? How is it done?

18. How are cams ground?

19. Describe the machines used for snagging.

20. When is grinding economical and when is it not?

21. Why is grinding not usually suitable to remove large quantities of stock?

22. For what degrees of accuracy and surface finish is grinding suitable?

Problems

1. A mild steel workpiece 12 in. long is to be ground on a 3 in.-diameter that is 10 in. long. It can be driven by a dog on a 2 in.-diameter that is 2 in.

long on one end. The machine is a 6 × 18 plain cylindrical grinder. It has a 10 hp motor and is 80% efficient. The workpiece is to be traversed past the 1½ in. wide grinding wheel at a rate of ½ in. for each revolution. Total stock removal is 0.015 in. on the diameter, of which 0.003 in. is to be removed in four finishing passes of the wheel over the workpiece. Ten horsepower are required at the wheel to remove one cubic inch of metal per minute. Select a work speed and a suitable infeed per pass for the roughing cuts within practical ranges and the capacity of the machine. How long should the grinding time be for this piece?

2. The workpiece described in Prob. 1 is to be ground on a centerless grinder with a 15 hp motor and 80% efficiency. Two passes will be taken with 0.010 in. of stock removed from the diameter in the first pass and 0.005 in. in the second. Ten horsepower at the wheel are required to remove one cubic inch of metal per minute. Select regulating wheel speeds and tilt angles for best utilization of the machine. How long should the grinding time be per piece?

3. A workpiece has a 1 in.-diameter for 3 in. of length from one end and a 2 in.-diameter for the remainder of its total length of 7 inches. A total of 0.015 in. of stock is removed to finish the 2 in.-diameter. Three minutes are required per piece on a 6 × 12 in. plain cylindrical centertype grinder and 1¾ min. on a centerless grinder. Set-up time is 20 min. per lot on the plain grinder, and 40 min. on the centerless grinder. The labor, over-head and depreciation rate is $8 per hr for both machines. No special tools are needed. What is the equal cost quantity for this part?

4. A short shaft with three diameters to be ground is produced in 12 lots of 1000 pieces each during the year. The procedure has been to grind one diameter on all pieces in one lot, then a second, and finally the third. The production rate has been 37½ pieces per hr. It is proposed to mount three wheels on the machine to grind the three diameters on one piece at the same time. This is expected to produce 75 pieces per hr, but requires a special wheel mount and one hour extra set-up time for each lot. The labor and overhead rate is $6 per hr, and the rate for interest, insurance, taxes, and maintenance is 25% per yr. What is the most that can be justified for the cost of the wheel mount?

5. Three adjacent diameters and shoulders must be ground on a shaft. One hundred thousand pieces are to be produced within the coming year. A grinding machine available can be tooled with three wheels in the con-ventional positions to grind the surfaces. A better action can be obtained if the wheelhead can be turned to allow the wheels to make contact with the work at an angle. It is estimated the production rate can be increased from 80 to 100 pieces per hr in that way. However, for that improvement the machine must be rebuilt at a cost of $2000. The labor and overhead rate in the plant is $5 per hr. Interest, insurance, taxes, and maintenance call for a rate of 35% per yr on an investment. Is it worthwhile to rebuild the machine for this job? It is assumed that it will not be impaired for any other work.

6. The regulating wheel of a centerless grinding machine is turning with a surface speed of 50 fpm, and its axis is inclined at an angle of 6° with the horizontal. What is the rate of thrufeed of the work between the wheels in inches per minute?

30

Surface Finishing Operations

Heavy cuts in a material leave rough and torn surfaces. The lighter and milder the cut, the better the surface and the smaller the tolerance. Good finishes can be obtained by operating cutting tools at light feeds, but that is slow. As has been explained, grinding is often faster for fine cutting because it removes material by the action of many grains taking small bites. Although grinding may be carried to the extreme to procure as fine finishes and as high a degree of precision as may be desired, other abrasive operations that have slower speeds and a milder action usually prove more economical for the best finishes. Such operations are lapping, honing, and Superfinishing.

The terms lapping and honing are often used interchangeably, and it is difficult always to make a clear distinction between them. In general but not always, lapping uses a loose abrasive and is applied to external surfaces, while honing is done on internal surfaces with bonded abrasives. Superfinishing is a proprietary operation.

When accuracy is not required, some of the costly aspects of grinding and other precision finishing operations may be eliminated, and abrasives applied in more economical ways to produce good surface finishes alone. This is done in the operations of polishing, buffing, brushing, tumbling, and shot- and sand-blasting.

LAPPING

Purpose of lapping. Lapping is an abrading process that leaves fine scratches arrayed at random. Its purpose is to improve surface quality by reducing roughness, waviness, and defects to produce accurate as well as smooth surfaces. Lapping pressure is light as compared to grinding, and the work is not overheated.

Lapping is done both by hand and by machines. Its range of usefulness is large. In same cases it may merely be an expedient to remove an occasional fault. It is a basic operation in job and tool shops where a typical application is to finish locating and wearing surfaces on precision tools and gages. Gage blocks, the standards of accuracy, are finished regularly by lapping. Machine lapping is common for production. Other typical lapping subjects are surfaces that must be liquid- or gas-tight without gaskets and those from which small errors must be removed, such as gear teeth.

How lapping is done. Only a small amount of stock normally is taken off by lapping, up to 0.003 in. for roughing and as little as 0.0001 in. for finishing. This is because the fine abrasive works slowly and the surface shape is hard to control if much stock is removed.

Fine loose abrasive mixed with a vehicle, bonded abrasive wheels, or coated abrasives are used for lapping. Wet lapping with clear or soapy water, oil, or grease may be as much as six times as fast as dry lapping.

Most lapping is done by spreading loose abrasive and vehicle on lapping shoes or quills, called *laps,* that are rubbed against the work. The face of a lap, usually of soft close grained cast iron, becomes charged with imbedded abrasive particles. Grooves cut across the lap face serve to collect excess abrasive and dirt. Loose abrasive lapping is not normally done on soft materials because the abrasive particles become imbedded in the workpiece.

In lapping, the work and lap are not rigidly guided with respect to each other, and their relative movements are continually changed. In *equalizing lapping,* the work and lap mutually improve each other's surface as they slide together. This is done in seating mushroom valves, machine lapping gears, and hand lapping plug and ring gages. In *forming lapping,* the work acquires a definite shape from the lap. That is the case for most lapping done with abrasive wheels.

Lapping machines. The *vertical lapping machine* of Fig. 30–1 laps flat or round surfaces between two opposed laps on vertical spindles.

Fig. 30–1. A No. 2 vertical lapping machine with a two piece work holder and adaptors for lapping rayon pump parts. (Courtesy Norton Co.)

The lower lap revolves at 45 to 65 rpm, and the upper one is lowered to float upon and adjusts itself to the work. Another type of vertical lapper uses coated abrasive cloth cemented to a horizontal vibrating disk. Workpieces may be applied to a vertical lapping machine by hand, but for production they generally are put in workholders. The pieces are moved about on the laps for even action. A machine like the one in Fig. 30–1 weighs around 2500 lb and costs about $9000.

The *centerless lapping machine* is designed for continuous production of round parts such as piston pins, bearing races and cups, valve tappets, and shafts. As an example of output, piston pins are produced at the rate of 40 pins per min. Tolerances of 0.000050 in. for diameters and 0.000025 in. for straightness and roundness are regularly obtained, with surface finishes of a few microinches and a selection of lusters and finishes.

The centerless lapping machine operates on the same principle as the centerless grinder, previously explained. Workpieces ride on a workrest blade as they pass between two 22 in.-long wheels revolving at speeds below 200 rpm. Such a machine weighs over 10,000 lb and costs about $25,000.

Abrasive belt lapping machines lap bearing and cam surfaces on such parts as crankshafts and camshafts by the application of strips of abrasive coated cloth or paper with short reciprocating motions to avoid continuous lines and refine finish.

HONING

Purpose of honing. Honing is an abrading operation mostly for finishing round holes by means of bonded abrasive stones. Because the bonded abrasive grains do not become imbedded in the work material, soft as well as hard and nonmetallic as well as metallic surfaces can be honed. Typical applications are the finishing of automobile engine cylinders, gear bores, connecting rod bearings, gun barrels, and ring gages.

Honing is a cutting operation and has been used to remove as much as ⅛ in. of stock but is normally confined to amounts less than 0.010 in. It normally is preceded by boring or reaming to establish true surfaces. Then size is commonly controlled to less than 0.0005 in. Surfaces can be finished to one microinch, but 8 to 10 microinches and even more are normal. A cross-hatched finish desirable for lubrication is characteristic of honed surfaces.

How honing is done. Honing stones are made from the common abrasive and bonding materials, often impregnated with sulfur, resin, or wax to improve cutting action and lengthen tool life. Grain sizes range from 80 grit for roughing to 320 for finishing hard materials to 500 for soft materials. A typical holder or toolhead on which the stones are mounted is shown in Fig. 30–2. The stones are expanded in the work by a cone or wedges inside the holder, actuated from the controls of the machine. This is done automatically to size on some machines.

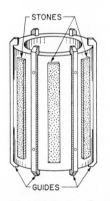

Fig. 30–2. A sketch of a typical honing toolhead for holes.

When honing is done manually, the tool is rotated, and the workpiece is passed back and forth over the tool. For precision production honing, the work usually is held in a fixture. The tool is rotated and reciprocated at the same time with the two movements purposely out of phase to cover all the surface without a regular pattern of scratches.

Honing machines. Honing is done on general-purpose machines, such as the lathe, drill press, and portable drills, as an expedient. More consistent and economical results can be obtained in production on honing machines. The two general types are the horizontal and vertical honing machines.

The *horizontal honing machine* of Fig. 30–3 has a rotating spindle to which workpieces are applied manually. The operator depresses a foot pedal to cause the stones to move outward in the holder. The dial above the spindle indicates the size to which the tool is working at any moment. A machine like this weighs 720 lb and costs about $1000.

On the *horizontal hydraulic honing machine* of Fig. 30–4, the workpiece is held in a horizontal position on the left. The honing tool is reciprocated and rotated by the head on the right. Machines of this type are made with strokes up to 75 ft and hone holes as large as 42 in. in diameter.

Vertical spindle honing machines hold the work and tools in a position where gravity has the least effect upon the action. In general appearance, a vertical honing machine resembles a drill press. It may have a single spindle or a number of spindles, like the one in Fig. 30–5

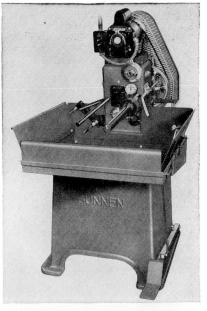

Fig. 30–3. A horizontal manually operated precision honing machine. (Courtesy Sunnen Products Co.)

for honing the cylinders of an engine block in production. The machine is capable of removing 0.004 in. of stock in each of 8 cylinders in 30 sec and of holding size to within 0.0005 in.

Fig. 30–4. A view of two No. 2 by 18 ft. horizontal honing machines for gun bores. (Courtesy Barnes Drill Co.)

SUPERFINISHING

Purpose of Superfinishing. Superfinishing is a trade name given an operation using bonded abrasive stones under certain conditions to pro-

Fig. 30–5. A vertical multiple spindle hydraulic honing machine
equipped with eight hydraulically actuated honing tools. An eight
cylinder engine block is held in a fixture during the honing operation.
(Courtesy Barnes Drill Co.)

duce fine quality finished surfaces on metals. It is not essentially a
dimension creating operation and removes on the average only from
0.0001 to 0.0002 in. of stock. Substantial geometrical and dimensional
accuracy must be created first, usually by grinding. Superfinishing is
intended to correct minute surface defects, is also effective in removing
amorphous, fuzzy, broken, or burned material from the surface, and
leaves a true surface of parent base metal. Practically perfect surfaces
with no apparent scratch pattern can be produced by Superfinishing. At
the other extreme, Superfinished surfaces can be made with readings of
30 microinches and more and a deliberate crosshatched scratch pattern.

How Superfinishing is done. For cylindrical surface Superfinishing a
fine grit stone with a soft bond is trued to match and is reciprocated
rapidly as it is pressed against a revolving workpiece. The motions are
arranged so that a grit never follows the same path more than once
around the workpiece.

The workpiece and tool in Superfinishing are flooded with cutting fluid to carry away heat and particles of metal and abrasive. At first the stone touches only a few high spots, the pressure on them is high, and the cutting action is rapid. The stone is able to bridge and equalize a large number of surface defects at one time and produces results reflecting the average form of the rough surface. When the surface becomes smooth, the pressure decreases, and the stone rides on a film of fluid and ceases to cut. A short surface may be refined to three microinches or better in less than one minute.

Flat surfaces are Superfinished with an abrasive cup wheel on a vertical spindle. Both the wheel and the workpiece, on a lower opposed spindle, rotate but do not oscillate. The wheel may be traversed radially on the workpiece. Precise but not optically flat surfaces may be produced. If the wheel spindle is inclined, spherical surfaces are generated.

Fig. 30–6. A 4 in. by 36 in. general purpose Superfinisher. (Courtesy Gisholt Machine Co.)

Superfinishing machines. Superfinishing may be done on a lathe with an attachment that mounts on the compound rest and presses and oscillates a stone on the work. An example of a machine specifically designed for Superfinishing is shown in Fig. 30–6. The workpiece is mounted and rotated between centers on the base. Above that the stone is carried on a head that presses it against and oscillates it along the workpiece. A machine of this type weighs around 4000 lb and costs about $10,000.

NONPRECISION FINISHING OPERATIONS

Polishing. Polishing is done to put a smooth finish on surfaces and may often involve removal of appreciable metal to take out scratches, tool marks, pits, and other defects from rough surfaces. Usually accuracy of size and shape of the finished surface is not important, but sometimes tolerances of 0.001 in. or less are held in machine polishing. Polishing is done with more or less flexible wheels to distribute cutting action and conform to curved surfaces on workpieces. A wheel of cloth, felt, rubber, leather, or similar material may have a layer of abrasive glued on or a coated abrasive belt running over its periphery. The application of abrasives here follows much the same principles as in grinding. Commonly several steps are necessary, first to remove the defects and then to put the desired polish on the surface. Much polishing cost can be saved by adequate surface preparation. (See pg. 642.)

The work may be applied to a wheel by hand for polishing on a floor-stand grinder like the one in Fig. 29–23. More production speed and consistency can be realized on semi-automatic polishing machines when there is enough work to justify the investment. The two general classes of such machines are: (1) those that carry the work in a straight line past one or more wheels and (2) those that revolve the pieces in contact with the wheels. The time needed by the operator to load a piece must be appreciably less than required to polish a piece by hand for a machine to be economical.

Buffing. Buffing gives a high luster to a surface. It is not intended to remove much metal and generally follows polishing. The work is pressed against cloth or felt wheels or belts on which fine abrasive in a lubricant binder is smeared from time to time.

Power brushing. High-speed revolving brushes are applied to improve surface appearance and remove sharp edges, burrs, fins and particles. This tends to blend surface defects and irregularities and rounds edges without excessive removal of material. Surfaces may be refined to around five microinches when desired. Brushing action helps avoid scratches that act as stress raisers.

Common power brushes are wire bristle, hard cord, and Tampico or tough fiber wheels. They are naturally flexible, able to conform to quite irregular surfaces, and can get into otherwise hard to reach places. Abrasive compounds are often put on brushes. Brushing is done by hand but is readily adaptable to semi-automatic machines, which are fast for production.

Tumbling. The operation called tumbling, rolling, or barrel finishing consists of loading workpieces in a barrel with abrasive particles, sawdust, wood chips, natural stones, cinders, sand, metal slugs, or other scouring agents depending on the work and action desired. Water is usually added, often mixed with an acid, a detergent, a rust preventative, or a lubricant. The barrel is closed or tilted and rotated at a slow speed from one to more than ten hours, according to the amount of treatment desired. As the barrel turns, the pieces inside slide over each other, and an abrasive or burnishing action takes place.

Tumbling is done to ferrous and nonferrous metals, plastics, rubber, and wood of small and large sizes. It cleans castings, forgings, stampings, and screw machine products; removes burrs, fins, skin, scale, and sharp edges; takes off paint and plating; improves surface finish and appearance; and has a tendency to relieve surface strains. Some reduction in size may be experienced. Results are uniform in each lot because all pieces in a barrel are subject to substantially the same conditions.

Although tumbling takes time, it is economical for medium and large quantities of parts because many pieces, depending on size, can be treated at the same time, and attention is required only for loading and unloading.

Shot- and sand-blasting. Shot- and sand-blasting are done by throwing particles at high velocity against the work. The particles may be metallic shot or grit, artificial or natural abrasive including sand, or agricultural products such as nut shells, depending upon what is to be done and the condition of the workpiece. A primary reason for blasting is to clean surfaces. This may mean removing scale, rust, or burnt sand from castings by means of shot or sand, stripping paint by sand-blasting from objects to be redecorated, cleaning grease or oil from finished parts by means of nut shells, or any number of similar operations. A clean, uniform, and in many cases final surface finish is obtained by blasting. In addition, shot-blasting peens surfaces and leads to the advantages of appreciably increasing fatigue strength and stress corrosion resistance, reducing porosity in nonferrous castings, improving surface wearability as on gear teeth, and improving the oil retentivity of some surfaces.

Four common ways of blasting are by compressed air, centrifugal action, high-pressure water, and a mixture of compressed air and water. Compressed air equipment can be used with any type of abrasive, is easily controlled, is simple and relatively inexpensive, and gives ready access to inside surfaces. For centrifugal action, particles are fed to and slung by a rapidly revolving wheel. A high flow and a rapid production rate can be obtained in this way, and it is the most popular method. Water with or without compressed air is used with fine particles to produce smooth, satin-like surface finishes.

Comparison of polishing, buffing, brushing, tumbling, and blasting.
Each finishing operation has certain areas in which it excels. Polishing
is suitable for removing large defects and heavy stock. Buffing and brushing are applied to get a higher luster after polishing. Tumbling is an
economical operation for small parts that can be treated in large lots.
Blasting is a quick way to improve even the worst surfaces, such as those
of rough castings. These are not the only applications of these operations, and often their provinces overlap. In such a case, an analysis
needs to be made in the same way as for any other operations.

As an example of a comparison, the time to polish and buff a part
may be three minutes per piece. The same pieces may be tumbled with
satisfactory results. Loading and unloading time is 15 minutes, and
tumbling time 4 hours. The labor and overhead rate is $6 per hr, and
the tumbling cost rate is $1.50 per hr. The number of pieces for which
the cost is the same by either method is N, and

$$(3N/60) \times 6 = (15/60) \times 6 + 4 \times 1.5 \quad \text{So} \quad N = 25 \text{ pieces.}$$

For a lot of fewer than 25 pieces, polishing is the more economical
method. It is assumed that at least 25 pieces can be tumbled at once.

Questions

1. What are the purposes of lapping, honing, and Superfinishing?

2. How is lapping done?

3. Describe three common forms of lapping machines.

4. What is the difference between lapping and honing?

5. How is honing done?

6. Describe two general types of honing machines.

7. What does Superfinishing do, and what does it not do?

8. How is Superfinishing done?

9. Describe several methods of finishing surfaces when precision is not important.

10. What determines the method best suited to finish a surface?

References

A.S.T.E., *Tool Engineers Handbook*, McGraw-Hill Book Co., Inc., New York.

Surface Cleaning and Coating

Manufactured products naturally collect oil, dirt, chips, etc. during processing. This soil must be removed for certain operations, such as inspection and painting, for assembly, and especially for salability. Thus cleaning is an important part of many processes, and the principal ways it is done will be discussed.

Coatings are commonly applied to the surfaces of articles for decoration, texture, corrosion-resistance, electrical insulation, lubricity, and protection against high temperatures. The common classes are conversion coatings formed by chemical reaction with the surface, organic coatings or paints, metallic coatings, and inorganic or vitreous coatings. The chief forms of these and the methods of applying them will be described.

CLEANING

Washing and degreasing. Cleaning may result more or less from mechanical operations like polishing or tumbling, but mostly it is done by washing or dissolving grease in a way not to attack the material of the workpiece.

The fluids used for washing and degreasing may be classified as *mineral* or *organic solvents* and *water solutions.* Solvents such as naphtha, kerosene, or chlorinated compounds (for low fire hazard) dissolve greases, oils, and waxes but not inorganic dirt. They are relatively expensive but do not harm most metallic surfaces. Water is cheap and the universal washing agent. Conditioners, such as softeners, may be added. In most washing processes, water is used freely for rinsing. Water *emulsions* of organic solvents combine the advantages of a solvent with those of a dispersing agent. They are economical for light degreasing. Alkaline solutions, such as caustic soda or trisodium phosphate with inhibitors and other additives, commercially available are strong enough to remove any soil but may attack some workpieces.

Methods of cleaning. Washing may be done hot or cold according to the action desired. The easiest way of cleaning and one that can be done with any fluid is *dipping* or *immersion*. This is not enough to dislodge clinging soil, and agitation or mechanical rubbing may have to be added. A tank of fluid into which parts are dipped becomes contaminated in time and less effective. Immersion in a series of tanks helps some.

Electrolytic cleaning is a form of immersion in alkaline solutions of high conductivity with a current passing through the part and solution. Gas is released in bubbles on the surfaces of the workpiece and acts to dislodge foreign substances. One patented process of this sort leaves a thin protective deposit of tin on the cleaned surfaces.

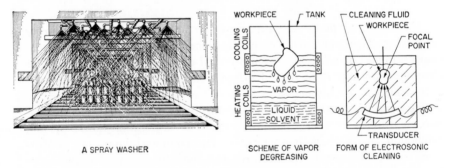

A SPRAY WASHER   SCHEME OF VAPOR DEGREASING   FORM OF ELECTROSONIC CLEANING

Fig. 31–1. Methods of washing and degreasing.

Spraying of all kinds of fluids forcefully acts to dislodge solid dirt. The spray may be directed by hand or be part of a conveyorized system as in Fig. 31–1.

Vapor degreasing is a method of applying solvents as indicated in Fig. 31–1. A quantity of the liquid in the bottom of a tank is vaporized at 200° to 250°F. Cooling coils up higher condense the vapor and keep it from rising above a desired level. When a relatively cool workpiece is lowered into the tank, vapor condenses on it. The clean condensate dissolves grease and runs off. Residue collects at the bottom and is not carried out with the work. Pieces are dry when they come out of the tank. Action is fairly rapid for removal of organic substances alone, but there is no manifest action to dislodge clinging dirt. The fluid is used over and over again, and its cost per piece is low; but the equipment and its operation are relatively expensive.

In *electrosonic cleaning,* high-frequency sound waves from a transducer are focused on a workpiece immersed in a cleaning fluid as indicated in Fig. 31-1. This is capable of jarring loose highly adherent smut which could otherwise be removed only by time consuming hand rubbing. With the application of a large amount of power and a dense fluid, this process is capable of deburring and rounding the edges of pieces, uniformly and quickly, in addition to cleaning.

The individual operations just described are commonly combined into processes to suit specific situations. For example, a typical sequence is: (1) pre-clean by dipping or spraying with an emulsifiable solvent to remove the bulk of the grease and dirt, (2) rinse by spraying with hot water, (3) dip and clean electrolytically to remove scale and oxide, (4) final hot rinse by dipping, and (5) dry in an air blast.

Pickling and oxidizing. Pickling is just the chemical removal of surface oxides and scale from metals by acid solutions. This is commonly done on rolled shapes, wire, sheets, heat-treated steel parts, wrought and cast aluminum parts, etc. In some applications, such as on aluminum, it is called *oxidizing.*

Common pickling solutions contain sulfuric or hydrochloric acids with water and sometimes inhibitors. Nitric and hydrofluoric acids are used for some applications. A solution may contain half acid for cold use but as little as 10% if intended for use at 200°F. Pickling is usually done by immersion for periods of several minutes or more.

In pickling, the acid cannot get to the surface if it is covered with dirt. Thus, parts must be cleaned first. After pickling, the parts must be rinsed and completely neutralized by an alkaline rinse. Any residue of acid will harm paint or other subsequent coating.

SURFACE COATINGS

Conversion coatings. Conversion coatings are inorganic films formed by chemical reactions with metallic surfaces. They are usually much less than 0.001 in. thick but are normally formed from the original surface and so are tightly bonded and cause no appreciable dimensional change. Common forms are phosphate, chromate, black oxide, and anodic coatings. The principal processes of applying such coatings are the following:

Phosphate coatings are essentially phosphate salts. They are mostly put on steel because they resist underfilm rusting and paint adheres well to their fine and uniform granular surface. Such coatings are applied by dipping, spraying, or swabbing with water solutions of acidic phosphate salts. Typical trade names are *Parkerizing, Granodising,* and *Bonderizing.*

Chromate coatings are obtained by applying chromium solutions to zinc, cadmium, aluminum, and magnesium surfaces, chiefly for corrosion resistance but sometimes as a paint base. They can be made highly colorful and decorative by means of dyes. Chromate coatings are more corrosion resistant but less wear resistant than anodic coatings.

Thin *black oxide coatings* are put on steel by immersion in a boiling solution of sodium hydroxide and mixtures of nitrates and nitrites. Several commercial processes are available, and each has its own formula. Typical are *Black Magic* and *Jetol.* Other methods entail heating the parts at temperatures between 600 and 1200°F in the presence of carburizing agents such as charred bone and oil. Oxide coatings serve as paint bases but when impregnated with oil or wax, furnish good corrosion resistance alone.

Anodic coatings applied to aluminum and magnesium alloys utilize electrical as well as chemical means. The workpiece is immersed in a solution, usually sulfuric acid for aluminum, and connected as the anode in an electrical circuit. Anodic coatings can be applied from 0.1 to over 1 mil in thickness and are good protection against corrosion because they are in reality the same as but only more of the thin oxide film that naturally protects the metal. The films provide a good paint base and can be colored readily.

Organic coatings. Organic coatings may be glued to surfaces in the form of thin plastic sheets or tapes but are best known as paints or inks. They go on almost all materials and offer unlimited color and gloss varieties. Thus, they provide more decorative possibilities than other coatings. In durability, strength, and corrosion resistance, they generally are superior to conversion coatings but not as effective as some metallic coatings. Usually they cost less than metallic coatings and thus are preferred if they serve satisfactorily.

Paint is the general term for an organic coating and consists of a vehicle of film forming materials and pigments for coloring, hiding power, and protection. Clear finishes lack pigments. Drying agents may also be added.

Oil paint is a dispersion of metallic pigments, such as white lead, in a vegetable drying oil, such as linseed oil, and solvent thinner and perhaps dryers. The thinner evaporates, and the oil oxidizes to form the film. Drying time depends on the oil used and drying agents added but is relatively long. Oil paints are not commonly used except for large structures like houses or bridges.

A *lacquer* is essentially a solution of plastic resins and plasticizers with or without pigments in a solvent. When the lacquer is applied, the solvent evaporates, and the remainder precipitates out as a dry film. Drying is quick, but the film is not as resistant to some solvents as other coatings.

Varnishes and *enamels* of the older kinds are like oil paints in that they form a film by oxidation of a resin-oil vehicle. Newer synthetic types have replaced oil paints and older types to a large extent because they are harder and more resistant and impervious to mechanical and chemical action. They are fairly fast drying but may require baking, which adds to the expense and makes them unsuitable for finishing plastic and wooden items. A typical synthetic varnish consists of a thermosetting resin in a solvent thinner. When it is applied to a surface, the thinner evaporates, and the resin polymerizes to form a clear dry film. An enamel is basically a pigmented varnish, and its film is generally harder, tougher, and less flexible than a varnish film.

Most varnishes, enamels, lacquers, and paints in industry today are based largely or entirely on plastic resins and elastomers. Almost all the principal substances described in Chap. 11 are used singly or compounded to obtain various degrees of corrosion-, chemical-, and environmental-resistance, colorability, durability, and other desired properties.

Dispersions and emulsions consist of synthetic resins, fillers, and pigments dispersed or emulsified in water or organic solvent. They have many forms, among which are heat-resistant pan coatings, odorless paints, and coatings to give smooth films on porous materials.

Sometimes only one coat of paint is enough, but mostly undercoats are applied to form a good base for the finish coat that provides color, luster, and appearance. Undercoatings include primers that form a bond and inhibit corrosion on the surface and intermediate coats that serve as fillers, smooth surfacers, or sealers. The composition of a paint depends largely upon its intended place in the layers on a surface.

Painting methods. Painting may be done by brush, knife, dip, roller, flow, tumble, silk screen, or spray methods. Brushing is easily done but is slow, and other methods are used for production. Dipping demands little equipment and can be mechanized easily but requires paint that films out, stirring, and workpieces that can be immersed easily and are without pockets.

Flow coating, by pouring paint onto workpieces and recirculating the runoff, is gaining in popularity because it is applicable to many kinds of pieces of small to medium sizes and is fast, thorough, and economical of material.

Paint spraying is the most used method of industrial painting because it is fast, dependable, versatile, and uniform. It is based on the principle that a liquid stream atomizes when it exceeds a certain speed. The most common system is to introduce the liquid into a high velocity stream of compressed air released through a nozzle. In another system, the paint is heated and discharged in a high velocity stream through a small orifice at pressures up to 5000 psi. In still another way, the paint may be slung off the edge of a rapidly revolving disk or bell shaped atomizer.

A spray gun or head may be directed by hand, but for continuous production many ingenious arrangements are in use to spray pieces automatically as they pass along a conveyor. Manual touch-up at the end of such a line is usually necessary, but the labor cost is normally less than if each piece were hand sprayed completely.

Because of the toxicity and flammability of most paints, painting is generally done in segregated enclosures or booths which are well ventilated. The exhausted air may be washed to remove fumes and waste.

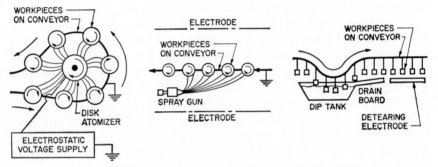

Fig. 31–2. Electrostatic painting systems.

Much paint is ordinarily lost when sprayed, particularly with automatic air spraying. The loss is reduced by imposing an electrostatic charge on the atomized paint. In one *electrostatic painting system* depicted at the left in Fig. 31–2, an 80,000 to 150,000 v-potential charges the paint emitted from a disk- or bell-shaped atomizer. The droplets are drawn to and deposited uniformly with almost no loss on the grounded workpieces of opposite polarity.

When paint is sprayed by air as in the center of Fig. 31–2, the particles may be discharged into an electrostatic field set up between charged electrodes and the grounded workpieces. The paint particles pick up the electrical charge of the electrode as they pass near it first and are attracted to the workpieces. Spray loss may be kept as low as 5 to 25%.

Drips and tears that collect at the bottoms of pieces that have been dipped can be drawn off electrostatically as indicated on the right in Fig. 31–2.

Paint may be baked in ovens heated by steam, gas, oil, or electricity. Infra-red lamps in banks have become quite popular for baking and drying because the method is fast, clean, and easily changed about and adjusted.

Painting costs. The first consideration in the selection of a paint is that it meets service requirements in regard to satisfactory corrosion protection, strength, durability, luster, color, etc. Often several paints can be found suitable for a particular application. The lowest cost is then the criterion; not the cost per gallon but the cost per square foot of surface covered adequately.

Most varnishes and enamels able to satisfy ordinary requirements cost from 1.5 to 2 cents and lacquers from 2.5 to 2.75 cents per sq ft per 0.001 in. thickness when dry for the material alone. In most cases 0.001 to 0.002 in.-thick varnish or enamel and 0.002 in.-thick lacquer gives satisfactory exterior durability on steel over a phosphate coating. A thickness of 0.001 in. will suffice for a purely decorative coat. If lacquer will serve as satisfactorily as enamel, it may be preferable in many cases because of its shorter drying time and lower cost for processing. The cost of applying a coating is normally much higher than the cost of materials. It is the total cost that must be considered.

Where special requirements must be met, the cost may have to be high. For instance, a silicone enamel for extraordinary heat resistance costs $0.06 per sq ft per 0.001 in.-thick coating when dry for material alone. A fluorocarbon dispersion coating with good heat resistance and exceptional wear resistance may cost as much as $0.15 for the same measure.

Hot-dip plating. One way of putting a protective coating on metal pieces is to dip them into certain molten metals, mainly zinc, tin, or an alloy of lead and tin. The same metals are also plated electrically.

Hot-dip galvanizing is done by dipping ferrous parts, such as outside hardware, into a bath of molten zinc. The parts are first cleaned and fluxed in a solution of zinc chloride and hydrochloric acid.

Zinc keeps iron from rusting even if the coating is broken because a galvanic action occurs in the presence of the moist carbon dioxide of the air. The zinc is the more active metal, and the iron does not rust until all the zinc is gone. Dipping is an economical way of putting on a heavy and enduring coat.

Tin plating or *dipping* is done by immersing cleaned and fluxed steel sheets in a bath of molten tin. They then are passed through rolls in a palm oil bath to remove excess tin. The tinned sheet furnishes adequate protection on the insides of food containers for which it mostly is used. It does not provide satisfactory outside protection like zinc because the rusting of the iron is hastened when the tin coating is broken.

Terne plate is steel dipped in an alloy of lead and about 25% tin. It is cheaper than tin plate but has satisfactory corrosion resistance. A heavy terne plate makes a good roofing. The lubricating quality of the lead is beneficial on sheets and wire that are going to be drawn.

Electroplating. Electroplating is done on all the common metals and even on many non-metals after their surfaces have been suitably prepared. Plating may be done for protection against corrosion or against wear and abrasion, for appearance, to rework worn parts by increase in size, to make pieces easy to solder, to provide a surface, usually of brass on steel, for bonding rubber, and to stop off areas on steel parts from being carburized during heat treatment. Most of these applications are evident in the articles about us every day. The common, but not the only, plating materials are cadmium, zinc, silver, gold, tin, copper, nickel, chromium, and their alloys.

The principle of electroplating is illustrated in Fig. 31–3. The piece to be plated is immersed in a water solution of salts of the metal to be applied and made the cathode in a direct current circuit. Anodes of the coating metal replenish the solution when the current is flowing, and ions of the metal are attracted to the workpiece to form the coating. The rate of deposition and the properties of the plate such as hardness, uniformity, and porosity depend upon getting a proper balance among the composition of the plating solution, current density, agitation, solution acidity, and temperature. For instance, the higher the current density, the faster the metal is deposited, but a rate above a critical level for a specific solution and temperature results in a rough and spongy plate.

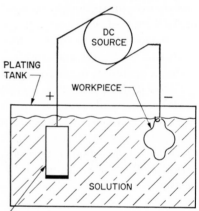

Fig. 31–3. The scheme of electroplating.

The electroplating process presents several difficulties of concern to the designer. One of these is that a plating is not always deposited uniformly. It tends to be thick on projections, thin in recesses, and almost non-existent in some corners. The designer must avoid irregularities as much as possible, but much can be done by good planning and control of the operation. Some solutions give better distribution of plating and are said to have better *throwing power* than others. The amount of plate deposited on a surface is related to the distance from an anode. Thus, anodes shaped to match the workpieces and suitably placed can help towards uniform plating.

Plating does not hide defects in the surface of the workpiece, and a surface must be fully finished if it is to be plated for appearance as well as corrosion resistance. Parts, such as automobile bumpers, nickel or chrome plated for appearance are commonly given an initial copper plating 0.0002 to 0.0006 in. thick. This adheres well to and effectively covers the steel, and its surface is easier to buff out than the steel. Decorative chrome plate is ordinarily only a few hundred-thousandths of an inch thick to maintain brightness over a protective undercoat of nickel. A combination gives the best results at lowest cost.

Hydrogen released at the cathode causes harmful embrittlement of hardened or cold-worked steel workpieces. The quantity of hydrogen can be kept at a minimum by proper control of the operation, and the embrittlement can be alleviated by heating the workpieces immediately after plating.

Electroplating equipment. The basic unit for electroplating operations is the tank to hold the solutions. Tanks are constructed of various materials such as lead sheet, rubber, plastics, and tile to resist alkaline and acidic solutions. Large pieces are suspended individually. Small pieces may be mounted on racks but mostly are barrel plated or tumbled. A batch of pieces is put in a non-conducting perforated barrel and in touch with suitable contacts. The barrel is lowered into the plating solution and revolved several times each minute, and the pieces tumble around and are plated uniformly.

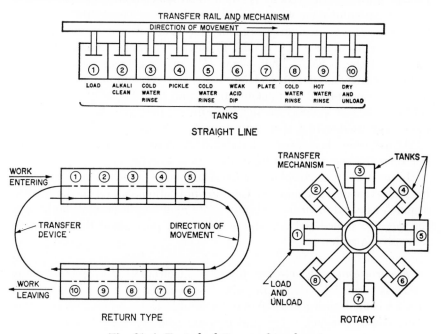

Fig. 31–4. Typical plating machine layouts.

The electroplating process entails cleaning, washing, rinsing, and other treatment in addition to the actual deposition of metal. This means each workpiece or batch must be dipped into and transferred among a number of tanks, whether plated individually, on racks, or in barrels. That is commonly done manually for small lots, but the labor is eliminated by automatic plating machines for large quantity production. The three general types of machines are illustrated in Fig. 31–4. The transfer devices for these machines raise the work from one tank, move it to the next, and then lower it into place at preset intervals. The straight line and return types may be single- or double-line machines, depending upon whether they have one or two rows of work carriers, one above the other. The rotary-type machine takes more floor space but can handle large parts. These machines can be tied in conveniently with conveyor systems.

In certain industries, specialized machines have been developed for continuously plating sheet metal or wire as it is guided by rollers and runs through a series of baths.

Costs of electroplating. Two major direct costs of electroplating are for the metal in the plate and for electricity. These and the other costs which depend upon time can be calculated readily from data given in hand-books. For instance, a square foot of zinc plate 0.001 in. thick is computed to weigh 0.6 oz or 17 grams from the specific weight of zinc.

One Faraday of electricity is equal to 96,540 coulombs (amp sec) and deposits an equivalent weight in grams of any metal at 100% cathode efficiency. The equivalent weight of zinc is its atomic weight (65.38) divided by its valence (2), or 32.7 grams. An average cathode efficiency for zinc plating is 85%. That means 85% of the current goes to deposit metal; the remainder into leakage, hydrogen generation, etc. The electricity to deposit 0.001 in. thickness of zinc on 1 sq ft then is $(17/32.7) \times (96540/3600) \times 1/0.85) = 16.4$ amp hr. At the usual potential of 6 v, the energy used is $16.4 \times 6 = 98.4$ whr.

At a permissible current density of 20 amp per sq ft, the time to deposit a thickness of 0.001 in. is $16.4/20 = 0.84$ hr.

In most cases electroplates of 0.001 to 0.002 in. and less are adequate for protection and appearance. Certain applications call for thicker plates; as much as 0.008 in. of hard chrome plate may be put on tools and gages for wear resistance and even more where the purpose of the plate is to increase dimensions.

Electroforming. Electroforming is an electroplating process whereby a part is formed by depositing metal on a mold or matrix. The matrix may be coated with a film or may be soluble to be removable from the plate. Copper, nickel, silver, and iron are commonly electroformed, but others can be processed if needed.

Electroforming is not economical for parts that can be made readily by casting, forming, machining, or other conventional methods. It does have a place in making parts that are too complicated to be made in one piece and too expensive by other methods. Among other advantages are that walls can be made thick or thin but always uniform in thickness. Small tolerances can be held with fine surface finishes and exceptionally good detail inside and outside. A wide range of metallic properties are obtainable by control of the process.

Vapor-deposited coatings. Several related processes exist for depositing thin, highly reflective, and decorative metallic films on plastics and metals for such products as costume jewelry, television set and interior automobile trim, and drawer pulls. *Evaporated* or *vacuum metallized* films of aluminum are commonest of these, although other metals are sometimes applied in similar ways. The aluminum is flash heated in a high-vacuum chamber containing the parts. The metal vapor condenses on all directly exposed surfaces in a film five microinches or less in thickness. Films as thick as 0.004 in. are obtainable from variations of the process. The film reproduces the original surface, which must be smooth and often is precoated with one or two layers of smooth lacquer. A final lacquer or enamel coating is applied to protect and even to tint the light metallic film.

Vacuum metallizing is fast; a large batch of parts can be treated in a few seconds. Little material is needed for the thin films. Operating costs are reported about one-half to one-fourth those of other plating processes, but initial equipment cost is high. A complete set of equipment to coat up to 10,000 small parts an hour costs about $40,000.

Other metal-plating processes. *Chemical reduction* is the means of precipitating metal from a chemical solution onto plastics or metals to form mirror-like films in thicknesses between those formed by vapor deposition and electroplating. Such films are typically used for mirror and reflector coatings and as a basis for further electroplating.

A *diffusion coating* is a hard and often brittle alloy-rich surface layer formed by heating a piece of metal in intimate contact with another metal in powder, liquid, or gaseous form. The purpose is to obtain corrosion resistance, in some cases against oxidation at high temperatures. Particular processes of this kind are *sherardizing* for zinc on steel, *chromizing* for chromium on steel, *calorizing* for aluminum on steel, and *siliconizing* for silicon on molybdenum.

Sheets or plates of corrosion-resistant metals are sometimes welded or brazed to base metals. This is known as *cladding.* Thicker coatings result than from other processes. A large variety of clad metal plate, sheet, strip, tubing, and wire is commercially available in many combinations of metals.

Vitreous coatings. Vitreous, porcelain or ceramic, enamel is a hard, glass-like, inorganic coating fused to metal. Such coatings consist mainly of silicates, feldspar, alumina for ceramics, fluxes like borax and soda ash, and various metallic oxides to provide specific properties. They can be applied only to certain grades of metals suitable for enameling. The ingredients of a coat are mixed with clay and water and brushed or sprayed on a surface. When dry, the coat is fired at temperatures up to 1500°F, depending on its composition and the part coated.

Vitreous coatings are smooth, hard, lustrous, and resist high temperatures. They are used on kitchenware because they are easily cleaned, on containers because they resist chemical attack, on surfaces subject to wear because they resist abrasion, and on the exhausts of jet engines because they protect metals from corrosion at high temperatures.

Questions

1. What are the principal cleaning fluids, and for what is each best suited?

2. What is the difference between electrolytic and electrosonic cleaning?

3. Why is spraying more effective than dipping for cleaning?

4. Describe vapor degreasing and state its advantages.

5. What is pickling and what precautions must be taken with it?

6. What are conversion coatings? Describe the principal ones.

7. How do anodic coatings differ from other conversion coatings?

8. What are organic coatings, and why are they popular?

9. Describe four major types of paint and their uses.

10. Describe the important industrial painting methods.

11. What are the benefits of electrostatic painting, and how is it done?

12. On what basis should a paint be selected?

13. Why and how are ferrous articles galvanized?

14. Cite examples from your experience of at least four different applications of plating.

15. Describe the principle of electroplating and specify the factors that influence its operation.

16. What can be done to help put a uniform plate on an object?

17. Why are some articles plated with several metals?

18. How can plating cause embrittlement of steel and how can it be alleviated?

19. Describe the common methods of plating.

20. What is electroforming, and what are its advantages?

21. Describe the process of vacuum metallizing and its uses.

22. Why is vacuum metallizing suitable only for large quantity production?

23. Briefly describe chemical reduction, diffusion coating, and cladding methods of coating metals.

Problems

1. A manufacturer is planning to produce an item at the rate of 50,000 pieces per yr. Each piece has an area of 3 sq ft and will be painted with two coats. Paint loss is 15%. A baking enamel that meets requirements costs 1.5 cents per sq ft for 0.001 in. thickness dry, and each coat is 0.0015 in. thick. A lacquer that is satisfactory costs 2.75 cents per sq ft per 0.001 in. thickness dry. A total thickness of 0.004 in. is needed for the lacquer. If the manufacturer chooses to use the enamel, how much can he afford to spend per year to bake the enamel? It is assumed that the cost of spraying either paint is the same.

2. An automobile bumper has an area of 15 sq ft and is to receive a copper plate 0.0005 in. thick. Copper has an atomic weight of 63.57, in this case a valence of 1, and a specific weight of 5.14 oz per cu in. The cathode efficiency is 50%. The process operates nominally at 6 v. How much copper and electrical energy are used for each bumper? How long should be the plating time for an allowable current density of 12 amp per sq ft?

3. An automobile bumper has an area of 15 sq ft and is to receive a nickel plate 0.0005 in. thick. Nickel has an atomic weight of 58.69, a valence of 2, and a specific weight of 5.09 oz per cu in. The cathode efficiency is 95%. The process operates nominally at 6 v. How much nickel and electrical energy are used for each bumper? How long should be the plating time for an allowable current density of 25 amp per sq ft?

4. An automobile bumper has an area of 15 sq ft and is to receive a final chromium plate 0.00002 in. thick. Chromium has an atomic weight of 52.01, a valence of 6, and a specific weight of 4 oz per cu in. The cathode efficiency is 15%. The process operates nominally at 6 v. How much chromium and electrical energy are used for each bumper? How long should be the plating time for an allowable current density of 150 amp per sq ft?

5. Instead of plating copper and nickel on a bumper as specified in Probs. 2 and 3, the requirements can be met by a single nickel plate 0.001 in. thick. In either case, a final chromium plate of 0.00002 in. must be applied. Copper costs $0.35 per lb and nickel $1.05 per lb. Electricity costs 1.5 cents per kwhr. Under what conditions would you recommend the single nickel plate rather than one of copper and one of nickel?

6. A system is being designed to cadmium plate parts to a thickness of 0.0005 in. at a rate of 700 sq ft per hr. Cadmium has an atomic weight of 112.41 and valence of 2. The system operates with a cathode efficiency of 90%. What must be the minimum capacity rating in kwhr of the d-c generator? If the current density must be 20 amp per sq ft, how many sq ft of work must the tank be able to accommodate at one time?

References

A.S.T.E., *Tool Engineers Handbook,* McGraw-Hill Book Co., Inc., New York.

CHAPTER 32

Chemical—Electrical—Mechanical Operations

Several processes for removing and forming metals in unique ways will be discussed in this chapter. One group is for cutting hard materials that cannot be cut as easily, and sometimes not at all, by other methods. This includes the electro-discharge, electro-chemical, and ultrasonic operations. A second group removes metal by etching or eating it away chemically, in the photo-etching and chemical milling operations.

OPERATIONS FOR CUTTING HARD MATERIALS

Electro-discharge machining. Electro-discharge, electro-spark, or electro-arc machining is a means of shaping hard metals and forming deep and complex shaped holes in soft metals and electroconductive materials. A typical system is illustrated in Fig. 32–1. The tool is held about 0.001 in. from the workpiece surface, and the gap is filled with a dielectric fluid, commonly a light oil. The rectified direct current builds up a charge in the condenser and raises the voltage between tool and workpiece. When the voltage across the gap reaches about 50 v, conduction starts, and within 30 microseconds the condenser discharges through the gap. This is repeated in a rapid succession of individual sparks of very high current density, 10^6 amp per sq in. or more. The gap required between tool and workpiece is maintained by a servo-control device that compares the average gap voltage to a reference voltage and seeks to keep their ratio constant.

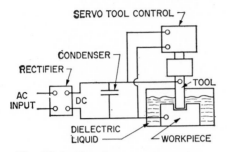

Fig. 32–1. The elements of an electro-discharge machining system.

The debris removed by electro-discharge machining is washed away by the dielectric fluid and is in the form of globules. This is evidence that material is removed by fusion rather than fracture. The tool is also eaten away by the sparking. Brass is the most co.n-mon tool material. If a hole is to be formed, its cross-sectional shape is determined by that of the tool.

For a flat surface, a revolving metal wheel acts as the tool, and the workpiece is reciprocated beneath its periphery as in surface grinding.

The electro-discharge method can machine any known material that conducts electricity and almost any shape. With no physical contact and therefore no forces between tool and workpiece, frail pieces such as honeycomb structures can be machined without distortion. Some change may occur in the composition of the workpiece surface because of high temperature, rapid cooling, and presence of dielectric and tool substances. Distortion has been observed to depths of as much as 0.050 in. in some materials but practically none in others. Fine surface cracks are induced in some hard brittle materials. Most defects have been found removable by light lapping.

The main disadvantage of electro-discharge machining is that it is slow. Grinding can remove material about 100 times as fast from hardened steel. On the other hand, electro-discharge machining removes stock almost as fast from cemented carbides as does grinding. Electro-discharge machining is not economical for soft materials except for shapes, such as complex holes, difficult to cut by other means but often is as fast as and therefore competitive all around with grinding for the hardest materials.

Electro-chemical grinding. Electro-chemical or electrolytic grinding is a method for removing hard materials by electrolytic attack. The machine used structurally resembles a surface grinder like the one in Fig. 29–12. In electro-chemical grinding, a metal-bonded diamond grinding wheel is connected as the cathode, and the workpiece as the anode, in a low voltage d-c circuit as indicated in Fig. 32–2. Both are flooded with an electrolyte, such as sodium nitrite-nitrate or sodium silicate solutions. The electrolytic action dissolves the metal at the anode, and the residue is wiped away by the slowly revolving wheel. A cut is taken deep

enough to remove all the stock desired, and the workpiece is traversed slowly past the wheel. Both rough offhand and fine precision grinding may be done by this method.

Much more power is required to remove a given quantity of material electrolytically than by grinding, roughly ten times as much in the case of steel. Thus for comparable equipment capacity, ordinary grinding is faster and more economical for most materials. However, that is not the case for quite hard materials, for which the limiting factors in grinding

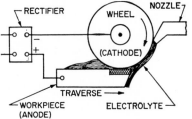

Fig. 32–2. An electrochemical machining system.

are what the abrasive can stand and the amount of heat the workpiece can take without damage. In such a case electrolytic grinding may be faster because there is little abrasion and no heat generated at the cutting edge. Electrolytic grinding has been found several times as fast as conventional grinding for cemented carbides in some cases. For plain grinding, such as finishing the top of a block, electro-chemical grinding is often faster than electro-discharge machining.

Because the abrasion action is negligible, electrolytic grinding does not leave fine scratches which may act as stress raisers. Because temperatures are low, there is no tendency to form cracks and checks. Surface finishes produced compare favorably with those of commercial grinding.

Most, but not all, electro-chemical grinding is done on external surfaces, straight in one direction but of almost any shape in the other. The work material must conduct electricity, so the process is limited to hard metallic alloys.

Ultrasonic impact grinding. Ultrasonic impact grinding is a means of cutting shapes of all kinds in hard materials of all kinds by the rapid motion of abrasive particles. A diagram of the device used is shown in Fig. 32–3. The tool is an image of the form to be cut, which may be a hole of almost any shape, a cavity, or figures in relief or intaglio. An abrasive slurry is fed between the tool and workpiece. The tool is brought up against the work and vibrated through a thousandth of an inch or so amplitude at from 15,000 to 30,000 cycles per sec. Tiny abrasive particles are thus driven against the work with acute pressures and chip or grind an exact counterpart of the tool face into the work. The tool is commonly of unhardened steel but usually wears relatively slowly, particularly on the sides, and the tool shape is maintained satisfactorily in most cases.

To generate the ultrasonic vibrations, an electronic driver consisting of an oscillator and high-output amplifier supplies high-frequency current to a coil around a laminated nickel core. Such a core has the property

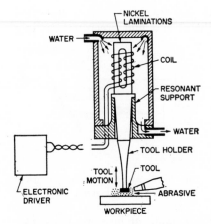

Fig. 32–3. Diagram of an ultrasonic transducer.

of expanding and shrinking under the influence of the alternating current.

Ultrasonic grinding is effective on non-metallic materials as well as metals. It has been applied to size shaping wire-drawing dies in cemented carbide in 15 min, cutting a cemented carbide stamp 0.025 in. deep in 2 min, and sinking a complete blanking die of intricate shape in hardened tool steel in 45 min, feats which could only be done more slowly by other methods. On nonmetals it has been applied to cutting holes in ceramics and duplicating delicately engraved patterns in glass or precious stones. The action does not heat the workpiece and does not disturb the material below the surface. This operation is not competitive for finishing flat external surfaces.

Comparison of operations. Some of the work done by each of the operations just described can be done by one or both of the others and by conventional grinding operations. A comparison of performance and costs for these alternatives is given in Table 32–1 to indicate their relative merits.

TABLE 32–1. PERFORMANCE AND COST COMPARISON OF OPERATIONS FOR CUTTING HARD MATERIALS

			Operation			
Item	Electro-discharge	Electro-lytic	Ultrasonic abrasive	Silicon carbide belt	Silicon carbide wheel	Diamond wheel
Performance:						
Surface finish (micro-in.)	30–150	10–30	5–30	5–30	5–30	5–30
Precision	4	3	4	2	2	1 (best)
Checking and cracking	some	no	no	little	some	some
Flat surfaces	yes	yes	no	yes	yes	yes
Holes	any shape	no	any shape	no	round	round
Costs:						
Min. capital investment	over $5000	$1500 to $5000	over $5000	under $1500	under $1500	under $1500
Tools and supplies	low to moderate	low	low to moderate	moderate	moderate	high
Direct labor	low	low	low	high	high	moderate
Maintenance	moderate	moderate	moderate	low	low	low
Electricity	10x+	3x	10x+	x	x	x

The operations described in this chapter for cutting hard materials involve fairly high investment, maintenance, and power costs but they can do the operations for which they are particularly suited at low costs for labor, tools, and supplies. Therefore, the criterion for investing in such equipment is that there must be sufficient work available on which enough can be saved to pay for the equipment.

CHEMICAL PROCESSES

Photo-etching. Photographic techniques for transferring designs and images to metal plates have been widely practiced in printing for many years. Similar methods have been developed for cutting parts like the ones shown in Fig. 32–4 from sheet metal up to about $\frac{1}{32}$ inch thick in moderate quantities. The sheet metal is coated with a photographic emulsion and exposed in a camera to a drawing of the part or parts desired. On development, the surface of the sheet is left covered with a protective film except on those lines or areas that are subsequently eaten away in an acid bath. The protective coat or *resist* may also be applied by printing. Printed circuits widely used in the electronic industry are fabricated in this manner, by etching away the unwanted areas of foil bonded to an insulating laminated board. Most metals, including aluminum, brass, copper, and steel, are subject to this process.

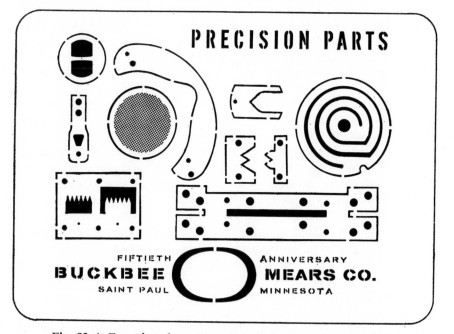

Fig. 32–4. Examples of precision parts made from sheet metal by photo-etching.

Parts made by photo-etching can also be cut by hand or die cut on a punch press. Photo-etching is economical for a quantity too large to be sheared out by hand but not warranting the cost of a die. For instance, a radio manufacturer needed 100 small contactor leaves from sheet brass. They were made 25 to the sheet by the photo-etching method for a total cost of labor, material, and overhead of $75. A die alone could not have been made for that amount.

Chemical milling. Chemical milling is the name given to a process for removing large amounts of stock by etching selected areas of complex workpieces. It was developed in the aircraft industry as one means of fabricating lightweight parts of large areas and thin sections but has been receiving attention in other industries. One kind of part chemically milled is the wing bulkhead depicted in Fig. 32–5. The large cavities are formed by removing metal from a thick slab.

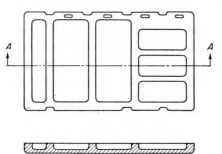

SECTION *A–A*

Fig. 32–5. An aircraft wing bulkhead that is chemically milled.

Chemical milling entails four steps: cleaning, masking, etching, and demasking. Maskant of neoprene rubber or vinyl plastic usually is sprayed over all surfaces and baked. It is then slit to a template and stripped from the areas to be etched. Different surfaces can be milled to different depths by removing parts of the maskant at different times during the process.

The size of workpiece that can be treated is limited only by the size of the tank into which it is dipped for etching. Caustic soda is the usual etchant for aluminum, and acids for steel, magnesium, and titanium alloys. The action proceeds at the rate of about 0.001 in. per min in the solution if proper concentration is maintained. A black smut that occurs may be removed by deoxidizing and rinsing. A variation of the process is to withdraw a long piece slowly from the etching tank to make a tapered or conical part.

Tolerances of ±0.001 in. have been reported obtainable in chemical milling, but ±0.060 in. on length and width and +0.005 −0.000 in. on depth and thickness are more practical. Surface finish ranges from 30 to 125 microinches. The deeper the cut, the rougher the finish, but the finer-grain material etches more smoothly.

Chemical milling can be done on all kinds of parts: rolled sections, forgings, castings, and preformed pieces. It is not limited by shape, direction of cut, or cutter, and different sizes and shapes of cuts can be made at one time. Both sides of a sheet can be cut at one time to minimize warping. The evidence points to a higher fatigue strength after chemical milling than after conventional milling because of lack of scratches. Chemical milling is advantageous for complex cuts and parts and makes feasible the future design of many more such parts where needed but is not superior for simple straightforward work because that can usually be done more economically on regular machine tools.

Chemical milling is simple and amenable to automatic operation. Equipment preparation time and costs are low. In one aircraft plant the usual period of three months to tool an average part for production has been reduced to less than one month where chemical milling is applicable. Masking costs may be high for each piece and chemicals add to the direct costs. Even so, chemical milling is economical in many cases. One manufacturer reported a cost of $9.36 per piece for chemical milling as against $25 per piece for machine milling in 60 to 150 piece lots.

Questions

1. How is electro-discharge machining done?

2. What are the advantages and disadvantages of electro-discharge machining?

3. Describe the operation of electro-chemical grinding.

4. What are the advantages and disadvantages of electro-chemical grinding?

5. What work can electro-discharge machining do that cannot be done by electro-chemical grinding? In what respect does electro-chemical grinding excel?

6. How is ultrasonic impact grinding done?

7. In what ways is ultrasonic impact grinding superior and in what ways inferior to competing methods?

8. How are parts made by photo-etching, and when is it economical?

9. What is chemical milling and how is it done?

10. In what cases is chemical milling advantageous, and when not?

Problems

1. In a manufacturing plant it costs $0.27 to remove a pound of metal by chemical milling based on a cost of $0.18 per lb of etchant. Any costs for masking must be added, including $0.05 per sq ft to apply the maskant

over the entire exposed surface, the prorated cost of the template, and $0.02 per lin ft of cut for slitting and removing the maskant.

Machine milling costs $1 per lb of metal removed. Set-up costs $5 for each lot. For each piece, let W = weight in lb of metal to be removed, A = the total surface area in sq ft, and L = the length in ft of cuts to be made in the maskant. Let T = the cost of the template to be used for all pieces. Set up and solve an expression for N, the number of parts in one lot for which the cost is the same by chemical or machine milling.

2. A part is to be milled under the conditions given in Prob. 1. Initially it is a slab of aluminum ⅝ in. thick, 32 in. wide, and 48 in. long. Three pockets each ½ in. deep by 10 in. by 30 in. are to be cut from one side. If one part only is to be made, how much can be spent on a mask for chemical milling? How much if 5 parts are to be made?

3. A mask for the part described in Prob. 2 costs $30. What process should be used if only two parts are to be made, both in one lot?

4. Cemented carbide cutting tools used in a certain plant must be ground on their rake faces to resharpen them. This can be done on an electro-chemical grinding machine in the time of 2 min, for each tool. The machine and equipment cost $5000. Depreciation for five years, interest, and taxes amount to $1500 per yr, or $6 per day.

The work can also be done in 4 minutes for each tool with a diamond wheel on a conventional grinder costing about $1500, prorated at $2 per day. The extra cost of the diamond wheel amounts to $0.01 for each tool ground. Electricity costs $0.005 per tool more for the electro-chemical method. Labor and related overhead costs amount to $4 for each hour of operation of either machine. Other costs are about the same for both machines.

How many tools must be ground each day to justify the electro-chemical method?

5. For the situation described in Prob. 4, which method should be selected if 25 tools are to be ground each day? If 50 tools are needed every day?

CHAPTER 33

Screw Threads
and Their Manufacture

SCREW THREADS AND SCREWS

Nature of screw threads. A *screw thread* is a ridge of uniform section that lies in a helical or spiral path on the outside or inside of a cylinder or cone. The groove between the ridges is called the *space*. A *straight thread* lies on a cylinder; a *tapered thread* lies on a cone. A thread on an outside surface is an *external thread*. A screw has an external thread. An inside thread is an *internal thread* and is found in a nut.

A *right-hand thread* is one that turns clockwise as it moves away from the observer. A *left-hand thread* turns counterclockwise from the same position. A thread is understood to be right-hand unless designated otherwise.

Uses of screw threads. Screw threads would be hard to give up for many purposes. They serve as fasteners, transmit power and motion, and act as measuring devices. Machine screws, bolts, studs, and nuts are universally used to fasten together parts of mechanical devices. They hold securely, yet can be removed easily without damage to the parts. Screw jacks increase forces. Leadscrews of lathes and other machine tools give controlled, precise, and uniform movements. Accurate screws in micrometer calipers, dividing machines, etc. magnify movements so that fine measurements can be made easily.

Features of a screw thread. The chief features of an external thread are illustrated in Fig. 33–1. Internal threads have corresponding features. They determine the size and shape of a thread. The important ones are described here.

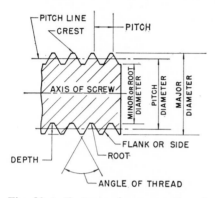

Fig. 33–1. Features of a screw thread.

The *pitch* is the distance parallel to the axis from any point on a screw thread to a corresponding point on the next ridge. The pitch is the reciprocal of the *number of threads* in a unit of length, usually an inch. Thus, a screw that has 8 threads per in. has a pitch of ⅛ in.

The *lead* is the distance a screw advances axially in one full turn. The lead is the reciprocal of the *number of turns* required to advance the screw axially an inch. Thus, a screw that requires 8 turns to move forward an inch in a nut has a lead of ⅛ in.

A *single-thread screw* has only one continuous thread on its surface, as on most commercial screws, bolts, and nuts. A *multiple-thread screw* has two or more adjacent threads. A *double-thread screw* has two threads, a *triple-thread screw* has three, etc. The lead of a single-thread screw is equal to its pitch, but the lead of a double-thread screw is twice the pitch, the lead of a triple-thread screw is three times the pitch, etc.

The *major diameter* of a straight thread is the diameter of a cylinder on which the crest of an external thread or the root of an internal thread lies. The *minor diameter* applies to the root of an external thread or the crest of an internal thread. The *pitch diameter* of a straight thread is the diameter of a cylinder that cuts the thread where the width of the thread is equal to the width of the space.

Screw thread forms. Screw threads are made with a number of cross sections. The most common are indicated in Fig. 33–2.

The *sharp V thread* has an angle of 60°, and each flank makes an angle of 30° with a radius of the screw. The thread and space have the same form. The depth $(D) = 0.866 \times$ pitch (P).

The *Whitworth* or *British Standard Screw Thread* has an angle of 55°. The crests and roots are rounded.

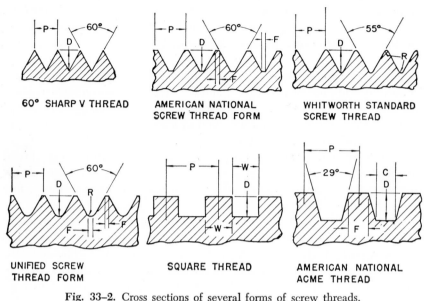

60° SHARP V THREAD

AMERICAN NATIONAL
SCREW THREAD FORM

WHITWORTH STANDARD
SCREW THREAD

UNIFIED SCREW
THREAD FORM

SQUARE THREAD

AMERICAN NATIONAL
ACME THREAD

Fig. 33–2. Cross sections of several forms of screw threads.

At one time the *American National Screw Thread Form* had flat crests and roots but now it is like the *Unified National Screw Thread Form*. The crests and roots may be flat or rounded, as formed by a tool as it wears. The Unified Standard applies to specified sizes from ¼ to 1½ in. The crest of the external thread is truncated by ⅛, and the root by ⅙, of the depth of a full V-thread. Thus, the basic depth of an external thread is $17\!/_{24}$ of the depth of a V-thread, or depth $(D) = 0.6135 \times$ pitch (P). Tolerance is negative on both crest and root diameters.

The internal thread of the Unified and American National Form is truncated in the root so that the flat $(F) = P/8$, but on the crest, $F = P/4$. Consequently for a nut the thread depth $(D) = 0.5413 \times P$. In effect this calls for cutting only 75% of a thread, which makes for easier machining with no appreciable loss in strength.

The *American National Acme Thread* has a 29° angle. The basic depth $(D) = P/2$. The width of the crest $(F) = 0.3707 \times$ pitch (P), and the width at the root (C) is 0.003 to 0.005 in. less.

Square and Acme threads are able to carry heavy loads. Typical uses are for jack screws and feed and operating screws of machine tools. The Acme thread is easier to machine with uniform accuracy than the square thread, which is not produced much.

Metric Threads resemble the National Screw Thread Form but are dimensioned in the Metric System, in millimeters instead of inches.

Threads developed on cones or tapers have specific applications, such as for pipe threads and wood screws. The *American National Taper Pipe Thread* has an angle of 60° between flanks of the thread. The crests and roots are cut to follow a taper of ¾ in. per ft.

Screw thread standards. At one time screw threads lacked uniformity in size and shape. Each manufacturer produced screws according to his own system and standards. One product could not be interchanged with another. Standardization of sizes, shapes, and pitches was undertaken to create a condition of order.

Following older standards, the American National Form Screw Thread Standard was adopted in 1924. It specified a series of coarse screw threads that came to be designated by the symbol NC, and a series of fine screw threads by the symbol NF.

An accord was reached by the United States, Britain, and Canada in 1948 on a uniform thread system to promote interchangeability of the products, particularly war matériel, of the three countries. The standard adopted is known as the Unified Screw Thread Form. Its coarse thread series is designated by UNC, and fine thread series by UNF.

Excerpts of American and Unified Screw Thread Standards

Nominal Size	Basic Major Diam. in.	Coarse Thread Series (NC and UNC)		Fine Thread Series (NF and UNF)	
		TPI	Basic Pitch Diam. in.	TPI	Basic Pitch Diam. in.
¼	0.250	20	0.2175	28	0.2268
⁵⁄₁₆	0.3125	18	0.2764	24	0.2854
⅜	0.375	16	0.3344	24	0.3479
⁷⁄₁₆	0.4375	14	0.3911	20	0.4050
½	0.500	13	0.4500	20	0.4675
⁹⁄₁₆	0.5625	12	0.5084	18	0.5264
⅝	0.6250	11	0.5660	18	0.5889
¾	0.7500	10	0.6850	16	0.7094
⅞	0.8750	9	0.8028	14	0.8286
1	1.000	8	0.9188	12	0.9459
1⅛	1.125	7	1.0322	12	1.0709
1¼	1.250	7	1.1572	12	1.1959
1⅜	1.375	6	1.2667	12	1.3209
1½	1.500	6	1.3917	12	1.4459

Fig. 33–3. Excerpts of American and Unified Screw Thread Standards.

Basic dimensions and threads per inch (*tpi*) for some of the standard sizes of the American National and Unified systems are given in Fig. 33–3. For each nominal size, the coarse-thread series has fewer threads per inch than the fine-thread series. In each series, the number of threads per inch decreases as the size increases. Another but less often used series is that for extra fine threads, designated by the symbol *NEF*.

Complete specifications for the dimensions, allowances, and tolerances of the various thread forms and sizes are given in standards bulletins and hand-books.

Classes of screw threads. Screw threads are divided into *classes* to designate the fits between internal and external mating threads. For some applications a nut may fit loosely on a screw; in other cases they must go together snugly. The different fits are obtained by assigning appropriate tolerances on the pitch, major, and minor diameters and allowances to the threads for each class.

The Unified Form Thread Standard recognizes several classes of threads. Those with A are for screws, B for nuts. Classes 1A and 1B are for a loose fit, where quick assembly and rapid production are important and shake or play is not objectionable. Classes 2A and 2B provide a small amount of play to prevent galling and seizure in assembly and use, and sufficient clearance for thin plating. Classes 2A and 2B are recommended for standard practice in making commercial screws, bolts, and nuts. Classes 3A and 3B have no allowance and 75% of the tolerance of Classes 2A and 2B. A screw and nut may vary from a fit having no play to one with a small amount of play. Only high-grade products are held to Class 3 specifications. Screws of one class may be used with nuts of another class, and that often gives desired results economically. Nine kinds of fits in all are possible.

Classes of threads have been set up for interference fits. A Class 4 has been included in the American National Form Standard as an interference fit. It requires close control of tolerances and has not been recommended for quantity production. A Class 5 fit for external and internal coarse threads from ¼ to 1½ in.-diameter provides positive interference on the pitch diameter with tolerances comparable to those for the Class 3 fit and considered reasonable. It is applicable for studs and thread locking screws in ferrous and nonferrous metals.

MEASURING SCREW THREADS

The size of a screw or bolt is designated by its outside diameter. A ½ in. *UNC* screw should fit a nut of the same nominal size. However, this does not mean that the outside diameter of the screw can be measured alone to determine whether the screw is correct. The major and minor diameters of screw threads are dimensioned to clear the corresponding surfaces of mating threads. Threads make actual contact with each other on their flanks. Measurements must be made in the space against the flanks of a thread to find its true and effective size. The dimensions that need to be measured or gaged directly, indirectly, or compositely are the outside and root diameters, pitch diameters, thread angle, and pitch or lead.

The outside diameter and pitch specify a thread's size. The other dimensions are calculated from these. Ways of computing the thread depth for the common forms of threads have been explained. The root diameter for a screw is equal to the outside diameter minus twice the thread depth.

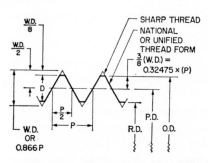

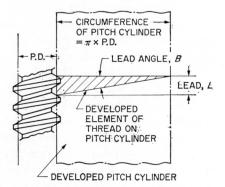

Fig. 33–4. Diameter and thread depth relationships for National and Unified Thread Forms.

Fig. 33–5. The basis for calculation of the lead angle of a screw thread.

The outside diameter of all National and Unified threads is specified over the thread crests truncated to a width equal to ⅛ of the pitch. Accordingly, the basic pitch diameter (PD) = outside diameter (OD) − 0.6495 × pitch (P). The basis for this relationship is given in Fig. 33–4. An allowance is subtracted from the basic pitch diameter to obtain the actual pitch diameter for any thread in Classes 1A and 2A.

If the pitch cylinder of a thread were slit along an element parallel to the axis and unrolled into a plane, it would be a strip having a width equal to π × the pitch diameter (PD). The pitch lines of the thread would lie at an angle across the strip. The angle between one of these lines and a normal to the sides of the strip is the lead angle of the thread, as shown in Fig. 33–5. This angle $(B) = \tan^{-1}[L/(\pi \times PD)]$.

The basic dimensions of a ⅜ − 16 UNC external thread will be calculated as an example. The thread depth $(D) = 0.6135 \times \frac{1}{16} = 0.0383$ in. The root diameter $(RD) = 0.375 − 2 \times 0.0383 = 0.2984$ in. The pitch diameter $(PD) = 0.375 − (0.6495/16) = 0.3344$ in. The lead angle $(B) = \tan^{-1}[1/(16 \times \pi \times 0.3344)] = 3°24'$.

Tolerances and allowances for National and Unified threads are computed by empirical formulas and are given in the tables set up for the standards.

Screw thread micrometer caliper. A screw thread micrometer caliper is like a standard micrometer caliper described in Chap. 15 but has a spindle with a conical point and an anvil with two V-shaped ridges. It makes contact on the sides of a screw thread and measures the pitch diameter directly. Any one anvil is limited to a small range of pitches. Even with the proper range, the readings are slightly distorted unless the micrometer is set to a standard thread plug and used to measure threads of the same diameter and pitch as the plug.

Measuring screw threads with three wires. The three wire method of measuring pitch diameters is more accurate but slower than the use of screw thread micrometer calipers. The arrangement of the wires is indicated in Fig. 33–6. Three wires of any one diameter that would fit within the space might be used, but the preferred diameter or *best wire* for each pitch makes contact on the flanks of the thread at the pitch diameter. A best wire has a diameter equal to ⅔ of the depth of a full V-thread. That depth is equal to 0.866 divided by the number of threads per inch. Thus, the best wire diameter is equal to 0.57735 divided by the number of threads per inch.

When a wire of diameter W touches a 60° thread, its center lies at a distance $W/4$ outside the points of contact as indicated in Fig. 33–6. Therefore, for a best wire size, the diameter (A) over wires is equal to the pitch diameter (PD) plus the product of ¾ times the diameter of the wire (W). The effect of the lead angle on the measurement usually is negligible for standard 60° single-thread screws. Sizes of best wires and measurements over wires are given in published tables.

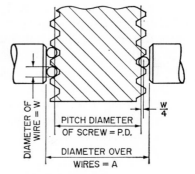

Fig. 33–6. Measuring a screw with three wires.

Effect of pitch, lead, and form errors. The standards do not specify tolerances for thread pitch, lead, or angle. Some error can be expected in these elements, and it detracts from the pitch diameter tolerance, which is specified. For instance, an error of 0.001 in. axially in the lead between any two threads in the length of engagement of a screw adds 0.0017 in. to the effective pitch diameter in mating with another thread.

Thus, measuring or gaging the pitch diameter alone across one or two threads is not enough to verify the functional worth of a screw.

The lead of a thread may be checked separately from the pitch diameter, and that is done to check precision gages and thread rolls. For production purposes, it is more meaningful to gage the high limit of the pitch diameter of a screw over the normal length of engagement at one time because that indicates how well the screw will fit in a nut. On the other hand, the low limit is gaged over one or a few threads only at one time to minimize the effect that lead and form errors have in making the pitch diameter seem large.

A typical device checks thread lead by comparing the thread on the workpiece with a precise master and showing any difference between the two on a dial indicator.

A set of *screw thread pitch gages* is shown in Fig. 15–12 (29). Such a gage is held up against a screw to check its pitch approximately.

Optical or projection comparators like the one in Fig. 15–31 are widely used for checking thread form and lead.

Thread gages. Typical plug, ring, and snap gages for threads are described in Chap. 15 in connection with Fig. 15–20. Such gages are made closely to theoretical sizes and forms of threads and check how screws and nuts will fit in service.

Thread snap gages like the one at the lower right of Fig. 33–7 are for rapid checking of screws. Two sets of rolls provide "go" and "not go" limits for the progressive type. A screw of correct size passes between the "go" threaded rolls but is stopped by the "not go" pair. The gages at the top of Fig. 33–7 are comparator types that are more sensitive. Their contacting members are threaded rolls or segments that bear against the workpiece, whose relative size is registered through a linkage on an indicator dial. "Go" rolls on gages like those in Fig. 33–7 each have a number of threads to indicate the effects of lead and form error over an appreciable length of screw. The "not go" rolls may have only one thread each.

WAYS OF MAKING SCREW THREADS

Screws may be cut or formed. They may be cut with single-point tools on a lathe or with multiple-tooth cutters that include dies, taps, and milling cutters on various types of machines.

Threads are formed on screws and bolts by rolling or pressing on thread rolling machines. Internal and external threads may be rolled in thin sheet metal and tubing, like those on a metal lid for a glass jar or the base of an electric light bulb.

Fig. 33–7. Functional gages for checking screws. (Courtesy Standard Pressed Steel Co.)

The methods just named for cutting and forming threads will be described in more detail in the remainder of this chapter. Threads also are ground, as described in Chap. 29. They may be hobbed like gears, as indicated in Chap. 34. Parts with threads are also produced by die casting and plastic molding.

Thread cutting on a lathe. Thread cutting on a lathe is called *chasing* a thread (Fig. 33–8). The single-point tool is ground with its cutting edge of the same shape as the thread space and enough relief to clear the helical sides. Practically every engine and toolroom lathe has an accurate leadscrew that drives the carriage, and the tool mounted on it, to chase the thread as the workpiece turns. The number of

Fig. 33–8. Cutting a screw thread on a lathe with the compound rest set at 29°. (Courtesy South Bend Lathe Works.)

threads per inch cut on a lathe depends upon the relative rates of rotation of the work spindle and leadscrew, as well as the lead of the leadscrew. The necessary rate of rotation of the leadscrew for any job is obtained by driving it through a selective gear train from the spindle as described in Chap. 18.

A modern lathe with a sliding gear transmission in the leadscrew drive has a plate that tells how to shift the levers to cut any of the threads it can produce. The engineer who designs the lathe must select the gear ratios for each lever position. This is a typical problem in machine design and deserves attention. The same problem must be solved on those lathes, usually older ones, that have pick-off change gears between the spindle and leadscrew. With *simple gearing,* as shown in Fig. 33–9, the rate of rotation of the leadscrew depends only upon the stud gear, driven at spindle speed, and the leadscrew gear. The idler gear may be any convenient size to connect the others together.

The proper ratio for simple gearing is found from the proportion that:

$$\frac{\text{the number of teeth on stud gear}}{\text{the number of teeth on leadscrew gear}} = \frac{\text{the number of threads per in. on leadscrew}}{\text{the number of threads per in. to be cut}}.$$

As an example, 13 threads per in. are to be cut, and the leadscrew has 6 threads. Then:

$$\frac{\text{stud gear}}{\text{leadscrew gear}} = \frac{6T}{13T} = \frac{12T}{26T} = \frac{18T}{39T} = \frac{24T}{52T}, \text{ etc.}$$

Sometimes simple gear ratios cannot be found to cut a desired thread. Then it is necessary to resort to *compound gearing.* One such arrangement is indicated in Fig. 33–9. Two idler or intermediate gears revolve together on one shaft. One is driven by the stud gear, and the other drives the leadscrew gear. The product of the ratios of the gear sets must equal the ratio between the number of threads on the leadscrew and on the workpiece.

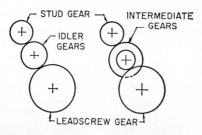

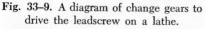

SIMPLE GEARING   COMPOUND GEARING

Fig. 33–9. A diagram of change gears to drive the leadscrew on a lathe.

A series of light cuts is taken to chase a thread accurately. The depth of the first cut or two may be as much as 0.005 in., but after that the tool is fed in only 0.002 to 0.003 in. for each cut, and finally 0.001 in. or less per pass for the last few finishing cuts. If the cuts are too heavy, the tool may be damaged, the workpiece distorted, or the threads torn. At the end of each pass the tool must be withdrawn and the feed stopped. The tool is then taken back to the beginning and set to depth, and the feed is engaged at the instant that starts the tool on the right path for the next pass. Most modern lathes have a *threading dial* on the front of the carriage. It is turned by a worm gear meshed with the leadscrew and shows the operator when to engage the half nut to start the tool in the right path.

Thread chasing is done at ⅓ to ½ the surface speed of turning. This is partly to conserve the tool and partly to give the operator time to do all that is necessary. The steps to chase a thread have been described in some detail to explain why thread cutting on a lathe is slow, requires skill, and is expensive. Its merit is that it is versatile and calls for little special equipment. External and internal, right- and left-hand, straight and tapered, and practically all sizes and pitches of threads can be chased on screw-cutting engine lathes with regular equipment. Quite accurate threads can be produced on a good machine. Other methods are faster but usually require special equipment that is not justified unless a moderate or large quantity of threads of one kind is needed.

As was mentioned, the feed must be stopped and the tool withdrawn at the end of the cut. This is most easily done if a *relief groove* is first cut, as indicated in Fig. 33–10. A designer should always specify a groove, if at all possible, at the end of a thread, whether it is to be made on a lathe or in any other way, to provide relief for the tools. It is common practice to make the groove as wide as the pitch of the thread, but it may be wider. If a tool having several teeth is used, such as a die, the groove should be wide enough to take the lead teeth and the first full tooth.

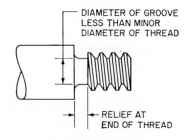
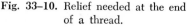

DIAMETER OF GROOVE LESS THAN MINOR DIAMETER OF THREAD

RELIEF AT END OF THREAD

Fig. 33–10. Relief needed at the end of a thread.

Thread-cutting dies. A threading die has an internal thread like a nut, but lengthwise grooves in the hole expose the cutting edges of the threads. Dies are made of hardened carbon tool steel or high-speed steel.

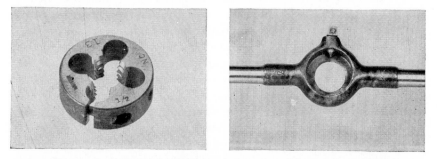

Fig. 33–11. A solid adjustable round split die and stock. (Courtesy Winter Bros. Co.)

A *solid adjustable die* is shown in Fig. 33–11. It is like a *solid die* except that it is split on one side and has an adjusting screw in a cross hole. Whereas a solid die cuts just one size, an adjustable die can be expanded or contracted slightly to change the size it cuts. Solid and adjustable dies are commonly sold for standard thread sizes up to 1½ in. and are used by hand in a holder called a *stock*. The entering end of the hole in the die is tapered to provide a throat to start the workpiece and distribute the cutting load over several teeth. The remaining teeth cut to full depth. Dies in common fractional sizes cost $1 to $5 depending on size and quality.

Spring adjustable dies and die heads are used on machines, mostly for production. A *spring adjustable screw threading die* resembles and can be sprung like a collet to cut to a desired size.

Fig. 33–12. A self-opening die head. (Courtesy Geometric Tool Co.)

A *die head* has a body in which four or more serrated blades or chasers are mounted. The blade may be carbon tool steel, high-speed steel, or cemented carbide. They are removed when dull, reground, replaced, and adjusted to cut to a desired size. The chasers are mounted radially in some heads but positioned tangentially to the workpiece in other heads.

A *self-opening die head,* like the one in Fig. 33–12, is arranged so that it is tripped, and its chasers snap outward when a thread has been cut to a predetermined length. The workpiece does not then have to be screwed out of the die head. The chasers are returned to cutting position by pulling the handle on the head before another piece is cut.

Threading machines. Dies and die heads are commonly used on lathes, turret lathes, and automatic bar and turning machines for cutting threads faster than they can be chased with single-point tools.

Universal threading machines like the one in Fig. 33–13 are used for threading bolts, studs, automotive parts, pipes, etc. They are made with one or two heads. Each head carries a revolving self-opening die head. Opposite each head is a carriage that slides on ways to carry the work to and from the dies. A standard vice is normally mounted on each carriage for holding work but may be replaced by a collet chuck or a special fixture. A leadscrew may be geared to the head to drive the carriage for cutting more accurate threads. The two carriages operate inde-

Fig. 33–13. The working zone of a threading machine with two heads. (Courtesy Landis Machine Co.)

pendently, and their operation cycles may be automatic or manually controlled. Cutting fluid is available to each head. An automatic double bolt threading machine for ¼ to 1 in.-diameters with equipment including leadscrews weighs about 4000 lb and costs around $8500.

Taps. Holes are usually threaded by taps. A *tap* has a shank and a round body with several radially placed chasers. Taps are made in many sizes and shapes to satisfy a number of purposes. They may be operated by hand or machine. They are made to cut all forms of threads. Small taps are solid; large taps may be solid or adjustable. A tap has two or more flutes that may be straight, helical or spiral, or spiral pointed. Taps are made of carbon tool steel for low first cost or high-speed steel for rapid production and endurance. Ground high-speed steel taps may be run up to drilling speeds. A tap works under strenuous conditions because it is buried in metal and fed at an invariable rate. It must be fully supplied with a cutting fluid suitable for the work material to operate successfully. The principal kinds of taps are described in the paragraphs that follow.

Hand taps have short shanks with square ends and are made in sets of three for each size. The three are the *taper, plug,* and *bottoming* taps,

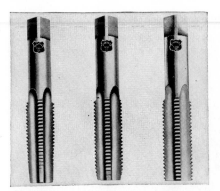

Fig. 33–14. Straight flute hand taps, from left to right; a taper, plug, and bottoming tap. (Courtesy Standard Tool Co.)

shown in Fig. 33–14. The taper tap is the easiest to start in a hole. It will cut a thread through a hole but not to the bottom of a blind hole. In the latter case, it must be followed by a plug tap and then by a bottoming tap. A high-speed steel tap with a ground thread for ½ in.-diameter costs about $2.50.

Hand taps are driven by machines as well as by hand. In either event, the tap must be started straight and be kept aligned with the hole for true threads. The smaller a tap, the more fragile it is. A tap breaks if it meets too much resistance and too much torque is applied. This is a major trouble in some operations. Skill is needed to tap small holes by hand and avoid breakage. Torque limiting tap drivers are commonly used on machines.

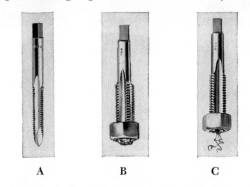

A   B   C

Fig. 33–15. (A) A spiral pointed tap. (B) The action of a straight flute tap. (C) The action of a spiral pointed tap, showing how the chips are driven ahead. (Pratt and Whitney Photo from Pratt and Whitney Division, Niles-Bement-Pond Co., W. Hartford, Conn.)

Straight flute taps are easiest to make and sharpen, but spiral or helical flutes help to clear away chips. A compromise is the *spiral pointed tap* illustrated in Fig. 33–15 with a negative helix on the end along the tapered teeth. This helps prevent chips from clogging the flutes.

Serial hand taps are made in sets of three. Two are undersize for roughing and are used first. A serial tap has one or more rings scribed around its shank to designate its place in the use sequence. Serial taps are used in tough metal, for threads like Acme threads that require a large stock removal, and to provide a light finishing cut for a smooth finish.

Pulley taps and *Nut taps* have long shanks to reach into inaccessible places. *Tapper taps* are used for tapping nuts in large quantities on specialized nut tapping machines and are made in a number of lengths and shapes for specific applications.

Fig. 33–16. A collapsible tap. (Courtesy Murchey Div., The Sheffield Corp.)

Collapsible taps operate like self-opening die heads and are used on turret lathes and automatics. Threads are cut by several chasers held in the body. The collapsible tap of Fig. 33–16 has two collars behind the chasers. The front collar may be set to trip the tap from the face of the workpiece or the rear one from a stop. When the tap is withdrawn, it is reset by a finger acting against the collar.

Pipe taps are tapered and are used to cut internal pipe threads. One style carries a short drill in front of the tap to clean out the hole to be tapped.

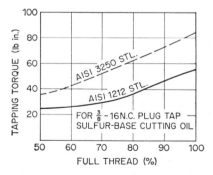

Fig. 33–17. Typical torque to percent depth of thread curves. (From Stuart E. Sinclair, "What Horsepower for Tapping?" *American Machinist*, May 20, 1957, p. 132.)

Design for tapping. The larger a hole is drilled for tapping, the easier the thread is to cut. Less thread depth means fewer chips in the hole and less torque with less tap breakage. A typical illustration of how the torque increases with thread depth is given in Fig. 33–17. Theoretically a full thread is only 5% stronger than a 75% thread and 20% stronger than a 50% thread. Common practice is to use, and the Unified Thread Standard is based on, a 75% thread, but in many cases even less is desirable. Experiments by M. L. Begeman and

C. C. Chervenka showed that steel threads from ¼ to ¾ in.-diameter and not over 40% full depth were as strong as the bolt for an engagement length equal to the diameter. This indicates that in many cases a 50% thread, to allow for tool runout and standard tap drill sizes, is adequate.

Tapping machines. Tapping is done on lathes, turret lathes, and automatics and on drill presses. Some machines called tapping machines are basically drill presses equipped with tap holders, reversing mechanisms, leadscrews, etc. to enhance their tapping ability. They may have one or more spindles.

A tapping attachment may be fastened to the spindle of a standard drilling machine that does not have built-in tapping accessories. Some attachments are of the speed-up type and revolve small taps at high speeds. Tapping attachments are arranged to rotate the tap in a forward direction when it is lowered into the hole and reverse the direction of rotation when the tap is withdrawn from the hole. This action may be obtained from opposed sensitive friction clutches in the tapping attachment head.

Machines for tapping nuts and other small parts are made with four, six, or eight vertical spindles in a row. The nuts are placed in fixtures under the spindles. The taps are lowered at a rate equal to the lead of the thread. The spindles advance one after another on one style of machine, and each station is loaded while its spindle is in a raised position. Straight shank tapper taps are used. Nuts collect on each tap shank, the tap is removed from the spindle when full, and the nuts are stripped off. Another style of machine has two sets of fixtures, and one set is unloaded and loaded while the workpieces in the other set are being tapped. The taps are all advanced at the same time, reversed at the end of the cuts, and screwed out of the workpieces and retracted at a fast rate. Production rates of as high as 150 pieces per min are achieved on multiple-spindle tapping machines.

An illustration is given in Fig. 33–18 of the mechanism of an automatic nut tapper that uses a bent tap to produce nuts continuously. Blanks pass from a hopper down a chute and enter an ejector that feeds them onto the tap one at a time. The tap is revolved continuously and is moved forward into each blank. The nuts are held in guides to keep them from turning and are not pulled along by the tap while the threads are being cut, to prevent binding. After one nut has been tapped, the tap with the nut on it is moved back ready for the next blank. The tap is always filled with nuts, which support and told the tap centrally in the revolving head. As each nut climbs onto the tap, it forces another off the bent end.

Fig. 33–18. A sectional view of the head of an automatic tapper that uses a bent tap. (Courtesy The National Machinery Co.)

Thread milling. A conventional thread milling machine, shown in Fig. 33–19, is like a lathe with a headstock and tailstock mounted on a bed. A carriage slides between the two on ways and carries a cutter head. The work may be mounted between centers or chucked on the headstock spindle.

Multiple-thread form cutters, like the one in Fig. 33–19, are used for rapid thread cutting. The cutter does not have a thread or lead. Instead its teeth are arrayed on a series of closed circles. The axis of the cutter and work are in parallel planes but at an angle equal to the lead angle of the thread. The revolving cutter is fed to depth in the work. It is longer than the thread. As the work revolves, the cutter is fed lengthwise to conform to the lead of the thread. At the end of $1\frac{1}{10}$ revolutions of the work, the cutter is withdrawn from the completed thread. An internal thread may be milled in a similar manner. Milling with multiple thread form cutters is often as fast as thread cutting with self-opening dies and collapsible taps and produces more accurate threads and better finishes. It is mostly confined to V-type threads (not necessarily sharp) because too much error is introduced in other threads.

Fig. 33–19. A view of an external thread milled with a multiple thread form cutter on a thread miller. (Pratt and Whitney Photo from Pratt and Whitney Division, Niles-Bement-Pond Co., W. Hartford, Conn.)

Coarse threads, like those on feedscrews and leadscrews, are milled with single cutters on a *universal thread miller*. The cutter is tilted to match the lead angle of the thread. As the work revolves, the cutter head and carriage are moved longitudinally on the machine by a leadscrew or cam to produce the desired lead. The cutter thus traverses the entire thread, and the length of thread is limited only by the capacity of the machine. Long threads are cut in this way faster than by chasing with a single-point tool, and the method is economical when enough pieces are needed to justify the single-purpose machine and cutters.

Threads can also be milled on a planetary milling machine described in Chap. 24.

Thread rolling. Thread rolling is a cold forging rather than a cutting process. It produces external threads by subjecting a blank to pressure between dies in the form of grooved blocks or threaded rolls. The work material is depressed to open the root and raised to fill the crest of the thread. Threads are rolled on machines built especially for the purpose, on lathes and drill presses, or in combination with other operations on

TYPES OF THREAD ROLLING MACHINES

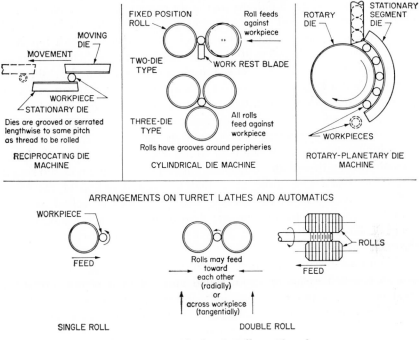

Fig. 33–20. Methods of Rolling Threads.

turret lathes and automatic bar machines. The principles of operation of the various methods are illustrated in Fig. 33–20.

The *rotary-planetary die machine* has a continuous action and is fast for screws of less than ½ in.-diameter. It can turn out ¼ in.-diameter screws at 400 to 1200 per min. The optimum ranges overlap, but the *reciprocating die machine* does well for diameters from ½ to 1 in. A typical rate for ¾ in.-diameter bolts is 40 to 60 per min. It is best for threads of all sizes with wide root flats, like wood screws, because the dies can be made to widen the flats gradually as the thread is formed. The *cylindrical die machine* is suited for large diameters, such as the production of 3 in.-diameter bolts at the rate of 4 per min. Cylindrical machines can roll long threads by thru-feeding. All types can be arranged with hoppers and automatic loading equipment. A typical basic thread rolling machine of ⅛ to 1½ in.-diameter capacity weighs 4000 lb and costs about $12,000.

Thread rolling offers a number of advantages. It is capable of producing accurate, uniform, and smooth threads of all classes at high rates of production on all kinds of screws, bolts, and studs. Rolling speeds are equivalent to cutting speeds with high-speed steel. No material is cut away to form the spaces, and up to 27% of material may be saved unless the screw blank is cut from a larger piece of stock anyway. The material is cold-worked; its grain pattern continuity is not cut away; and a smooth wearable surface is left on the thread flank. Wear life is lengthened; tensile strength may be increased 10%; and fatigue strength has been found raised as much as 5 to 10 times for hardened alloy bolts with rolled instead of cut threads. The dies roll rather than rub and retain their original sizes a long time, often for millions of pieces. Thread rolling is more convenient than die cutting for some set-ups on automatic bar machines, such as for cutting a thread behind a shoulder.

Thread rolling requires some care and has several limitations. A blank for rolling must be made with an initial diameter less than the pitch diameter of the thread and to a close tolerance. The action of the rolling operation must be carefully controlled to avoid bending of the blank and seams or slivers on the thread. Threads cannot be rolled easily in material with an elongation of less than about 5% or a hardness over about 32 Rockwell C. The last fraction of a turn on the end of a rolled thread is truncated.

Almost all threads are rolled in large quantities because that is fastest and cheapest. Threads are both rolled and cut in moderate quantities on standard semi-automatic machines, and the total cost is not much different for either method. Commercial self-opening thread rolling heads and rolls for standard sizes of threads are comparable in price to self opening die heads and chasers. A head with capacity of ½ to 1 in.-diameter costs around $400, and a set of rolls for a specific size about $50. General-purpose threading in small quantities is seldom done by rolling because cutting is more adaptable and versatile for varieties of requirements and circumstances.

Formed internal threads. An *X-Press* tap is a proprietary tool that does not have grooves or flutes like an ordinary tap. It cold-forms and swages the threads in a hole instead of cutting them. Sizes run up to ⅜ in.-diameter. The material is compacted and burnished, the grain fibers are unbroken, and the threads are strong like rolled threads. No chips are present to clog the bottom of a blind hole; lead is easy to control, and speeds up to twice those for cutting have been found practical. Holes must be tap drilled larger than for conventional tapping and countersunk because the material is extruded.

Questions

1. Define a screw thread, a right-hand thread, and a left-hand thread.

2. Describe three general uses of screw threads.

3. What is meant by the pitch and lead of a screw thread? How do the pitch and lead agree for a single-thread screw and for a multiple-thread screw?

4. Define the major, minor, and pitch diameters of a thread.

5. Make a sketch of a Unified Screw Thread Form and name its parts.

6. What is the Unified Screw Thread Form Standard?

7. Why are screw threads divided into classes? What are common classes?

8. Describe four ways of measuring or checking screw threads.

9. What effect do pitch, lead, and form errors have on a screw thread?

10. In what ways can threads be cut or formed?

11. How is a lathe arranged to cut threads?

12. Why is thread cutting on a lathe slow and costly? When is it done?

13. Why should a groove be cut at the end of a thread?

14. Describe the principal types of dies. How are they used?

15. Describe the operation of a universal threading machine.

16. Describe the three styles of hand taps. How are they used?

17. What are serial hand taps, pulley taps, collapsible taps, and pipe taps?

18. Describe three types of tapping machines.

19. In what two ways may threads be cut on thread milling machines?

20. How is thread rolling done? What are its advantages and disadvantages?

Problems

1. What is the nominal thread depth for each of the following threads?
   (a) #5 (0.125)—40 NC   (b) ¼—20 UNC   (c) ½—13 UNC
   (d) ⅝—11 UNC   (e) ⅞₆—20 UNF   (f) ¾—16 UNF

2. The basic addendum of a thread is the radial distance from the outside diameter to the pitch diameter. The basic dedendum is the radial distance from the pitch diameter to the root diameter. What are the basic addenda and dedenda of external threads with the specifications listed in Prob. 1?

3. Specify the basic outside diameter, root diameter, pitch diameter, and helix angle for each of the external threads listed in Prob. 1.

4. Calculate the basic minor diameters of external screw threads with the specifications listed in Prob. 1.

5. Find the size to bore a hole for a 1¼—6 UNC internal thread.

6. Show that the best wire size for a 60° thread has a diameter $(W) = \frac{2}{3} \times$ the depth of a full V thread of the same pitch, and thus that the best wire diameter $(W) = 0.57735/\text{TPI}$.

7. Prove that the diameter (A) over best wires on a 60° thread is equal to the pitch diameter (PD) plus the product of $\frac{3}{2} \times$ the diameter of the wires (W).

8. Find the best wire size and measurement over three wires for a ⅝—11 UNC thread.

9. What is the error in the answer to Prob. 8 from neglecting the lead angle?

10. Find the best wire size and diameter over three wires for a ⅞—9 UNC thread.

11. Wires of 0.050 in.-diameter are available for checking a ⅝—11 UNC thread. The dimension measured over these wires is 0.6315 in. What does this indicate the pitch diameter to be?

12. The leadscrew on a lathe has four threads per inch. Specify the gear ratios required to cut each of the following numbers of threads per inch. (a) 4   (b) 5   (c) 6   (d) 7   (e) 8   (f) 12   (g) 16   (h) 18   (i) 20 (j) 25.

13. It is desired to cut a fine thread of 56 TPI on a lathe with pick off gears and a leadscrew with 6 threads per in. The smallest gear available has 20 teeth, and the largest 100 teeth, with all ratios available in between. How should the lathe be geared, and with what ratios?

14. What nominal size would you select for a tap drill for a ½—13 NC thread? Give your reasons for your choice if the material is steel.

15. Six H.S.S. taps are to be driven at 60 fpm by a multiple-spindle drill press. They include (2) ⅜—16 NC, (2) ½—13 NC, and (2) ¾—16 NF thread taps. Maximum torque per tap is estimated to be 140, 220, and 230 in-lb respectively. Machine efficiency is 70%. What size motor should be supplied?

References

A.S.T.E., *The Tool Engineers Handbook*, McGraw-Hill Book Co., Inc., New York.

Unified and American Screw Threads, Proposed American Standard ASA B1.1, American Standards Association, New York, 1949.

Gears and Gear Manufacture

A gear is a machine element that transmits motion in a positive manner through teeth around its periphery. The *spur gear* is the simplest form with teeth parallel to its axis as shown in Fig. 34–1. A *rack* is a gear with an infinite radius; it moves in a straight line.

Fig. 34–1. A spur gear and rack. (Courtesy Foote Bros. Gear and Machine Co.)

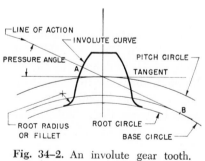

Fig. 34–2. An involute gear tooth.

Gear tooth curves. The contact surfaces of gear teeth are curved to transmit motion uniformly as they roll and slide together. Most gear teeth today have or approximate an involute form because it is simple,

735

easy to reproduce, and allows variations in center distances of mating gears. A gear tooth with the involute curve modified at the extremities is said to have a *composite* form.

An *involute curve* is generated by a point on a straight line rolling on a *base circle*. The line AB in Fig. 34–2 is tangent to the base circle, and point A traces the involute profile of one side of the gear tooth as the line is rolled on the circle. In the position shown, the angle between the *line of action AB* and the tangent to the pitch circle is called the *pressure angle*. A *pitch circle* is an imaginary ring of the same diameter as a smooth disk that would transmit the same relative motion by friction as the gear does when meshed with another gear. The radius or fillet adds strength to the root of the tooth.

Elements of gear teeth. Gear teeth have been standardized so they mesh together. Two shapes of gear teeth are recognized. One is called the *full depth tooth* and is longer than comparable sizes of the other, known as the *stub tooth*. Stub teeth are stronger but do not overlap as much as full depth teeth.

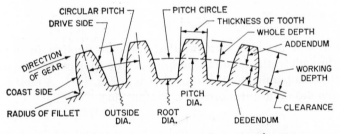

Fig. 34–3. The elements of gear teeth.

The important dimensions of gear teeth are called elements and are designated in Fig. 34–3. They are related to a factor called *diametral pitch*, which is defined as the number of teeth on the gear divided by the pitch diameter in inches. Any two standard gears of the same diametral pitch and tooth shape will mesh if mounted with the proper distance between their centers. The formulas for finding the sizes of the main elements of full depth and stub gear teeth are given in Table 34–1.

Table 34–1 shows that the circular pitch and tooth thickness at the pitch line are the same for all gears of the same diametral pitch whether they have full depth or stub teeth. On the other hand, the addendum, dedendum, and whole depth that determine tooth height are smaller for a stub tooth than for a full depth tooth of the same diametral pitch. Also, tooth size decreases as diametral pitch increases.

TABLE 34–1. Formulas for Calculating the Dimensions
of Diametral Pitch Gears

Element name	Symbol	Formula for: Full depth teeth with 14½° pressure angle	Stub teeth with 20° pressure angle
Addendum	a	$a = 1/P$	$a = 0.8/P$
Circular pitch	p	$p = \pi/P = \pi D/N$	$p = \pi/P = \pi D/N$
Clearance	c	$c = 0.157/P$	$c = 0.2/P$
Dedendum	b	$b = a + c = 1.157/P$	$b = a + c = 1/P$
Diametral pitch	P	$P = N/D$	$P = N/D$
Number of teeth	N	$N = P \times D = \pi D/p$	$N = P \times D = \pi D/p$
Outside diameter	D_o	$D_o = (N + 2)/P = D + 2a$	$D_o = (N + 1.6)/P = D + 2a$
Pitch diameter	D	$D = N/P = (N \times p)/\pi$	$D = N/P = (N \times p)/\pi$
Root diameter	D_R	$D_R = D_o - 2b_t = (N - 2.314)/P$	$D_R = D_o - 2b_t = (N - 2)/P$
Tooth thickness	t	$t = 1.5708/P$	$t = 1.5708/P$
Whole depth	b_t	$b_t = a + b = 2.157/P$	$b_t = a + b = 1.8/P$
Working depth	b_k	$b_k = b_t - c = 2/P$	$b_k = b_t - c = 1.6/P$

What a gear must do determines the diametral pitch, number of teeth, and tooth width. From these the other dimensions can be calculated by means of the formulas in Table 34–1.

Spur gear tooth form systems. Various systems have been advocated for standardizing gear tooth shapes and sizes. Four are generally accepted now and are described in detail in reference- and hand-books on the subject. Essentially they are based upon the choice of either 14½° or 20° pressure angle with either full depth or stub teeth.

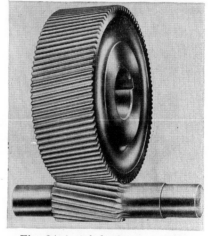

Fig. 34–4. A helical gear and pinion. (Courtesy Foote Bros. Gear and Machine Co.)

Types of gears. Spur gears are the easiest and cheapest kind to make. They must be mounted on parallel shafts. A *helical gear*, like the one in Fig. 34–4, has teeth along helices on a cylinder. The angle between a helix and an element of the pitch cylinder is called the *helix angle*. Helical gears are more expensive than spur gears but are stronger and quieter because the teeth engage gradually and more teeth are in mesh at the same time. They may be mounted on parallel shafts or on non-parallel and non-intersecting shafts.

A helical gear has a decided side thrust that is neutralized in a *herringbone gear*, like the one in Fig. 34–5, that has teeth on right- and left-hand helices.

Fig. 34–5. A continuous tooth herringbone gear. (Courtesy Foote Bros. Gear and Machine Co.)

A *worm* is like a screw and may have one or more threads, each a tooth. A high ratio can be obtained by engaging a worm with a *worm gear*, as shown in Fig. 34–6. Their axes are non-intersecting and usually at right angles. A worm gear with a small helix angle cannot drive the worm, which is an advantage for some applications.

Bevel gears operate on axes that intersect at any required angle but most commonly at right angles. A bevel gear is conical in form. A *straight bevel gear* has straight teeth like the one on the machine in Fig. 34–14. If all the lines along its teeth were extended, they would pass through a common point called the *apex*. This apex point coincides with the point of intersection of the axes of mating bevel gears. A pair of bevel gears with equal numbers of teeth and perpendicular axes are called *miter gears*.

A *crown gear* is a bevel gear with a plane instead of a conical pitch surface. A crown gear is in the form of a disk and corresponds for bevel gears to the rack for spur gears.

Fig. 34–6. A worm and worm gear. (Courtesy Foote Bros. Gear and Machine Co.)

Fig. 34–7. A spiral bevel, hypoid, and Zerol bevel gear. (Courtesy Gleason Works.)

The teeth of a *spiral bevel gear* are curved and oblique. One is shown on the left of Fig. 34–7. Spiral bevel gears run smoothly and quietly and are strong because their teeth have what is known as spiral overlap.

They are relatively easy to manufacture. A *Zerol bevel gear* has curved teeth, but they lie in the same general direction as straight teeth, as shown on the right of Fig. 34–7.

Hypoid gears resemble bevel gears but their axes do not intersect, as indicated in the middle view of Fig. 34–7. They are quiet and strong. A common application is for automobile rear axle drives.

The gears described so far are the important *external gears*. An *internal gear* is one with teeth inside a cylinder or cone. Internal gears are used for clutches, speed train reducers, and planetary gear trains.

Methods of making gears. Gears are produced by casting, molding, pressure forming, flame cutting, and machining.

Gears may be cast in sand or in permanent molds. Cast iron gears are rough, inaccurate, and low in strength but large sizes can be made at relatively low cost. Many small gears for light service are die cast of zinc, tin, aluminum, and copper alloys. They can be made to a high degree of accuracy and finish.

Gears are sometimes molded of plastic materials where quietness, insulating properties, and only moderate strength for light service are needed. Some gears are pressed and sintered from metallic powders.

Gears are made by several kinds of hot- and cold-forming operations. Gear stock of brass or aluminum is extruded, to be cut to desired lengths. Small and fine pitch worms, involute splines, and gears are rolled from soft steel in the manner described for threads in Chap. 33. As an example, involute splines on the ends of automobile axle shafts are cold-rolled in soft steel at the rate of 6 sec each in quantities of 2½ million pieces per year. Some attempts have been reported of hot-pressing or -rolling relatively coarse pitch gears to finished sizes.

Large gears, such as the ring gear on the base of a revolving crane, are successfully made by flame cutting from thick steel plates. Tolerances reported held are ±0.005 in. with plate up to 4 in. thick and ±0.010 to 8 in. thick.

Gears are cut from cast and forged blanks, bar stock, sheet metal, laminated plastic, and molded shapes. Sometimes machining is the most economical method for small quantities. Sometimes it is most economical for large quantities, such as for gears stamped from sheet metal for watches, clocks, toys, and appliances. Generally gears are machined because that is the only way of getting the degree of accuracy or processing the hard material required by modern exacting mechanisms like internal combustion engines, automotive transmissions, machine tools, etc.

Gear cutting methods may be divided into three classes as follows:

1. The *forming* method, which uses a cutter having the same form as the space between the teeth being cut. The cutter may be a single-point tool on a planer or shaper, a rotating cutter on a milling machine, or a broach.

2. The *template* method, in which a reciprocating cutting tool is guided by a master former or template on a machine called a gear planer. This method is slow and has been displaced for all but quite large and coarse pitch gears.
3. The *generating* method, in which the cutting profile of the tool is like that of a mating gear or rack tooth. The cutter and work roll together as though in mesh to develop the tooth form.

FORM CUTTING

Cutting gear teeth on a milling machine. Spur, helical, worm, and straight bevel gears may be cut on milling machines with standard dividing heads and arbors. Gear cutters are the only tools needed that are not used for other kinds of operations, and their cost is low, from $10 to $60 each depending on size. A cutter will cut many gears, if needed. Set-up is easy. At one time most gears were form cut, but during the present century generating has proven to be a more efficient method of manufacturing gears. Milling machines are not used in modern gear manufacture except when one or a few gears are made at a time and when more efficient equipment is not available. That is because the cutting of gears on a milling machine is a relatively slow and inaccurate process.

When a gear is cut on a milling machine, it is mounted on a dividing head, usually but not always between centers, and the cutter is carried on an arbor as illustrated in Fig. 24–7. That picture shows the table swivelled to align the teeth of a helical gear with the cutter. The table is not swivelled for a spur gear. The dividing head is geared to the table for a helical gear, but not for a spur gear, so that the helical gear revolves as it passes the cutter. One tooth space is cut at a time. After each cut on any gear, the dividing head is manipulated in the usual manner to index the gear to the next space, and so on.

Bevel gears with theoretically correct tooth forms cannot be cut with rotary cutters on a milling machine. Occasionally, a bevel gear may be gashed out on a milling machine in an emergency, but then the teeth must be filed by hand after being cut to make them perform satisfactorily.

Gear tooth form cutters. Commercial form-relieved cutters for spur gears with a 14½° pressure angle and composite form are available in sets. Each set covers one diametral pitch. Each cutter in a set covers a range of certain numbers of teeth and is only an approximation for all but one of the gears in the range. Gear tooth cutters appear in Fig. 24–2. Those made particularly for heavy rough cuts are called *stocking cutters*.

Production form cutting. Gears sometimes are roughed out by form cutting and then finished by generating when manufactured in quantities.

Form-cutting machines are made for the specific purposes of roughing gears rapidly. One type uses a circular form cutter and operates like a milling machine, but has a built in indexing mechanism and roughs out gears automatically. The operator has only to unload and load the work. Such machines are also commonly used for cutting slots and grooves around parts other than gears.

A high-production machine called the *Shear Speed gear shaper* form cuts spur and helical gears. A number of single-point cutters, each with the form of a tooth space of the gear to be cut, are arrayed in a circle in a hollow vertical head. The gear blank is mounted on a fixture below and is reciprocated into the head. The tools are fed in uniformly at each stroke of the work and are retracted when they have cut to depth. All tooth spaces are cut at the same time.

The Shear Speed gear shaper is the fastest gear cutter today and can turn out gears in 15 to 50 seconds each. It is economical for large quantity production. The machines are made in several sizes to take gears up to 10 in.-diameter. A medium-size model with a capacity of 7 in.-diameter by 2¾ in. stroke weighs 22,500 lb and costs around $25,000. A high degree of accuracy is obtained because it depends mostly on the tooling, which is made up especially for each job. The tooling for a job costs several hundred dollars, but the cutters can be resharpened easily and many times. Experience has been that tool costs per piece for large quantities are no more and may be less than for other methods.

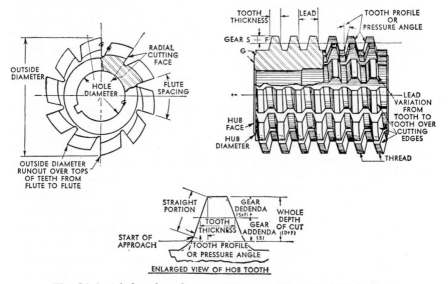

Fig. 34–8. A hob and its elements. (Courtesy Illinois Tool Works Co.)

GEAR GENERATING

Gear hobs. Hobbing is a generating process done with a cutter called a *hob* that revolves and cuts like a milling cutter. Its teeth lie on a helix like a worm. A typical hob is illustrated and its elements are designated in Fig. 34–8. Lengthwise gashes expose the cutting faces that have a contour simulating a rack. The teeth are form-relieved behind the cutting edges. As the hob revolves one turn, the effect is as though the simulated rack were to move lengthwise an amount equal to the lead of the thread on which the teeth lie. When a gear is cut, it is positioned and revolved as if it were in mesh with such a rack. The hob teeth take progressive cuts relative to each tooth space in the manner illustrated in Fig. 34–9. A hob cuts all gears having the same tooth form and diametral pitch as the rack it represents.

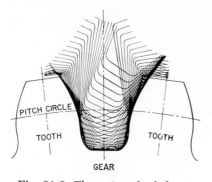

Fig. 34–9. The action of a hob as its teeth progress through and cut the tooth space in a gear.

A hob may have one, two, or more threads. When a spur gear with N teeth is being cut, it can turn only one revolution when a single thread hob turns N times, once when a double thread hob turns $N/2$ times, and so on. Thus a single-thread hob does not produce at as high a rate as a multiple-thread hob turning at the same speed but cuts a more accurate thread because more of its teeth act in each tooth space.

Hobs are made of high-speed steel or with carbide-tipped teeth in several standard classes of accuracy. Hardened but unground hobs are satisfactory for average work, especially for roughing. High-speed steel hobs cost about $50 to $250 from small to large sizes. Hobs finish ground all over for accuracy cost from $10 to $50 more. Hobs are made in several styles. The most common is the straight hob shown in Fig. 34–8.

Hobbing machines. A gear is being hobbed on a hobbing machine in Fig. 34–10. The hob is set at an angle in a horizontal plane so its teeth line up with the tooth spaces of the gear. A constant speed motor drives the hob through speed change gears which are selected to make the hob rotate at the proper speed. Generally hob surface speeds are about the same as milling cutter speeds for comparable materials and other conditions and are governed by the same principles.

The hob spindle and work spindle are connected through index change

Fig. 34–10. A gear being hobbed on a hobbing machine. (Courtesy Barber Colman Co.)

gears that are selected to make the work gear rotate at the proper speed in relation to the hob. Usually the hob is set to cut to depth alongside the gear and then fed across the width of the gear as the gear and hob rotate together. The feed is expressed in inches per revolution of the gear. Common feed rates are between 0.040 and 0.080 in. per rev. The feed rate is obtained from feed change gears in a drive from the work spindle to the leadscrew that moves the hob carriage. The feed must be set in relation to the index ratio between the hob and gear to cut a helical gear.

Hobbing machines are made in many sizes and styles from small ones for watch and instrument gears to huge ones for gears over 10 ft in diameter. Some are general-purpose machines; others are specialized. For large quantity production, hobbing machines are made with several work stations and often are arranged for automatic operation. A medium-size general-purpose hobbing machine for gears up to 16 in.-diameter by 16 in. wide has a 5 hp motor, weighs 6300 lb and costs about $13,000.

Gear shaping. A gear is shaped by a reciprocating cutter in the form of a single tooth, rack, or pinion. The gear blank and cutter move to-

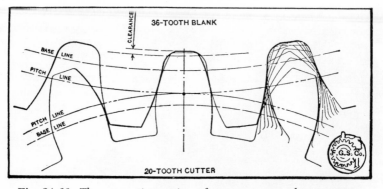

Fig. 34–11. The generating action of a rotary gear shaper cutter. (Courtesy The Fellows Gear Shaper Co.)

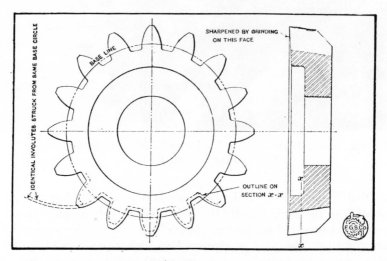

Fig. 34–12. A pinion type gear shaper cutter. (Courtesy The Fellows Gear Shaper Co.)

gether as though in mesh, and a series of cuts are taken as depicted in Fig. 34–11.

The teeth of the typical pinion-type gear shaper cutter of Fig. 34–12 have a true involute form in any section normal to the axis and are form-relieved on the sides, outside, and root for clearance. The face of the cutter is dished to provide rake. As this face is ground to resharpen the cutter, the outside diameter becomes smaller, but the teeth retain their involute form and pitch. Cutters for helical gears have helical teeth. A spur gear cutter is capable of generating any gear of the same pitch in the same system, but a helical gear cutter can generate only gears having one pitch and helix angle.

Gear shapers. The cutter is mounted on the lower end of a reciprocating vertical spindle in the housing on the front of the gear shaper of Fig. 34–13 and is revolved as it reciprocates up and down. Cam guides may be attached to the spindle to guide the cutter in a helical path to cut a helical gear. The workpiece on the vertical spindle below and to the right of the cutter is made to rotate in unison with the cutter by index change gears in the drive between cutter and work spindles.

Fig. 34–13. A 6A type Fellows gear shaper. (Courtesy The Fellows Gear Shaper Co.)

The cutter is fed inward to depth while revolving with the workpiece when the machine is started. Two cuts to depth around a gear are necessary for best results. Both may be taken in one setting, but economical results are obtained in production from a roughing cut on one machine and a finishing cut on another.

The medium-size gear shaper of Fig. 34–13 takes spur gears up to

18 in.-pitch diameter and 5 in. wide, has a 5 hp motor, weighs around 7000 lb, and costs about $16,000.

A number of varieties of gear shapers serve various purposes. Some are made with multiple work stations for large quantity production. Some gear shapers use rack-type cutters which are relatively easy to make because the teeth have straight sides. However, a *rack shaper* is one that cuts racks but uses a pinion shaped cutter. The machine has a long table that feeds the work past the cutter.

The *Sykes gear generator* has two pinion type reciprocating cutters on horizontal in line opposed spindles that thrust and withdraw alternately. The work is also carried on a horizontal spindle. This gear shaper cuts gears up to 12 feet in diameter and can cut continuous tooth herringbone gears. Such a gear is stronger than one with a gap in the middle.

Comparison of gear hobbing and shaping. Spur, helical, and worm gears, worms, ratchet wheels, and sprockets for chain drives are produced by hobbing and shaping. In addition, the processes are capable of machining a variety of other shapes including straight side and involute splines, square and hexagonal shafts, and cams.

Except for the methods described for production form cutting, gear generating methods are faster and more accurate than form cutting. Many gears semifinished by hobbing and shaping are finished by burnishing, shaving, or grinding, which are described later.

About 70% of all cut gears are hobbed. The continuous action of the hobbing process makes it generally faster and more accurate than competing processes. The heat generated in hobbing is dispersed uniformly over the workpiece and cutter. The nature of hobbing requires a relatively simple machine with few motions, but a hobbing machine must be rugged because of the large cutting forces that act in various directions as a gear is cut. Fairly long shafts, splines, or a batch of gears on one mandrel can be accommodated on most hobbing machines. Herringbone gears of the gap type only can be hobbed.

Gear shaping is capable of producing internal gears, gears close to a flange, cluster gears, and continuous herringbone gears, all of which cannot be hobbed. Among other products of the gear shaper are interrupted tooth gears, elliptical gears, face gears, racks, cams, and pawls. The width of gear that can be cut is limited by the relatively short stroke on many gear shapers. Tooling costs about the same for gear shaping as for hobbing.

BEVEL GEAR CUTTING

Machines for cutting bevel gears may be divided into two classes: (1) for straight, and (2) for curved teeth. The basic machines of universal type are the two-tool straight bevel generator and the spiral bevel and hypoid generator. Others are available for special or supplementary purposes, and the most important of them will be described briefly.

Machines and methods for straight tooth bevel gears. A view of the cutting tools and a gear in position on a two-tool *straight bevel generator* is shown in Fig. 34–14. Two tools are used, one on each side of a tooth, to make the tooth taper in the desired manner. They reciprocate along slides on a cradle, and their tips travel along paths directed through the apex of the gear being cut. The tools have straight cutting edges and simulate the sides of a tooth space of an imaginary crown gear. The cradle and tools roll upward with the workpiece as though the simulated crown gear were in mesh with the gear being cut. During the roll, the tools make a series of cuts to develop the tooth shape in a manner similar to that demonstrated for spur gears. A gear with any number of teeth within the capacity of the machine may be cut by arranging the proper relative motions between the tools and blank. One tooth is generated from the bottom to the top of the roll. The gear is then withdrawn and indexed. The cradle is returned to the bottom position, and the gear is fed into full depth with the cutting tools. Another tooth is cut during the next roll, and so on.

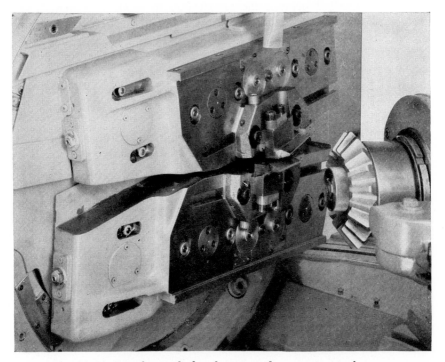

Fig. 34–14. Straight tooth bevel gear and generating tools on a straight bevel gear generator. (Courtesy Gleason Works.)

One design of generator for small straight tooth bevel gears employs two disk-type milling cutters with interlocking teeth instead of reciprocating tools. The cutters are rolled with the blank to generate the teeth. Straight bevel gear generators are available in several sizes for gears from about $\frac{3}{16}$ to $35\frac{1}{2}$ in.-diameter. One with a capacity for gears up to 24 in. pitch diameter, $3\frac{1}{2}$ in. face width, and 12 in. cone weighs 15,250 lb, has motors with a total of $4\frac{1}{2}$ hp, and costs about $28,000.

On some straight bevel generators, the teeth can be slightly crowned from end to end to localize the tooth contact. A gear with crowned teeth may be displaced slightly in assembly or under load without the load being concentrated at the ends of the teeth where it is dangerous. The same effect is obtained from a difference in curvature of the mating surfaces of bevel gears with curved teeth.

Fine pitch straight bevel gears are mostly cut from the solid in one operation. Certain methods combine roughing and finishing in one operation, even for fairly large teeth. Otherwise, all straight bevel gears must be rough-cut prior to finish cutting. They may be roughed in small quantities on the two tool straight bevel generator without generating motion. On the other hand if quantities are large, machines and tools especially designed for rapid roughing without generation are commonly used to prepare bevel gears for finishing.

The *Revacycle Process* is the fastest way to produce straight bevel gears in large quantities. The rotating Revacycle cutter roughs and finishes a tooth space during each revolution it makes. The machine burrs each gear and automatically presents a new one to the cutter. Such a machine for gears up to 7 in.-diameter, 1 in. face, and 5 in. cone weighs 13,000 lb, and costs about $35,000. Automatic loading and handling devices often are added to enable one operator to take care of a number of machines.

Straight bevel gears too large for generating machines and large spur gears are cut on the *gear planer*. This is the oldest type of machine capable of cutting bevel gears with teeth tapering in the correct manner. A single planing tool with rounded point is reciprocated across the face of a gear and is controlled by a template or former to produce the profile shapes of the teeth. The mass that has to be accelerated and decelerated is much less than necessary for generating large gears.

Machines for curved tooth bevel and hypoid gears. A *spiral bevel gear and hypoid generator* employs a special form of face mill like the one on the machine of Fig. 34–15. The cutter represents a tooth of a mating gear and is rolled with the gear being cut to generate the tooth profile. The machine can be adjusted for spiral bevel, Zerol, and hypoid gears. Sometimes both sides of a tooth space are finish cut in one oper-

Fig. 34–15. A spiral bevel gear, rotating cutter, and cradle on a Gleason hypoid generator. (Courtesy Gleason Works.)

ation, and sometimes only one side, depending on the tools available or the quality and quantity of gears required. Machines and cutters are available for gears from ³⁄₁₆ to 33 in.-diameter. A spiral bevel gear and hypoid generator arranged for job cutting gears up to 18 in.-diameter and 1⅜ in. face has a 5 hp motor, weighs 15,000 lb, and costs about $38,000.

Spiral bevel gears, except those of fine pitch, are usually first rough cut and then finish cut. *Spiral bevel roughers* rough cut gears without, and pinions with, a generating motion.

For large quantities of spiral bevel and hypoid gears of ratios of 3:1 and larger, the larger member of a pair is often finish cut without generation on a machine especially designed for that purpose. This decreases the cutting time and cost. The pinion is generated to suit the gear. Such pairs are called *Formate gears.*

Spiral bevel, Zerol, and hypoid gears too large for generators with rotating cutters are cut on the *planing generator*. It employs a single planing tool that cuts tooth after tooth around the blank that rotates continuously. The tool is carried on a cradle that is rolled with respect to the workpiece to provide the generating action.

Spiral bevel grinders are available in both generating and Formate types. They finish grind the teeth after the gears have been semi-finished and hardened. This corrects inaccuracies caused by hardening and promotes uniformity in the gears. A Formate gear grinder for gears to 24 in.-diameter and 3½ in. face weighs 13,720 lb and costs about $60,000.

GEAR FINISHING

A gear tooth surface that is hobbed or shaped is composed of tiny flats. Such a surface is satisfactory for some purposes but is not good enough where a high degree of accuracy and stamina is required. The flats can be made very small by cutting at low feeds, but the operation then becomes slow and costly. Often the lowest net cost can be realized by cutting a gear fast with a less accurate and less expensive tool to tolerances of around 0.001 in. Then a finishing operation is added to obtain the necessary tooth straightness, size, concentricity, spacing, and involute form with small tolerances. Furthermore, gears often are heat treated for hardness and strength, and that tends to warp them and form scale. Finishing after hardening corrects these deficiencies.

Finishing operations are performed to make gears accurate, quiet, smooth running, and dependable. They include shaving and burnishing for soft gears and grinding and lapping for hard gears. Only a few thousandths of an inch or less of stock are left on gear teeth for finishing.

Gear shaving. A gear is shaved by running it at around 400 fpm in mesh with and pressed against a cutter in the form of a gear or rack with gashes or grooves on its tooth faces as typified in Fig. 34–16. The edges of these grooves are sharp and actually scrape fine chips from the faces of the teeth of the workpiece. Some sliding normally takes place between gear teeth in mesh, and this action is augmented in gear shaving by crossing the axes of the cutter and work gear, generally from 5° to 15°, and by reciprocating the workpiece as it is revolved in mesh with the shaving cutter. The tooth form of the cutter is accurately ground and reproduces a correspondingly accurate conjugate form on the workpiece. Shaving can be made to crown gears slightly at their centers to localize tooth contact and keep it away from the ends of the teeth.

The gear in Fig. 34–16 is being shaved by a gear-type shaving cutter on a *rotary shaving machine.* The workpiece is loaded between live centers, raised against the cutter, and reciprocated while being driven in one direction and then the other. Gear shaving machines are made in many sizes, to finish external and internal gears for the smallest to over 16 feet in diameter. A rotary gear shaving machine for external gears up to 12 in. in diameter weighs 10,600 lb and costs $15,000.

A shaving cutter in the form of a rack is reciprocated lengthwise at high speed in mesh with a workpiece on a *rack-type shaving machine.* At the same time the workpiece is reciprocated sideways and fed into

the rack. A rack-type shaver produces uniformly precise gears because the rack form is easier to
make accurately and has fuller contact with the work than a rotary
shaver. The rack-type shaver cannot
accommodate cluster or large gears.
The cutters are large and expensive
but have long lives and low cost
per piece. They are more suitable
for long runs, and circular-type tools
are better for job lots.

Gear shaving is a low cost rapid
production process. Many gears can
be shaved in less than half a minute apiece, some in as short a time
as five seconds. Each cutter is suitable only for a single pitch and
tooth form, and a demand for many
gears is necessary to warrant its
cost.

Fig. 34–16. A camshaft gear being
shaved on a Red Ring rotary gear shaving
machine. (Courtesy National Broach and
Machine Co.)

Gear burnishing. A gear is mounted on a burnishing machine on an
upright floating spindle in mesh with three hardened burnishing gears,
one of which is power driven. The burnishing gears are forced inward
against the work gear and turn a few revolutions in each direction. The
tooth surfaces of the workpiece are smoothed and slightly hardened but
are left with a layer of weak smear metal.

Gear tooth grinding. Hardened gear teeth are ground by forming and
by generating. Three variations of grinding gear teeth with formed
wheels are depicted at the top of Fig. 34–17. The results depend upon
the accuracy to which the wheel is trued. This is done by guiding the
truing diamonds on the machine through a pantograph mechanism from
templates six times the gear tooth size. A workpiece between centers is
reciprocated under the grinding wheel which is fed down at each stroke
until desired size is reached. Then the workpiece is cleared from the
wheel and indexed to the next tooth space. Usual procedure is to rough
grind around a gear in this way, and then finish grind with the trued
wheel set to depth. Form grinding is done on external and internal spur
gears, splines, and similar parts.

When spur or helical gears are ground by generating, the wheel or
wheels are trued to simulate a mating rack. On one type of machine
that uses a single wheel, as at the lower left in Fig. 34–17, the workpiece

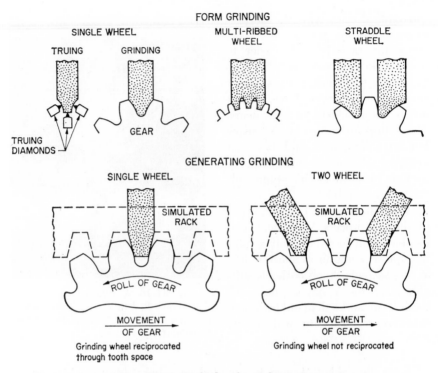

Fig. 34–17. Methods of grinding gears.

is carried under a reciprocating wheel and rolled as though it were in mesh with the rack. A spur gear is ground with its axis in line with the wheel movement, and a helical gear is swivelled. A machine of this type for gears 10 in. in diameter has motors totaling 7½ hp, weighs 7800 lb, and costs around $29,000.

Another type of generating gear grinder has two wheels as indicated at the lower right of Fig. 34–17. It operates on the same principle as just described, but the wheels are not reciprocated. They are large enough to cover an entire tooth working surface on gears not over about 1¼ in. wide. It is faster for work of that kind than the one wheel grinder.

Form grinding has been found faster in some cases, generating in others; but the differences are not large. The area of wheel contact is small for generating, and there is less likelihood of burning and cracking hardened steel, for which care must be exercised in form grinding. The root of a gear space can be finished and blended with the tooth profile better by forming than by generating. Generating leaves small flats on the teeth, and subsequent lapping is necessary if they must be removed.

Gear tooth lapping. Gears are commonly lapped after heat treatment to remove scale and correct small errors. Occasionally some gears may

Fig. 34–18. A gear lapping machine. (Courtesy National Broach and Machine Co.)

be salvaged by lapping to correct gross errors, but mainly the process is one to put the final touches on already good gears. This is done with all forms of gears by running them with mating gears or with one or more cast iron toothed laps under a flow of fine abrasive in oil.

The basic operation of lapping spur and helical gears is illustrated by the machine in Fig. 34–18. On it the lap meshes with and drives the gear above it. Their axes are crossed, and the workpiece is reciprocated axially to increase the sliding between the tooth surfaces. The work is turned first in one direction and then in another, to lap both sides of the teeth. Various machines embody refinements for particular advantages. Among these are *cramp lapping* or forcing the workpiece hard against the lap to speed the action, braking the workpiece to lap more on one side of the teeth than the other, and running several laps at once on one gear to break up tooth spacing errors.

A gear lapping operation usually takes one to several minutes. The laps are subject to wear, but on average work a lap can finish several thousand gears.

Comparison of finishing operations. Basically the finishing method for a gear is dictated by the degree of accuracy required and the available equipment. Invariably greater precision demands more costly operations for gears. It has been found that economical results are realized in modern mechanical devices when errors in gear tooth form or spacing do not exceed 0.0002 in. In most cases, tolerances smaller than that give a little but not worthwhile gain. On the other hand, errors of 0.0005 in. or larger lead to a pronounced inferiority in the running qualities of hardened gears.

Shaving is by far the cheapest method of obtaining accuracy within 0.0002 in. for spur and helical gears. Common practice for hardened gears is to shave, heat treat, and finish lap to touch them up. Heat treatment can be expected to add errors, but these are kept within limits by modern methods, particularly flame and induction hardening. That this process gives satisfactory results is evidenced by the fact that most such gears are produced in this way in the automotive, agricultural equipment, aircraft, machine tool, and similar industries.

Gears, such as worms, that cannot be shaved and spur and helical gears that require the highest degree of accuracy must be ground after hardening. This is commonly done to make master gears, shaving cutters, etc. Tolerances of 0.0002 in. or less can be held dependably.

Good quality straight and spiral bevel and hypoid gears are produced by lapping mating pairs together. Bevel and hypoid gears may be ground for best results.

Care should be taken that gears are not made too much better than necessary. A machine tool manufacturer found that some gears case hardened to 60 Rockwell C hardness and ground were not appreciably better than others through hardened to only 38 to 48 Rockwell C. The softer but tougher and stronger gears could be finished by hobbing. The tolerances held by hobbing were 0.0003 to 0.0005 in. but proved adequate at less cost.

GEAR INSPECTION

The inspection and measurement of gears involve some techniques not common for other products. Gears are tested for:

1. The accuracy of linear dimensions such as outside and root diameters and tooth thickness and depth.
2. Tooth profile.
3. Positions of the teeth as reflected by tooth spacing, runout, radial position, backlash, and helix angle or lead.
4. The bearing and finish of the tooth faces.
5. Noise.

Gear testing can be divided into two kinds; functional and analytical. Functional checking shows how errors affect the way the gears work together, as when they are rolled together to test them for freedom or noise. It is usually the easiest way of testing for acceptable gears. Analytical checking actually measures the important elements. That may be done by making absolute measurements or by finding how much a gear differs from a master. Analytical checking is usually required to adjust or correct gear cutting or finishing equipment in setting it up to produce. Examples of these forms of testing are given in the following descriptions of typical gear checking equipment and methods.

Checking the sizes of gears and gear teeth. A *gear tooth vernier caliper* measures the thickness of a gear tooth at the pitch line as is done in Fig. 34–19. A *gear tooth comparator* is a similar device that measures the addendum depth to a specified tooth thickness.

Ground rolls of precise diameter to make theoretical contact at the pitch line may be placed in opposite tooth spaces of a gear, and the distance across them measured by a micrometer or comparator. This is like measuring threads across wires. Formulas and table of proper roll sizes and measurements are given in hand-books.

Fig. 34–19. An application of a gear tooth vernier caliper. (Courtesy Brown and Sharpe Mfg. Co.)

Checking gear tooth profile. An optical comparator like the one in Fig. 15–31 offers one way of checking the profiles and positions of gear teeth by comparing their enlarged shadows on a screen with a large scale drawing. Fixtures are commonly used to position the gears.

The machine of Fig. 34–20 for measuring gear tooth involute profiles has a vertical spindle carrying the gear above a disk of the same diameter

Fig. 34–20. An involute profile measuring machine. (Courtesy Illinois Tool Works Co.)

as the base circle of the involute to be checked. The disk bears against a bar on a slide on the front of the machine. As the bar moves in a straight line, friction causes the disk to roll along it, and a point on the bar establishes the locus of a true involute in relation to the disk. The bar slide carries an indicator and tracer finger that touches a gear tooth at a point directly above the edge of the bar. As the slide is moved, the disk and gear roll together, and the indicator registers deviations in the profile of the tooth from a true involute. Some machines are arranged with an electrical recorder to trace the deviations on a chart.

Checking the positions of gear teeth. A typical device to check tooth spacing carries a gear freely between centers. A tapered block is brought in on a slide to locate a tooth space. An indicating finger previously set to a master makes contact with the face of the next tooth. Error in tooth spacing displaces the finger and is indicated on a dial.

The lead and helix angle of a helical gear may be compared with a master cam through an indicating mechanism on one type of machine.

To check backlash, a work gear and master gear may be mounted on shafts at fixed center distances. The master gear is held still, and the slight movement or backlash of the engaged gear teeth is measured by an indicator.

Composite errors in tooth spacing, thickness, profile, runout, interference, and eccentricity are reflected in changes either in velocity or center distance when gears are run together. A common way of checking these errors is to run a gear with a master. One gear shaft is fixed, and the other can move, but the two are drawn together by a spring. The movement between the centers of the two gears can be measured by an indicator. The *Red Liner Gear Checker* of Fig. 34–21(A) operates on this

(A)

(B)

Fig. 34–21. (A) A Red Liner gear checker. (B) Examples of Red
Liner chart indications. (Courtesy The Fellows Gear Shaper Co.)

principle. Movement of the master gear shaft as the gears are run together is magnified and recorded on a chart. Each cause of error can be
identified from the features of the curve traced on the chart, as depicted
in Fig. 34–21(B).

Checking gear tooth bearing and surface finish. Bevel and hypoid
gears commonly and other gears at times are inspected by running them
together or with masters to determine where the teeth bear. Localized
tooth bearing near the center of each face is desirable to avoid concentrating loads at the ends of teeth. The teeth are painted with marking
compound that is rubbed away at contact to show bearing areas.

The surfaces of finished gear teeth may be checked with a profilometer.

Checking for noise. Faulty gears are noisy and can be checked on
machines in which they are run in a sound chamber together or with a

master. Power is applied to one gear, and a brake loads the other. Characteristic sounds have such descriptive names as squeal, whine, growl, knocks, nicks, and marbles; and each indicates certain kinds of gear errors to an experienced inspector.

Questions

1. What curve is found on most gear teeth, what are its advantages, and what are its characteristics?

2. Name the important elements of a gear tooth and specify the size of each for a full depth tooth.

3. Define spur gear, helical gear, herringbone gear, worm, worm gear, bevel gear, crown gear, and hypoid gear.

4. By what processes are gears made?

5. What are the three classes of gear cutting methods?

6. How is a gear cut on a milling machine and under what circumstances?

7. How are gears form cut in large quantities?

8. Describe a hob and the way it generates gear teeth.

9. Describe the action of a vertical gear shaper and the pinion type cutter used on it.

10. Compare gear hobbing and shaping with each other and with other methods of gear cutting.

11. Describe the actions of the two basic machines of universal type for generating bevel gears.

12. Why are gear finishing methods used after gear cutting?

13. How are gears finished?

14. Describe the principle of gear shaving.

15. How and why are gear teeth ground?

16. When and how are gear teeth lapped?

17. What determines the methods used to finish a gear?

18. For what kinds of errors and in what basic ways are gears tested?

19. Describe the common methods of checking gear teeth.

Problems

1. Calculate the elements of a 12 diametral pitch gear of 36 teeth
   (a) with full depth teeth and 14½ ° pressure angle,
   (b) with stub teeth and 20° pressure angle.

2. Compute the important dimensions for an 8 diametral pitch, 14½ ° pressure angle full depth tooth gear that has 32 teeth and a width of ¾ in.

3. Compute the important dimensions for a 8 diametral pitch, 20° pressure angle stub tooth gear that has 32 teeth and a width of ¾ in.

4. An 1.187 in.-diameter involute spline in SAE 1040 steel with a 20 Rc hardness can be form-rolled in 18 sec. A set of forming dies costs $350 but can turn out 200,000 pieces in its lifetime with no reconditioning necessary. The spline can be hobbed at a rate of 1 min and 36 sec per piece. A hobbing cutter costs $95, must be ground after cutting 200 pieces, and can be resharpened 50 times. The time to sharpen and replace the hob is 20 min. Capital charges are 50% for interest, insurance, taxes, and losses. Labor and overhead are worth a total of $6 per hr. If machines are available in the plant for either method, what is the smallest number of pieces in a year's production that justifies the roll-forming method?

5. In the situation described in Prob. 4, hobbing machines are available with sufficient available time for the job, but machines must be purchased at a cost of $25,000 each if the parts are to be form-rolled. Each machine can be operated 1600 hr per yr. If 750,000 pieces are required per year, how long should it take to pay for the machine out of expected savings?

6. A 12 pitch gear with 36 teeth and ⅞ in. wide can be cut on a Shear Speed gear shaper at the rate of 2 gears in 55 sec. The machine and tooling cost $23,000. On a hobbing machine that costs $5800, best results are obtained from two cuts for each gear. Six gears are cut at a time, but the total time for each gear is six minutes. One man operates four hobbing machines or two Shear Speed shapers.

   Tool maintenance and overhead is assumed the same for either machine. Man time costs $2 per hr. Twenty per cent of the cost of a machine is charged each year for depreciation, interest, insurance, and taxes. A machine can be operated 2000 hr per yr.
   (a) Which type of machine should be selected to produce 15,000 gears per year if the machines are used for other work when not needed for this job?
   (b) Which type of machine should be selected to produce 15,000 gears per year if the machines have no other use and must be charged all to this job?
   (c) Which type of machine should be selected to produce 100,000 gears per year even if the machines cannot be used for other jobs?

7. A soft steel spur gear with 40 teeth, 3.500 outside diameter, 14½ ° pressure angle, and 1 in. width is to be cut on a milling machine. What should be:

    (a) the diametral pitch, addendum, tooth thickness, and whole depth?

    (b) the specifications of the cutter?

    (c) the number of turns of the dividing head crank to index each tooth?

    (d) the cutting time with a feed rate of 0.003 ipt? Refer to a manufacturer's catalog for cutter specifications.

8. A 30 teeth spur gear is to be hobbed with a 4 in.-diameter hob at 90 fpm. What is the work speed in rpm if the hob has a single thread? A double thread?

9. A 4 diametral pitch, 8 in. pitch diameter, full depth, 14½ ° pressure angle spur gear is made of mild steel. Two gears each ¾ in. wide are put next to each other on a mandrel and cut in one pass by a single-thread hob having a 4 in. outside diameter and running at 90 fpm. Calculate:

    (a) The rpm of the hob;

    (b) the rpm of the gears;

    (c) the pitch diameter of the hob;

    (d) the time to cut the gears with a feed of 0.060 in. per rev of the work and a distance for approach and overtravel of 1.6 in.

References

Buckingham, Earle, *Analytical Mechanics of Gears,* McGraw-Hill Book Co., Inc., New York, 1949.

Modern Methods of Gear Manufacture, National Broach and Machine Co., Detroit, 1950.

Automation

AUTOMATION is a word that has many meanings in industry today. The term was coined shortly after World War II at the Ford Motor Co. to describe the automatic handling of materials and parts between process operations. Even now the original concept is the most common. Most automation at this time comprises the automatic fabrication and handling of large quantities of parts over series of single-purpose machines. That is said to be *fixed programming*.

Automatic machines of all kinds existed long before the term automation was conceived. Some people consider automatic machines of all kinds within the definition of automation. Examples of automatic machines are given throughout this text. Automatic bar and chucking machines are examples. The discussion of fixed programming in this chapter will deal mainly with groups of machines.

Automation in manufacturing is found in foundries, press plants, and molding rooms as well as in machine shops. It is still more advanced in the process industries, such as petroleum and chemical industries, where production is high, processes are simple, not changed often, and straightforward, and the product is easy to move.

Automation has come to include more than fixed programming. A step forward has been to make some machines self-regulating to correct themselves when they err. A further advance has been the development of systems and machines each of which does a variety of jobs in response to prepared and recorded instructions. Such a system is not limited to making one particular product or part but can produce a number of kinds of products, and only a few of each at low cost, still without constant human attention. This is called *selectable programming.*

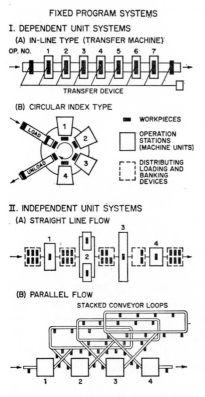

FIXED PROGRAM SYSTEMS

I. DEPENDENT UNIT SYSTEMS

(A) IN-LINE TYPE (TRANSFER MACHINE)

OP. NO.   1   2   3   4   5   6   7

TRANSFER DEVICE

(B) CIRCULAR INDEX TYPE

LOAD   UNLOAD   1 2 3 4

■ WORKPIECES

☐ OPERATION STATIONS (MACHINE UNITS)

⌐ ¬ DISTRIBUTING LOADING AND BANKING DEVICES

II. INDEPENDENT UNIT SYSTEMS

(A) STRAIGHT LINE FLOW

(B) PARALLEL FLOW

STACKED CONVEYOR LOOPS

Fig. 35–1. Diagrams of fixed program systems of automation.

Fixed programming. Fixed program automation performs a certain specific operation or series of operations on a particular part or group of similar parts. Both the operations and the transfer of parts from station to station are automatic. Two forms are the *dependent* and *independent unit systems* as depicted in Fig. 35–1.

The dependent unit system may have a series of machine units in line, in a *transfer machine,* or around an indexing table, on a *circular index machine.* Normally a workpiece is at each station during the working cycle. When the work is completed at all stations, all the parts are moved simultaneously to succeeding stations, and another cycle is started. A much less common arrangement is for the workpieces to travel continuously through a machine, with the tools moving alongside at intervals.

A circular index system may take less floor space and be cheaper to construct than an equivalent in-line system and has loading and unloading stations together but is limited to a few stations. With both these types the time for a cycle depends upon the slowest operation, and the most efficiency occurs when all operation times are made the same and minimal. For tool changes and breakdowns, all stations are shut down, and efficiency decreases as the number of stations increase.

An independent unit system provides for a bank of parts to supply each machine and permit it to operate at its fastest rate. Any machine may be shut down temporarily without stopping the others. This system has a high overall efficiency and can be planned for the best combination of the machines. For *straight line flow,* the banks of parts between machines may be contained in hoppers, magazines, elevators, etc. *Parallel flow* is an arrangement of conveyor stored banks between machines. The conveyors may be stacked one above the other in the least possible space adjacent to the line.

Transfer machines. Transfer machines have a number of favorable features and have been widely adopted in high-production manufacturing plants. The straight line workflow conforms naturally to continuous production and fits readily into desirable plant layouts. Considerable flexibility is permitted in planning for the number, kinds, and positions of stations with floor space and cost being the only limiting factors. Workpieces can be reoriented readily at desired stations in the line, and the least restriction is imposed upon approach of the tools to the part from any direction. Vibration, heat, and strain at any one station can be isolated from the others.

In addition to the unfavorable factors already cited for dependent unit systems, transfer machines have some of their own. Some parts can only be handled on pallets or fixtures, and that is expensive. All parts and pallets need to be relocated and reclamped at each station. Usually gaging and self-regulation require extra stations, and that adds to cost.

Fig. 35–2. A 24 station transfer machine which does most of the operations on cast iron compressor bodies. The insert in the upper left corner shows the rough workpiece on the left and two views of the finished part. (Courtesy Greenlee Bros. and Co.)

Transfer machines exist in sizes from those with only a few stations and costing less than $100,000 to some with several score stations and valuations of several millions of dollars. Each is special for a particular job, and scarcely any two are identical. A transfer machine with 24 stations is illustrated in Fig. 35–2 along with the refrigerator compressor body on which it does most of the machining. The workpieces are located in pairs on fixtures that are transferred from station to station, automatically positioned for the various cuts, and at the end unloaded and brought back to the beginning on a conveyor. On each pair of compressor bodies, 152 separate operations are performed in 19 working, 2 inspection, 1 loading, and 2 idle stations. These operations require 50 drills, 12 face mills, 2 side mills, 2 end mills, 12 boring tools, 38 chamfering tools, and 36 taps. The machine produces 188 pieces per hr at 88% efficiency.

The biggest saving from a transfer machine is in labor costs. Some prefer to turn the emphasis around and say that more output can be obtained from the same labor. The transfer machine of Fig. 35–2 probably needs no more than two or three set-up and maintenance men. In contrast, a conventional line to do the same work would employ no less than 21 operators, and perhaps a set-up man or so. Other savings may result from better quality, less scrap, less floor space, inspection on the machine, and scrap disposal through a conveyor.

The largest cost in transfer machine operation comes from the relatively heavy investment required. Even large savings can be more than eaten up by the heavy burden unless care is taken. One large user has found that no profit is returned unless a transfer machine is kept running 80% to 90% of the time, and even so it takes two to three years to recover the cost of a machine. The loss may very well be over $100 for every hour a half million dollar transfer machine is down. The engineer who plans and designs a transfer machine has much at stake. He must provide for a minimum first cost, long enough life, and as little down time as possible. The main considerations to these ends are the following.

A transfer machine starts with the design of the product. The part or parts to be made must not be subject to change often and must be designed to be made in the easiest way with all needed surfaces for locating and handling. Even so, the machine must be as flexible as possible, should changes occur.

The extent of automation should always be subject to scrutiny. For example, hand loading of a transfer machine for machining several million automobile connecting rods a year was found more economical than a loading device that cost $90,000.

Every provision must be made for the safety of the equipment and personnel. This includes foolproofing and interlocks to prevent wrecks and personal injuries, pre-inspection of rough workpieces, and means to stop the machine when it misses. The machine must take over everything done by an operator. This included cleaning and disposing of chips, rough checking and orienting of workpieces, and watching for trouble.

Tool problems must be solved before a transfer machine is designed to assure as much dependability as possible. Even so, tools become dull and breakdowns do occur. To minimize interruptions, provisions are made to preset sharp tools before they are put on the machine, to mount them in quick change holders, for tool racks to make the preset tools readily available when needed, for signals to alert the attendants to the times to change tools, and for schedules for changing the tools in batches. An example of quick change tooling is given in Fig. 21–14. The best of components and adequate means for lubrication help prevent breakdowns.

Although each transfer machine is a special project, many of its units, such as tool heads, hydraulic drive units, controls, and slides can and should be standard items at considerable saving in construction cost and facility of repair.

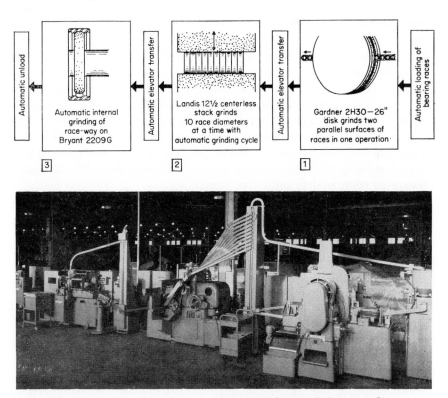

Fig. 35–3. An independent unit system made up of three grinding machines to finish bearing races. (Courtesy Gardner Machine Co.)

Independent unit systems. An independent unit system for an integrated line for grinding bearing races is illustrated in Fig. 35-3. In general, such a system altogether costs about 20% more than the total for
the machines, which are mostly standard items. Because such a system
utilizes standard components, even some of the conveyors and loading
devices, it can be put together in the relatively short time of from four
to six months. The standard units are easy to service, and repair parts
are always available.

Other advantages of the independent unit systems are that parts can
be positioned readily in the best way for each operation, there is plenty
of room for chip removal, and units are easily isolated from one another.
Good scrap control can be had by including inspection units in the connecting devices.

On the negative side, an independent unit system is not compact and
some floor space is wasted. It is not suitable for some sizes and shapes
of parts, such as large engine blocks.

Selection of automated systems. When an appreciable quantity of
pieces is to be produced, the question usually is not whether to automate
but rather how much is justified. An illustration is furnished by a case
for blanking and then notching electric motor laminations. Seventeen
different round blanks are needed in lots of 1300 to 8100 pieces: a total
of 70,000 blanks a week. There may be anywhere from 18 to 58 notches
required around the outside of a blank, in 50 different shapes and sizes.

One blanking press and four notching presses are capable of meeting
production requirements. Several arrangements are possible, and all have
been studied, but for simplicity only the two most feasible will be explained here and are indicated in Fig. 35-4. A detailed study shows that
the following annual savings may be expected from the fully automated
system as compared to no automation:

At blanking press (760 hr @ $1.80 per hr).............	$1,368
Overhead saved at blanking press.....................	243
At notching presses (8320 hr @ $1.80 per hr)..........	14,976
Overhead saved at notching presses...................	2,660
Total annual savings from full automation.............	$19,247

All four notching presses must process the same blanks being turned
out by the blanking press at any one time. This necessitates three additional sets or 150 notching dies. The costs of equipment for the fully
automated system are:

150 duplicate notching dies @ $250 each..............	$37,500
Automatic distribution mechanism....................	15,000
Annual cost of set-up and maintenance of aut. dist. mech.	2,000

I. FULLY AUTOMATED SYSTEM

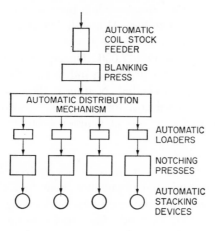

II. PARTIALLY AUTOMATED SYSTEM

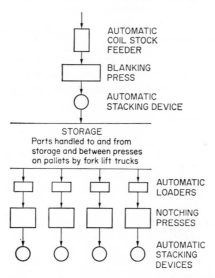

Fig. 35–4. A diagram of two arrangements for producing motor laminations.

Automatic press loading, feeding, and stacking devices..	29,800
Annual set-up and maintenance costs.................	500
Total cost of equipment for full automation...........	$84,800

A partially automated system, also depicted in Fig. 35–4, dispenses with the automatic distribution mechanism and requires handling and storing the blanks in lots by means of pallets and fork trucks. With this system the blanking press can be run at its fastest speed because it is not held back by the notching presses when they are turning out laminations with large numbers of notches. Although handling costs are more, the annual saving for partial automation is not much less than for full automation and is estimated to be $17,636. The equipment expenses are much less. The notching presses can be run independently, and the 150 duplicate notching dies are not needed. Neither is the distribution mechanism required. The total annual cost for partial automation is $30,300. Thus, the return on the investment is at a much higher rate for partial than for full automation in this case.

Self-regulation. A fact that must be recognized is that all physical systems, whether organisms or machines, contain within themselves the seeds of decay. The tools and machines performing an operation wear and deflect and thus err in producing precise results. As time goes on, the decadence increases. This is taken care of in conventional systems with fixed programs by changing tools at predetermined intervals and by building rugged machines that deteriorate very slowly. However, to go beyond fixed programs and the usual goals of precision, some means must be added to make corrections when errors begin. This is done by *self-regulation* through *feed-back* and *compensation*. A sensory device is incorporated in the system to detect discrepancies in the output and send back signals to prompt adjustments to counter the deviations.

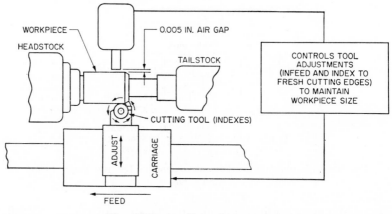

Fig. 35–5. A self-regulating system.

Self-regulation in simple forms has been applied for many years to machines with fixed programs. A typical example is described here to illustrate the principles. Figure 35–5 is a sketch of an actual arrangement for chamfering and turning a workpiece on an automatic lathe with a single-point tool. A gage head checks the diameter of each piece and prompts an adjustment in the position of the tool if indications are that the size of the piece is going out of limits. The unloading mechanism puts the pieces into slots for oversize, undersize, and good pieces according to the gage findings.

A prerequisite for self-regulation of a fixed program is a stable machine that can hold closely to size for many pieces without being regulated. If the machine were quite erratic, the regulating device would continually be activated, then tend to overcompensate, and soon compound the errors. Some consider it desirable that the machine be able to run at least forty pieces without adjustment and still hold within one half of the tolerance.

The tool depicted in Fig. 35–5 can be moved inward by a solenoid actuated cam a total distance of 0.002 in. in steps of 0.0002 inch. The increments are small so that adjustment from one limit back into the tolerance zone through one step does not push the dimension outside the opposite limit. The tool can also be indexed around its axis in 100 steps to bring fresh bits of cutting edge into action. When the gage head senses a workpiece close to or over the high limit, it closes contacts to transmit an impulse to a storage relay system. If the next piece is well within size, the relay system returns to its starting position; but if the next piece is near but not over the high limit, the relay system energizes the solenoid that sets the tool in a notch. If the second piece is oversize, a chipped tool is indicated, the machine is shut off, and a signal is turned on to show trouble.

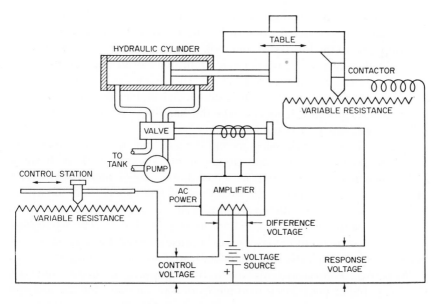

Fig. 35–6. A simple servo-mechanism.

Self-regulation through feedback is necessary for successful selectable programming and is accomplished by means of a device called a *Servo mechanism*. It appears in many forms, but they are all based on the same principles which will be explained by illustration of the simple application in Fig. 35–6. The figure depicts a machine tool table positioned by an order from a remote control station, at which a variable resistance setting determines a control voltage. The position of the table sets the rheostat that determines the response voltage. Their difference is passed through an amplifier and then through a solenoid that shifts an equalized hydraulic control valve from its neutral position. This causes the hydraulic piston to push the table in the direction to make the response voltage equal to the control voltage. When the two voltages are equal, there is no difference to be amplified, the hydraulic valve returns to its neutral position, and the table stops.

The Servo mechanism literally solves an equation. The controlled quantity is always driven so that its response equals the amount of the input. Instead of or in addition to resistance, the circuits may depend on variations in reactance or capacitance. The controlled variable may be linear position, angular position, velocity, torque, temperature or anything desired with proper transducers to convert the variable into electrical quantities. Instead of voltage differences, circuits may be set up to act on the bases of voltage phase differences or frequency differences of alternating currents. The Servo principle is also carried out hydraulically. In all cases, the basic principle is the same as explained for this case.

Selectable programming. About 75% of the manufacturing in the United States is estimated done in lots of 15 to 50 pieces and mostly is not adaptable to the form of automation described so far. What is needed is a form that can be changed easily from one job to another, and that is what selectable programming offers. The older forms of automation are in reality extensions of mechanization. Selectable programming goes a step further because it mechanizes the handling of information or instructions necessary to initiate and carry on a job.

Numbers on a part drawing specify the size and shape of a workpiece that is to be made. Selectable programming systems work with these and supporting numbers and are given the name of *numerical control systems*. Information about the quantities of feed, speed, length, width, flow, temperature, and other variables is stored, coordinated, and issued automatically to control an operation, process, or device. The name *tape control* also is given to these systems because most of them make use of punched paper or plastic tape, punched cards, or magnetic tape.

Numerical control systems are of two classes. The simpler includes those capable of positioning workpieces or tools, usually for the location of holes. The other class is composed of those able also to do continuous

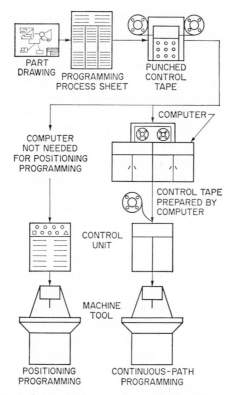

PART DRAWING

PROGRAMMING PROCESS SHEET

PUNCHED CONTROL TAPE

COMPUTER

COMPUTER NOT NEEDED FOR POSITIONING PROGRAMMING

CONTROL TAPE PREPARED BY COMPUTER

CONTROL UNIT

MACHINE TOOL

POSITIONING PROGRAMMING

CONTINUOUS-PATH PROGRAMMING

Fig. 35–7. Typical steps in the two classes of selectable programming.

path machining, either profiling or contouring. Typical arrangements for these two classes are indicated in Fig. 35–7. In both cases the specifications from the part drawing are entered on the programming process sheet in columns of numbers expressing coordinate positions, feeds, speed, etc. that must be imposed in sequence on the machine to meet requirements. These instructions are then punched in code form on a tape. Tape punching devices may cost several hundred dollars or more. The simplest resemble punchboards full of holes; the more elaborate look and operate like typewriters.

For simple positioning, the original punched tape is put directly on the machine control unit. In some systems, even a tape may not be used; the operator turns dials on the control unit to control the machine.

One major difference between *positioning programming* and *continuous path programming* is that the latter requires a computer to prepare the instructions for the machine control unit. When a curved path is shown on a part drawing, usually the first and last points and sufficient data to identify the curve are given. The computer must calculate the coordinates of sufficient points so that the machine can go from point to point and duplicate the curve within the required tolerance. Also, the instructions fixing the x and y, and even z, coordinates for each point must be synchronized when sent to the machine. This is done both by the computed instructions and the control unit. The computer prepares the information for the control unit on tape or cards. A person may make the computations for the simplest curves, but the work soon becomes laborious, and usually electronic computers are needed. A general-purpose computer may be adapted to this work if already available, but if one must be purchased, its cost may be as much as $70,000. Custom computer service is available at upwards of $50 per hr.

The information carried by the tape or other medium is converted into and transmitted by signals, which may be of two kinds. One is called *analog;* the other *digital.* An analog signal is continuous and constitutes a quantity analogous to the variable it controls. A common example is an electric potential. If a voltage controls a spindle speed, for instance, it is varied in proportion to the amount the speed is expected to change. A digital signal consists of discrete pulses. That might be a series of dots as in a telegraph signal. To control a speed, a certain number of pulses in a certain time specifies the quantity.

An analog quantity cannot be made to an exact desired amount; it always is an approximation but usually can be made to fall well within practical tolerances. On the other hand, a digital signal can readily be made up exactly of any desired number of pulses. Analog systems are simple and comparatively inexpensive, especially when a number of signals must be handled. General practice is to use each kind where it fits best, and usually both are found in different parts of any one installation.

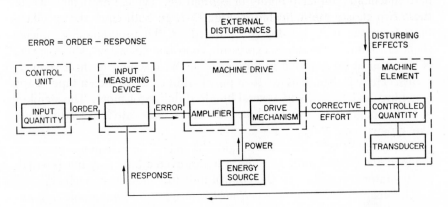

Fig. 35–8. A typical machine control circuit for selectable programming.

Figure 35–7 depicts the overall system and Fig. 35–8 the nature of the control at the final stage, at the machine. A signal which is an order for a certain action is issued by the control unit at the command of the tape. This travels through to the drive mechanism which imposes the action upon the controlled element of the machine. For an example, that might be a leadscrew that positions a table. A transducer measures and reports the position to the input measuring device. The response is compared to the order, and any difference or error is amplified and prompts the drive mechanism to correct the position until the desired condition is reached. An actual system includes a number of circuits like this, one for each element and aspect, such as speed, feed, position, etc.

What has been described is typical. Many ways of applying the principles with many modifications in details are in existence. The systems have been applied to all kinds of machine tools, including engine and turret lathes, turret punch presses, drilling and boring machines, milling machines, spot welders, and riveting machines. All operate from the same fundamentals. Two illustrations will be given here; one simple and the other elaborate.

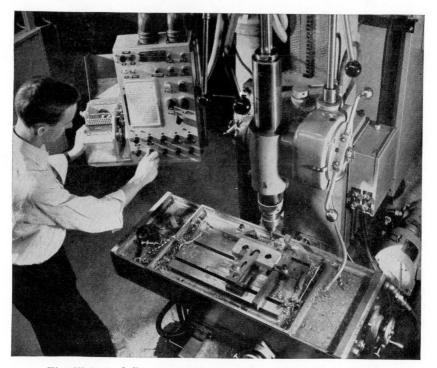

Fig. 35–9. A drill press equipped with a numerically controlled positioning table. (Courtesy Jone and Lanson Machine Co.)

Numerical-controlled positioning. A numerical-controlled positioning table under the spindle of a standard drill press is shown in Fig. 35–9. It is capable of locating holes within 0.001 in. and of repeating to less than 0.0005 in. Hole to hole speed is 150 in. per min. The control unit on the left may be actuated by punched tape or by setting the knobs in the bottom two rows. The table follows orders to go from hole to hole in any desired order, to go around a pattern of holes in any mixed manner, and to omit any holes as desired. The cost of this system is in the twenty-five to thirty thousand dollar range.

Fig. 35–10. A 5-axis Gantry Type skin milling machine equipped with numerical control for continuous cutting of profiles and contours. (Courtesy Cincinnati Milling Machine Co.)

Numerical-controlled continuous cutting. The five-axis milling machine shown in Fig. 35–10 with its control unit is the final stage in a system for positioning or cutting profiles and contours on aircraft parts. A typical job for this machine is to mill the top of a wing with its skin and ribs from a solid slab of aluminum. It utilizes a combination digital-analog system. The input data on punched cards from a computer are fed into memory units, converted into analog form, interpolated, and compared to distinct and unambiguous signals from feedback units. All dimensions are absolute from a reference line and can be held to 0.001 in. in 20 in. or 0.002 in. in 100 in. Complete systems of this sort are quoted at several hundred thousand dollars. Some contouring systems are arranged so that if the operator manipulates the controls to turn out a piece, his procedure is recorded on a tape that can be run back as often as desired to produce additional pieces.

Economics of numerical control. Numerical-controlled machines do not compete successfully with fixed program machines to produce large quantities of parts. The latter, such as an automatic bar machine controlled by cams, are simple, direct, and rugged and can produce faster. The place for numerical control is in the production of small and medium quantities of parts that otherwise would require human attendance on general purpose machine tools.

For some operations little or no special tooling is required for conventional machining, but preparation is needed for numerical control. As an example, a milling operation may require only one hour for set-up on a standard machine but four hours to program a numerical-controlled machine. Once set up, the standard machine takes three hours to make a piece, and the numerical-controlled machine only one hour. For one piece the standard machine is more economical. In such cases a rough rule is that the breakeven point is between 2 and 25 pieces.

For other operations, appreciable special tooling such as jigs for positioning or templates for contouring may be needed even for small quantities on conventional machines. In such cases, the preparation cost may be less for numerical control. Even more important, the lead time may be less, and it may be possible to get the job done sooner by numerical control rather than wait a month for conventional tools if the tool shops are busy. In one case, the time to prepare the tools was reported to be 210 hours for a conventional machine, but only 118 hours for a numerical-controlled machine. Of the 118 hours, only one hour was on an electronic computer. In operation, 5½ hours were required per piece for manual control, and 2 hours for numerical control. It must be remembered that the 2 hours probably cost more per hour than each of the 5½ hours because of the large cost of the numerical-controlled equipment.

Numerical-controlled machines can often work faster than manually operated machines because idle time is a minimum (the machine does not demand a coffee break), fatigue is not present, human mistakes are avoided, rejects are fewer, and less time is needed for inspection. Tool life may be better because of constant and controlled loading of the tools. Multiple control of several machines and even remote control, say for dangerous materials, is practicable. The tooling in the form of tape is easily stored and preserved.

Although numerical-controlled machines and accessories are substantially more costly than bare standard machines, their cost may even be less than for template-controlled contouring machines when the cost of the equipment to make the templates is taken into account.

Maintenance of numerical-controlled equipment may be a problem because it requires a high order of skill, and special personnel may have to be trained. Tool breakage can cause serious complications because there is no direct and easy way to stop the unknowing automaton from trying to drive a broken tool into the workpiece. As a device that saves labor, numerical control may meet with opposition from some workmen.

Profile scanning machines. Several makes of machines are available to cut pieces, such as cams, to shapes in two dimensions directly from line drawings. Whether they are automata or forms of tracing machines is debatable. Essentially they operate on the pantograph principle, with a tracer to follow a line on a drawing and direct a tool through a linkage to cut a workpiece. The drawings for one of these machines are made with a conductive ink. A tracer disk maintains contact with the line through control of a spark gap. Regular ink lines are scanned on another type of machine by electric eyes.

Questions

1. What is meant by automation, and how does it differ in the forms of fixed and selectable programming?

2. Describe the principal fixed program systems.

3. What are the advantages and disadvantages of transfer machines?

4. How can the costs of a transfer machine be minimized?

5. What are the advantages and disadvantages of the independent unit system of automation?

6. How would you make an analysis to determine whether to automate an operation?

7. What is self-regulation, and how is it accomplished?

8. Describe a typical system for self-regulation of a fixed program machine.

9. What is the principle of operation of a Servo mechanism?

10. What are numerical-control and tape-control systems?

11. What are the two classes of numerical-control systems and how are they arranged?

12. Describe analog and digital signals and state their relative merits.

13. Sketch and describe a typical control circuit for a numerical-controlled machine.

14. What is the place for numerical control?

15. What are the advantages and disadvantages of numerical control as compared to conventional methods?

Problems

1. Rough and finish operations on a workpiece include boring a hole and profiling the front and two sides. For a conventional milling machine, 210 hours are required to design and make a jig, fixture, and template at a toolroom rate of $8 per hr. Cycle time is 5½ hr per piece at a rate of $15 per hr.

    For a numerical-controlled machine 71 hours are required in the tool room for a fixture, 46 hours at $10 an hr for the drawing, process sheet, and punched tape, and 1 hour at $50 per hr on an electronic computer. The cycle time is 2 hr per piece at $45 per hr.

    For how many pieces should the numerical-controlled system be used?

2. A job can be set up on a standard jig boring machine in one hour. Each piece takes six hours for boring. If the job is done on a tape-controlled jig boring machine, two hours are needed for programming in the office. Then each piece can be bored in five hours. The shop rate is $12 per hr on the standard jig borer and $14 per hr on the numerical-controlled jig borer. Office work costs $9 per hr. When is the numerical-controlled machine justified?

References

Kaplan, Julius Y., "Automation of Machine Tools," *A.S.T.E. Trans. No. 21T18–1*, March, 1953.

La Joy, Millard H., *Industrial Automatic Controls,* Prentice-Hall, Inc., Englewood Cliffs, N.J., 1953.

Nixon, Floyd E., *Principles of Automatic Controls,* Prentice-Hall, Inc., Englewood Cliffs, N.J., 1953.

Index